SECOND EDITION

# READINGS IN POPULATION AND COMMUNITY ECOLOGY

**WILLIAM E. HAZEN**

*Professor of Biology, Dan Siege State College*

1970    W. B. SAUNDERS COMPANY · PHILADELPHIA · LONDON · TORONTO

W. B. Saunders Company:    West Washington Square
                           Philadelphia, Pa.   19105

                           12 Dyott Street
                           London W.C.1

                           1835 Yonge Street
                           Toronto 7, Ontario

Readings in Population and Community Ecology

Print No.:    1    2    3    4    5    6    7    8    9

# PREFACE

This volume of readings had its inception at the College of the University of Chicago where I taught a course in field biology which relied heavily on original source material. I have continued to revise and extend this list while teaching general ecology at San Diego State College. The purpose of a collection such as this is to introduce students to the literature of ecology as soon as they begin their study of the subject. The study of ecology, which is one of the great theoretical subject matters of biology, thereby gains interest, currency, and intellectual vigor. These readings are intended for use by third and fourth year students, in conjunction with a text and lectures. I attempt to use laboratory and field work to supplement the rest of the course.

I am grateful to my former colleagues at the University of Chicago for their continued interest, particularly to Gerson Rosenthal, who first suggested several of the readings. Discussions with fellow faculty members teaching general ecology at San Diego State College have been helpful in this revision; Boyd Collier, Richard Darby, and Richard Ford have been generous with time and suggestions. I remain indebted to Nelson Hairston, Laurence Slobodkin, and Frederick Smith, who first introduced me to the nature and scope of ecology.

It has again been difficult to reduce this volume to a reasonable size, particularly since I had to eliminate some useful and important papers. The errors of omission are entirely my own.

*San Diego, California*                                   WILLIAM E. HAZEN

# CONTENTS

# EDITOR'S INTRODUCTION

The current focus of interest in ecology, which emphasizes populations and communities as the proper objects of study in the science, is largely due to the stimulus of two books published in the 1920's: Lotka's *Elements of Physical Biology* and Elton's *Animal Ecology*. Both these volumes stressed the role of populations, with population dynamics or kinematics having central positions. Volterra's classic study should also be mentioned; its influence was more marked after 1931, when a translation of it appeared as an appendix to Chapman's *Animal Ecology*. In the next decade such works as Gause's *The Struggle for Existence* and Boden-heimer's *Problems of Animal Ecology* redirected the attention of investigators to theoretical problems and to their experimental solutions. In plant ecology, the discussions of Tansley, who proposed the term ecosystem for the fundamental ecological unit, had a similar function. It is difficult to point to particular recent authors, but Lindeman should be mentioned as one who directed the activity of working ecologists to the problems of productivity and efficiency. Intellectually, I am particularly indebted to Slobodkin's *Growth and Regulation of Animal Population,* which was the immediate stimulus for my current interests in ecology.

The collection of papers in this volume attempts to explore some of the avenues that research and speculation in population and community ecology have taken. The articles are grouped under four substantive headings, with one of Hutchinson's papers and an article by Harper acting as a general introduction. The rubrics under which the papers fall are: "Single Species Populations," "Relationships Between Species," "Community Metabolism," and "Community Structure and Population Regulation." Because of the arbitrary nature of the divisions, some of the articles do not fall neatly into place. For example, the Smith paper treats models for predation, as well as those for growth of a single species. Engelmann's work might equally well be treated as a study in community energetics; it is placed where it is because it could not be understood without a prior knowledge of MacArthur's theoretical analysis of the niche. In general, I have placed the papers to permit their being read sequentially.

By using different criteria, the papers could be grouped differently than they appear here. One of these possible groupings would correspond to the different kinds of activities which the authors undertake. Thus there are theoretical papers, which use the rational processes of logic and mathematics to investigate the possible ways of ordering ecological subject matters, and empirical ones, which investigate the world of art and nature; that is, ecology is studied by experiment or simple observations. I have made no attempt to "cover" ecology. My lack of familiarity with plant ecology has made it impossible to include the more detailed portions of that part of the science. The papers are uneven in their level of difficulty and some will be too difficult for undergraduates. For this I offer the defense that it is better for students to be shown the scope of the science in all its difficulty and particularity than to be fed predigested pap.

The introductory paper by G. E. Hutchinson, after discussing the general significance of structure, analyzes in more detail two kinds of patterns, stochastic and coactive, the former dependent on random environmental forces, the latter on interaction between species. Competition, an example of coaction, is discussed and related to the niche. The final portion discusses the patterns found in the enumeration of individuals belonging to different species found in samples. As it stands, this article introduces all the topics found in the rest of the book other than energetics and productivity. For these areas, Lindeman is an adequate introduction.

In the first group of papers, "Single Species Populations," the unit of study is the population; both the individual, with its private environment, and the community, with its complex of populations, are excluded. The patterns studied here are (1) distributions in space and (2) changes in time. Cole's study of the animals found under boards placed in a woodland analyzes the spatial patterns of the different species found there by use of the Poisson series. For a more complete discussion, see Grieg-Smith's text, *Quantitative Plant Ecology*.

I have chosen to begin the study of changes of populations in time with concrete examples of life histories as found in life tables. Such tables have the advantage of being easy to understand, and information from them is necessary for the calculation of the intrinsic rate of increase. From such tables, with the additional knowledge of the distribution of fecundity with age, the intrinsic rate of natural increase can be estimated. The calculation and theoretical importance of this statistic are adequately discussed by Birch. Hall estimates under different conditions of diet and temperature, using these estimates to investigate the biology of *Daphnia* in a lake. Finally, Smith discusses various mathematical formulations related to population dynamics and the experimental methods appropriate to testing these models. Among the cases he considers are growth of a single species and interactions of species in predation, thereby serving as a bridge to the next major section.

In *Elements of Physical Biology*, Lotka considered the types of relationships that can occur between species and attempted to formulate equations expressing these relationships. I have included papers which treat competition and predation; neither symbiosis nor commensalism has yet received adequate theoretical treatment. I believe that, in this portion, the importance and general relevance of each of the selected papers are self-evident. Theories of competition lead most directly to a consideration of niches as is evident in both field and laboratory studies. Theories of predation lead to a consideration of energy flow in ecosystems. Since the first edition was published, I have become familiar with Holling's remarkable studies of predation, which bridged the gap between theoretical models and field studies.

The section on "Community Metabolism and Productivity" is also largely self-explanatory. It begins with Lindeman's pioneering study of energy flow and efficiency in lakes. Although the details of his formulation and of his estimates may be open to criticism—the decomposers are not treated separately, and net productivity rates seem high—this is too important a piece of work to omit. Slobodkin derives a set of equations applicable to three different kinds of efficiency: ecological, population, and growth. These relationships are applied to experimental *Daphnia* populations. The last two papers discuss how to estimate productivity in two different kinds of ecosystems: the oceans and old fields.

The last and most difficult portion is entitled "Community Structure and Population Regulation." Two kinds of attempts to analyze communities are included. The first, more closely connected logically to the earlier sections, proceeds from considerations of competition and energy flow through an attempt to analyze the ecological meaning of "niche" to an understanding of community structure. The second uses statistical associations of species for the analysis of communities.

If one can speak of a community as being "structured," this means that the populations of organisms present are not mere haphazard assemblages, but are functionally related to one another. The question arises, "What are the parts that constitute the whole?" In an abstract community either the populations can be so conceived, or the activities of the encompassed populations can play the role of structural elements. I believe that in ecology the sets of activities—that is, the niches corresponding to the populations present—are fundamental in a functional concept of community. The first set of papers here, that is, through Engelmann, deals with the structure and function of communities and attempts to relate the niches to the populations found in nature. The model of the community proposed by MacArthur, a model deduced from simple biological premises, has been useful in that it led to a great deal of research by ecologists.

In conclusion, my bias in favor of the concept of biological control of the numbers of species in nature and of the necessity of treating communities as wholes is evident. Although it seems clear that there is now no ready solution to the problem of constructing a general theory covering the kinds and numbers of organisms present at a place, progress is being made toward a solution. The construction of such a theory is a problem of sufficient difficulty and interest to occupy the best scientific minds of any age. I believe the articles presented in this book show that ecology has attracted a fair share of such minds in the middle of the twentieth century.

*San Diego, California*                                                    WILLIAM E. HAZEN

# PART I

# INTRODUCTION

# THE CONCEPT OF PATTERN IN ECOLOGY *

BY G. EVELYN HUTCHINSON

*Director of Graduate Studies in Zoology, Yale University*

In any general discussion of structure, relating to an isolated part of the universe, we are faced with an initial difficulty in having no a priori criteria as to the amount of structure it is reasonable to expect. We do not, therefore, always know, until we have had a great deal of empirical experience, whether a given example of structure is very extraordinary, or a mere trivial expression of something which we may learn to expect all the time.

If, with the surrealists, we imagine ourselves encountering in the middle of a desert a rock crystal carving of a sewing machine associated with a dead fish to which postage stamps are stuck, we may suspect that we have entered a region of the imagination in which ordinary concepts have become completely disordered. Macroscopically, we are in the realm of what Elizabeth Sewell (1951), in her remarkable book *The Structure of Poetry*, defines as nightmare. On a smaller scale, since we can recognize the individual objects and give them names, we are still in the familiar world. The fish may be expected to have the various skull bones which have been enumerated by vertebrate morphologists; if it departed too radically from the accepted structure, we should see at once that it was not a fish. The rock crystal would have the ordinary physical properties of quartz; if it did not, we should not recognise and name it as such.

---

* An address given upon presentation of the Leidy Medal to the author on December 4, 1952, at the Academy of Natural Sciences of Philadelphia. (See notice of the award in *Proceedings* of the Academy, vol. 104, p. 249, 1952.)

When we push our analysis as far as we can, we end up with a series of statements of relations between entities, which at the present state of development of science are apparently unanalysable. What we call knowledge appears to consist of a series of known relationships between unknown elements. The latter may become known as new techniques permit their study, but it is reasonable to suppose that they too will become in the process of investigation relationships between new unknown entities of a higher degree of abstraction. Actually, the degree of abstraction which has been reached in modern theoretical physics is already so great that it is practically impossible to say anything intelligible in words about what the universe is made of. Our preliminary exploration thus suggests that the completely disordered is unimaginable and that the known consists of a collection of relationships between temporarily unknown entities. If we are going to say anything at all, some structure is certain to be involved, but, as has already been indicated, the amount of structure per unit volume cannot be guessed in advance.

Very roughly, in an empirical and qualitative way, we may distinguish a number of kinds of structure. The ordinary small-scale structure of the inorganic world, as exemplified in crystals, we may call, as is usually done, *order*. *Disorder* in physical science usually means random as opposed to placed in a particular order, such as that of a crystal lattice.

There is another important kind of structure in purely physical systems, which is in a sense a sort of converse of order, and which may be called *arrangement*. By this is meant the kind of structure exhibited by having the sun in one place, radiating energy, the earth in another receiving some of it. *Arrangement* in this limited sense decreases as entropy increases. Measured as negative entropy it is essentially what organisms eat. It is obviously a very different concept from order, thought the two are often confused by biologists.

The order of a system increases as we lower its temperature and is maximal at absolute zero. Order is an equilibrium phenomenon. Arrangement in the energetic sense in which it has been used, decreases as the *whole* system exhibiting it approaches absolute zero. It is essentially a non-equilibrium phenomenon, and most of modern cosmology is devoted ultimately to trying to find out how it came or comes into existence.

The characteristic structure of the living world will be called *organization*. Much order is also present, and, as organisms lay up an energy supply, arrangement is there also. The really characteristic structure of organisms, however, only exists near transition points. The art of living consists fundamentally of just crystallizing or just going into solution at the right time and place. Living matter is poised precariously between the solid and liquid states. Organization is never an equilibrium phenomenon in the physical sense.

The structure which results from the distributions of organisms in, or from, their interactions with, their environments, will be called *pattern*. As is organization, pattern is essentially a steady state rather than an equilibrium phenomenon, though it will be convenient to speak of equilibrium and non-equilibrium communities in a later paragraph when the phenomena are completely abstracted from physico-chemical categories. Pattern is obviously closely related to the arrangement of the inanimate world in which it developed.

The structure which organisms may impose on material systems to convey information, or in the construction of tools, may be called *design*. Human artifacts of all sorts, including works of art, come into this category. Design may be an equilibrium phenomenon and may be unchanged by cooling. A sentence written with appropriate materials is still the same sentence in the neighborhood of absolute zero, though the organization of the man who wrote it and the pattern of the community in which he lived, could not survive such extensive cooling. There are, however, remarkable formal mathematical analogies between arrangement and design.

These categories are to be considered as qualitative and suggestive; they are set up mainly to indicate how complex the problem of structure becomes even when an effort is made to keep the matter as simple as possible. The justification for the use of such categories is that confusion may often be avoided by asking which are appropriate to any structure under discussion.

Pattern, in the sense used above, appears to be of five kinds. The distribution of organisms and of their effects on their environment may be determined by external forces, such as light, temperature, humidity or density gradients, changes of state in certain directions, currents, winds, etc. Patterns produced in this way will be termed *vectorial*. The distribution may be determined by genetic continuity, offspring remaining near the parent, giving a *reproductive* pattern. The distribution may be determined by signalling of various kinds, leading either to spacing or aggregation, producing *social pattern*. The distribution may be determined by interaction between species in competition leading to *coactive* pattern. The distribution may depend on random forces producing a *stochastic* pattern.

The main theme of the present address is the coactive and stochastic types of pattern and their interaction.

*Stochastic patterns.*—The distribution of a plankton organism by night is commonly conceived as becoming increasingly random. Moreover, when horizontal distribution across a vertical light gradient is considered, many investigators have unconsciously assumed the same random distribution to hold. It is a mistake to consider such a random distribution to be structureless or lacking in pattern. The probabilities involved may be regarded as quite definite. Only if such probabilities were completely indeterminate, could we get an irrational series of surprises and enter the world of nightmare above a certain size level.

If a number of samples of a habitat is considered, and the probability of the occurrence of any particular species is low, the incidence of that species will appear at first very irregular. Examination of the number of samples containing no specimen, one specimen, two ... $n$ specimens, etc., however, will indicate the existence of stochastic patterns. The simplest of such patterns is that in which the number of samples of each rank from 0 to $n$ approximates to a Poisson series. It is the property of such a distribution that the variance in the statistical sense is equal to the mean. Where the variance is much greater than the mean (*superdispersion*) the organisms are grouped together more than would be expected on the simple random hypothesis; where the variance is much less than the mean (*infradispersion*) they are much more evenly spaced than in a randomly distributed population (fig. 1).

In the plankton of lakes, the distribution of different species of animals has been studied from this point of view by Ricker (1937), by Langford (1938) and perhaps most beautifully by Tonolli (1949). The last-named investigator made series of horizontal tows with the Clarke-Bumpas plankton sampler in Lago Maggiore in November, three series of tows being made at each depth. The results of some of his investigations are shown in figures 1 and 2. Out of a large number of series of comparisons, ninety-three in all, infradispersion appeared to be significantly demonstrated in only two. Since the significance limit was set as the degree of infradispersion which would occur by chance only in 1% of the cases studied, we are probably at liberty to regard infradispersion as a chance phenomenon. Superdispersion was observed far more often and is certainly significant. In three common species, *Eudiaptomus vulgaris*, *Daphnia longispina* and *Asplanchna priodonta* there is a very obvious tendency for the superdispersion to be most marked in the 5-10 m. layer. Presumably in these species, the tendency of the individuals to disperse at random in a horizontal plane, to move like the molecules of a gas, is modified by some hydrographic factor, probably turbulent movement, itself a random phenomenon. The organisms may be supposed to react to such random turbulent movements, so that they collect in certain regions and not in others. In *Cyclops strenuus* the superdispersion is differently distributed and must be due to different factors. Bliss (1953) in a very important recent paper

6

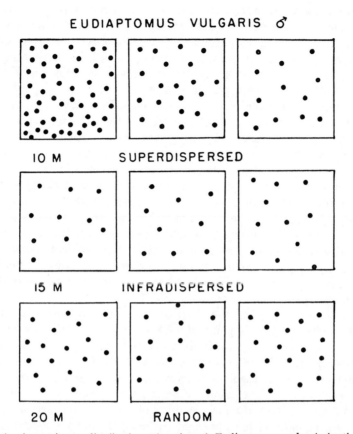

EUDIAPTOMUS VULGARIS ♂

10 M    SUPERDISPERSED

15 M    INFRADISPERSED

20 M    RANDOM

Fig. 1.—Approximate distribution of males of *Eudiaptomus vulgaris* in three successive plankton samples at three different depths in Lago Maggiore, showing *super-dispersion, infradispersion* and *random distribution*. (From the data of Tonolli 1949.)

has shown that in one marine copepod the superdispersed distribution approximates to the so-called negative binomial, which is to be expected when one stochastic process is superimposed on another. Tonolli's data are not appropriate for testing this particular distribution, but it is very likely that stochastic patterns dependent on the superimposed operation of random events involving different size dimensions, of the microorganisms themselves and of much larger convention cells for instance, may ultimately be found to produce a number of different kinds of stochastic pattern.

*Coactive Pattern.* The fundamental regularity underlying the distribution of all organisms in a community is Gause's principle, or, as it is more properly termed, the Volterra-Gause principle, that in an equilibrium

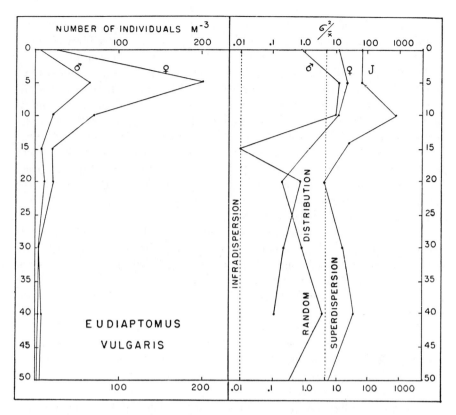

Fig. 2.—Vertical distribution of males and females, and of the ratio of the variance to the mean for males, females and immature individuals of *Eudiaptomus vulgaris* in Lago Maggiore. The absolute numbers of immature specimens are much greater than of mature individuals but are similarly distributed. The dotted lines indicate superdispersion and infradispersion significant to the 1% level. (From the data of Tonolli 1949.)

community no two species occupy the same ecological niches. A formal statement of the principle emerged early in Volterra's mathematical studies of biological associations (Volterra 1926), and Gause (1934, 1935) showed by an elegant series of experiments that in cultures of protozoa under conditions in which two species were forced to occupy a space of such simple structure that no niche diversification was possible, only one species could survive indefinitely.

In natural communities of a kind in which equilibrium may be expected, all subsequent studies have indicated that the generalization is true. Recently a number of studies largely by ornithologists have indicated that allied species which apparently live together under equilibrium conditions, may actually be occupying niches which are largely distinct. A particularly beautiful case is provided by three species of African weaver birds, *Ploceus intermedius cabanisi*, *P. collaris nigriceps* and *P. melanocephalus duboisii*, which all live together near Lake Mweru, the last two species even sharing the same communal nests. All feed on different foods; in the case of the two species which share a communal nest, one is a seed-eater and one is insectivorous (White 1951). A similar situation has recently been described among the owls, the Saw-whet, *Aegolius a. acadicus* and the Long-eared, *Asio otus wilsonianus*, in coniferous plantations in Ohio. Both occupy the same sleeping territory by day, but by night the Saw-whet hunts mainly in wooded areas catching large numbers of *Peromyscus*; the Long-eared owl mainly in open land catching many more *Microtus* and *Cryptotis* (Randle and Austing 1952).

Instances of this sort can be multiplied indefinitely and, where apparent exceptions to the Volterra-Gause principle of niche-specificity occur, we may legitimately suspect that a true equilibrium between the species is not established. We can in fact speak of *equilibrium* and *non-equilibrium* communities which may be distinguished by observing whether the principle holds.

Whenever two species are competing, the direction of competition is largely dependent on environmental factors. This is critically shown in
\* Gause's (1935) experiments in which *Paramecium candatum* tended to replace *P. aurelia* in frequently renewed media, and *P. aurelia* to replace
\* *P. candatum* when metabolic products were allowed to accumulate.

Precisely similar results have been long recognised in plant ecology. Many species which appear to be calciphil or calciphobe in nature can actually grow quite well when isolated in cultivation in soils of a wide range of calcium contents. The apparent restriction shows up only when the plants have to enter into competion with the rest of the flora to which they belong.

Ecological zonation is largely dependent on the competitive relations of species as controlled by the environment, and so is as much a coactive as a vectorial type of pattern. The production of a discontinuous discrete type of biological zonation in a continuous gradient of salinity, soil moisture or other physical variable is easily understood in terms of competition theory, since the direction of competition will change at a definite point on the gradient, below which one species, above which another species, will be successful (Gause and Witt 1935). It is probable that this process plays a considerable part in regulating the invasion of fresh waters from the sea. It is often apparent that species exhibit far greater salinity tolerances in the laboratory than in nature. In Joseph Leidy's day, the Schuylkill near Philadelphia contained a serpulid worm *Manayunkia*

---

\*Author's note: Candatum should have been caudatum.

*speciosa* Leidy, one of the very few species of fresh-water polychaets. Allied species occur in the Great Lakes drainage, in Lake Baikal and in salt water in the Arctic. The nearest local marine ally of *M. speciosa* is *Fabricia sabella*, a marine species found on the Atlantic seaboard. J. P. Moore (in Johnson 1903) long ago showed that at least the adults of these worms could be acclimated to water of the normal salinity of each other's environments. Similar situations are found among the amphipoda of western Europe (Sexton 1939, Reid 1939, Beadle and Cragg 1940). It is probable that, when two species of slightly different tolerances compete in a salinity gradient, selection will cause the optima of values of the salinity of the two species to diverge. The operation of selection on a zonal pattern has doubtless played an immense part in evolution (cf. also Brooks 1950).

The very definite types of pattern which we have just considered are characteristic of equilibrium communities in biotops which contain physico-chemical gradients. Much of the diversity of the living world is due to this sort of pattern, but much is also probably due to the existence of non-equilibrium communities. The first type of non-equilibrium community characterizes those regions in which certain more or less catastrophic events are continually creating new empty biotops. If such biotops are colonized by more than one species, and if the species occupy the same niche, competition will begin and one species will tend to exterminate its weaker competitors. If before this happens, a new adjacent habitat is opened, a new mixed population may be set up. If the original habitat is now destroyed by a catastrophic event, and the process is repeated indefinitely, the mixed population will appear to persist. It is probable that, in order for this to happen, the tendency for the weaker species to disappear by competition must be balanced by a tendency for it to spread a little more easily than the stronger; it must in fact be a *fugitive species* (Hutchinson 1951). Wynne-Edwards (1952) has concluded that the co-existence of very closely allied species of birds in the Arctic, where local populations are easily exterminated by adverse climatic conditions, actually provides a case of this sort.[1]

A more widespread type of non-equilibrium population is dependent on the relation of the life-span or generation time to the seasonal cycle. If we consider two competing species with an annual or longer life cycle, such as is found in mammals, birds, many insects, the larger marine invertebrates, and some quite small aquatic animals such as many copepods, it is obvious that the species must be adapted throughout their life histories to a great variety of conditions. In these circumstances, we can properly

---

[1] I am indebted to James Bond for calling my attention to this case.

consider the two species to compete under some long term mean condition; transitory fluctuations may alter temporarily the direction of competition, but the final result will be the elimination of one of the competitors.

If we now consider two species with exceedingly short life histories, such as those of bacteria dividing rapidly in a favorable medium, it is quite possible that competition leading to extermination might occur so rapidly that no environmental change sufficient to reverse the direction of competition, would have time to occur before one species had been exterminated by the other.

The Volterra-Gause principle of one species per niche should, therefore, hold for very rapidly reproducing and very slowly reproducing organisms. In the intermediate region, in which a number of generations may occur in a year, but the generation time of several days or weeks is sufficient to permit considerable variation in environment in the course of a few generations, there is no reason to suppose that the law would hold. If one species displaced the other at low temperatures and the reverse at high, it is easy to see that, if both appeared from some resting stage in Spring, competition would first favor the first, then the second, and then again the first species.

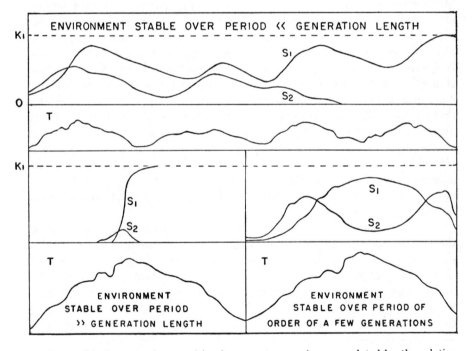

Fig. 3.—Ideal course of competition between two species as regulated by the relation between generation length and the period over which the environment may be taken as stable.

There can be little doubt that the great diversification of the phyto-plankton of lakes, the turbulent epilimnia of which can hardly provide to autotrophic euplanktonic organisms greater niche diversity than existed in Gause's culture tubes, is due to the fact that phytoplanktonic organisms in nature probably divide at a mean rate of once every few days or every few weeks (see particularly Grim 1950) and so fall in the intermediate or potentially non-equilibrium category of the three which we have been considering.

It is also probable that some species of limnetic zooplankton form a non-equilibrium community, but here the situation is complicated in some cases by a tendency for the reproductive rate to vary, but with a lag-period, with the feeding rate. Very marked non-equilibrium populations of single species must often be set up during the Spring; the oscillations which follow and which are slowly damped out, may be extensive enough to prevent the species, in the time available for active feeding and repro-duction, from ever achieving equilibrium, even with a constant food supply. This phenomenon, which has been most ingeniously studied by Slobodkin (1951) emphasizes the non-equilibrium nature of the plankton, though in its details it differs somewhat from the coactive non-equilibrium of the phytoplankton.

\* THE DIVIDING OF THE BIOTOPHY COACTIVE PROCESSES

If we consider, not a single species but a whole series of species of a certain taxonomic group, and examine a large collection made at random in some specified habitat, we can enumerate the species which occur once, twice, three times and so on. Recently a good deal of attention has been paid to the regularities exhibited by such an enumeration. Designating the number of specimens per species as $r$, the rank of the species and the number of species which have that rank as $n$, Fisher, Corbet and Williams (1943) have concluded that for many kinds of organisms

$$n = \frac{R}{r} x^r$$

where $x$ is a number slightly less than unity, and $R$ a number which char-acterizes the diversity of the population under examination. The existence of the relationship, which is related to the negative binomial already men-tioned, is attributed to a combination of random processes determining the incidence of a species and of individuals of that species in the collection.

Preston (1948), however, has shown that, when the rank coordinate is graduated logarithmically (he used $\log_2 r$) the resulting curves do not take the form implied by the expression given by Fisher, Corbet and Williams. What Preston finds is that there is a definite mode in the number of species for one of the logarithmic rank categories, the precise rank depending on the size of the collection. He believes that

$$n = n_0 e^{-(aR)^2}$$

when R is the logarithmic rank measured from the mode. This is, of course, the well-known log normal distribution. It is not entirely clear intuitively what such a distribution means biologically. In discussing the matter with Dr. E. S. Deevey, he suggested that in such cases what we are dealing with is not primarily a distribution of specimens, but rather a distribution of fractions of environments. Actually, nearly thirty years ago Dr. C. F. A. Pantin expressed the same idea (he has now probably forgotten it) when we were discussing the same general type of problem, which was beginning to interest biologists owing to the work of J. C. Willis. Every specimen, whether of diatom, moth, bird or elephant, will have required a certain amount of space for its development. The number of specimens, provided we stick to a single taxonomic group, gives in a certain sense, a measure of the space needed by the successful members of that species. It is probably reasonable that, in dividing up a space by coactive processes, a log normal type of distribution should result. What is really extraordinary is that the constant $a$, which is actually the reciprocal of $\sqrt{2}$, * should have practically the same numerical value wherever it is encountered. In collections of moths from North America and Europe, Preston found values from 0.152 to 0.227; in a local bird census he obtained 0.194. Dr. Ruth Patrick, who is making very important studies along these lines, using the statistics of diatoms settling on slides submerged in streams, tells me that the constants found by her group of investigators are always close to 0.2. The value, therefore, appears to be independent of the size and reproductive rate of the organisms under investigation and probably applies to both equilibrium and non-equilibrium communities. It is likely that something very important is involved here, but for the present what it may be is a mystery, a very good thing with which to end a discourse.

*Author's note: $\sqrt{2}$ should have been $\sqrt{2\sigma^2}$

### REFERENCES

BEADLE, L. C. and J. B. CRAGG. 1940. The intertidal zone of two streams and the occurrence of Gammarus spp. on South Rona and Raasay (Inner Hebrides). *Jr. Animal Ecol. 9:* 289-295.

BLISS, C. I. 1953. Fitting the negative binomial distribution to biological data. To appear in *Biometrics.*

BROOKS, J. L. 1950. Speciation in ancient lakes. *Quart. Rev. Biol. 25:* 30-60, 131-176.

FISHER, R. A., A. S. CORBET, and C. B. WILLIAMS. 1943. The relation between the number of species and the number of individuals in a random sample of an animal population. *Jr. Animal Ecol. 12:* 42-58.

GAUSE, G. F. 1934. *The Struggle for Existence.* Baltimore. ix + 163 pp.

————. 1935. Verification expérimentales de la théorie mathématique de la lutte pour la vie. *Actualités scientifiques et industrielles,* no. 277. Paris. 63 pp.

GAUSE, G. F. and A. A. WITT. 1935. Behavior of mixed populations and the problem of natural selection. *Amer. Nat. 69:* 596-609.

GRIM, J. 1950. Versuche zur Ermittlung der Produktionskoeffizienten einige Planktophyten in einem flachen See. *Biol. Zentralbl. 69:* 147-174.

HUTCHINSON, G. E. 1951. Copepodology for the ornithologist. *Ecology 32:* 571-577.

JOHNSON, H. P. 1903. Fresh-water nereids from the Pacific coast and Hawaii, with remarks on fresh-water Polychaeta in general. *Mark Anniversary Volume.* New York. pp. 205-224.

LANGFORD, R. R. 1938. Diurnal and seasonal changes in the distribution of the limnetic crustacea of Lake Nipissing, Ontario. *Univ. Toronto Studies, Biol. Ser. 45:* 1-142.

PRESTON, F. W. 1948. The commonness, and rarity, of species. *Ecology 29:* 254-283.

RANDLE, W. and R. AUSTING. 1952. Ecological notes on the long-eared and saw-whet owls in southwestern Ohio. *Ecology 33:* 422-426.

REID, D. M. 1939. On the occurrence of *Gammarus duebeni* Lillj. (Crustacea, Amphipoda) in Ireland. *Proc. R. Irish Acad. 45 B:* 207-214.

RICKER, W. E. 1937. Statistical treatment of sampling processes useful in the enumeration of plankton. *Arch. f. Hydrobiol. 31:* 68-84.

SEXTON, E. W. 1939. On a new species of *Gammarus* (*G. tigrinus*) from Droitwich District. *Jr. Mar. Biol. Ass. 23:* 543-551.

SEWELL, ELIZABETH. 1951. *The Structure of Poetry.* London. Routledge and Kegan Paul Ltd. x + 196 pp.

SLOBODKIN, L. B. 1953. Population dynamics in *Daphnia obtusa* Kurz. (Yale thesis 1951.) To appear in 1953.

TONOLLI, V. 1949. Stuttura spaziale del popolamento mesoplanctico, eterogeneità delle densità dei popolamenti orizzontale e sua variazione in funzione della quota. *Mem. Ist. ital. Idrobiol. "Dott. Marco de March" 5:* 189-208.

VOLTERRA, V. 1926. Variazioni e fluttuazioni del numero d' individui in specie animali conviventi. *Mem. Accad. Lincei* (6) 2: 31-113.

WHITE, C. M. N. 1951. Weaver birds at Lake Mweru. *Ibis 93:* 626-627.

WYNNE-EDWARDS, V. C. 1952. Zoology of the Baird Expedition (1950). I: The birds observed in central and south-east Baffin Island. *Auk 69:* 352-391.

# A DARWINIAN APPROACH TO PLANT ECOLOGY

## By J. L. HARPER

*Department of Agricultural Botany, University College of North Wales, Bangor*
(*Being the Presidential Address to the British Ecological Society on* 5 *January* 1967)

The theory of evolution by natural selection is an ecological theory—founded on ecological observation by perhaps the greatest of all ecologists. It has been adopted by and brought up by the science of genetics, and ecologists, being modest people, are apt to forget their distinguished parenthood. Indeed, Darwinian plant ecology has been largely neglected and a changeling child nourished and brought to adulthood by Schimper and Warming who asked geographical questions about vegetation, and answered the questions by demonstrating correlations between climate and soils on the one hand and comparative physiology on the other.

By contrast with the 'vegetationalist' and his concern to describe and interpret areas of land, Darwin's ecological observations and the questions he asked were based on a consideration of individuals and populations—a preoccupation with numbers. 'Look at a plant in the midst of its range, why does it not double or quadruple its *numbers*?' '. . . if we wish in imagination to give the plant the power of increasing in *number*, we should have to give it some advantage over its competitors, or over the animals which prey on it'. 'Look at the most vigorous species; by as much as it swarms in *numbers*, by so much will it tend to increase still further' (Darwin, *Origin of Species*, Chapter III).*

These quotations, with their emphasis on numbers, pose problems of population biology—of a demography which has never gained a momentum in plant ecology, although it has played a vertebral role in animal ecology.

Two interlinked properties of higher plants have seriously hindered the development of plant demography—plasticity and vegetative reproduction. Darwin found a 26-year-old pine tree on heathland which 'had during many years tried to raise its head above the stems of the heath and had failed'. It is clearly not fair to count such a plant as a unit equal to a full grown tree in a population census. A mature plant of an annual weed such as *Chenopodium album* may produce four seeds or 100 000 seeds, depending on the nutrient and water status of the soil. It can therefore be argued that a statement about numbers of plants implies very little about the real nature of the population. Vegetative reproduction is a further obstacle to census making, because the vegetative offspring remain to some extent a part of the parent, often for a long period. When is such a ramet to be counted as an individual? Arbitrary decisions have to be made if plant populations are to become numerable and the arbitrariness of the decisions has often discouraged attempts to count plants.

These problems are, however, not peculiar to plants and have had to be faced in animal demography where they arise in only a slightly less acute form. Plasticity in individual size and reproductive capacity have to be taken into account in population studies of fish and even of *Drosophila*. Vegetative reproduction in *Hydra*, where the 'ramets' slowly develop independence, has not prevented its use in model population studies.

* All quotations in this paper are from Chapters III and IV of *The Origin of Species* (1859), the text being the Everyman edition of 1928. Italics are mine.

The very few population studies which have been made of plants in natural populations suggest that the difficulties are not overgreat in practice and the results can be very revealing. Tamm's study of perennial plants in forests and meadows is a classic (Tamm 1948, 1956) (Fig. 1a, b and c). Over a period of 13 years he counted 'individuals' of selected species in permanent quadrats. Many of the populations were remarkably constant in total numbers over this period and yet displayed a high turnover rate including losses both of seedlings and of mature (flowered) plants and gains from new recruits both as seedlings and from vegetative reproduction.

Tamm's study of a declining population of *Centaurea jacea* (Fig. 1c) is equally remarkable for the insight it gives to the process of disappearance of a species from a community. These data have been recalculated and presented as the change in plant numbers (as logarithms) with time (Fig. 2). The relationships are almost startlingly linear, indicating that the chance of an individual dying remains the same through the period of the study. It shows elimination as a steady, not jerky, process, with some individuals remaining vigorous enough to reproduce vegetatively to the bitter end. It suggests that the exodus of a species from a community is not due to the occasional occurrence of extreme conditions but to a slow process of elimination of which the causes act with surprisingly constant intensity. Such population changes may be characterized like the decay of a radioisotope, by a 'half-life'. The half-life of *C. jacea* calculated from Tamm's data is *c.* 1·9 years. Similar calculations made from more constant populations in Tamm's study show widely different half-life values. For example, the individuals of *Filipendula vulgaris* present at the start of Tamm's observations had a half-life of *c.* 18·4 years, and *Sanicula europaea* > 50 years (Fig. 2). In these cases the population decay was at least matched by new recruitment from seedlings or vegetative reproduction.

Sagar (1959) made a shorter but more detailed study of populations of *Plantago lanceolata* in 'permanent' grassland near Oxford which had been under essentially constant management over the preceding 10 years. Using pantograph techniques for mapping plants and seedlings and following the fates of all the seedlings and rosettes in replicate sample plots A and B, he attempted to extract life table data (Table 1).

On both of the two replicate areas sampled, the number of plants of *P. lanceolata* increased but much more strikingly in Area B than in Area A. The behaviour of those plants which were present at the start of the observations was, however, very similar on the two areas. Of the plants recruited to the population as seedlings within the 2-year period, two-thirds died when less than 12 months old. The mature plants present at the start of the period of study had a half-life of *c.* 3·2 years. This is a measure of the dynamic character of such superficially stable vegetation.

Antonovics (1966) has studied the dynamics of population of *Anthoxanthum oderatum* in the open communities of metal mine spoils—in this case marking individuals present along line transects. This was again a short-term study and typical results are given in Fig. 3. As with many of Tamm's examples (and Sagar's plantains) the new recruitment from seedlings compensated for (might indeed be determined by) the rate of loss of the initial population. Such attempts to trace the fate of individuals within populations necessarily involve detailed and frequent mapping so that a seedling which appears where another has just died is recognized as a new individual, and that individuals do not both appear and die in the interval between observations. Probably the first serious observation of this sort was that of Darwin '. . . on a piece of ground three feet long and two wide, dug and cleared, and where there could be no choking from other plants, I marked all the seedlings of our native weeds as they came up, and out of 357 no less

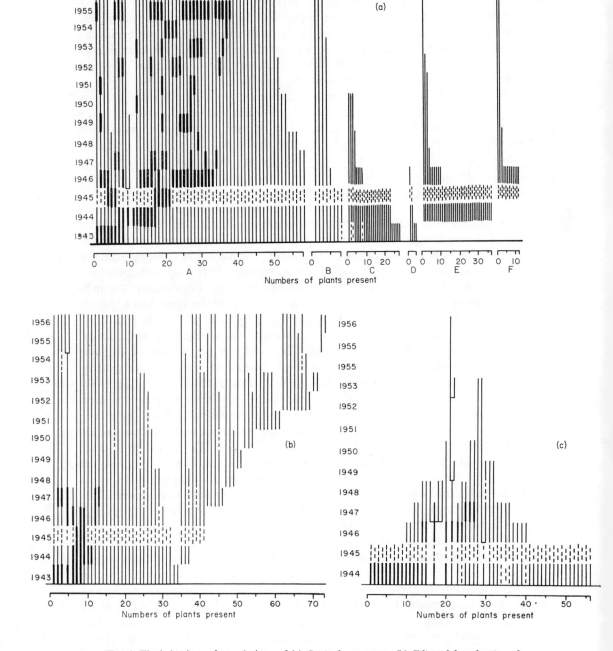

FIG. 1. The behaviour of populations of (a) *Sanicula europaea*, (b) *Filipendula vulgaris* and (c) *Centaurea jacea* within a ¼ m² quadrat in woodland from 1943 to 1956. Group A includes specimens that were large or intermediate in size at the first inspection, Group B rather small plants, Group C very small plants and Groups D–F different crops of seedlings. Heavy lines indicate that the plant flowered in that year. Branching of a line indicates vegetative reproduction. (Redrawn from Tamm 1956.)

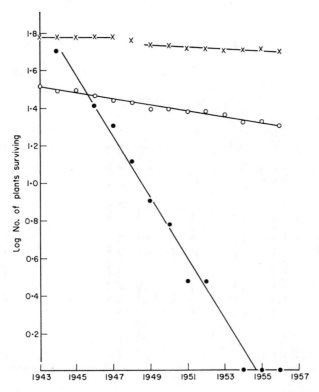

FIG. 2. The decay rate of populations of *Sanicula europaea* (×, half-life > 50 years), *Filipendula vulgaris* (○, half-life *c.* 18·4 years) and *Centaurea jacea* (●, half-life *c.* 1.9 years) calculated from data given by Tamm (1956).

Table 1. *The behaviour of a population of* Plantago lanceolata *in an alluvial meadow near Oxford* (*adapted from Sagar* 1959)

|  |  | Area A | Area B |
|---|---|---|---|
| (a) | Number of individuals per m² present, April 1957 | 238 | 149 |
| (b) | Number of individuals per m² present, April 1959 | 249 | 211 |
| (c) | Net gain | +11 | +62 |
|  | % gain ($\frac{c}{a} \times 100$) | 4·6 | 41·6 |
| (d) | New individuals appearing between April 1957 and April 1959 | 576 | 487 |
| (e) | Individuals lost from population between April 1957 and April 1959 | 565 | 425 |
| (f) | Individuals present at April 1957 and surviving April 1959 | 83 | 52 |
| (g) | Individuals present at April 1957 but lost by April 1959 | 155 | 97 |
| (h) | Percentage survival of individuals from April 1957 to April 1959 ($\frac{f}{a} \times 100$) | 34·9 | 34·9 |
| (i) | Calculated half-life (years) of mature plants present at start of observation | 3·2 | 3·2 |
| (j) | Fate of plants appearing between April 1957 and April 1959 |  |  |
|  | (i) % dying when less than 12 months old | 68·2 | 66·2 |
|  | (ii) % dying when 12–24 months old | 2·3 | 1·2 |
|  | (iii) % still surviving April 1959 | 29·5 | 32·6 |

18

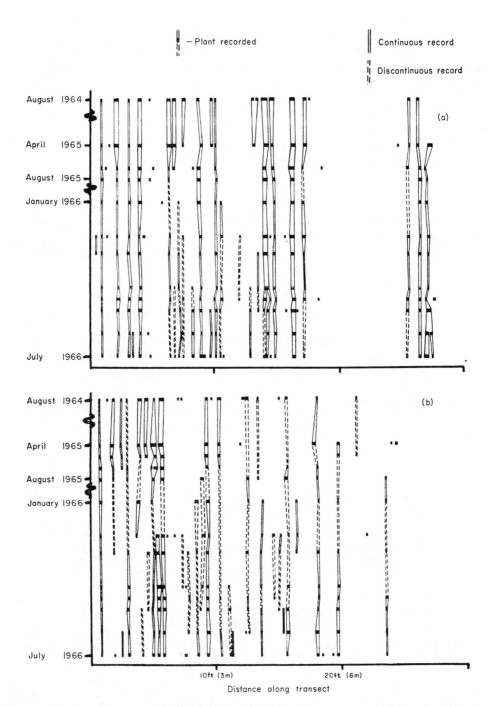

FIG. 3. (a) and (b) The pattern of change in two populations of *Anthoxanthum odoratum* over a period of 2 years in open vegetation on a copper mine site at Trelogan, Flintshire (from Antonovics 1966). Note abbreviation of time scale.

than 295 were destroyed, chiefly by slugs and insects.' Demographic study of this sort focuses attention on the life span of individuals, focuses attention on the causes as well as the time of death, and particularly on the enormous fungal and animal roles in plant mortality.

Measures of population turnover can only be obtained by the detailed observation of individuals—they are totally obscured by vegetational study and revealed by population studies only if plants are marked for repeated observations. They bring measurements of flux into ecological studies in terms which are meaningful to the selection geneticist and the evolutionist. Stable vegetation is then seen to be in a state of continuous flux in which the rates of turnover are critical characteristics of the stability.

The early seedling phases of a plant's life are usually considered the most risky, and the hazards are often strikingly exaggerated by increasing plant density; 'seedlings suffer most from germinating in ground already thickly stocked with other plants'. I have discussed the density dependent mortality of seedlings in other papers (Harper & McNaughton 1962; Harper 1960; Harper 1964a), and this self-regulating property of plant populations is becoming increasingly well documented although the ultimate causes of density-induced death are still very obscure.

One of the earliest attempts to study self-regulation of numbers in populations of plants was made by Sukatschev (1928), who sowed *Matricaria inodora* at two densities in fertilized and unfertilized soil. At the end of a season's growth the percentage loss from the population was greater at the higher density, and in the fertilized soil. (Sukatschev had also observed that the density of mature fir trunks in Leningrad forests declined steadily with *increasing* soil fertility.) Yoda *et al.* (1963) extended this type of observation on natural and artificial populations of plant species (see, for example, Fig. 4). They found that:

(a) The chance of a seed producing a mature plant declined with increasing density.

(b) That irrespective of the density of seeds sown there is a maximum population size of plants produced, and densities beyond this level cannot be realized no matter how many seeds are sown.

(c) The densities of overcrowded populations converge with the passage of time, irrespective of the differences in initial density. The converging densities are always lower on the more fertile soil.

(d) The converging (or asymptotic density) is closely correlated with plant size—so that plants having a certain average size always maintained a more or less similar level of surviving density regardless of the differences in stand age, initial density and fertilizer level.

A particular achievement of this group of Japanese workers was that they were able to formulate a hypothesis linking the numbers of plants and their weight in pure stands which could be expressed as a mathematical relationship—susceptible to experimental test—the major step in transforming a wordy descriptive science into a rigid discipline.

The empirically derived relationship of Yoda *et al.* is

$$w = Cp^{-3/2}$$

where $w$ = mean weight per plant, and $p$ = existing plant density or

$$y = wp = Cp^{-1/2}$$

where $y$ = mean weight per unit area.

It remains to be seen whether this formal relationship holds good for a wider range of species than those studied by Yoda *et al.* which did, however, include such different forms as pure populations of *Betula* sp., *Pinus densiflora*, *Abies sachalinensis*, *Erigeron canadensis*, *Amaranthus retroflexus* and *Plantago asiatica*. It is of great interest to know how far this type of generalization, made for populations of a simple species, can be extended to include populations of several species. The studies of density-dependent mortality in *Papaver* spp. made by Harper & NcNaughton (1962) suggest that pure stands behave in essentially the same way as that suggested by Yoda *et al.*, but that in

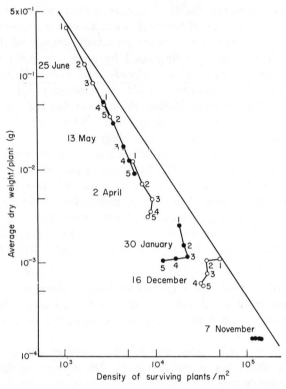

Fig. 4. Changes in numbers and individual plant weight of *Erigeron canadensis* with time. Observations on an abandoned field at Osaka, Japan. The field contained a steep fertility gradient and the plot numbers 1–5 represent an order of decreasing fertility which was exaggerated by the addition of N–P–K–Mg fertilizer in the ratio 5:4:3:2:1 on the plot numbers 1–5. Seed of *E. canadensis* was distributed evenly over the ground $1-2 \times 10^5$ seeds/$m^2$. (Redrawn from Yoda *et al.* 1963.)

mixed stands the processes of self-thinning and alien-thinning (intra- and interspecific effects) are subtly different. A very important aspect of the work of Yoda *et al.* is that it examines both the response of numbers and of individual plant size (i.e. both mortality and plasticity) to changing density. Most previous attempts to study density effects in plant populations have looked at changes in mean plant weight while density is artificially regulated, or have examined changes in plant numbers whilst ignoring plant weight. Because of the comment made earlier that the study of plant demography is hindered by plant plasticity, the attempt by Yoda *et al.* to take plasticity into account in a generalized theory is important. Their experiments suggest that mortality is a continuing risk through the life of the plant, continually adjusting the numbers in the population in relation to the increasing size of the plants. This to an extent contradicts Darwin's view that mortality is concentrated in the seedling stage, and much work is needed to clear up this point and obtain accurate life tables for a number of plant species.

'There is no exception to the rule that every organic being naturally increases at so high a rate that, if not destroyed, the earth would soon be covered by the progeny of a single pair.'

'Lighten any check, mitigate the destruction ever so little, and the number of the species will almost instantaneously increase to any amount.'

'A struggle for existence inevitably follows from the high rate at which all organic beings tend to increase.'

The manner in which potentially explosive plant populations are regulated or controlled in nature is obscure. The pattern of population growth is commonly taken to be logistic

$$\frac{dN}{dt} = rN\left(\frac{K - N}{K}\right)$$

Rate of growth of population = Intrinsic rate of natural increase ×
Degree of realization of the potential increase

In environments in which there is a recurrence of natural hazards, populations may spend most of their time recovering from the hazards—increasing their population size at a rate near to the intrinsic rate of natural increase. The size of such populations may frequently be a function of the magnitude of the last catastrophe and the time available for recovery. Regulation preventing an excessive population size may then be a relatively rare occurrence. This may well be true for many annual plant species of disturbed habitats such as arable weeds. More stable environments are likely to contain populations which spend most of their time near to the $K$ value or saturation level of the population and then density-dependent regulating processes may control population growth continuously.

The intrinsic rate of natural increase of higher plants is a function of seed output and of vegetative reproduction. These two forms of increase represent different values of $r$, the one appropriate for increase over a broad geographical range and the other for immediate and local colonization. The higher (seed) value of $r$ is associated not only with high risk but also with a spread of the risk over a large, sometimes very large, number of small capital investments (or bets!). The lower (vegetative) value of $r$ is often associated with heavy and continuous capital investment, a 'cautious' policy of placing the investments and a low risk. I know of no attempts to compare the capital investment in seed and vegetative reproduction in any species that possesses both. Comparisons of the seed output of a range of species were made by Salisbury (1942) and these are invaluable starting material for a study of the reproductive strategy of higher plants. However, numbers and seed size are not all of the qualities needed to assess or compare reproductive strategy of different species and perhaps the most important is some measure of the proportion of the annual capital increment of a plant which is invested in reproduction. Cody (1966) and R. H. MacArthur (unpublished) have argued that the way in which the resources of an organism are proportioned may be of profound ecological importance, particularly in comparative biology. Cody was concerned with clutch size in birds and argued that available energy may be partitioned between three ecologically important ends (amongst others): (a) contributions to $r$, the intrinsic rate of natural increase (in plants this represents energy put into seed and ramet production); (b) contributions to competitive ability, adaptations in relation to the $K$ value (in plants this presumably represents energy spent in putting leaves higher than neighbours—long petioles, tall stems, or in possessing roots which grow and search faster and further than neighbours); and (c) contributions to predator avoidance (which in plants presumably corresponds to energy spent producing unpalatable structures, defensive chemicals, spines, stinging hairs, etc.).

Few attempts have been made to compare the ways in which different species of plant allocate their limited resources. The procedural difficulties are immense—it is necessary to estimate roots (always an ecologist's nightmare) and to estimate tissues which are shed as the plant grows; there is much difficulty in determining seed output because so many plants shed their seeds over a long period instead of being neat and tidy like crops and holding all their seeds until harvest.

Two examples of attempts to partition a higher plant's activities are shown in Figs. 5 and 6. I suggest that these represent ways of describing the behaviour of a plant which will be of great ecological interest when sufficient examples have been studied for generalizations to be made. It should then be possible to answer such ecological questions as the following:

(1) Is the proportion of a plant's output that is devoted to reproduction higher in colonizing species than in those of mature habitats?

(2) Is the proportion of a plant's output that is devoted to reproduction fixed or plastic? Is it changed by inter- and intraspecific density stress?

(3) Does the proportion of a plant's output that is devoted to reproduction differ between plants of hazardous climatic conditions and those of more stable environments such as a tropical rain forest?

(4) Do plants adapted to competitive environments devote a greater proportion of energy to non-photosynthetic organs (such as support organs)?

(5) Do plants with vegetative reproduction sacrifice a proportion of the energy which would otherwise be expended on seed? Are the two processes competitive within the plant?

(6) What is the relative energy expended in producing a vegetative propagule and a seed? Can this expenditure be related to the relative risks of establishment by the two means and the relative ecological importance of local and long-distance spread?

(7) What is the expenditure on organs ancillary to reproduction—the economic cost to the plant of attractive flowers, a pappus or the massive woody cones of conifers? Is this expenditure a measure of the selective advantages due to possessing these organs?

A whole branch of plant ecology lies almost untouched in attempts to understand the significance of the strategy of reproduction (a very different matter from the tactics—the significance of specific dispersal mechanisms, etc.).

'The only difference between organisms which annually produce eggs or seeds by the thousand, and those which produce extremely few, is that slow breeders would require a few more years to people under unfavourable conditions, a whole district, be it ever so large.'

The strategy of the life cycle itself is an ecologically fascinating but neglected subject of study. Cole (1954) and, more recently, Lewontin (1965) have examined the consequences to population growth of changes in the life cycle of plants and animals. Their studies show that a high intrinsic rate of natural increase ($r$) can be obtained by producing a few offspring early in life—precocious reproduction is all important. For example, a population of which the individuals produce two offspring in the 1st year of life and then die, will have a potential rate of increase as high as if the individuals produce one offspring every year for ever.

It is instructive to examine the consequences of life cycle strategy in such a species as

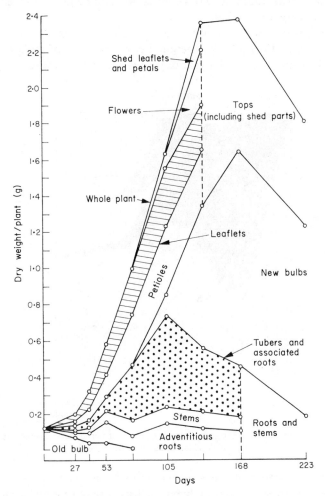

FIG. 5. The pattern of dry weight addition and distribution in *Oxalis pescaprae* L. from the time of planting of the bulb. (Redrawn from Michael 1965.)

the foxglove, which is commonly monocarpic, and under favourable conditions is biennial. In an unexploited environment an annual species producing $S$ seeds per annum could theoretically show a population growth of $1, S, S^2, \ldots, S^n$ in succeeding years. To achieve the same rate of population growth a biennial species would require to produce $S^2$ seeds at the end of each 2-year period. Thus if a biennial such as the foxglove (*Digitalis purpurea*) produces 100 000 seeds every 2 years, its annual counterpart would require to produce only 333 seeds to achieve the same population growth rate. However, if there is a significant mortality risk which is concentrated in the seed and seedling stage, the annual will experience this risk every year and the biennial only in its 1st year of growth. Thus if the 1st year mortality risk is high, a biennial with seed production $S^{<2}$ will maintain the same population growth rate as an annual with seed production $S$. Fig. 7 shows the calculated relationships between $x$, the probability of a seed producing a plant that survives through the first season, and $p$, the power by which the seed production $S$ of an annual would need to be raised to permit equivalent biennial reproduction. This is shown for various values of $S$.

The following points emerge: (1) Where $x = 1$, and all seeds produce a mature plant, the biennial must bear the square of the number of the seeds of the annual. (2) As the chance of the plant surviving the 1st year decreases $p$ decreases. (3) At $p = 1$ the biennial

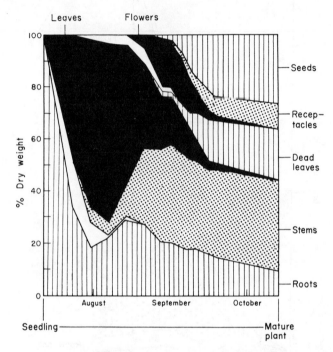

FIG. 6. The proportional distribution of the dry weight of plant parts through the life cycle of *Senecio vulgaris* (data of J. Ogden).

produces the same number of seeds as the annual—this corresponds to the state at which each plant, whether annual or biennial, leaves only one replacement. (4) When $p < 1$ the mortality rate exceeds the seed production and the populations decline. It is apparent that a population of annuals producing $S$ seeds per plant will decline faster than one of biennials bearing $S$ seeds per plant.

This sort of theoretical argument, even in the simple case argued above, emphasizes the rather subtle interplay between the strategy of the life cycle, the population parameters and the timing of the mortality risk.

Similar arguments can clearly be made for a wide variety of alternative strategies. For example: (a) If seed number is sacrificed in favour of seed size, what increase in survival value of a seed is required to maintain the same potential for population increase? (b) In the face of recurrent hazard conditions, of specified frequency and magnitude, what is the optimal fraction of seeds remaining dormant or undergoing dispersal (see Cohen 1966). (c) In what ways is the optimal strategy altered if overcrowding is a more common experience than unhindered population growth?

The great value of this type of theoretical approach lies in the extent to which it focuses attention on quantitative aspects of the life history and behaviour of species which are of acknowledged importance but have remained part of natural history rather than of science.

Even though a high intrinsic rate of natural increase is of great importance to a colonizing species—and such a high rate can be obtained by precocious reproduction

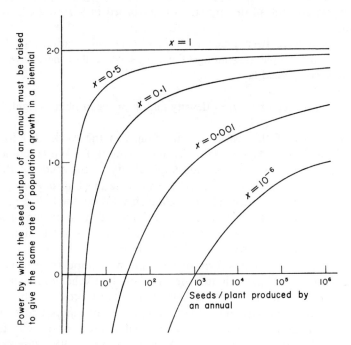

Fig. 7. The theoretical relationship between the seed output of an annual and a biennial for an equal intrinsic rate of natural increase at various values of density-independent mortality ($x$) where this risk is confined to the 1st year of development (data of R. Oxley).

—very few plants use all their reproductive output for immediate multiplication. Seed dormancy is widespread, and it is clear from an elementary consideration of life cycle strategy that a precociously produced seed loses the advantage of precocity if it is unable to start the new generation quickly. An annual colonizing species like *Avena fatua* loses much of its potential rate of population increase by the seed dormancy mechanism which ensures one to several years delay in germination. The adaptive gain from dormancy must be set against an adaptive loss in the intrinsic rate of natural increase. It is all the more interesting that *A. fatua* in the more predictable agriculture and climate of central California seems to lack seed dormancy (Harper 1965).

Much of Darwin's concept of the behaviour of organisms in nature centres around the concept of struggle, '. . . as more individuals are produced than can possibly survive, there must in every case be a struggle for existence, either one individual with another of the same species, or with the individuals of distinct species, or with the physical conditions of life.'

Intraspecific struggle, in which individual development is restricted because of interference from neighbours, has been studied as an agronomic problem—what is the optimal density of plants per unit area needed to achieve maximal dry matter production per area, or maximal economic yield per unit area? At low plant densities plants may not interfere with each other, but as density increases the growth of the population becomes limited by a shortage of environmental supply factors—such as light, water and nutrients —and the growth made by the population becomes a function of the availability of supplies rather than the number of individuals. In many agronomic experiments, self-thinning is absent, so that all density stress is absorbed in the plastic development of the individuals.

Various attempts have been made to fit mathematical relationships to the yield/density responses of crop plants. Amongst the most successful of these have been various forms of the reciprocal yield law

$$\frac{1}{w} = a + bx \text{ where } x = \text{density and } w = \text{mean plant weight.}$$

Various modifications of this basic law are found in the work of Kira, Ogawa & Sagazaki (1953), and other papers of this Japanese School, De Wit (1960) and Holliday (1960). This relationship, which has wide applicability to the study of the behaviour of plants in pure stands, assumes that: (1) the increase in plant dry weight is logistic, (2) the initial growth rate is independent of plant size, (3) the final yield per unit area is constant at high density, (4) time is measured from a common time of sowing, and (5) density-dependent mortality does not occur. If it does, a model similar to that of Yoda *et al.* (1963), discussed earlier, may be preferable.

The major disadvantage of this form of description of population behaviour is that it focuses attention on yield per unit area, or on mean plant behaviour, usually measured by dividing yield per unit area by the number of plants present. This obscures the existence of plant to plant variation. When populations of plants under density stress are examined by sampling and measuring individual plants, curious effects of density on the frequency distribution are revealed. Koyama & Kira (1956) showed that populations of plants which at low density showed normally distributed plant weight, progressively developed log-normal distributions with the passage of time and with increase in density. This phenomenon is shown in Fig. 8 for populations of a variety of fibre flax (Obeid 1965). Stern (1965) has shown the same phenomenon in populations of subterranean clover. It seems that under conditions of density stress not only is there a forced sharing of limited resources with a compensating plastic reduction in individual development, but that a hierarchy emerges amongst the individuals in the population. This hierarchy consists of a few large individuals and an excessive number of small. Such a hierarchy develops in natural habitats as well as in the model crop experiments. R. Oxley has recently shown strikingly log-normal distributions for capsule number per plant in *Digitalis purpurea* in natural habitats and R. Bunce for hazel shoot length in coppices. Apart from the significance of these observations to the interpretation of population samples (in a log-normal distribution the mean plant is *not* the most representative) they show that dominance and suppression may develop within a single species stand. The direct consequences of density stress on a plant population are therefore three-fold: (i) to elicit a plastic response from the individuals as they adjust to share limiting resources, (ii) to increase mortality, and (iii) to exaggerate differentials within the population and encourage a hierarchy of exploitation.

Just as in a population of a single species the stress of density intensifies the expression of small differences (genetic or environmental) between individuals, so in mixed populations density stress may exaggerate and exploit interspecific differences. The experimental models of De Wit (1960) are superbly designed to study the behaviour of two species in mixture and so to begin the exploration of natural diversity. In these models two species are sown together in varied proportions while the overall density of the sown or planted mixture is maintained constant. The behaviour of a species can then be compared in pure stand with its performance in variously proportioned mixtures, and the mutual aggressiveness of two forms may be measured.

Fig. 9 illustrates the use of such an experimental design for the study of the interaction of *Chenopodium album* with barley and with kale. The results of experiments designed

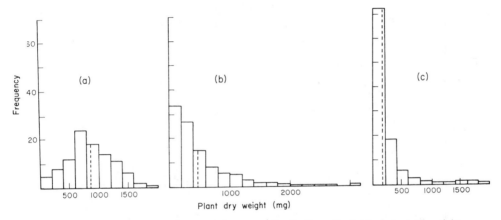

FIG. 8. The influence of density on the frequency distribution of individual plant dry weight in *Linum usitatissimum* sown at densities of (a) 60/m², (b) 1440/m² and (c) 3600/m², and harvested at seed maturity (from Obeid 1965).

in this way may also be conveniently expressed as 'ratio diagrams' relating the sown proportions of two species to the harvested proportions. Such a diagram has considerable value in understanding both the progress of extinction of one species by another and the processes by which an equilibrium between species may be produced. Fig. 10 illustrates some idealized forms of ratio diagrams which are considered in more detail in De Wit (1960).

Darwin was clearly aware that in nature there is a frequent ousting of one form by another, either over long periods as witnessed in the palaeontological record, involving extinction, or over short periods, involving successional changes of vegetation and purely local elimination. At times he gives the impression that the struggle for existence between forms must lead to a winner and a loser. He sees this as particularly likely between closely related species or varieties. 'In the case of varieties of the same species, the struggle will generally be almost equally severe (*cf. members of the same species*). and we sometimes see the contest soon decided.' But he is also aware that in nature diversity is everywhere, and far from this involving perpetual struggles to extinction 'Battle within battle must be continually recurring with varying success; and yet in the

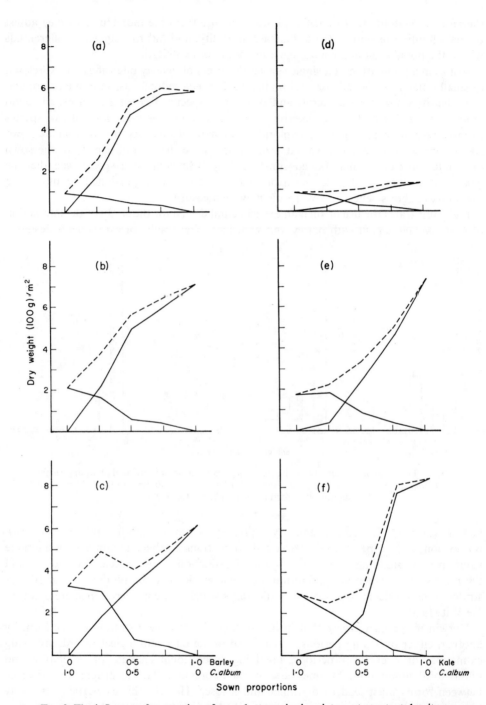

Fig. 9. The influence of proportion of two plant species in mixture at constant density on dry weight per unit area of each component and combined yield (– – – –). (a), (b) and (c) *Chenopodium album* and barley at three successive harvest dates. (d), (e) and (f) *C. album* and kale at three successive harvest dates (from Williams 1964).

J.E.    B

long run the forces are so nicely balanced that the face of nature remains for long periods of time uniform, though assuredly the merest trifle would give the victory to one organic being over another.'

The existence of natural diversity implies that the struggle for existence is not regularly forced to decide between stronger and weaker brethren—and that the struggle between some forms living in the same area is either evaded or does not occur. This poses the question which has worried so many zoologists, most notably Gause (1934), Gause & Witt (1935) and Hutchinson (1966) and his various colleagues, what are the characteristics of species which permit them to co-occur in the diversity of nature? This has been

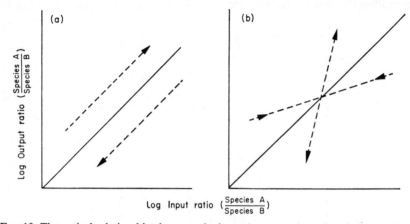

Fig. 10. Theoretical relationships between the input (sown or planted) ratio between two species and the output (seed harvested) ratio. (a) Frequency independence in which the empirical relationship has unit slope (– – →) lying above or below the continuous line which represents input ratio = output ratio. Such situations lead to the progressive extinction of one or other component of the mixture. (b) Frequency dependence in which the empirical relationships have a slope > or < unity (– – →) and intersect the line of input ratio = output ratio. A slope of > 1 implies that the population moves towards the extinction of the minority component. A slope of < 1 implies equilibration and stabilization of the mixed condition.

examined in great and fascinating detail in experiments and theoretical models and a conclusion is conveniently expressed by Hutchinson in the modified logistic equation of growth for two species living together:

$$dN_1 = r_1 N_1 \left( \frac{K_1 - N_1 - \alpha N_2}{K_1} \right)$$

$$dN_2 = r_2 N_2 \left( \frac{K_2 - N_2 - \beta N_1}{K_2} \right)$$

where $N_1$ and $N_2$ are the numbers of individuals of species $S_1$ and $S_2$.

The conditions under which both $S_1$ and $S_2$ survive is that $\alpha < K_1/K_2$ and $\beta < K_2/K_1$, or that the growth of each species population inhibits its further growth more than it inhibits that of the other species. This solution assumes a linear competition function, and there are likely to be further solutions where the function is not linear. This solution generalizes a host of differences between organisms which may permit them to evade a struggle to the death and so permit diversity. In animals it is easy to see that differences in food taken or in feeding habits, differences in habitat preference, differences in prey (or in predators) may prevent an exclusive struggle by focusing the intensive battles within rather than between the species. In plants it is less easy to see how a group of species which all require the same basic food requirements—light, water and mineral nutrients—may possess sufficiently diverse biologies to prevent a best species from excluding all others. There are, however, a number of experiments which show that mixtures of two plant species may form stable associations and indeed possess self-stabilizing properties.

Van den Bergh & De Wit (1960) grew *Phleum pratense* and *Anthoxanthum odoratum* together in field plots at a range of proportions and compared the ratio of tillers of the two species after the first winter with the ratio after the second winter (Fig. 11). In plots

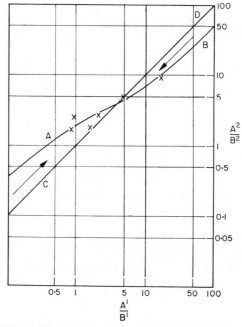

Fig. 11. The relationship between the ratio of the number of tillers of *Anthoxanthum odoratum* (A) and *Phleum pratense* (B) after the first winter ($A^1/B^1$) and after the second winter ($A^2/B^2$). (Redrawn from Van den Bergh & De Wit 1960).

in which *A. odoratum* had been in excess, the proportion of *Phleum pratense* increased. Where *P. pratense* was in excess, *Anthoxanthum odoratum* increased. Thus the mixture possessed self-stabilizing properties—the stable mixture under this set of environmental conditions being the point at which the experimentally obtained ratio line A–B on Fig. 11 intersects with the line of unit slope C–D (cf. Fig. 10). In a similar experiment performed in a controlled environment chamber, *A. odoratum* was at a slight advantage over *Phleum pratense* at all relative frequencies, and at all proportions and the population changed regularly towards increasing dominance by *Anthoxanthum*.

A stabilizing situation is also found in mixtures of *Lolium perenne* and *Trifolium repens*. Lieth (1960) has described how in pastures these two species form a moving mosaic in which patches of the mosaic dominated by grass tend to be invaded by clover, while patches dominated by clover are overrun by grass. Ennik (1960) grew *Lolium perenne* and *Trifolium repens* in mixtures of varying proportions in controlled environments at high and low light intensities. Ratio diagrams relating the proportion of the two species at the beginning and end of the treatment are shown in Fig. 12. At high light intensity the populations changed regularly towards extinction of the grass. At low light intensities the populations equilibrated, those with excess clover tending to increase their grass content, and those with excess grass tending to increase in clover. In this example the ecological differentiation between the species which permits this stabilization is almost certainly due to differences in their nitrogen nutrition.

A further example of stabilizing action in mixture has been demonstrated by P. D. Putwain for the sexes of the sexually dimorphic *Rumex acetosella*. In permanent grass-lands this species only rarely reproduces by seed and the main means of spread is by

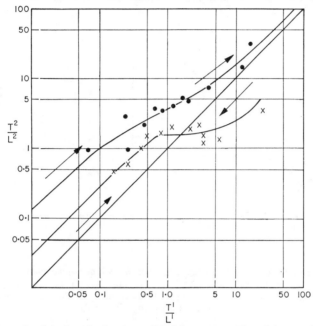

FIG. 12. The ratio of the length of stolons of *Trifolium repens* (T) and the number of tillers of *Lolium perenne* (L) in the first winter ($T^1/L^1$) plotted against the same ratio in the second winter ($T^2/L^2$). ●, At high light intensity; ×, at low light intensity. (Redrawn from Ennik 1960.) The same data are presented with calculated linear regressions in De Wit *et al.* (1960).

root buds. In dense stands the two sexes are therefore the equivalent of two species with different biologies, one having the whole task of seed production and the other the apparently light responsibility of producing pollen. It might be expected that two such forms would differ in aggression in the community and that in old pastures the 50 : 50 sex ratio of seedlings would become biased. In fact, natural populations have been shown by Löve (1944) and many others to have a sex ratio not departing significantly from equality.

An experiment was designed on the 'De Wit' model to study the population balance of the sexes in this species. Clonal populations of males and of females were obtained from root fragments and were grown at various proportions at low and high densities. The results of the high density treatment are shown in Fig. 13. Populations with an excess of males increased the proportion of females, and those with excess females increased the proportion of males. Experimental distortion of the sex ratio from equality led to readjustment towards equality as a result of the more vigorous reproduction by the minority sex.

In the three experiments described above, reproduction was clonal and the adjustment of balance between the species (or sexes) was by differential vegetative reproduction. All these examples illustrate the essential criterion for a balanced 'co-occurrence' of two species—that the minority component should always be favoured.

A similar model was shown by Harper & McNaughton (1962) for the survival of *Papaver* spp. sown in mixture. In this case each individual of a species in a mixture of two species had the greatest likelihood of becoming an adult plant when it was in the minority. In the discussion of the poppy experiments we contrasted 'self-thinning' (the

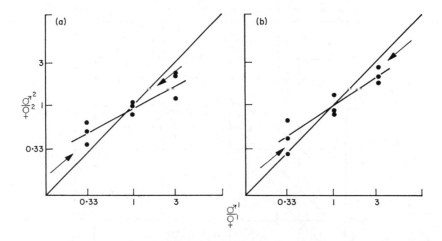

FIG. 13. The ratio of male to female plants of *Rumex acetosella* planted in the spring ($\male^1/\female^1$) plotted against the same ratio in the autumn ($\male^2/\female^2$). (a) Dry weight of above ground parts, (b) number of inflorescences (data from P. D. Putwain). Values for three replicates are shown individually.

reaction of a species to an increase in its own density) with 'alien-thinning' (the reaction of a species to the density of its associated species). These experiments suggested that each species in a mixture suffered more severely from intra- than from interspecific interference. It was argued that this was a necessary condition for stable diversity. It is interesting to find that a similar differentiation between self- and alien-thinning occurs in mixtures of *Medicago sativa* and *Trifolium pratense*. Black (1960) sowed these two species in variously proportioned mixtures, and recorded plant survival. From his data it is possible to calculate the chance of a seed forming a plant and this is shown for two ranges of density in Fig. 14. The nature of the differences between poppy species and between *Medicago sativa* and *Trifolium pratense* which alleviate interspecific interference are obscure. It is presumably an understanding of these critical differences between species that will provide the 'explanation' of stable diversity in nature.

In the various models of the behaviour of two species in mixture, the existence of a stable equilibrium depends on *frequency-dependent* 'competition'. This phenomenon has recently been recognized by Pavlovsky & Dobzhansky (1966) in *Drosophila* cultures, and, as they point out, it plays havoc with the Sewall Wright concept of adaptive values.

Selection genetics is therefore forced to take account of fundamental ecological phenomena and the convergence of population genetics and population ecology provides one of the most exciting fields of development in modern biology.

Recently there has been growing interest in the genetic consequences of a struggle for existence between two populations and the ecological significance of these changes. The experiments have all involved flies, and in a lecture on plant ecology I have assumed that *Drosophila* (by usage) and all flies (by analogy) are appropriate objects for botanical study!

Pimentel *et al.* (1965) allowed populations of blowflies and houseflies to multiply with a controlled food supply in a network of interconnected population cages. He

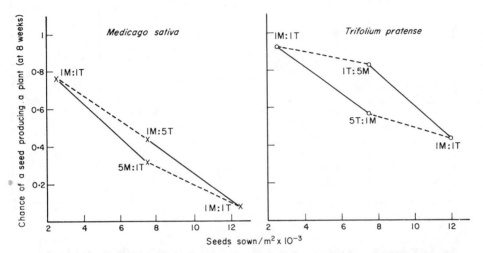

Fig. 14. The influence of density on 'self-thinning' and 'alien-thinning' in mixed populations of *Trifolium pratense* (T) and *Medicago sativa* (M). The extreme densities, 2500 and 12 500 seeds/m², were composed of equal numbers of the two species. The intermediate density, 7000 seeds/m², was either with a preponderance (5:1) of one species or the other.

The difference between the chance of a seed producing an 8-week-old plant at the two differently constituted intermediate densities reflects the different degrees of thinning in predominantly 'self' and predominantly 'alien' populations. In each diagram the broken line indicates 'alien-thinning' and the continuous line 'self-thinning' (i.e. inter- and intraspecific effects respectively). Calculated from data in Black (1960).

observed oscillation in the populations of the two species. By sampling and testing his two populations against each other at intervals he was able to show that there was an oscillation in the 'competitive ability' of the two species. He argued that in a mixture the minority species faces predominantly interspecific interference, and is therefore under selection to improve its performance relative to the majority species. The majority species, however, experiences predominantly intraspecific interference and hence selection within it is concentrated on qualities important in the intraspecific struggle. The minority species eventually gains the majority because of its newly selected qualities, and interspecific selection immediately concentrates on the new minority species. The two species thus oscillate in relative abundance. Pimentel shows that the amplitude of oscillations may become progressively damped and he suggests that the two species are attaining an equilibrium.

Seaton & Antonovics (1967) reared wild type and 'dumpy' *D. melanogaster* in milk bottle cultures. The two forms were reared in mixtures, but care was taken that mating did not occur between them (by removing virgin females and mating them with males of the same type from their own culture). Each succeeding generation was started with six wild type and six dumpy flies from the preceding experiment, and the food supply was limited. After four generations the two mutually selected populations were tested against each other and against stock populations using a 'De Wit' model for the experimental testing. The results are shown in Fig. 15.

The results of mutual selection were at first sight surprising. Instead of one type of fly acquiring increased success in a struggle for existence the selection process seems to

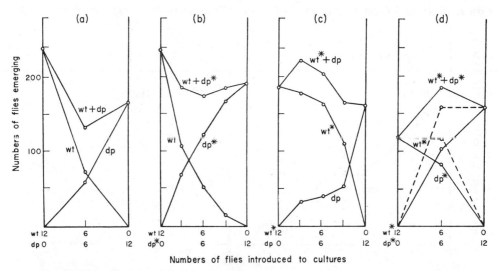

FIG. 15. The results of a replacement experiment (cf. Fig. 9) involving wild type and dumpy *Drosophila melanogaster* grown in pure cultures and mixtures. The two forms were prevented from mating with each other.

The success of each component in mixture and pure culture was assessed as the number of offspring hatched in the first generation of progeny. (a) Stock 'wild type' with stock 'dumpy'. (b) Stock 'wild type' with selected 'dumpy'. Selected 'dumpy' had experienced four repeated generations in mixed culture with 'wild type'. (c) Selected 'wild type' with stock 'dumpy'. Selected 'wild type' had experienced four repeated generations in mixed culture with 'dumpy'. (d) Selected 'wild type' with selected 'dumpy' (after one further generation of relaxed selection). – – –, Replicate experiment; wt, Stock wild type; wt*, selected wild type; dp, stock dumpy; dp*, selected dumpy. (From Seaton & Antonovics 1967.)

have resulted in an ability of the wild type and the 'dumpy' fly to avoid interference from each other. At the end of the experiment neither wild type nor dumpy had as depressive effect on the other, as did mutually unselected strains. Moreover, the mutually selected strains grown together achieved a greater output of offsprings than did either of the stock types grown in pure culture.

This would appear to be a case of direct selection for some difference in niche occupancy, the evolutionary process which Ludwig (1950) has called 'annidation'.

The experiments of Pimentel and of Seaton & Antonovics illustrate three different evolutionary solutions to the problem of intergroup struggle for limited resources: (i) extinction of one group, (ii) mutual oscillating inter-group selection leading to increased stability of the mixture (the Pimentel solution), and (iii) mutual divergence in behaviour leading to the avoidance of inter-group struggle (the Seaton–Antonovics solution).

Both (ii) and (iii) imply that in the process of natural selection the reaction to the other species may be a critical force '. . . . the structure of every organic being is related, in the most essential yet often hidden manner, to that of all the other organic beings, with which it comes into competition for food or residence, or from which it has to escape, or on which it preys.' Goodall (1966) has recently argued a similar point, though he despaired of the chance of demonstrating such coadaptive evolution in action.

The concept of natural selection operating between groups of organisms and adjusting their mutual strategies to permit increasing diversity and more efficient environmental exploitation strengthens the image of the community as an integrated whole rather than a Gleason-type assemblage of individuals.

The logical extension of the view that community stability and diversity depend on niche specialization, is that complex ecosystems are more efficient than simple in using environmental resources. Yet the rigid demonstration that mixtures of plant species outyield pure stands seems not to have been made. Darwin wrote 'It has been experimentally proved that if a plot of ground be sown with one species of grass, and a similar plot be sown with several distinct genera of grasses, a greater number of plants and a greater dry weight of herbage can be raised in the latter than in the former case.' More than 100 years later, the Director of the Grassland Research Institute writes 'No research, as far as I am aware, has yet shown that a mixture of two or more grass species, when sown together, will outyield the crop that can be obtained from a single bred variety' (Woodford 1966). Perhaps the answer to this contradiction lies in the degree to which the forms that are grown together have been mutually selected. It may be too much to hope that any pair of species grown together will already possess the precise biological differences needed to interniche or annidate effectively. Perhaps special breeding programmes are needed to develop 'ecological combining ability' (Harper 1964b) in agricultural crops.

With the exception of examples of mutual exploitation of the light environment shown by the studies of Salisbury (1916) in woodland—there are few demonstrations that stable mixed vegetation is compounded of ecologically complementary species. Recently, a number of experimental designs have been suggested which permit the 'ecological combining ability' of groups of species to be examined, in the same way that a plant breeder explores the 'genetic combining ability' of a range of genotypes (Sakai 1961; Williams 1962; McGilchrist 1965; Harper 1964b; Norrington Davies 1967). These are all based on diallell analysis, in which a number of species are grown in all possible combination of pairs and their yield as mixtures is contrasted with the yield of pure stands. In this way the ecological equivalents of the genetic concepts of dominance, recessiveness, overdominance and interaction can be detected and—more important—measured. These techniques seem likely to bring to experimental synecology a refinement and subtlety appropriate for a science which has outgrown its qualitative and descriptive youth.

It is impossible in the time of one lecture to do justice to the range of ecological thought and the stimulus to modern experimental ecology to be found in just two chapters of *The Origin of Species*. I have wholly omitted the fascinating matter of animal–plant interactions that play so large a part in Darwin's ecology. I am not amongst those very few ecologists since Darwin who are intellectually equipped to deal with the plant–animal interface. My aim has been to try to show that much of what is exciting to me in the science of plant ecology in the late sixties has a highly respectable origin in the ecological thinking of Darwin. 'It is never safe for a biologist to announce a discovery if he has not read and mastered *The Origin of Species*.' (Keith 1928). A presidential address is a rare opportunity for a personal expression of belief. My own is that *The Origin of Species* states precise questions which plant ecologists can usefully spend the next hundred years answering.

## ACKNOWLEDGMENTS

I am grateful to J. Ogden, P. D. Putwain and R. Oxley for allowing me to use material which has not yet appeared in thesis form.

## REFERENCES

**Antonovics, J. (1966).** *Evolution in adjacent populations*. Ph.D. thesis, University of Wales.

**Black, J. N. (1960).** An assessment of the role of planting density in competition between red clover (*Trifolium pratense* L.) and lucerne (*Medicago sativa* L.) in the early vegetative stage. *Oikos*, **11**, 26–42.

**Bergh, J. P. van den & Wit, C. T. de (1960).** Concurrentie tussen Timothee en Reukgras. *Meded. Inst. biol. scheik. Onderz. Lundb Gewass.* **121**, 155–65.

**Cody, M. L. (1966a).** A general theory of clutch size. *Evolution, Lancaster, Pa.* **20**, 174–84.

**Cohen, D. (1966).** Optimising reproduction in a randomly varying environment. *J. theor. Biol.* **12**, 119–29.

**Cole, L. C. (1954).** The population consequences of life history phenomena. *Q. Rev. Biol.* **29**, 103–37.

**Ennik, G. C. (1960).** De concurrentie tussen witte klaver en Engels raaigras bij verschillen in lichtintensiteit en vochtvoorziening. *Meded. Inst. biol. scheik. Onderz. LandbGewass.* **109**, 37–50.

**Gause, G. F. (1934).** *The Struggle for Existence*. Baltimore.

**Gause, G. F. & Witt, A. A. (1935).** Behaviour of mixed populations and the problem of natural selection. *Am. Nat.* **69**, 596–609.

**Goodall, D. W. (1966).** The nature of the mixed community. *Proc. ecol. Soc. Aust.* **1**, 84–96.

**Harper, J. L. (1960).** Factors controlling numbers. *The Biology of Weeds* (Ed. by J. L. Harper), pp. 119–32. Oxford.

**Harper, J. L. (1964a).** The individual in the population. *J. Ecol.* **52**(Suppl.), 149–58.

**Harper, J. L. (1964b).** The nature and consequences of interference amongst plants. *Proc. XIth int. Conf. Genet.*, pp. 465–81.

**Harper, J. L. (1965).** Establishment, aggression and cohabitation in weedy species. *The Genetics of Colonising Species* (Ed. by H. G. Baker and G. L. Stebbins), pp. 243–268. New York.

**Harper, J. L. & McNaughton, I. H. (1962).** The comparative biology of closely related species living in the same area. VII. Interference between individuals in pure and mixed populations of *Papaver* species. *New Phytol.* **61**, 175–88.

**Holliday, R. (1960).** Plant population and crop yield. *Nature, Lond.* **186**, 22–4.

**Hutchinson, G. E. (1965).** *The Ecological Theater and the Evolutionary Play*. Newhaven and London.

**Keith, (1928).** Introduction to Everyman Edition of C. Darwin, *The Origin of Species*.

**Kira, T., Ogawa, H. & Sagazaki, N. (1953).** Intraspecific competition among higher plants. I. Competition–density–yield interrelationship in regularly dispersed populations. *J. Inst. Polytech. Osaka Cy Univ.* Ser. D, **4**, 1–16.

**Koyama, H. & Kira, T. (1956).** Intraspecific competition among higher plants. VIII. Frequency distribution of individual plant weight as affected by the interaction between plants. *J. Inst. Polytech. Osaka Cy Univ.* Ser. D, **7**, 73–94.

**Lewontin, R. C. (1965).** Selection for colonising ability. *The Genetics of Colonising Species* (Ed. by H. G. Baker and G. L. Stebbins), pp. 77–94. New York.

**Lieth, H. (1960).** Patterns of change within grassland communities. *The Biology of Weeds* (Ed. by J. L. Harper), pp. 27–39. Oxford.

**Löve, A. (1944).** Cytogenetic studies on *Rumex* sub-genus *acetosella*., *Hereditas*, **30**, 1–127.

**Ludwig, W. (1950).** Zur Theorie der Konkurrenz. Die Annidation (Einnischung) als fünfter Evolutionsfaktor. *Neue Ergebnisse in Probleme der Zoologie* (*Klattfestschrift*), 516–37.

**McGilchrist, C. A. (1965).** Analysis of competition experiments. *Biometrics*, **21**, 975–85.

**Michael, P. W. (1965).** Studies on *Oxalis pes-caprae* L. in Australia. I. Quantitative studies on oxalic acid during the life cycle of the pentaploid variety. *Weed Res.* **5**, 123–32.

**Norrington Davies, J. (1967).** The analysis of competition experiments. *J. appl. Ecol.* (In press).

Obeid, M. (1965). *Experimental models in the study of plant competition.* Ph.D. thesis, University of Wales.

Pavlovsky, O. & Dobzhansky, T. H. (1966). Genetics of natural populations. xxxvii. The coadapted system of chromosomal variants in a population of *Drosophila pseudoobscura.* *Genetics, Princeton,* **53,** 843–54.

Pimentel, D., Feinberg, E. G., Wood, P. W. & Hayes, J. T. (1965). Selection, spatial distribution, and the coexistence of competing fly species. *Am. Nat.* **94,** 97–109.

Sagar, G. R. (1959). *The biology of some sympatric species of grassland.* D.Phil. thesis, University of Oxford.

Sakai, K. (1961). Competitive ability in plants: its inheritance and some related problems. *Symp. Soc. exp. Biol.* **15,** 245–63.

Salisbury, E. J. (1916). The oak-hornbeam woods of Hertfordshire: a study in colonisation. *Trans. Herts nat. Hist. Soc. Fld Club,* **17.**

Salisbury, E. J. (1916). *The Reproductive Capacity of Plants.* London.

Seaton, A. J. P. & Antonovics, J. (1967). Population interrelationships. I. Evolution in mixtures of *Drosophila* mutants. *Heredity, Lond.* (In press).

Stern, W. R. (1965). The effect of density on the performance of individual plants in subterranean clover swards. *Aust. J. agric. Res.* **16,** 541–55.

Sukatschev, V. N. (1928). [*Plant communities*] (in Russian). Moscow.

Tamm, C. O. (1948). Observations on reproduction and survival of some perennial herbs. *Bot. Notiser,* **3,** 305–21.

Tamm, C. O. (1956). Further observations on the survival and flowering of some perennial herbs. *Oikos,* **7,** 273–92.

Williams, E. J. (1962). The analysis of competition experiments. *Aust. J. biol. Sci.* **15,** 509–25.

Williams, J. T. (1964). *Studies on the biology of weeds with special reference to the genus* Chenopodium *L.* Ph.D. thesis, University of Wales.

Wit, C. T. de (1960). On competition. *Versl. landbouwk. Onderz. Ned.* **66,** 8.

Wit, C. T. de, Ennik, G. C., Bergh, J. P. van den & Sonneveld, A. (1960). Competition and non-persistency as factors affecting the composition of mixed crops and swards. *Proc. 8th int. Grassld Congr.,* pp. 736–41.

Woodford, E. K. (1966). The need for a fresh approach to the place and purpose of the ley. *J. Br. Grassld. Soc.* **21,** 109–15.

Yoda, K., Kira T., Ogawa, H. & Hozumi, K. (1963). Self-thinning in overcowded pure stands under cultivated and natural conditions. *J. Biol. Osaka Cy Univ.* **14,** 107–29.

# PART II

# SINGLE SPECIES POPULATIONS: PATTERNS IN SPACE AND TIME

# A STUDY OF THE CRYPTOZOA OF AN ILLINOIS WOODLAND

LAMONT C. COLE

*Hull Zoological Laboratory, University of Chicago*

## THE DISTRIBUTION OF THE CRYPTOZOIC ANIMALS WITHIN AREAS

It has been shown that different experimental areas representing slightly different habitats might contain faunas distinct from each other in species composition, seasonal aspects, and in relative abundance of various forms. Faunal variations within specific areas where conditions may be presumed to have been relatively constant may also be examined with respect to individual species to see to what extent individual animals were distributed at random in the available cryptozoic habitat.

A discontinuous integral variate such as the frequency of occurrence of a species of animal in field plots should be expected to correspond to a Poisson distribution (Poisson 1837, Student 1907, Svedberg 1922) if the individual animals are distributed at random. The application of the Poisson frequency distribution to cases where the number of samples is not very great or in cases such as would arise in field plot sampling of a fairly abundant species has sometimes been questioned (Whitaker 1914), but such applications have been vigorously defended by Arne Fisher (1922) and now seem to be generally accepted (Snedecor 1938, R. A. Fisher 1941). It is only profitable to investigate the distribution of the more abundant species because comparisons of observed and theoretical distributions are unsatisfactory for forms so rare that there is little probability of ever finding more than one individual under a particular board.

The distribution of spiders under the boards regularly corresponded to a Poisson distribution indicating a random distribution of individuals. Table 8 shows the distribution of 108 spiders encountered in 240 inspections of boards in Area H for the month of August, 1942.

TABLE 8. The distribution of spiders in Area H—August, 1942. P $=$ 0.527.

| | Number of spiders per board | | | | |
| --- | --- | --- | --- | --- | --- |
| | 0 | 1 | 2 | 3 | More |
| Observed frequencies... | 159 | 64 | 13 | 4 | 0 |
| Expected (Poisson)..... | 157.0 | 66.5 | 14.2 | 2.0 | 0.3 |

The test of the observed distribution by the Chi-square test indicates that as great a deviation from the Poisson distribution could be expected about 53 percent of the time due to chance alone so there is certainly no reason for assuming a non-random distribution of the spiders under the experimental boards. In all experimental areas and at all seasons the spiders were distributed at random.

Editor's Note: Of the nearly 40 pages of this study, only the section dealing with the distribution of members of the Cryptozoic fauna under boards is reprinted. The terms of the Poisson series, formally written

$$P_{(x)} = \frac{m^x \, e^{-m}}{x!}, \text{ are for } 0, 1, 2, 3 \ldots. \text{ occurrences } \frac{1}{e^m}, \frac{m}{e^m}, \frac{m^2}{2e^m}, \frac{m^3}{3 \times 2e^m} \ldots.$$

For a further discussion of this series in ecology, see Andrewartha's Introduction to the Study of Animal Populations (University of Chicago Press) and Greig-Smith's Quantitative Plant Ecology (New York, Academic Press).

Reproduced and excerpted with permission from Ecological Monographs, 16: 70-75 (only), 1946. Published by The Duke University Press, Durham, North Carolina.

No other prominent species exhibited a random distribution of individuals. The chilopod Lithobius, which is generally considered to be a solitary animal, was never common enough under the boards to permit a rigid test of the randomness of distribution but, as already observed, they form winter aggregations which certainly indicates a non-random distribution for at least a part of the year.

All of the other important animals exhibited non-random distributions of the type termed "contagious" by Polya (1931). The distribution of 254 diplopods (Scytonotus) in Area H for a series of 360 inspections made between September 12 and September 22, 1942 will serve as an example of a contagious distribution. This distribution is shown in Table 9 and in Figure 3.

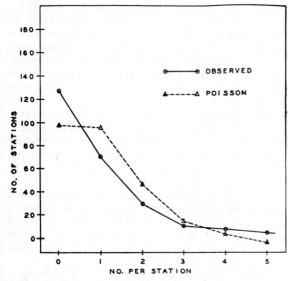

Fig. 3. The contagious distribution of *Scytonotus*.

Contagious distributions are characterized by a tendency for the animals to form aggregations so that the larger numbers of animals under single boards occurred more often than would be the case if the distribution were random.

TABLE 9. The distribution of *Scytonotus granulatus* in Area H. P = 0.0000.

| | Number of *Scytonotus* per board | | | | | | |
|---|---|---|---|---|---|---|---|
| | 0 | 1 | 2 | 3 | 4 | 5 | More |
| Observed frequencies | 128 | 71 | 34 | 11 | 8 | 5 | 3 |
| Expected (Poisson) | 100.5 | 94.5 | 45.4 | 14.4 | 3.4 | 0.7 | 0.1 |

In testing randomness of distribution there is danger of confounding the results by lumping together data collected on different days or in different areas. For example, if data from the grazed part of the woods were included in the Scytonotus table, the form of the distribution would be radically altered because nearly all of these boards would show a zero-frequency for diplopods. For this reason, interpretations based on such frequency distributions must be limited to the more common species and to as homogeneous samples as possible.

In the case of Scytonotus distributions were always contagious and showed a tendency to cross the theoretical Poisson distribution at about the level of the frequency class "3 diplopods per board." More detailed investigation might reveal that when about 3 Scytonotus are present under a board of this size they serve to attract other diplopods to the board or influence wandering individuals to remain once they find that particular board. Thus any "social instinct" on the part of the animals would lead to contagious distributions of the type observed.

In the case of the isopod Trachelipus the number of aggregations found usually did not exceed expectation until groups of 7 or 8 individuals were attained. Table 10 illustrates this for Area TP on June 12, 1942.

TABLE 10. Distribution of *Trachelipus rathkei* in Area TP—June 12, 1942.

| | Number per board | | | | | | | | |
|---|---|---|---|---|---|---|---|---|---|
| | 0 | 1 | 2 | 3 | 4 | 5 | 6 | 7 | 8 |
| Observed | 28 | 28 | 14 | 11 | 8 | 11 | 2 | 3 | 3 |
| Expected | 5.7 | 17.5 | 26.8 | 27.3 | 20.9 | 12.8 | 6.5 | 2.8 | 1.1 |

| | Number per board | | | | | | | | |
|---|---|---|---|---|---|---|---|---|---|
| | 9 | 10 | 11 | 12 | 13 | 14 | 15 | 16 | 17 |
| Observed | 3 | 3 | 2 | 0 | 1 | 2 | 1 | 0 | 2 |
| Expected | Total expected over 8 = 0.5 | | | | | | | | |

The isopods obviously tended to form larger aggregations than did the diplopods. The largest aggregation ever encountered under one board contained 56 isopods.

It is obvious that social insects such as the ants are not distributed at random but, aside from a social instinct, there are several other conditions which could cause animals to exhibit contagious frequency distributions. If an animal deposits its eggs in clumps, the newly hatched young will occur in groups and will be contagiously distributed. Neyman (1939), reasoning from this type of situation, has developed a class of theoretical frequency distributions which have been shown by Beall (1940) to give good fits when applied to certain contagiously distributed animals. Neyman's "type A" curve may be thought of as a generalized expression of the Poisson law with another parameter added. This type of distribution, however, seldom gave good fits in the present study where the basic assumptions were not realized. In highly contagious distributions such as those shown by the ants and isopods the fit was little better than that given by the Poisson distribution.

*Author's note: 360 inspections should have been 260 inspections.

**Author's note: Corrected figures are: 97.8  95.4  46.5  15.1  3.6  0.7  0.9

Another condition leading to contagious distributions is heterogeneity in the experimental areas. Unequal suitability of the boards for a particular species may cause the individuals to become aggregated under the boards with the more favorable habitat. This condition may be very difficult to detect because seemingly trivial factors might exert a great effect. It was found that boards over soil with a moisture content of less than 10 percent were definitely deficient in isopods so, at least at certain times, this factor would tend to produce a contagious distribution of isopods. The data on soil moisture are not sufficient for a detailed quantitative analysis of the effects of moisture on isopod distribution but part of the contagiousness of the observed distributions probably results from this factor.

Although soil moisture, and perhaps additional undetected factors, may lead to contagious distributions under the conditions of this study, it seems probable that a considerable part of the aggregating tendency observed is attributable to a mutual attraction between members of the same species. When mating is in progress paired animals are certain to occur more often than would be expected on an assumption of randomness. This is illustrated in Table 11 which shows the distribution of 60 small carabids in 500 inspections made during September, 1942.

Three of the seven observed pairs of small carabids were copulating when found and it is obvious that the frequency of pairs causes this distribution to depart from randomness.

In addition to mating, there are other advantages of associations between members of a species which could be operated upon by natural selection (Allee 1931, 1938) to accentuate aggregating tendencies. In the winter aggregations of centipedes, for example, no survival value is obvious but these aggregations are probably formed as a result of tendencies inherent within the individuals.

TABLE 11. The distribution of small carabid beetles—September, 1942.

|  | Number per board | | | |
|  | 0 | 1 | 2 | More |
|---|---|---|---|---|
| Observed | 447 | 46 | 7 | 0 |
| Expected | 443.4 | 53.2 | 3.2 | 0.2 |

Whatever the cause of contagious distributions their occurrence considerably complicates statistical analysis of the data. Mean numbers of animals in different areas or time intervals cannot be compared by the usual methods employing standard errors because these methods assume random distribution of the populations. Also, the correlation coefficient cannot be used to measure association between species when the populations are not normally distributed. Consequently, it has been necessary to use presence or absence in samples as a criterion in making such comparisons.

The fact that nearly all of these species are contagiously distributed also makes it extremely hazardous to use sample collections in estimating any larger population. Even in a mildly contagious distribution this factor may be of considerable importance. For example, in an area of 20 boards such as Area H, 5 boards might be selected at random and the total population estimated by mutiplying the observed number of animals by four. The results which could be obtained in this way can be calculated. As an example the distribution of 39 isopods in Area H on May 3, 1942 is shown in Table 12.

There are 15,504 different ways of drawing a sample of 5 boards from the 20 in this area and, by

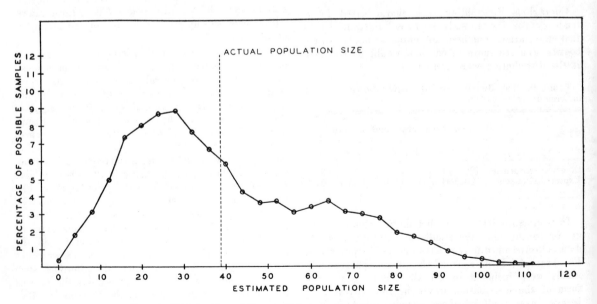

FIG. 4. Distribution of the possible samples for population estimation.

using such a sample to estimate the total isopod population of the 20 boards, 29 different estimates ranging from no isopods to 112 isopods could be obtained. The most frequent estimate of the total population would be 28 isopods and this value would be obtained 8.79 percent of the time. The distribution of the 15,504 possible samples is shown in Figure 4, and it illustrates that such a method of population estimation may lead to very great errors even when the distribution is not highly contagious. It is probably a general characteristic of contagious distributions that the population will tend to be underestimated from the mean of sample collections. This is to be expected because a disproportionately large percentage of the fauna is concentrated into a few units which are unlikely to be included in samples.

Because the observed contagiousness of these distributions seemed to result largely from a social instinct or attraction between individuals, it is very desirable to find some mathematical expression for the tendency to aggregate shown by a species at a particular time. This tendency is not constant but varies from day to day or even from hour to hour and also between experimental areas.

In a Poisson distribution the variance $(\sigma^2)$ is equal to the mean (m) and the deviation of a frequency distribution from the Poisson distribution may, therefore, be expressed by the ratio: $\dfrac{m-\sigma^2}{m}$ or $\dfrac{\sigma^2}{m}$ —1. This expression will have the value 0 in a true Poisson distribution, will be positive when aggregation occurs, and negative when the animals are more evenly distributed (overdispersed) than would occur in the Poisson case. This expression is closely related to a number of others which have been employed such as the Lexis ratio (Arne Fisher 1922, Beall 1935), the second parameter in Neyman's "type A" contagious distribution (Neyman 1939), and the expression used by Svedberg (1922) and discussed by Gause (1936).

Attempts to use the above expression as a measure of aggregating tendency indicated that its value was greatly affected by the number of animals present, an effect also described by Arne Fisher (1922) and by Beall (1935). Since the formula for the variance of a distribution may be written as: $\sigma^2 = \dfrac{\Sigma x^2 - m\Sigma x}{n}$ where x is the size of any sample and n is the number of samples, the expression: $\dfrac{\sigma^2}{m}$ —1 will reduce to $\dfrac{\Sigma x^2}{\Sigma x}$ —m —1 in which form it is obvious that the ratio will tend to increase as the size of the samples increases. The Charlier coefficient of disturbance which may be written: $C = \dfrac{100\sqrt{\sigma^2 - m}}{m}$ is independent of the number of animals and in the present study, as also found by Beall (1935), proved to be a much more satisfactory index of aggregating tendency. Positive values of C indicate aggregation while C becomes imaginary with overdispersion.

Imaginary values would be inconvenient for investigating animals if individuals showed actual antagonism toward each other but in this study all species were typically either underdispersed or randomly distributed so the occasional imaginary values of C were merely taken to indicate zero tendency to aggregate.

TABLE 12. Distribution of isopods in Area H—May 3, 1942.

| Number per board | 0 | 1 | 2 | 3 | 4 | 6 | 12 |
|---|---|---|---|---|---|---|---|
| Observed frequency | 8 | 4 | 2 | 3 | 1 | 1 | 1 |

A number of attempts were made to correlate values of C with physical or climatic conditions. Because many species tend to form autumn and winter aggregations one might expect to find values of C considerably influenced by low temperatures. Moisture conditions, in the laboratory at least, also influence the formation of aggregations by certain forms such as isopods.

For the period from September 16, 1942 to September 22, 1942 the boards in Area H were inspected every six hours. During this period there was an interval of hard rain and rapid temperature fall. These data then seem well suited for comparing variations in aggregating tendency and weather conditions. In Figure 5 the Charlier coefficient for isopods is plotted along with the air temperature taken some 30 cm. above the soil surface. This temperature was not necessarily the same as the microhabitat temperature to which the animals were responding and the significant parallelism between the two lines is, therefore, all the more striking.

Another way of looking at aggregating tendency is to consider how the quantity $\Sigma x^2$ varies with the amount of aggregation. If aggregation is complete so that all of the animals are under a single board we will have: $\Sigma x^2 = (\Sigma x)^2$ while if the animals are distributed as evenly as possible so that there is zero aggregation we shall have approximately: $\Sigma x^2 = nm^2 = m\Sigma x$. Therefore, the increment representing amount of aggregation for any observed value of $\Sigma x^2$ is approximately $\Sigma x^2 - m\Sigma x$ and the maximum possible amount of aggregation is represented approximately by $(\Sigma x)^2 - m\Sigma x$. Expressed as a proportion, the observed degree of aggregation is then the ratio of the observed amount to the possible amount, or: $\dfrac{\Sigma x^2 - m\Sigma x}{(\Sigma x)^2 - m\Sigma x} = \left(\dfrac{n}{n-1}\right)\dfrac{\Sigma x^2}{(\Sigma x)^2} - \dfrac{1}{(n-1)}$ which is nearly equal to $\dfrac{\Sigma x^2}{(\Sigma x)^2}$.

At the time these data were being collected the writer made the then purely empirical observation that the quantity $\dfrac{\Sigma x^2}{(\Sigma x)^2}$ seemed to give a better representation of aggregating tendency as evidenced by significant correlations with air temperature than did the Charlier coefficient. This quantity was not used analytically because of its purely empirical nature

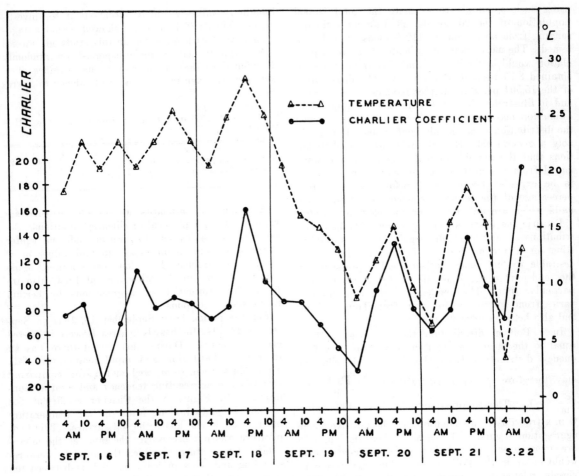

Fig. 5. Relation of isopod aggregating tendency to temperature.

and the lack of a rationale for ignoring the amount of aggregation which would be expected to result from chance. It now appears, however, that some investigation might profitably be devoted to answering the question of whether it is the absolute degree of aggregation or the degree of excess aggregation which tends to vary with environmental factors.

The correlation coefficient between C and temperature was not significant, apparently because the downward trend in temperature was not accompanied by a general downward trend in the tendency of the isopods to aggregate, but the parallelism between the two lines may be tested for statistical significance by comparing the number of times the two lines rise or fall simultaneously. These data give the 4-fold table shown in Table 13.

TABLE 13. Significance test of the parallelism between air temperature and C—the contagiousness of the distribution of isopods. P = 0.00007.

|  | Increase in C | Decrease in C |
|---|---|---|
| Temperatures increase..... | 10 | 1 |
| Temperature decrease...... | 1 | 13 |

If C were independent of temperature we should expect to find the two increasing together only about 4.8 times instead of the 10 times observed. The probability value as calculated by Fisher's "exact method" (R. A. Fisher 1941) shows that a parallelism as great as that observed should occur by chance only about 7 times in 100,000 observations. Thus it appears that increases in temperature did increase the tendency of isopods to form aggregations in the cryptozoic niche.

This effect of temperature on aggregation tendency must be independent of any effect on the total number of isopods present because C is independent of this factor. Increases in aggregation then were almost necessarily brought about by isopods leaving slightly occupied boards and moving under boards where more isopods were present. There are evidently two ways in which weather conditions might effect this change. Either some inherent social tendency within the isopods must have been altered, or, as temperature changed, some boards must have become less favorable as habitats so that isopods left them. In this case there was no evidence of heterogeneity in Area H as evidenced by certain boards being consistently more occupied than others. Furthermore, in the entire study, whenever heterogeneity was demonstrable in any experimental area, it tended to disappear when the soil became wet. Figure 5 shows a closer parallel between temperature and isopod aggregation in the period following the rain (the rain stopped at noon September 20) when the area should show less heterogeneity than in the earlier days. Thus the evidence favors the conclusion that some social tendency inherent within the isopods was increased by rising temperature. This is certainly not the only factor affecting the isopod aggregations or a much closer correlation should have been obtained but the temperature effect was highly significant.

This complicated behavior of the isopods, leaving shelter and moving to boards harboring larger numbers of isopods, as well as the vertical migration from unfavorable conditions, suggests that the complexity of aggregation phenomena has been underestimated in attempts to reduce these phenomena ot mechanical responses such as altered rates of turning (Waloff 1941).

Any relationship between weather and aggregating tendency in other species was much less clear than for isopods. In Figure 6 the Charlier coefficient for the diplopod Scytonotus is plotted for the same period shown in Figure 5. A comparison with the isopod graph makes it clear that the factors affecting the aggregating tendency of diplopods differed from those affecting the isopods. It is interesting to note the common tendency of the diplopods under the boards to be unaggregated (imaginary values of C) at the time of the 4 A.M. inspection which parallels the observation that Scytonotus may come out at night to aggregate on top of the boards or to wander in the grass. The early morning frost on September 20 may have been responsible for keeping the diplopods aggregated under the boards and at other times low atmospheric humidity might operate in this way. We do not at present, however, have sufficient data to correlate the aggregating tendency of Scytonotus with external conditions.

No species except Trachelipus and Scytonotus were common enough in this series of data to permit a satisfactory analysis of aggregating tendency. The Charlier coefficient becomes erratic when the mean number of animals per sample is very small and it would also be impossible to detect heterogeneity within the area from such limited data. Larger samples would be necessary to obtain satisfactory results with most of the other species.

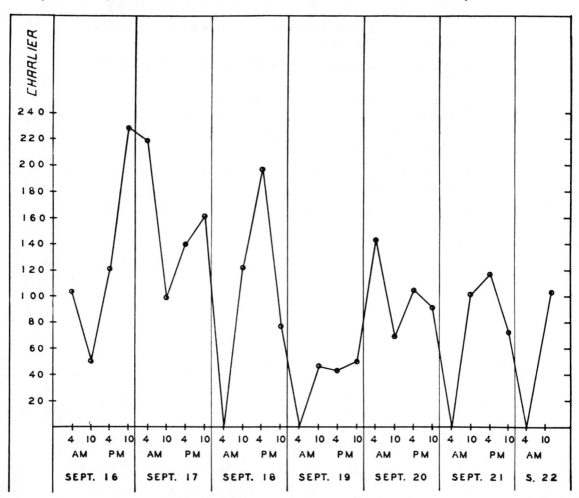

FIG. 6. Tendency of *Scytonotus* to aggregate.

# LITERATURE CITED

Allee, W. C. 1926. Studies in animal aggregations. Causes and effects of bunching in land isopods. Jour. Exp. Zool. 45: 255-277.

1931. Animal aggregations. A study in general sociology. Univ. of Chicago Press. Chicago.

1938. The social life of animals. Norton, N. Y.

Beall, G. 1935. Study of arthropod populations by the method of sweeping. Ecol. 16: 216-225.

1940. The fit and significance of contagious distributions when applied to observations on larval insects. Ecol. 21: 460-474.

Fisher, Arne. 1922. The mathematical theory of probabilities. N. Y.

Fisher, R. A. 1941. Statistical methods for research workers. 8th ed. Edinburgh.

Gause, G. F. 1936. Principles of biocenology. Quart. Rev. Biol. 11: 320-338.

Neyman, J. 1939. On a new class of contagious distributions applicable in entomology and bacteriology. Ann. Math. Stat. 10: 35-57.

Poisson, S. D. 1837. Recherches sur la probabilité des jugements en matières criminelles. Paris.

Polya, G. 1931. Sur quelques points de la théorie des probabilités. Ann. de l'Inst. Henri Poincaré. 1: 117-162.

Snedecor, G. W. 1938. Statistical methods applied to experiments in agriculture and biology. Ames. Iowa.

Student. 1907. On the error of counting with a haemocytometer. Biometrika. 5: 351-355.

Svedberg, The. 1922. Ett Bidrag till de statistiska methodernas anvandning inom vaxtbiologien. Svensk Botanisch Tidskrift. 16: 1-8.

Waloff, N. 1941. The mechanisms of humidity reactions of terrestrial isopods. Jour. Exp. Biol. 18: 8-135.

Whitaker, L. 1914. On the Poisson law of small numbers. Biometrika. 10: 36-71.

# LIFE TABLES FOR NATURAL POPULATIONS OF ANIMALS

By EDWARD S. DEEVEY, JR.

*Osborn Zoological Laboratory, Yale University*

(Contribution No. 384 from the Woods Hole Oceanographic Institution)

At sperat adulescens diu se victurum, quod
sperare idem senex non potest.  Insipienter sperat;
quid enim stultius quam incerta pro certis habere,
falsa pro veris?

—Cicero, *De Senectute*

## INTRODUCTION

"THE certainty of death", remarks Sir
Thomas Browne, "is attended with uncertainties, in time, manner, places."
The same refrain, audible in classical
authors from Horace to Hoffenstein,
embodies immutable truth.  But the rise of life
insurance has taught us to ask the fatal question
differently.  We now substitute "probability" for
"certainty," and have exchanged our fates for parameters of populations.  The dictum of Galilei,
"to measure what can be measured, to make
measurable what can not be measured," has been
applied to the product of Lachesis' loom, with
interesting results.

There is no evidence that man's maximum life
span has been lengthened a particle since antiquity.
The celebrated cases of fantastic longevity, from
Methuselah to Thomas Parr, do not withstand
critical scrutiny.  The mean length of life, however, differs widely among the races of men, is notably lower for most primitives than for civilized
populations, and has been increasing by leaps and
bounds in the United States during the last century.  In ancient Rome, according to Macdonell's
analysis (1913), the expectation of life at age 10 was
an additional 22 years, compared to an additional
55 years for a male resident of the United States in
1929–31 (Dublin and Lotka, 1935).

The Romans, in fact, knew more about such
matters than might be supposed from their super-
stition that "ten times twelve solar years were the
term fixed for the life of man, beyond which the
gods themselves had no power to prolong it; that

the fates had narrowed the span to thrice thirty
years, and that fortune abridged even this period
by a variety of chances, against which the protection of the gods was implored" (Hodge, 1857,
cited from Niebuhr's *History of Rome*).  A table
showing the expection of life at birth, at age 20, and
at 5-year intervals thereafter, evidently based on
real experience and intended for the computation
of annuities, was in use in the third century A.D.;
it is attributed to Ulpian (Trenerry, 1926).  Even
the Babylonians seem to have known about insurance contracts, though this does not necessarily
imply any actuarial knowledge, and Horace's reference to "Babylonian numbers"—"Tu ne quaesieris
(scire nefas) quem mihi, quem tibi finem di
dederint, Leuconoe, nec Babylonios temptaris
numeros" (*Odes*, I: 11)—may mean more than he
intended.

Having gained some idea of the limits circum-
scribing his own mortality, man has turned to look
at the other animals.  In 1935 Pearl and Miner, in
their discussion of the comparative mortality of
lower organisms, attempted to formulate a general
theory of mortality.  They quickly gave up the
attempt upon realizing that the *environmental*
determinants of life duration can not, at least as
yet, be disentangled from such *biological* determinants as genetic constitution and rate of living.
They ended with a plea for "more observational
data, carefully and critically collected for different
species of animals and plants, that will follow
through the life history from birth to death of each
individual in a cohort of statistically respectable
magnitude."  Thus by implication Pearl and
Miner appealed to the ecologists, who for the most
part have been busy elsewhere.  Accounts of the
conceptions and methodology of life tables have not
yet found their way into textbooks of ecology, and
while field naturalists have devoted increasing
attention to the dynamics of natural populations

most of them have been content to leave the construction of life tables to the statisticians and laboratory ecologists.

This article, which is designed as an introduction to the subject rather than as a formal review, brings together from the ecological literature a mass of information bearing on the survival of animals in nature. This information has not heretofore been considered relevant by biometricians working with human populations, nor has it ever been considered in its context by ecologists. In collecting the material it was immediately obvious that it is still too early to formulate general theories. Serious deficiencies are only too apparent in the data. But the difficulties differ from case to case, and are therefore not insurmountable. Moreover, the bibliography will show that virtually all of this knowledge has been acquired in the twelve years since the appearance of the review by Pearl and Miner. By taking stock now, and by calling attention to gaps in our information, it is hoped that some guidance can be given to ecologists and others in the gathering of new material.

### THE MEANING OF THE LIFE TABLE

A life table is a concise summary of certain vital statistics of a population. Beginning with a cohort, real or imaginary, whose members start life together, the life table states for every interval of age the number of deaths, the survivors remaining, the rate of mortality, and the expectation of further life. These columns are symbolized by $d_x$, $l_x$, $q_x$ and $e_x$, respectively, where $x$ stands for age. Additional columns which may be tabled include the age structure ($L_x$) or the number of persons living who are between ages $x$ and $x + 1$.

Because all the life table functions can be calculated from each other, it makes little difference where one begins in summarizing the method of construction. It is convenient to begin with deaths at given ages ($d_x$), since these usually make up the "raw data." A curve obtained by plotting number of deaths against age is obviously a histogram showing the frequency distribution of deaths. It is customary to reduce the data to a relative basis by expressing the observed number of deaths at any age as a fraction of the total number of deaths. Such fractions stated as percentages and carried out to three figures include a decimal place; in this review and elsewhere where small samples are involved, it is the practice to drop the decimal

point and put deaths, etc., on a "per thousand" basis. Starting, then, with a cohort of 1000 individuals born together, survivorship ($l_x$) is obtained by successive subtraction of deaths in the age interval from survivors at the beginning of the age interval. Mortality rate ($q_x$) is the fraction of those living at the beginning of the age interval who die during the interval, $q_x = d_x/l_x$, and is usually expressed here on a per thousand basis, $1000\,q_x = 1000\,d_x/l_x$.

The calculation of expectation of life is more complicated. For individuals at age 0 (at the beginning of their life span), it is the same as the mean length of life of the cohort. For older individuals, it is the mean life span remaining to those attaining a given age. It could therefore be calculated for any age $x$ by measuring the area under the survivorship curve beyond $x$ and dividing by the number of survivors attaining age $x$,

$$e_x = \frac{\int_x^\omega l_x \cdot dx}{l_x}$$

However, a life table, among other things, is a device for obtaining such integrals arithmetically, being divided into age intervals so small that changes between age $x$ and $x + 1$ can be regarded as linear functions of $x$. It is therefore assumed that the *age structure*, $L_x$, or the number of persons alive who are between ages $x$ and $x + 1$, which is exactly given by

$$L_x = \int_x^{x+1} l_x \cdot dx$$

is in practice given by

$$L_x = \frac{l_x + l_x + 1}{2} \qquad *$$

Successive values of $L_x$ obtained in this way are then summed from the bottom of the column up to each age $x$. This gives $T_x$, the total number of (persons × age units), or person-years if age is expressed in years still to be lived by persons of age $x$. Dividing by $l_x$, the number of persons, gives the expectation of life in age units,

$$e_x = \frac{T_x}{l_x}$$

Farner (1945) calculates $e_x$ directly for each year of a bird's age by obtaining the mean after lifetime

*Author's note: Corrected equation is $L_x = \dfrac{l_x + l_{x+1}}{2}$

of birds alive on their first November 1, doing the same for birds alive on their second November 1, and so on. This procedure is cumbersome, and is more accurate than the method given here only if the deaths in any year are so unequally distributed through the year that a serious error results from ignoring the fact (Lack, 1943b).

Nice (1937) gives, as Table XXVIII, the "theory as to age composition of a population of breeding birds; theoretical numbers of each age according to annual survival rate." As this table has been frequently used by students of bird populations, it is as well to understand its construction. Actually, it consists of a group of life table $d_x$ columns, constructed on the assumption of mortality rates

the number of deaths. For the ratio of the living at any age to the total number living must equal the ratio of the dead at any age to the total number of deaths,

$$\frac{l_x}{\Sigma l_x} = \frac{d_x}{\Sigma d_x} \, .$$

But $\Sigma d_x = 100$, by convention; therefore

$$100 \, \frac{l_x}{\Sigma l_x} = d_x \, .$$

By the same reasoning it can be shown that

$$100 \, \frac{L_x}{\Sigma L_x} = d_x \, .$$

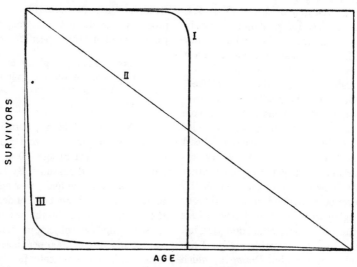

FIG. 1. SCHEMATIC REPRESENTATION OF THEORETICAL TYPES OF SURVIVORSHIP CURVE, ADAPTED FROM PEARL AND MINER (1935)

The survival axis can be graduated either arithmetically or logarithmically, but the logarithmic scale is more instructive, in that a straight line implies equal *rates* of mortality with respect to age.

which are *constant with respect to age*, but change from column to column between 75 and 25 per cent per year. It may seem surprising that a table of deaths should show the age composition of the living, but this is merely a consequence of starting with a round number of births, 100 in this case. Nice takes a cohort of 100 individuals and obtains their survivorship by successive applications of the assumed mortality rate until the number of survivors is reduced to 1. She then expresses the number living at any age as a percentage of the total number living at all ages, and thus the age composition of the living becomes identical with

Nice's table is convenient for ornithologists, since the assumption of constant age-specific mortality rates proves to be approximately true for adult birds. When mortality rates change with age, as they normally do, the table is inapplicable, though of course the age composition computed as percentage will always bear the same relationship to the $d_x$ column. Nice states that her table applies to species breeding at one year of age, but this is not a necessary condition, as Farner (1945) has pointed out: it merely implies that the birth rate cannot be deduced from the life table age composition unless all members of the population breed every year.

The fact that the various life table columns are interconvertible makes it unnecessary to discuss all of them in dealing with a given species. Usually it is sufficient to focus attention on the survivorship curve, since this is most readily comprehensible. Pearl and Miner (1935; see also Pearl, 1940) have made it clear that there are three possible sorts of distribution of survivorship with respect to age, as shown diagrammatically in Fig. 1. Type I, the *negatively skew rectangular*, is shown by members of a cohort which, having been born at the same time, die more or less simultaneously after a life span which is presumably characteristic of the species. Type II is *diagonal* (when the logarithm of the number of survivors is plotted against age), implying a constant mortality rate for all age groups, or no one age as a favored time of dying. Type III, the *positively skew rectangular*, shows extremely heavy mortality beginning early in life, but the few individuals which survive to advanced ages have a relatively high expectation of further life.

Most survivorship curves hitherto published, including those for man, *Drosophila, Hydra, Agriolimax*, the mouse (Pearl and Miner, 1935), the vole (Leslie and Ranson, 1940), the black widow spider (Deevey and Deevey, 1945), *Tribolium* (Pearl Park, and Miner, 1941), and other laboratory animals, are variants of the diagonal type, or rather are intermediate between Type I and Type II. Type III has never been obtained with a laboratory population, though marine species with pelagic eggs and larvae, such as the oysters, would doubtless fall here if complete data were available. Type I has been observed in the case of adult *Drosophila* which were given no food, but this sort of survivorship is probably to be thought of as a laboratory curiosity.

### KINDS OF LIFE TABLES

Life tables for human populations, which differ in certain important respects from animal populations in nature, are calculated by roundabout methods, most of which have little relevance to ecology. Some understanding of them is nonetheless essential. Census data show the number of persons born in a given year living in various political areas. Published vital statistics give the number of deaths in the same areas each year and the ages of those dying. By combining the two sets of figures it is possible to arrive at estimates of the rate of mortality ($q_x$) suffered by persons of a given age *at the time of the census*. Using a smooth curve fitted with exquisite precision to the $q_x$ data,

a life table can be constructed on the assumptions: (1) that a standard cohort (100,000 persons) is born alive uniformly throughout the year of the census; (2) that its members will be exposed throughout life to these particular mortality rates; and (3) that there is no immigration or emigration.

A life table so derived exposes to view a purely theoretical population, one which might have existed at the time of the census, but which ceased to exist even before the census was complete. For human populations are notably subject to immigration and emigration; the best known ones are growing, and their age structure is therefore changing; and what is even more important, the mortality rates observed at the time of the census are certain to change with the passage of time. An example will make clear how ordinary life table procedure crystallizes an imaginary population from a series of "time-specific" death rates.

This example is a paraphrase of Merrell's lucid exposition delivered at the symposium on "Life Tables and Their Application" held at Boston on December 27, 1946.

In 1940 the individuals, born in 1890 and now living in a certain state, were exposed to a risk of death at their current age (50 years) which works out at 12.58 per thousand. By 1950 the survivors of these same individuals, now aged 60 years, will be exposed to a different risk of death, say 27.03 per thousand. Eventually the last survivor will be dead, having been subject, in his last year of life, to a mortality rate of 1000 per thousand, and at that time it will be theoretically possible to construct a survivorship curve for the original group of individuals born in the state in 1890 and suffering age-specific mortality rates which changed systematically throughout their lives. But this will be impossible to do in practice, since (1) the birth records for 1890 are incomplete, and (2) many of those whose births were recorded will have left the state and died elsewhere. Moreover, (3) they will have been replaced by a number (probably a larger number) of persons born elsewhere in 1890, subjected to different mortality risks for varying fractions of their lives, who appear in the death records merely as "born in 1890."

In 1940, however, we also know the mortality rate for individuals born in 1900, and now 40 years of age. By 1950, when these persons are 50 years old, their age-specific mortality rate at age 50 will be obtainable. It will not be 12.58 per thousand, but probably a slightly lower figure. In fact, the mortality rates for all ages will have changed slightly, some more, some less, by 1950, partly because of immigration and emigration and partly because of improvements in public health technique. The same applies, mutatis mutandis, to 1960, when the 1900 year-class are 60 years old. In actuarial practice *this does not matter.* By drawing a vertical line, as it were, through all the age-classes present in 1940, and taking their age-specific mortality rates as the basis of a life table, the actuary seizes the only way out of a troublesome situation. He erects a hypothetical population and tables its survivorship, its mortality rates, its age structure, and the expectation of life of its members, and his figures serve for ordinary purposes. In any case they are the best available until the next census, when they have to be completely revised.

A very different life table would result if, instead of arbitrarily halting the flow of events at some particular time, as 1940, we followed all the individuals born in a certain state in a particular year, and recorded their deaths as they occurred. This would be a "horizontal" life table. Human biologists are less interested in this type, for from their standpoint, life being long and patience short, it is more worth while to be able to predict the future than to describe the past. The life table for persons born in 1840 is not of pressing concern to medical scientists (or to insurance salesmen) in 1940, conditions having meanwhile changed profoundly. The two sorts of life table approach identity as the age structure of the population approaches stability in a uniform environment, but these considerations have no real meaning to the actuary, who deals with expanding populations in which births exceed deaths and which are constantly improving their own environmental conditions. The ecologist, on the other hand, is bound to be interested in both kinds of life table. If there is no change in the environment from year to year, and if the natural population is at equilibrium, with recruitment of each age class always kept exactly balanced by deaths, a horizontal life table for the year-class born in 1940 or any other year will be identical with a vertical life table drawn up for all year-classes present in 1940 or any other year. But normally there will be good years and bad years, both the birth rate and the age-specific death rates will oscillate more or less reciprocally, and the

resulting differences in the two sorts of life tables will be large.

Since the data necessary for a vertical life table include both a census of the age distribution of the living members of the population and a record of the deaths by ages, the horizontal life table is easier to construct. The experimental ecologist, in particular, can go at the problem directly, by allowing a large cohort to be born at the same time, keeping its members under observation throughout their lives, and recording deaths as they occur. Thus survivorship ($l_x$) and deaths ($d_x$) make up the raw data of his experiment. Mortality rates are then easily obtained as the ratio of the dying to the living at any age, and other life table functions follow just as readily. The environment having been maintained constant artificially, there should be no difference between such a life table and one built up vertically from a census made when the age structure becomes stable.

### ECOLOGICAL LIFE TABLES

The field ecologist deals with populations which are by no means so elementary as those inside *Drosophila* bottles. Even the total size of the population of a species cannot be easily ascertained for an area large enough to be representative, and calculations of the birth rate and death rate are uncertain at best, largely owing to immigration and emigration. It is seldom indeed that the ecologist knows anything of the age structure of a natural population. In a few cases, growth rings on the scales or otoliths (fish) or horns (ungulates) make it possible to determine the age of an animal. Moore (1935) has shown that annual growth rings occur in the genital plates of sea-urchin tests, as they do in the shells of some molluscs. Moore checked the validity of the age determination by reference to the size-frequency distribution in his catches, and the separation of modal size classes in a population often affords a clue to age, particularly for younger age groups. The age of adult females can be determined in the case of certain mammals (whales, Wheeler, 1934, Laurie, 1937; seals, Bertram, 1940) by counting the corpora lutea in the ovaries. But for most animals it is possible to find out the ages of individuals only by marking them in some way.

Even when the age of a member of a natural population is known, it is not a simple matter to obtain accurate vital statistics. The source of greatest confusion lies in the impracticability of keeping the individuals under continuous observation. Migratory birds, for example, are easy to band as nestlings, but nearly impossible to find between fledging and the time they leave for winter quarters. Often they can not be found at all unless they return to the same area to breed, when they can be trapped in nest boxes. Their mortality between fledging and breeding can be calculated, but the calculation is rendered uncertain by the tendency of young birds not to return to their birthplaces as breeding adults.

As sources of data for the construction of life tables, the ecological information falls into three groups: (1) cases where the age at death $(d_x)$ is directly observed for a large and reasonably random sample of the population; (2) cases where the survival $(l_x)$ of a large cohort (born more or less simultaneously) is followed at fairly close intervals throughout its existence; (3) cases where the age structure is obtained from a sample, assumed to be a random sample of the population, and $d_x$ is inferred from the shrinkage between successive age classes. It should be noticed that only the second sort of information is statistically respectable, since in so far as the breeding can safely be assumed to be simultaneous, it is comparable to that obtained from a *Drosophila* bottle. The first and third types can be used only if one is prepared to assume that the population is stable in time, so that the actual age distribution and the life table age distribution are identical. This assumption would certainly not be true of a human population; it may be approximately true for many natural populations of animals. When it is definitely not true, e.g., when certain age classes are stronger or weaker than they should be, to take the ages at death or the actual age structure as observed at any "instant" of time will give erroneous estimates of the age-specific mortality rates. In these cases it would be better to construct a series of horizontal life tables, one for each year class. A vertical life table could be constructed from the average age composition observed over many years, if the ages at death were also known. But the ecological information does not yet give both the census by ages and the deaths by ages for any one population.

In making comparisons between species that have widely different life spans, Pearl's device is very useful. This consists in shifting the origin of the age axis from zero to the mean length of life and regraduating the age scale so that age is expressed as percentage deviation from the mean.

In this way $l_x$ values (and other life table functions, should they be desired) can be shown on the same graph in equal detail for rotifers, which live for a matter of days, and for birds, which live for many years. In connection with this method it has been customary to work with a fitted curve, the life table functions being calculated for equal percentage deviations, as $-80\%$, $-60\%$, $-40\%$, etc. This procedure, applied to the natural populations considered in this review, would entail an enormous amount of arithmetical labor which does not seem to be justified by the end in view. Curve fitting minimizes observational error and generalizes the sweep of the observations, but in this case the generalization goes too far, in that it seems to confer a universality on the resulting life table which is not supported by the facts. The published life tables for *Drosophila*, the flour beetle, and other lower organisms apply only to the particular experimental conditions under which they were obtained. Under other conditions, e.g., with different population densities, the longevity will be different and different life tables will result. Accordingly, all life tables presented below have been treated simply, and age intervals, though expressed as percentage deviation from the mean longevity, have been entered in the tables only for values corresponding to the original observations. The only exception is the life table for *Balanus balanoides* (see footnote, Table 6).

### Age at Death Directly Observed

In the course of his careful investigation of the wolves of Mt. McKinley, Murie (1944) picked up the skulls of 608 Dall mountain sheep (*Ovis d. dalli*) which had died at some time previous to his visit, and an additional 221 skulls of sheep deceased during the four years he spent in the Park. The age of these sheep at death was determinable from the annual rings on the horns. "Time, which antiquates antiquities, and hath an art to make dust of all things, hath yet spared these minor monuments" (Sir Thomas Browne, *Urn Burial*). Most of the deaths presumably occurred directly as a result of predation by wolves. Many skulls showed evidence of a necrotic bone disease, but it is not possible to say whether death was due solely to the disease or whether the disease merely ensured death by predation.

The mean longevity of the later sample is significantly greater (7.83 years) than that of the earlier (7.09 years), but the interpretation of this fact is not clear. The form of the distribution of deaths is sensibly the same in the two samples. As the survival of the members of this population is astonishingly great, it seems best to be conservative, and attention has been focussed on the larger, earlier sample. Except for the "lamb" and "yearling" classes, which are doubtless under-represented in the data owing to the perishability of their skulls, there is no reason to suppose that either group is anything but a fair sample of the total population, i.e., the probability of finding a

predation and that only the very young, which have not learned by experience, and the very old, which are too feeble to escape, suffer heavy losses. This survivorship curve is decidedly not of the positively skew rectangular type.

The second case to be discussed is that of an aquatic invertebrate, the sessile rotifer *Floscularia conifera*. This species has been studied by Edmondson (1945) under conditions which are fully as natural as those enjoyed by Murie's mountain sheep. *Floscularia* lives attached to water plants,

TABLE 1

*Life table for the Dall Mountain Sheep (Ovis d. dalli) based on the known age at death of 608 sheep dying before 1937 (both sexes combined)\*. Mean length of life 7.09 years*
*Data from Murie (1944)*

| $x$ AGE (years) | $x'$ AGE AS % DEVIATION FROM MEAN LENGTH OF LIFE | $d_x$ NUMBER DYING IN AGE INTERVAL OUT OF 1000 BORN | $l_x$ NUMBER SURVIVING AT BEGINNING OF AGE INTERVAL OUT OF 1000 BORN | $1000\,q_x$ MORTALITY RATE PER THOUSAND ALIVE AT BEGINNING OF AGE INTERVAL | $e_x$ EXPECTATION OF LIFE, OR MEAN LIFE-TIME REMAINING TO THOSE ATTAINING AGE INTERVAL (years) |
|---|---|---|---|---|---|
| 0–0.5 | −100 | 54 | 1000 | 54.0 | 7.06 |
| 0.5–1 | −93.0 | 145 | 946 | 153.0 | — |
| 1–2 | −85.9 | 12 | 801 | 15.0 | 7.7 |
| 2–3 | −71.8 | 13 | 789 | 16.5 | 6.8 |
| 3–4 | −57.7 | 12 | 776 | 15.5 | 5.9 |
| 4–5 | −43.5 | 30 | 764 | 39.3 | 5.0 |
| 5–6 | −29.5 | 46 | 734 | 62.6 | 4.2 |
| 6–7 | −15.4 | 48 | 688 | 69.9 | 3.4 |
| 7–8 | −1.1 | 69 | 640 | 108.0 | 2.6 |
| 8–9 | +13.0 | 132 | 571 | 231.0 | 1.9 |
| 9–10 | +27.0 | 187 | 439 | 426.0 | 1.3 |
| 10–11 | +41.0 | 156 | 252 | 619.0 | 0.9 |
| 11–12 | +55.0 | 90 | 96 | 937.0 | 0.6 |
| 12–13 | +69.0 | 3 | 6 | 500.0 | 1.2 |
| 13–14 | +84.0 | 3 | 3 | 1000 | 0.7 |

\* A small number of skulls without horns, but judged by their osteology to belong to sheep nine years old or older, have been apportioned *pro rata* among the older age classes.

skull is not likely to be affected by the age of its owner. A life table for the 608 sheep has accordingly been prepared (Table 1). The survivorship curve, plotted logarithmically in Fig. 2, is remarkably "human" in showing two periods of relatively heavy mortality, very early and very late, with high and nearly constant survival ratios at intermediate ages.

The adult sheep have two principal methods of defense against wolves, their chief enemies: flight to higher elevations, where wolves can not pursue; and group action or herding. It is clear that these recourses confer a relative immunity to death by

especially *Utricularia*, surrounded by a tube constructed by itself out of pellets of detritus. The tube is added to at the top continuously throughout life, and Edmondson was able to identify all the members of a population living in a pond by dusting the *Utricularia* plant with a suspension of powdered carmine. On subsequent visits the *Floscularia* present at the time of dusting were conspicuously marked by bands of carmine-stained pellets in the walls of their tubes, each band being surmounted by new construction of varying widths. Thus in one operation the stage was set for an analysis of growth, age, birth-plus-immigration, and death in a natural population. Among other spectacular results, Edmondson found that the expectation of life of solitary individuals was only half as great as that of members of colonies of two or more, and he presented separate life tables for each component of the population, calculated from the age at death. To facilitate comparison with other species, however, solitary and colonial individuals have been lumped together (for Edmondson's "Experiment 1") in the life table of Table 2.

The survivorship curve (Fig. 2), like that of the Dall sheep, shows unexpectedly good survival. As Edmondson has pointed out, it is not so good as that of other rotifers reared in the laboratory under

(*Larus argentatus*) has recently been prepared by Paynter (*in press*). These gulls, banded as chicks at the Bowdoin Scientific Station, Kent Island, Bay of Fundy, have been recovered dead from all over North America. No special effort was made to recover banded gulls at their birthplace, and the colony is a large one (ca. 30,000 birds). The fact remains, however, that the first-year birds are perhaps more likely to be picked up than older birds near the place of banding, and perhaps less likely to be picked up elsewhere, so that some doubt can be cast on the reliability of the first-year recoveries as truly representative of the deaths in the first year. This troublesome point is probably

TABLE 2

*Life table for the sessile rotifer Floscularia conifera based on the known age at death of 50
rotifers, both solitary and colonial. Mean length of life 4.74 days
From Edmondson (1945), Experiment 1*

| $x$ | $x'$ | $d_x$ | $l_x$ | 1000 $q_x$ | $e_x$ |
|---|---|---|---|---|---|
| AGE (days) | AGE AS % DEVIATION FROM MEAN LENGTH OF LIFE | NUMBER DYING IN AGE INTERVAL OUT OF 1000 ATTACHING | NUMBER SURVIVING AT BEGINNING OF AGE INTERVAL OUT OF 1000 ATTACHING | MORTALITY RATE PER THOUSAND ALIVE AT BEGINNING OF AGE INTERVAL | EXPECTATION OF LIFE, OR MEAN LIFE TIME REMAINING TO THOSE ATTAINING AGE INTERVAL (days) |
| 0–1 | −100 | 20 | 1000 | 20 | 4.76 |
| 1–2 | −78.9 | 200 | 980 | 204 | 3.78 |
| 2–3 | −57.8 | 60 | 780 | 77 | 3.70 |
| 3–4 | −36.7 | 0 | 720 | 0 | 2.98 |
| 4–5 | −15.6 | 300 | 720 | 416 | 1.97 |
| 5–6 | +5.4 | 140 | 420 | 333 | 2.02 |
| 6–7 | +26.7 | 60 | 280 | 214 | 1.79 |
| 7–8 | +47.7 | 140 | 220 | 636 | 1.14 |
| 8–9 | +68.8 | 40 | 80 | 500 | 1.25 |
| 9–10 | +90.0 | 20 | 40 | 500 | 1.00 |
| 10–11 | +111.0 | 20 | 20 | 1000 | 0.50 |

standard conditions (*Proales decipiens, P. sordida, Lecane inermis*), but it is only a little less good, and life tables for these rotifers are notorious (Pearl and Miner, 1935) for their close approach to a Type I distribution.

The case of *Floscularia* is almost above reproach as an example of a life table obtained under natural conditions. It is, of course, open to the objection that only the age at death is known, and the age structure of the living animals must be assumed to be constant. Apart from this deficiency, it should also be realized that the origin of the life table is not at birth. The pelagic larval life of the rotifer, like the larval life of barnacles and insects, is omitted from consideration in such a table.

A life table for a population of herring gulls

less serious than with the songbirds to be discussed below; moreover, it is overshadowed by another difficulty, the fact that the study is not complete, and many of the banded birds are still alive. Paynter minimized this error by a compensatory adjustment; since banding began ten years ago and is still being carried out, first-year recoveries were divided by 10, second-year recoveries by 9, etc. Birds dying at ages greater than 10 years have naturally not yet been recorded, though a few are to be expected.

That these older birds will probably not change the life table appreciably is shown by Marshall's independent study (1947) of the longevity of the herring gull. Marshall used all available records of American herring gulls banded as young during the last 25 years and subsequently recovered dead. Thus his data probably include most of the returns from the Kent Island population. Returns before September 1 of the first year of life were excluded, so that the life table refers to adult birds only. It differs from Paynter's chiefly in that it includes birds older than 10 years, one bird having lived as long as 17 years. Despite two factors which might be supposed to enhance the apparent longevity (exclusion of juvenile mortality; inclusion of older birds) the expectation of life is markedly lower than that of the Kent Island colony, 1.5 years on the first

tality before 1936, and Marshall's recoveries may have been predominantly from the earlier years, before banding started at Kent Island. The simplest explanation is that (3) an appreciable number of bands are lost by older birds, so that the mean age at death is actually higher than appears from the returns of banded birds.

These questions will doubtless be discussed by Paynter on the basis of direct observation of juvenile mortality, planned for the coming summer (1947) at Kent Island. Meanwhile, taking his life table at face value, the figures have been entered in

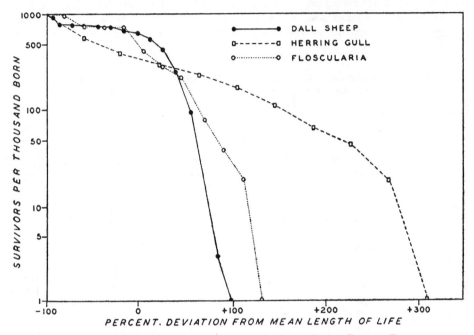

FIG. 2. SURVIVORSHIP ($l_x$) CURVES FOR THE DALL MOUNTAIN SHEEP, THE SESSILE ROTIFER FLOSCULARIA CONIFERA, AND THE HERRING GULL, AGE BEING EXPRESSED AS PERCENTAGE DEVIATION FROM THE MEAN LENGTH OF LIFE

September 1 of life as against 2.44 years at banding age.

Probably neither set of data for the herring gull is wholly reliable. Paynter's calculations suggest that the Kent Island population is just replacing its losses, assuming a rather high reproductive potential and a rather low rate of mortality between hatching and fledging, while a similar calculation applied to Marshall's figures implies that the population as a whole must be declining. Several reasons may be suggested for the discrepancy between the two life tables: (1) the mortality of the Kent Island gulls may actually be lower than average; (2) there may have been greater total mor-

Table 3, and the survivorship curve is plotted in Fig. 2 for comparison with the Dall sheep and the rotifer. In contrast to those cases, the curve for the gulls is of the diagonal type, the mortality rate being approximately constant throughout life. This feature seems to be characteristic of birds, as will appear below. The causes of death of these birds have been discussed in detail by Paynter, who finds that there is no significant difference in mean length of life between gulls dying through human interference (shooting, trapping, etc.) and those dying through "natural" or unknown causes.

In his delightful book, *The Life of the Robin* (1943a) and in two admirable papers, Lack (1943b,

c) has investigated the age at death of certain British birds, as obtained by recoveries of individuals banded as nestlings. Because banded nestlings are likely to be picked up near the banding stations or not at all, it is impossible to estimate the whole of the mortality in the first year of life with any accuracy, and Lack begins his life tables on August 1. The proportion of birds banded which are later recovered is small, ranging from 1.0 per cent for the robin to 18.4 per cent for the cormorant; but after August 1 of the first year it is considered that the ages at death of birds recovered are not likely to differ from the ages at death among the total population. The samples are small and of course become progressively smaller with increasing age,

they suffer more or less severe depredations from shooting.

The striking feature of these survivorship curves is their diagonal form. The mortality in the first year varies from 380 per thousand for the lapwing to 723 per thousand for the robin, but for a given species the mortality remains approximately constant throughout life, or at least for as long as the data are reliable.

When the ages of these birds are transformed into percentage deviations from the mean, as in Fig. 4, it becomes obvious that the mortality per unit of life span is constant for all the birds studied. This does not tell us anything new, for any series of diagonal lines will become the same when replotted

TABLE 3

*Life table for the Herring Gull (Larus argentatus) based on returns of 1252 birds banded as chicks at Kent Island, Bay of Fundy, 1936–1945. Mean length of life 2.44 years*
*From Paynter (in press)*

| $x$ | $x'$ | $d_x$ | $l_x$ | 1000 $q_x$ | $e_x$ |
|---|---|---|---|---|---|
| AGE (years) | AGE AS % DEVIATION FROM MEAN LENGTH OF LIFE | NUMBER DYING IN AGE INTERVAL OUT OF 1000 BORN | NUMBER SURVIVING AT BEGINNING OF AGE INTERVAL OUT OF 1000 BORN | MORTALITY RATE PER THOUSAND ALIVE AT BEGINNING OF AGE INTERVAL | EXPECTATION OF LIFE, OR MEAN LIFE TIME REMAINING TO THOSE ATTAINING AGE INTERVALS (years) |
| 0–1 | −100 | 419 | 1000 | 419 | 2.44 |
| 1–2 | −59 | 181 | 581 | 312 | 2.84 |
| 2–3 | −18 | 95 | 400 | 238 | 2.90 |
| 3–4 | +23 | 65 | 305 | 213 | 2.65 |
| 4–5 | +64 | 69 | 240 | 288 | 2.22 |
| 5–6 | +105 | 60 | 171 | 351 | 1.92 |
| 6–7 | +146 | 45 | 111 | 405 | 1.68 |
| 7–8 | +187 | 21 | 66 | 318 | 1.48 |
| 8–9 | +228 | 26 | 45 | 578 | 0.93 |
| 9–10 | +269 | 19 | 19 | 1000 | 0.53 |

so that Lack does not regard the mortality rates and expectation of life as reliable beyond the fourth or fifth year.

Several of Lack's life tables are reproduced in Table 4, and the survivorship curves are shown in Fig. 3. Three of the species are familiar British songbirds belonging to the Turdidae, the robin (*Erithacus rubecula melophilus*), the blackbird (*Turdus m. merula*), and the song thrush (*T. e. ericetorum*). The others are the starling (*Sturnus v. vulgaris*) and the lapwing (*Vanellus vanellus*), taxonomically though not ecologically a "shorebird" (Charadriidae). Lack's remaining species, the woodcock, black-headed gull, lesser black-backed gull, and cormorant, have been omitted, as

in this way, but it is helpful none the less. A line fitted by eye to the survivorship points plotted in this figure has a slope corresponding to a mortality of about 320 per thousand per 100 per cent deviation. If the divergence of the points for older ages is ignored as being due to inadequate data, and this line projected, it cuts the age axis at about +560 per cent, implying that if the mortality of birds is really constant throughout life, the oldest bird in a group of 1000 adults should survive about 6.6 times as long as the average bird.

The American robin (*Turdus m. migratorius*), a larger bird than its distant English relative, has been studied by Farner (1945), using U. S. Fish and Wildlife Service data on 855 birds banded as young

TABLE 4

*Life tables for several British birds, based on returns from all Britain of birds banded as nestlings and known to be alive on August 1 of their first year. Age reckoned from August 1*
From Lack (1943a, b, c)

| SPECIES; SIZE OF SAMPLE; MEAN LENGTH OF LIFE AFTER FIRST AUGUST 1 | $x$ AGE (years) | $x'$ AGE AS % DEVIATION FROM MEAN LENGTH OF LIFE | $d_x$ NUMBER DYING IN AGE INTERVAL OUT OF 1000 ALIVE ON AUGUST 1 | $l_x$ NUMBER SURVIVING AT BEGINNING OF AGE INTERVAL OUT OF 1000 ALIVE ON AUGUST 1 | 1000 $q_x$ MORTALITY RATE PER THOUSAND ALIVE AT BEGINNING OF AGE INTERVAL | $e_x$ EXPECTATION OF LIFE, OR MEAN LIFE-TIME REMAINING TO THOSE ATTAINING AGE INTERVAL (years) |
|---|---|---|---|---|---|---|
| Blackbird (352) 1.58 years | 0–1 | −100 | 545 | 1000 | 545 | 1.57 |
| | 1–2 | −37 | 170 | 455 | 374 | 1.85 |
| | 2–3 | +27 | 142 | 285 | 498 | 1.66 |
| | 3–4 | +90 | 57 | 143 | 398 | 1.82 |
| | 4–5 | +153 | 34 | 86 | 396 | 1.80 |
| | 5–6 | +216 | 20 | 52 | 385 | 1.65 |
| | 6–7 | +280 | 17 | 32 | 531 | 1.38 |
| | 7–8 | +343 | 9 | 15 | 600 | 1.33 |
| | 8–9 | +405 | 0 | 6 | 0 | 1.50 |
| | 9–10 | +470 | 6 | 6 | 1000 | 0.50 |
| Song Thrush (374) 1.44 years | 0–1 | −100 | 556 | 1000 | 556 | 1.44 |
| | 1–2 | −31 | 185 | 444 | 417 | 1.61 |
| | 2–3 | +39 | 136 | 259 | 525 | 1.40 |
| | 3–4 | +108 | 72 | 123 | 585 | 1.39 |
| | 4–5 | +178 | 21 | 51 | 411 | 1.65 |
| | 5–6 | +245 | 13 | 30 | 433 | 1.43 |
| | 6–7 | +316 | 11 | 17 | 647 | 1.12 |
| | 7–8 | +385 | 3 | 6 | 500 | 1.17 |
| | 8–9 | +455 | 3 | 3 | 1000 | 0.67 |
| Robin (130) 1.01 years | 0–1 | −100 | 723 | 1000 | 723 | 1.03 |
| | 1–2 | −2 | 131 | 277 | 472 | 1.41 |
| | 2–3 | +97 | 108 | 146 | 740 | 1.23 |
| | 3–4 | +196 | 23 | 38 | 605 | 2.29 |
| | 4–5 | +294 | 8 | 15 | 533 | 4.0 |
| | 5–6 | +392 | 0 | 15 | 0 | 3.0 |
| | 6–7 | +491 | 0 | 15 | 0 | 2.0 |
| | 7–8 | +590 | 0 | 15 | 0 | 1.0 |
| | 8–9 | +689 | 8 | 7 | 1000 | 0.5 |
| Starling (203) 1.49 years | 0–1 | −100 | 487 | 1000 | 487 | 1.49 |
| | 1–2 | −33 | 261 | 513 | 509 | 1.43 |
| | 2–3 | +34 | 113 | 252 | 448 | 1.40 |
| | 3–4 | +102 | 89 | 139 | 640 | 1.12 |
| | 4–5 | +168 | 25 | 50 | 500 | 1.22 |
| | 5–6 | +236 | 20 | 25 | 800 | 0.92 |
| | 6–7 | +302 | 0 | 5 | 0 | 1.60 |
| | 7–8 | +370 | 5 | 5 | 1000 | 0.60 |
| Lapwing (460) 2.36 years | 0–1 | −100 | 380 | 1000 | 380 | 2.37 |
| | 1–2 | −58 | 213 | 620 | 344 | 2.51 |
| | 2–3 | −15 | 128 | 407 | 314 | 2.56 |
| | 3–4 | +27 | 78 | 279 | 280 | 2.50 |
| | 4–5 | +70 | 67 | 201 | 334 | 2.28 |
| | 5–6 | +112 | 56 | 134 | 418 | 2.17 |
| | 6–7 | +154 | 24 | 78 | 308 | 2.37 |
| | 7–8 | +196 | 20 | 54 | 370 | 2.20 |
| | 8–9 | +239 | 7 | 34 | 206 | 2.20 |
| | 9–10 | +282 | 9 | 27 | 333 | 1.63 |
| | 10–11 | +324 | 7 | 18 | 389 | 1.17 |
| | 11–12 | +366 | 11 | 11 | 1000 | 0.55 |

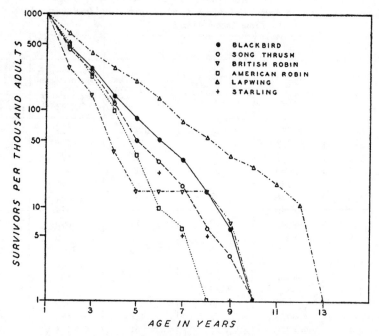

FIG. 3. Survivorship ($l_x$) Curves for the British Robin, Song Thrush, Blackbird, Starling, Lapwing and American Robin, Age being Expressed in Years

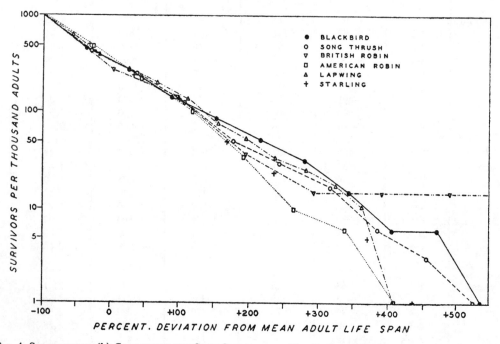

FIG. 4. Survivorship ($l_x$) Curves for the Same Species as in Fig. 3, Age being Expressed as Percentage Deviation from the Mean Length of Life

within the breeding range of the type subspecies between 1920 and 1940, and subsequently recovered dead. Farner's method of treatment of the data is analogous to Lack's, except that November 1 is taken as the starting point for the life table. The figures for the American robin have been entered in Table 5, and Figs. 3 and 4 indicate that this species suffers a mortality which is not only uniform with respect to age but is approximately the same as that of the British birds with respect to units of the mean life span.

Lack (1946) has recently discussed anew the question whether the disproportionately high mortality found among birds in their first year of life is real, or is due to the greater likelihood of their being

portionate" mortality in the first year, starting from August 1, is really very little greater than in later years; it is scarcely visible on a logarithmic plot of survivorship (Figs. 3 and 4). The significant differences between juvenile and adult mortality, which would give a marked initial dip on such a plot, have been left out of account altogether, and August 1 is not too early, but too late a starting point.

Additional information on the lapwing is given by Kraak, Rinkel, and Hoogerheide (1940), who studied the age at death of 1333 continental birds banded as juveniles. The life table is not published, but the survivorship curve is reproduced, and is shown to be closely fitted by a line corres-

TABLE 5

*Life table for the American Robin (Turdus m. migratorius), based on returns of 568 birds banded as nestlings and known to be alive on November 1 of their first year. Age reckoned from November 1. Mean length of life after November 1—1.37 years*
*From Farner (1945)*

| $x$ | $x'$ | $d_x$ | $l_x$ | $1000\,q_x$ | $e_x$ |
|---|---|---|---|---|---|
| AGE (years) | AGE AS % DEVIATION FROM MEAN LENGTH OF LIFE | NUMBER DYING IN AGE INTERVAL OUT OF 1000 ALIVE ON NOVEMBER 1 | NUMBER SURVIVING AT BEGINNING OF AGE INTERVAL OUT OF 1000 ALIVE ON NOVEMBER 1 | MORTALITY RATE PER THOUSAND ALIVE AT BEGINNING OF AGE INTERVAL | EXPECTATION OF LIFE, OR MEAN LIFE TIME REMAINING TO THOSE ATTAINING AGE INTERVAL (years) |
| 0–1 | −100 | 503 | 1000 | 503 | 1.38 |
| 1–2 | −27 | 268 | 497 | 539 | 1.26 |
| 2–3 | +46 | 130 | 229 | 567 | 1.16 |
| 3–4 | +119 | 63 | 99 | 636 | 1.03 |
| 4–5 | +192 | 26 | 36 | 722 | 0.94 |
| 5–6 | +265 | 4 | 10 | 400 | 1.10 |
| 6–7 | +338 | 5 | 6 | 1000 | 0.50 |

picked up near the banding station. Analysing the returns between August 1 and January 1 for the blackbird, the song-thrush, the starling, and the lapwing, he found that most of these returns were of first-year birds, but that the proportion of first-year birds is no higher among those found by the bander or found near the banding station than it is among those found at a distance. The annual mortality is greater for first-year birds than for older birds when the calculations begin on August 1, and it remains greater when November 1 is the starting date, but by January 1 the constant level of adult mortality is reached. Calculations of adult mortality should therefore start on January 1, but from a comparative point of view this adjustment is of minor importance. The "dispro-

ponding to a constant mortality rate of 40 per cent per year, reckoned from the first January 1 of life. This value is slightly higher than that found by Lack for the British population, but as the mean length of life is slightly lower, the mortality per unit of life span is the same.

It may be mentioned that the mortality rates for adult song sparrows, dealt with in the next section because the original data give $l_x$ and not $d_x$, are fully consistent with the picture given by Fig. 4. The same may be said of Paynter's herring gull data, which have been presented separately because juvenile mortality is not specifically excluded, as it is for the other birds. All natural populations of birds so far investigated in any detail appear, therefore, to be alike in suffering a constant annual risk of death from early adult life to the end of the life span, this mortality being constant for birds at about 320 per thousand per hundred centiles of life span. Little is known of the seasonal distribution of these deaths, and it will be very interesting to discover whether non-migratory tropical birds suffer death in similar fashion.

## Survivorship Directly Observed

The cases now to be discussed differ from the preceding in the character of the original observations.

observations, so that births can be assumed to be simultaneous, as in a *Drosophila* bottle, a horizontal life table can be directly constructed from the survivorship data. Unfortunately, most of the species which have been studied in this way have short spans of natural life, and when census data are obtained only once a year the number of points on the survivorship curve is too small to be satisfactory.

The best example of such observed survivorship comes from Hatton's work (1938) with the barna-

TABLE 6

*Life table for a typical population of Balanus balanoides, based on the observed survival of adult barnacles settling on a cleaned rock surface in the spring of 1930. The population is that at Cité, (St. Malo, France), a moderately sheltered location, at Level III, at half-tide level. The initial settling density (2200 per 100 cm²) is taken as the maximum density attained on May 15. Mean length of life 12.1 months*

Data from Hatton (1938)

| $x$ | $x'$ | $d_x$ | $l_x$ | $1000\,q_x$ | $e_x$ |
|---|---|---|---|---|---|
| *AGE (months) | *AGE AS % DEVIATION FROM MEAN LENGTH OF LIFE | NUMBER DYING IN AGE INTERVAL OF 1000 ATTACHING | NUMBER SURVIVING TO BEGINNING OF AGE INTERVAL OUT OF 1000 ATTACHING | MORTALITY RATE PER THOUSAND ALIVE AT BEGINNING OF AGE INTERVAL | EXPECTATION OF FURTHER LIFE (*months*) |
| 0–2 | −100 | 90 | 1000 | 90 | 12.1 |
| 2–4 | −83.5 | 100 | 910 | 110 | 11.3 |
| 4–6 | −67.0 | 50 | 810 | 62 | 10.5 |
| 6–8 | −50.4 | 60 | 760 | 79 | 9.1 |
| 8–10 | −33.9 | 80 | 700 | 114 | 7.8 |
| 10–12 | −17.4 | 160 | 620 | 258 | 6.7 |
| 12–14 | −0.9 | 80 | 460 | 174 | 6.7 |
| 14–16 | +16.0 | 100 | 380 | 263 | 5.9 |
| 16–18 | +32.2 | 50 | 280 | 179 | 5.7 |
| 18–20 | +49.0 | 40 | 230 | 174 | 4.7 |
| 20–22 | +65.4 | 100 | 190 | 526 | 2.4 |
| 22–24 | +82.0 | 60 | 90 | 667 | 1.9 |
| 24–26 | +98.8 | 20 | 30 | 667 | 1.8 |
| 26–28 | +115.0 | 8 | 10 | 800 | 1.4 |
| 28–30 | +132.0 | 2 | 2 | 1000 | 1.0 |

* Survivorship data given graphically by Hatton were smoothed by eye, and values at every other month were then read from the curve. The original observations were made at irregular intervals during three years.

Instead of a fairly large sample of individuals about which little or nothing can be told except their age at death, we have a group of individuals known to have been born at a particular time and to have been present or absent at some later time. Their presence gives their survivorship, their absence implies death in the interval since they were last observed. This is the best sort of information to have, since it does not require the assumption that the age composition of the population is stable in time. Provided only that the season of birth is a small fraction of the age interval between successive

cle, *Balanus balanoides.* This work will be examined in great detail in a later section, and it is here necessary to say only that the case is very nearly ideal. The barnacle settles on rocks during a short time (two to six weeks) in early spring. Test areas were scraped clean one winter, and after new populations had settled, the survival of their members was followed at intervals of one to four months for three years. Barnacles which disappeared from the areas between observations were certainly dead, for emigration does not complicate the problem. Immigration, however, does present difficulties, though since it is confined to the attachment seasons of subsequent years it should be possible to control it in subsequent work. There is one further disadvantage in that the life tables necessarily start at metamorphosis, leaving out of account mortality during pelagic larval stages. A life table for a typical population of barnacles is presented in Table 6.

The remaining examples suffer from more serious defects, and the data do not justify extended treatment. Green and Evans (1940) in their important study of the snowshoe rabbit (*Lepus americanus*) in Minnesota, followed the survival of marked individuals of several year classes, the total population present on the area and the number in each age-class being obtained by the mark-and-recapture method—also known as the "Lincoln index" (Jackson, 1939). Marking was done during most of the winter, and the annual census was made in February. It is perhaps unnecessary, and certainly uncharitable, to point out two sources of error in this excellent and ingenious work. In the first place, when marked individuals are released into a population and later recaptured, the calculation of the total population from the fraction

$$\frac{\text{size of sample when recapturing}}{\text{number recaptured}} \times \text{number marked}$$

depends on two assumptions, neither of which is likely to be true in this case: that there is no mortality between marking and recapturing; and that the marked individuals disperse at random through the whole population. Secondly, the flow of vital events in this population was so rapid, very few rabbits more than three years old ever having been found, that observations made annually can give only a very rough idea of the life table.

The latter objection applies with equal force to the study of a pheasant population made by Leopold et al. (1943) in Wisconsin. The former objection, though doubtless it could be urged, has less validity here, since the population, as ascertained by trapping, was checked by census drives.

Nice's thoroughgoing work (1937) on the song sparrow (*Melospiza melodia*) included a consideration of the survival of banded birds from year to year. The number of individuals which could be kept under continuous observation was necesarily* small, and to find a sample large enough to use as the basis of a life table, it is necessary to take the 144 males banded in the breeding season between 1928 and 1935. Unfortunately, some of these

males were of unknown age when first banded. Even if one assumes, (and the assumption is not far from the truth) that all new males appearing are first-year birds born elsewhere, the survival ratios from year to year will be too low if any adult males were still alive but failed to return to the area. Evidently such emigration is of minor importance with adult male song sparrows. With adult females, however, it is so serious that Nice did not think it worth while to publish the data on their return. Clearly, work on the survival of migratory birds is full of uncertainties, though the same may be said of resident species such as the wren-tit (Erickson, 1938) and the robin (Lack, 1943a).

All of these cases, snowshoe rabbit, pheasant, and song sparrow have one defect in common. This is the necessity of calculating the survival between birth and the first year of adult life from other data than those given by banding. For the snowshoe rabbit, the initial strength of the year-class is calculated from the estimated breeding population present and its known fertility. Leopold et al., lacking observations of their own on the pheasant mortality between birth and the first census period, used the estimates given by Errington for pheasants in another state. Nice calculates the survival of fledged young song sparrows to their first breeding season, by assuming a stable population and combining the estimated mean length of life of adults with their average nesting success. These procedures, while perfectly defensible as approaches to the problem, are inadequate substitutes for direct observation.

The three sets of data, with all their uncertainties, have been used as bases for synthetic life tables, and the survivorship curves are presented in Fig. 5. The snowshoe rabbit curve is that for the 1933 year class, the only one for which data are available on rabbits as old as four years. The juvenile mortality for 1933 is calculated by Green and Evans as 77 per cent between birth and the following February; for most other years it was higher, and for a few it was lower. Adult mortality, amounting to 70 per cent per year, was essentially constant throughout the study. The data for the pheasant are the average survival values for adults (30 per cent per year), combined with Errington's estimate of 84 per cent mortality between hatching and maturity. The song sparrow curve is calculated in two ways, the first including only the estimated mortality between fledging and the first breeding season (80 per cent) and the

---

* Corrected spelling is: necessarily

second also including the loss (40 per cent) between the laying of the eggs and fledging. The adult part of the life span is taken from the survival of the 144 males banded in 1928–1935.

The three curves show a pronounced diagonality from the adult stage onward. Initially, however, since the juvenile mortality in all cases is greater than the adult mortality, the curves show a dip which is most emphatic for the song sparrow reckoned from the egg, but which is invariably present. Here, then, we have for the first time sur-

between successive age classes, has not been directly observed. This kind of information lends itself just as well as either of the others to the computation of life tables. As in the group where only the age at death is known, of course, it is necessary to assume the age composition to be unchanged with time. When this assumption is unreasonable, as it often is for fish populations, with their outrageous fluctuation in strength of year-classes, average age compositions obtained from several years' work can often be used. As it happens,

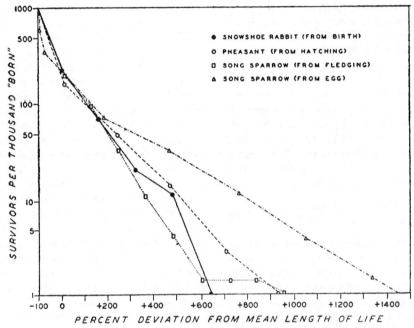

Fig. 5. Synthetic Survivorship ($l_x$) Curves for the Snowshoe Rabbit, the Pheasant, and the Song Sparrow, the Latter Calculated from Two Different Biological Ages
Data for different parts of the life spans are derived in different ways, as explained in the text.

vivorship curves which approach the positively skew rectangular type expected in theory from animals in nature. It is surprising that the approach is not closer, but it may well be true that the theoretical curve, in its most extreme form, is not to be looked for among terrestrial vertebrates.

### Age Structure Directly Observed

Ecological information of a third sort is available for a number of natural populations, principally of fishes and birds. In these cases the investigator has been able to determine how many individuals of each age are living in the population, and the age at death, though calculable from the shrinkage

however, all the life tables which fall in this third group are incomplete for one reason or another, and the data do not bear close comparison with such examples of natural life tables as those of the Dall sheep and the barnacle.

Kortlandt (1942) has recently given a very elaborate analysis of the Netherlands population of cormorants (*Phalacrocorax carbo sinensis*). Birds banded as nestlings were later observed in their breeding and playing colonies, the numbers on the bands being read with the aid of a telescope. The age distribution of the banded birds being known in 1940 and 1941, it should be possible to infer the age distribution of the total population and from this to compute the annual mortality suffered by each year-class. A number of complicating conditions are present in this case, however, making direct calculation unreliable and necessitating a more circuitous approach: (1) the size of the Dutch cormorant population is not constant, but has been increasing by about 10 per cent per year, as estimated by counts of nests at the breeding colonies; (2) differences between the observed sex ratio among sexually mature birds and the sex ratio predicted on the basis of estimated mortality by sex and age class show clearly that there is some *band mortality*; that is, some birds either lose bands or die because of the band, making estimates of natural mortality too high by a factor of about 2; (3) it is not possible to infer the complete age structure from observations made at breeding colonies, since the one- and two-year-old birds occupy "colonies" elsewhere, returning to their birthplaces to breed no sooner than their third year.

In view of these difficulties, and others which need not be discussed·here, Kortlandt's results must be regarded as schematic and preliminary only, and scarcely warrant the construction of a life table. His computations suggest that cormorants suffer mortality somewhat as follows: 17 per cent between fledging and the first May 1; 8 per cent in the first year; 6 per cent in the second year; and about 4 per cent per year in the third to twelfth years. These are astonishingly low figures for a natural population, but it must be remembered that the population is increasing rapidly. It is interesting to find that the slight differential death rate between the sexes from the third year onward appears to favor the female rather than the male sex. It is not known whether this is true of birds generally, in contrast to most other animals (Geiser, 1923, 1924). MacArthur and Baillie (1932) have maintained that there is no evidence that differential mortality is correlated with the sex-determining chromosome mechanism, and that among moths and birds the male longevity is generally lower in conformity with the "rate of living" theory.

Huge numbers of returns of the common tern (*Sterna hirundo*) have been obtained at the Austin Ornithological Research Station on Cape Cod (Austin, 1942), where terns have been banded for over twenty years. Unfortunately the data are inadequately published, and in any case can yield only an incomplete life table, since terns, like other sea birds, scatter widely after birth and do not return to their birthplace until breeding age. Inspection of Austin's table, in which all returns are given by ages for the four years 1938–1941, suggests that the annual mortality is not constant from the fourth year onward, but varies from 178 to 636 per thousand even between the fourth and eighth years, when the numbers are large. It is not clear, however, whether or not the tern population has remained statistically constant during the period of study, i.e., whether the table really reflects the true natural mortality of an average or of any one year-class.

The literature of fisheries biology is full of attempts to estimate the mortality of fishes, to distinguish natural mortality from rate of exploitation, and to determine the rate of exploitation which, given certain mortality rates and certain relationships between age and size, will steadily yield an optimum catch. These complex questions are fully discussed in the important works of Russell (1942), Thompson and Bell (1934), and Ricker (1940, 1944), and by various authors in the *Rapports et Procès-Verbaux of the International Council for the Study of the Sea*, Volume 110, 1939. Little of this information can be directly used for our purpose. The explanation is as simple as it is regrettable: although the age of a caught fish can be ascertained with more or less complete confidence, fishes of all ages can not be caught with equal facility. Inevitably the methods so skilfully developed for catching fish of desirable sizes will fail to catch fish of undesirable sizes. It is true that on various occasions the whole fish population of a lake has been removed by poisoning or drainage. The estimates given by Eschmeyer (1939) for the abundance of large-mouth black bass (*Huro salmoides*) in Howe Lake, Michigan, at the time of its poisoning in 1937, may be cited as an example:

| Age | Number |
|---|---|
| 0 | 18,374 |
| 0 (cannibals) | 229 |
| I | 25 |
| II | 10 |
| III | 105 |
| IV | 7 |
| V and older | 9 |
| Total | 18,759 |

The implication of enormously greater mortality in the first year of life is plain from these figures, but such data can not be taken as they stand, partly because of very variable annual recruitment, and partly because young of the year were removed from the lake at various times for hatchery purposes.

Lacking satisfactory observations of the complete age structure of the population, and faced with the obstacle of variable yearly recruitment in its most massive form, it is not surprising that fisheries workers have not attempted the construction of life tables, and have so far been content with the estimation of natural mortality among fishes of certain sizes only. This mortality is generally assumed to be constant with respect to age, and it may well be so for middle-aged fishes exposed to fishing; but a life table constructed from the available observations would certainly be lacking both head and tail.

As an example of the kind of information yielded by fisheries statistics, and of the methods used in their analysis, we may first take the data given by Ricker (1945) for the bluegill sunfish (*Lepomis macrochirus*) in Muskellunge Lake, Indiana. This is an especially instructive case, for it shows that despite great technical advantages not enjoyed by students of marine fisheries (a small, isolated, self-contained population; size and character of catch known with certainty by the investigator; age structure of the population checked by tagging methods), the difficulties remaining are still embarrassing.

Ricker first determined the rate of exploitation and the total mortality between one year and the next by what he called (rather inappropriately) the "direct" method, involving marked fish. In 1942, of 140 fish 145 mm. and larger (mostly 3 years old and older) marked prior to the opening of the season, 25 were recaptured by fishermen during the season, giving a rate of exploitation of 18 per cent. Estimated autumn fishing raises this figure to 19 per cent. Of 230 blue-gills 125 mm. and larger, marked prior to the 1942 season, 14 were recaptured in 1943. The rate of exploitation of fish in the same size group (then 155 mm. and larger) in 1943 was 15.1 per cent. It is necessary to calculate the number of 1942-marked fish present at the beginning of the 1943 season; this number is given by dividing the number recaptured in 1943 by the rate of exploitation in 1943, or $\frac{14}{0.151} = 93$. These 93 fish were the survivors of 230 marked fish present before the 1942 season, so the rate of mortality from one season to the next was $\frac{230 - 93}{230} =$ 60 per cent. Subtracting the 19 per cent rate of

exploitation leaves 41 per cent as the natural mortality.

Ricker's "indirect" method is the life-table method in a crude form. A collection of scales from 529 blue-gills caught by fishermen in 1942 gave the following as the age structure of the sample:

Age....... I II III IV V VI VII VIII
Number... 1 293 151 54 20 7 2 1

The age I fish was presumably caught by accident, and those of age II were not equally vulnerable to fishing during the first part of the season. From age III onward the age structure may be used to yield an estimate of the age-specific mortality rates (assuming uniform recruitment and mortality rates from year to year). These mortality rates in early ages, where the data are more reliable, are nearly constant at about 65 per cent. A weighted geometric mean by Jackson's method gives

$$\frac{1 + 2 + 7 + 20 + 54}{2 + 7 + 20 + 54 + 151} = 36\% \text{ survival}$$

$$= 64\% \text{ mortality.}$$

This is close to the 60 per cent mortality calculated by the "direct" method. However, both methods contain unproved and rather unlikely assumptions, and the agreement merely shows the order of magnitude of the total annual mortality. Moreover, the natural mortality as calculated so far is too low, as some of the fish caught by anglers would have died anyway. By making the additional assumption that the natural mortality is synchronized with the fishing mortality, Ricker calculates the former to be of the order of 50 per cent per year for bluegills age III and older in four Indiana lakes. This is an important result, and one which will doubtless surprise many fisheries supervisors. It is not sufficient as the basis for a life table, however, since it does not include the mortality from birth to the third year of life, and since the method of weighting underrates the age-specific mortality at advanced ages. Ricker, in fact, thinks it not unlikely that the older fish are subject to a still higher mortality, but his data give no clear answer to the question.

It is a generally accepted conclusion that *adult* fishes, from the time they enter a fishery to the age at which they cease to be caught in significant numbers, suffer a more or less constant mortality with respect to age. Thus for these intermediate ages the survivorship curves, whether constructed vertically for a series of year-classes in any one fishing season, or horizontally for particular year-classes followed through several seasons, tend to fall on straight lines when plotted logarithmically. Such straight lines, with slopes changing according to the rate of exploitation, are implicit in Raitt's treatment of the statistics on the haddock (1939) and are conspicuous in Jensen's review (1939) of data on the cod, haddock, plaice, and herring in the North Sea. Whether the natural mortality, as distinguished from the fishing mortality, also is constant at all adult ages is an open question, but most fisheries workers would probably be prepared to assume that this is the case, in the absence of evidence to the contrary.

Direct observations of *juvenile* mortality in fishes are not easy to make, but a mass of indirect evidence points to the conclusion that it must be very much greater than adult mortality in many species. Some idea of this mortality can be had from Sette's work (1943) on the mackerel. Eggs and larvae of this pelagic species were caught on several systematically conducted cruises over the continental shelf between Martha's Vineyard and the Chesapeake Capes. Several broods spawned at short intervals during the season of 1932 were recognizable at later times and at geographically remote stations as separate modes in the frequency distributions of size and age. Assuming that the technique of plankton sampling gives a reliable estimate of the abundance of eggs and larvae of particular stages in the sea, their reduction in numbers gives a measure of their mortality. Sette's calculations show that the mortality is very great, and is substantially the same per unit time at all egg and larval stages. There is a noticeable rise in mortality rate, from about 10 to 14 per cent per day up to about 30 to 45 per cent per day, at the transition from larval to post-larval stages, when the fins are developing rapidly, but it falls again to the original level. The total mortality from the beginning of development to the 50 mm. stage, when the baby fish school like the adults and seek out their nursery grounds, is 99.9996 per cent. This fantastically high figure refers to a time interval of about *70 days*, and may be compared with values of 50 to 90 per cent *per year* estimated as the total mortality suffered by several species of commercial fishes as adults. Clearly, Pearl was correct in supposing that the survivorship curve for pelagic fishes may be of the J-shaped or positively skew rectangular form.

Though it can not be doubted that survivorship curves for fishes in nature will in general have an initial dip, it would be incorrect to conclude that this dip is invariably as pronounced as in the case of the mackerel. Barnaby (1944), for example, has considered the mortality of the Karluk River population of red salmon (*Oncorhynchus nerka*). Marking experiments suggest a total mortality in the ocean of about 79 per cent, while a calculation based on the reproductive potential yields a figure for the mortality in fresh water, between birth and seaward migration, of 99.55 per cent. The problem is complicated by the fact that the salmon may spend their lives in fresh water and in the ocean in various combinations of years, as 3 + 2 years, 3 + 3 years, 4 + 2 years, etc., so that these mortality rates refer to varying intervals of age. Thus there is no proof that the *annual* mortality rate is other than constant, and while no such deduction should be made from the data, it is evident that the age-specific mortality in fresh water can not be *very much* greater than in the ocean.

The data just presented have been grouped together because they give some conception of the form of the life table for certain species of fish, and the fact has been ignored that some of the information is not based on the age structure of the population, but on other kinds of evidence. This section may logically be concluded with a brief reference to the data for the fin whale, in which, as recent investigations have shown, the age of the female can be determined from the number of old corpora lutea in the ovary. By this method Wheeler (1934) arrived at the following as the age structure, observed over five seasons, 1926–1931, of the catch of female fin whales in the Antarctic:

| Age | Number caught |
|---|---|
| 3–4 years | 130 |
| 5–6 years | 95 |
| 7–8 years | 72 |
| 9–10 years | 53 |
| 11–12 years | 37 |
| 13–14 years | 28 |
| 15–16 years | 10 |
| 17–18 years | 4 |
| 19–20 years | 1 |
| 21–22 years | 1 |

The data imply (subject to the usual qualifications) a biennial mortality of about 26 per cent, increasing beyond the 15th year to much higher values. The author considers that the increased rate of loss with age is not real, but is due to failure of the older whales to return from their winter quarters in the north. This belief may or may not be well founded, but one suspects it to be predicated on the idea that mortality, at least when it is primarily due to exploitation, is constant among animals with respect to age. Edser (to whom the statistical analysis is credited) assumed, for the purpose of a rough calculation of the necessary rate of replacement, that the mortality between birth and breeding age is also 26 per cent. The improbability of this assumption may be surmised by reference to the life table for the Dall sheep (Table 1). Edser's calculation has the great merit of yielding a minimal estimate of the alarming exploitation being conducted by the whaling industry in the Antarctic. More realistic assumptions would darken the picture even more. In any case the data can not yet be cast into a life table.

### Miscellaneous Survivorship Data

By means of the mark-and-recapture method, Jackson (1936, 1939) has given an analysis of the population of a tsetse fly (*Glossina morsitans*) in Tanganyika. Jackson was chiefly interested in determining the size of the population and its fluctuations from season to season. The death of flies in the one-week intervals between marking and recapturing struck at the foundation of the method, which assumes no such mortality. But by taking a geometric average of the survival of marked flies in successive weeks, and extrapolating backward one week, the number theoretically recapturable on the date of marking was calculable. From this figure, the first term in a geometric survival series, the population could be directly calculated for each week during the year over which the study was conducted. But the flies were of unknown ages when first marked, being recognizable simply as adult males (plus a few females) having had their first meal. Evidently the operation was designed to smooth out of existence those systematic changes in age-specific mortality in which we are interested here. A few males were marked *before* their first meal, and the returns of these should permit the construction of a life table beginning at early adult life, but the data are not published separately, and in any case are probably inadequate statistically.

Two other points of interest are raised by this resourceful study. The first deals with the sex ratio in the wild population. Data on the return of marked females are not numerous, but so far as they go they suggest a considerably lower mortality than among males, the calculated survival ratio being 0.716 for females and ranging from 0.307 to 0.622 (depending on the season) for males. Expressed as mortality rates, these values are equal to 284, and between 693 and 378 per thousand flies per week, respectively. As a result, the normal sex ratio among the wild flies must vary from 1.5 to 2.0 in favor of females. Yet the sex ratio at emergence from the pupa is unity. There is no evidence that emigration, though always a complicating factor, is performed differentially by the two sexes, and it is not improbable that here also, as in man and in so many other animals studied in the laboratory, the female is significantly more long-lived than the male. The oldest fly captured lived $13\frac{1}{2}$ weeks after marking, and was a female.

The second point is that Jackson used two methods for the calculation of $a$, the initial term in a survivorship series. "Instead of considering the survival curve of flies marked in any one week and recaptured in subsequent weeks . . . we can equally well consider the recaptures of flies marked in previous weeks and recaptured in any one week. Subject to sampling errors, both methods should give the same value of $a$." The difference between the latter "negative" method and the former "positive" method is essentially the difference between a vertical and a horizontal life table. The two methods, while equally applicable to a series of mortality rates assumed to be constant and equal to the geometric mean, as in this case, will give different results for animals of known ages if the age-specific mortality rates change with time. Inasmuch as the smoothed mortality rates for flies of all ages in the population appear to change regularly with the season, being greater in the dry season, real life tables constructed for similar populations would have to be distinguished with care.

An elaborate program of trapping and marking has been carried out with a population of long-tailed field mice (*Apodemus sylvaticus*) by Hacker and Pearson (1946). This sort of work is full of pitfalls, arising mainly from the fact that the traps are attractive to the mice and tend to drain them from distances which are frequently too great to be safely negotiated a second time. As the mice were of unknown ages when first marked, the results need not be summarized in any detail here, but some of the conclusions are of interest in giving an indication of the form of the field mouse life table in nature.

The "standard" survival ratio for mature mice,

as determined from repeated recaptures between December 1938 and April 1939, was 0.879, i.e., the mortality was 121 per thousand per month. But returns of these same mice in December and in March of the following year were much lower than expected from this ratio, implying that the mortality rate increases with age. Data for other years also show that the survival of the winter population is lower in the summer. Moreover, a study of returns of small, middle-sized, and large mice over three winter periods shows that the rates of loss are higher at both ends of the size distribution. Such scanty information can not be cast into a life table, but it is noticeable that a survivorship curve with two inflections fits well with that of the vole (*Microtus agrestis*), as established in the laboratory by Leslie and Ranson (1940).

### Survival of Barnacles

Some of the advantages of the life table notation will now be illustrated by an analysis of the survivorship of the barnacle *Balanus balanoides*, as studied at St. Malo by Hatton (1938). The technical advantages presented by intertidal barnacles as objects of population research have been discussed in an earlier section, and a typical example of a barnacle life table has been given in Table 6. The relevant information about the biology of the species, as elucidated by Runnström (1925), Moore (1934), and Hatton, may be briefly summarized:

*Balanus balanoides* is a typical intertidal species, occurring primarily within the mean range of neap tides, where it often makes dense incrustations on all solid objects. It breeds in the fall, the nauplii being held in the mantle cavity for some time before liberation, while attachment and metamorphosis of the cyprid larvae takes place in the early spring, the exact time doubtless depending on the temperature. The attachment season lasts about six weeks. The intensity of attachment varies with the exposure to surf and the tidal level, being greatest at most exposed localities and at lower levels. The growth rate after attachment is greatest at lower tidal levels in the first year of life, but in subsequent years the growth at higher levels surpasses that at lower levels. Mortality, however, is also greater at lower levels, as shown by survival of barnacles of known ages from year to year, and thus the few barnacles at high levels (up to the mean level of high-water neap tides) are larger after a year's growth and live longer than those lower

down. The maximum longevity appears to be about 5 years, but is much less at lower levels.

It is not clear which of these facts are simple responses to the physical ecology of the intertidal zone, and which are biotic effects. It is easy to suppose that the growth rate might be best at lower levels, where the barnacles are more continuously submerged and therefore take food more frequently. It is not so easy to explain the decline of growth rate with age at these levels (or the increase of growth rate with age at higher levels), unless it is in some way related to the population density; yet the growth differences are said to be observable in the absence of crowding. The low attachment densities at high levels presumably reflect the time necessary for a cyprid to attach, for the time available on any one tide decreases with the height. But after attachment the higher levels are exposed for longer periods to desiccation, direct sunlight, and rainwater, and the enhanced survival under these conditions is difficult to understand except as a function of the low population density.

The relation between population density and longevity is well known for certain laboratory animals. In general the length of life is curtailed by overcrowding (Pearl, 1946; Davis, 1945). In certain well-studied cases, however, the mean length of life has been found to increase at densities above the minimum, to decrease at very high densities, and to be greatest at some intermediate density (Pearl, Miner, and Parker, 1927). Pratt's proof of an optimum density for longevity of *Daphnia magna* (1943) is particularly convincing, since the densities were actually maintained constant throughout the life of the animals, and were not permitted to decrease with the gradual extinction of the initial cohort.

It is of considerable importance, therefore, to examine Hatton's data, which fortunately are published in full, for evidence of the relationship between longevity and population density in *Balanus balanoides*. Hatton studied nine different populations, allowed to settle on cleaned areas in 1930, and followed for three years. Three different levels were chosen at each of three localities as follows:

| Localities | Levels |
|---|---|
| Décollé Ouest, exposed | II—mean high-water neap tide |
| Décollé Est, sheltered | III—half-tide |
| Cité, moderately sheltered | IV—mean low-water neap tide |

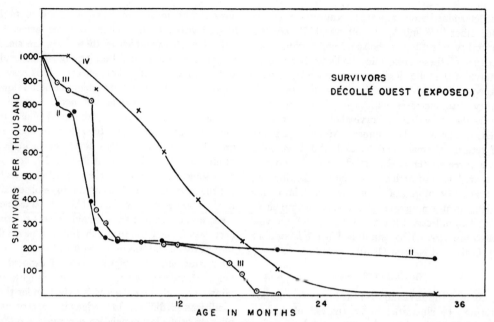

FIG. 6. SURVIVORSHIP ($l_x$) CURVES FOR THREE OF THE NINE POPULATIONS OF BALANUS BALANOIDES STUDIED AT
ST. MALO BY HATTON (1938)

The locality, Décollé Ouest, is exposed to surf. The initial density of attachment, taken as the maximum density attained on May 15, 1930, was as follows: II (at mean high-water neap tide level), 790 per 100 cm²; III (at half-tide level), 2330 per 100 cm²; IV (at mean low-water neap tide level), 1500 per 100 cm².

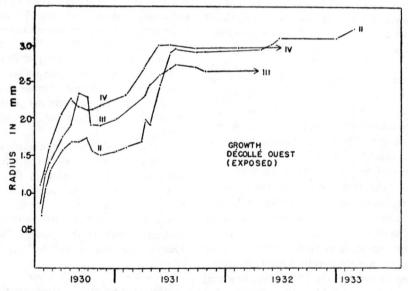

FIG. 7. GROWTH CURVES FOR BARNACLES CORRESPONDING TO THE THREE POPULATIONS OF FIG. 6, BUT OBTAINED
FROM UNCROWDED SPECIMENS

The measurements began on April 1, 1930, and the points plotted are the average lengths (at the base, in the rostro-carinal axis), divided by 2. Each point represents an average of about 50 measurements.

Survivorship curves for the three populations at Décollé Ouest, converted to a relative (per thousand) basis, are shown by way of illustration in Fig. 6. It may be seen that the only population having surviving members after three years was that at Level II, where the initial population density was also least. The same relationship between density and survival was observed at the other two localities. But the matter is not so simple as it looks, for the growth rates must be taken into account in evaluating the degree of crowding on the areas. The corresponding growth curves for the Décollé Ouest populations are shown in Fig. 7. The measurements were made, not on the original populations, but on barnacles from adjacent cleaned areas, where the initial density was not allowed to exceed 100 per square decimeter, so that the growth was uninfluenced by crowding. The measurements given are the average lengths (in the rostro-carinal axis) of 50 individuals. This explains the curious fact that the sizes decrease during the winter: negative growth is biologically impossible in this case, and evidently there was a relatively great loss of older barnacles each winter. For purposes of calculation the radius of a barnacle has been taken to equal half the length, and the reasonable growth figures (ignoring negative increments) have been fitted to equations of the form

$$r = at^b$$

where $r$ is the radius and $t$ is the time in months.

Hatton's survivorship curves give the population per unit area at any time. The area at the base of an average uncrowded member of the population at any time can be calculated from the growth curve on the assumption, which is sufficiently accurate for the purpose, that the barnacles grow as expanding circles. The degree of crowding attained at any time can be evaluated as follows: (Grateful acknowledgment is due to Dr. John Ferry, of the University of Wisconsin, for the elegant following formulation.)

If barnacles of radius $r$ settle at random within distance $D$ of each other, and grow as expanding circles, so that at any time the radii $r$ are equal, any barnacle which settles within distance $2r$ will be in contact with or overlap another. The number of binary contacts per barnacle will be given by:

$$\int_0^{2r} \frac{N}{A} \cdot 2\pi D \cdot dD$$

or, evaluating:

$$4\pi r^2 \frac{N}{A} \cdot$$

where $\frac{N}{A}$ is the density per unit area. The total number of binary contacts per unit area will be this expression times the density times $\frac{1}{2}$ (because each contact is counted twice):

$$C = 2\pi r^2 \left(\frac{N}{A}\right)^2$$

This value $C$, the *crowding coefficient*, can be evaluated in terms of contacts per square centimeter, and is a function of the density and of the radius of an individual barnacle.

The crowding coefficients for Hatton's nine populations are given for selected times in Table 7, together with the observed density and the average radius of a barnacle at the same times. The expectation of life of a barnacle at the time in question is calculated by ordinary life table methods. Plotting $C$ against $e_x$ gives the graph shown in Fig. 8.

Evidently the population density, when considered in this way, has a definite effect on the survival of *Balanus balanoides*. The effect is not linear, but becomes less marked at higher degrees of crowding. Evidently, too, the relationship between survivorship and crowding is less definite at advanced ages, for the points for 18 months diverge from the curve.

It seems fairly certain that this discrepancy is due to the fact that the treatment has ignored the new settlements of barnacles which were added to the populations in subsequent years. The new arrivals can be treated by an extension of Dr. Ferry's mathematical approach, but it becomes necessary to decide whether there is any super-incrustation, i.e., whether the area exposed to settlement, $A$, is (1) the same as the original area, (2) equal to the unoccupied area, or (3) has some intermediate value. No decision can be reached on this point from Hatton's account, which moreover gives only the second-year settlements, without subsequent data on the survival of the 1931 year-class or any information on the 1932 year-class. The data, however, are suggestive in that all the populations which diverge widely at 18 months from the curve of Fig. 8 received high second-year settlements, while the "good" points are from populations which received relatively little recruitment in 1931. Since in general the populations with highest initial densities will receive the most considerable reinforcement in subsequent such as the one drawn in Fig. 8, is an illusion. But only further work will permit a deeper analysis of this exceptionally interesting case.

### TABLE 7

*Population density, calculated radius, crowding coefficients, and expectation of life at selected times for nine populations of Balanus balanoides at St. Malo*

*Original data from Hatton (1938)*

| POPULATION (Locality and Level) | t TIME (months)* | N/A DENSI- TY PER CM² | r RADIUS (mm.) | C CROWDING COEFFICI- ENT: contacts per cm² = $2\pi r^2(N/A)^2$ | $e_x$ EXPECTA- TION OF FURTHER LIFE (months)† | POPULATION (Locality and Level) | t TIME (months)* | N/A DENSI- TY PER CM² | r RADIUS (mm.) | C CROWDING COEFFICI- ENT: contacts per cm² = $2\pi r^2(N/A)^2$ | $e_x$ EXPECTA- TION OF FURTHER LIFE (months)† |
|---|---|---|---|---|---|---|---|---|---|---|---|
| Décollé Est II | 0 | 4.0 | 1.08 | 1.17 | 23.1 | Décollé Ouest IV | 0 | 15.0 | 1.74 | 42.55 | 12.6 |
| | 6 | 2.4 | 1.65 | 0.98 | 29.6 | | 6 | 12.6 | 2.20 | 48.41 | 8.2 |
| | 12 | 2.1 | 1.92 | 1.02 | 27.2 | | 12 | 7.3 | 2.40 | 19.35 | 5.6 |
| | 18 | 1.9 | 2.11 | 1.01 | 23.7 | | 18 | 3.0 | 2.54 | 3.65 | 3.7 |
| | 24 | 1.5 | 2.27 | 0.73 | 23.1 | | 24 | 0.6 | 2.64 | 0.16 | 2.9 |
| | 30 | 1.5 | 2.39 | 0.81 | 17.7 | | 30 | 0.08 | 2.73 | 0.03 | 2.0 |
| Décollé Est III | 0 | 11.9 | 1.12 | 11.24 | 13.8 | Cité II | 0 | 10.0 | 1.24 | 9.61 | 14.3 |
| | 6 | 8.3 | 1.59 | 10.87 | 12.8 | | 6 | 3.4 | 1.67 | 2.03 | 28.6 |
| | 12 | 5.4 | 1.80 | 5.92 | 12.6 | | 12 | 2.9 | 1.89 | 1.88 | 27.2 |
| | 18 | 4.2 | 1.94 | 4.09 | 9.1 | | 18 | 2.8 | 2.00 | 1.97 | 22.5 |
| | 24 | 2.0 | 2.06 | 1.07 | 9.9 | | 24 | 2.5 | 2.10 | 1.73 | 19.0 |
| | 30 | 1.0 | 2.16 | 0.29 | 12.2 | | 30 | 2.2 | 2.19 | 1.45 | 15.2 |
| Décollé Est IV | 0 | 15.0 | 1.41 | 27.91 | 9.5 | Cité III‡ | 0 | 22.0 | 1.32 | 53.22 | 12.1 |
| | 6 | 8.4 | 1.80 | 14.35 | 7.5 | | 6 | 16.7 | 1.66 | 48.05 | 9.1 |
| | 12 | 4.8 | 1.97 | 5.61 | 4.9 | | 12 | 10.1 | 1.80 | 20.70 | 6.7 |
| | 18 | 1.8 | 2.08 | 0.88 | 1.2 | | 18 | 5.1 | 1.89 | 5.85 | 4.7 |
| | | | | | | | 24 | 0.7 | 1.96 | 0.11 | 1.8 |
| Décollé Ouest II | 0 | 7.9 | 1.34 | 7.07 | 11.0 | | | | | | |
| | 6 | 1.9 | 1.82 | 0.75 | 31.2 | Cité IV | 0 | 23.8 | 1.44 | 74.10 | 11.2 |
| | 12 | 1.7 | 2.03 | 0.75 | 28.5 | | 6 | 12.9 | 1.71 | 30.68 | 12.2 |
| | 18 | 1.5 | 2.18 | 0.67 | 24.5 | | 12 | 11.0 | 1.82 | 25.29 | 7.9 |
| | 24 | 1.4 | 2.29 | 0.65 | 20.3 | | 18 | 6.1 | 1.90 | 8.41 | 5.4 |
| | 30 | 1.3 | 2.38 | 0.61 | 15.8 | | 24 | 2.6 | 1.95 | 1.62 | 2.5 |
| Décollé Ouest III | 0 | 23.3 | 1.50 | 76.28 | 7.0 | | | | | | |
| | 6 | 6.3 | 1.94 | 9.34 | 8.7 | | | | | | |
| | 12 | 4.9 | 2.12 | 6.81 | 4.7 | | | | | | |
| | 18 | 1.2 | 2.25 | 0.46 | 1.0 | | | | | | |

\* These are the times corresponding to the density figures (read from the survivorship curves), beginning at 0 = 15 May. The growth curves begin on 1 April, and the time values for radius as stated are actually 1.5, 7.5, 13.5, 19.5, 25.5, and 31.5 months.

† Computed on the assumption that those populations still having surviving members after 3 years would have terminated at 5 years.

‡ Life table for this population given in Table 6.

years, it is easy to imagine that over the years the effect of unit change of crowding on survival, $\dfrac{de_x}{dC}$, will be greatest for these populations. This argument carries the implication that a single curve, Returning to the original question, whether there is a density above the minimum which is optimal for the longevity of *Balanus balanoides* in nature, Fig. 8 indicates that there is not. The expectation of life is greatest when the crowding coefficient is least, and the curve does not rise before it falls. This negative evidence is probably not conclusive, and a larger body of data, preferably obtained under conditions which are less variable as regards factors other than crowding, might give a different answer. But there is no particular reason to expect that a species such as this one would benefit greatly from mutual support. It is possible to point to another barnacle in which the case may be otherwise. This is *Chthamalus stellatus*, which flourishes best at an intertidal level above that of

this phenomenon was never observed with *Chthamalus*.

Hatton's work included survival studies of *Chthamalus* as well as of *B. balanoides*, but as the longevity of the former is greater (see also Moore and Kitching, 1939), few of the populations had run their courses when the experiments were terminated at the end of three years. As a result, the expectation of life cannot be calculated with any confidence. Annual mortality rates for six populations (three at Level I, above the *B. balanoids*

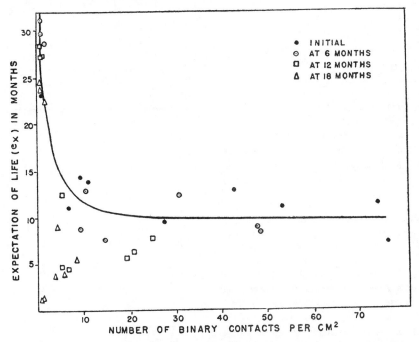

Fig. 8. Relation Between Expectation of Life ($e_x$) of Balanus balanoides at Selected Times and the Crowding Coefficient (Contacts per Square Centimeter) at the Same Time
Data in Table 7, calculated from data of Hatton.

*B. balanoides.* Here it is exposed to sun and drought for long periods, and Monterosso (1930) has found that it is remarkably hardy, specimens having survived for three years on a laboratory table with only one or two days' immersion in sea water each month. Hatton suggests that the chances of survival of a young *Chthamalus* are improved if it settles in the shade of a larger individual; at any rate, the larvae tend to attach in the shade in greater numbers, when ridges of cement are built upon the rocks. Moreover, while attached and growing *B. balanoides* were frequently found to dislodge each other from the substratum,

zone; and three at Level II, where densities of *B. balanoides* were low) are arranged in Table 8 for direct comparison with the density. The table shows that the populations having very low densities suffered higher mortality rates on the average than those below the dashed line in the table, which had higher densities. The difference is more pronounced when the first year's mortality is omitted, but in neither case is the difference significant statistically. The predicted relation between density and survivorship of *Chthamalus* is therefore not proven, and the question remains open.

Mention has been made in an earlier section of a

defect inherent in the life tables calculated from experiments like Hatton's, in that the observations much greater, reaching 95 per cent (survival ratio 0.05) at the greatest densities observed.

TABLE 8

*Annual mortality of Chthamalus stellatus at St. Malo in relation to population density*
*Data from Hatton (1938), Tables XXXVI–XXXVIII*

| POPULATION (LOCALITY AND LEVEL) | FIRST YEAR | | SECOND YEAR | | THIRD YEAR | |
|---|---|---|---|---|---|---|
| | Initial density per 100 cm² | Mortality % | Density per 100 cm² | Mortality % | Density per 100 cm² | Mortality % |
| Décollé Ouest I | 21 | 4.8 | 20 | 10.0 | 18 | 16.6 |
| Décollé Est II | 39 | 10.3 | 35 | 20.0 | 28 | 28.6 |
| Cité I | 44 | 9.1 | 40 | 17.5 | 33 | 9.1 |
| Décollé Est I | 48 | 31.2 | 33 | 9.1 | 30 | 36.7 |
| Cité II | 184 | 11.4 | 163 | 13.5 | 141 | 8.5 |
| Décollé Ouest II | 270 | 17.4 | 223 | 11.2 | 198 | 14.1 |

start with metamorphosis, and the pelagic larval life is neglected. Some idea of the mortality during the earliest attachment stage, the interval between attachment of the cyprid and its transformation to an adult barnacle, can be gained from the unpublished studies of Weiss at Miami Beach, Florida.

Permission to present these results in advance of publication has been courteously granted by Mr. C. M. Weiss of the Woods Hole Oceanographic Institution.

Weiss observed the daily attachment of cyprid larvae (mainly *Balanus improvisus*) to glass slides exposed each twenty-four hours for more than three years. At the same time, records were kept of the attachment of adult barnacles to glass panels exposed each month at the same locality. The time required for a cyprid to grow into an adult barnacle large enough to be counted varies from one to two weeks according to the season. By summing the daily cyprid attachments over a two- to three-week period, therefore, and comparing the figures with the number of adult barnacles found on the panels at the end of the month, a measure of the survival between cyprid and adult stages was obtained. The results are shown in Fig. 9, the ratio of surviving barnacles to cyprids being plotted against the intensity of cyprid attachment. The curve shows clearly that a cyprid's chances of successful growth to maturity vary inversely with the density of attachment: when few cyprids attach most or all of them survive to become barnacles, but when cyprid densities are high the mortality is

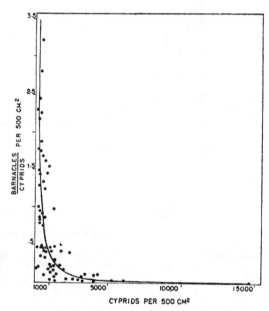

FIG. 9. RELATION BETWEEN SURVIVAL OF BARNACLES TO MATURITY AND THE INTENSITY OF CYPRID ATTACHMENT AT MIAMI BEACH, FLORIDA

Cyprid attachment was observed on glass slides exposed for twenty-four hours; the barnacles were counted on glass panels exposed for twenty-eight days. Daily cyprid attachment figures have been summed over two or three weeks, according to the season, for comparison with the number of surviving barnacles. From unpublished results of C. M. Weiss, Woods Hole Oceanographic Institution.

Inspection of the scale of barnacle:cyprid ratios in Fig. 9 brings out an apparent paradox in that ratios above 1.0 were frequently observed, i.e., in some months more barnacles survived than can be accounted for from the cyprids attaching. Weiss takes this to mean that the longer exposure of the one-month panels made them more suitable for the attachment of barnacles than the twenty-four-hour slides. Such a result of exposure can reasonably be attributed to the facilitating effect of a "slime film" (of diatoms and bacteria) on the attachment of larvae of fouling organisms, an effect of which there is independent evidence. This complication, interesting as it is, makes it impossible to use the data further for an analysis of the mortality of barnacles in early stages. For if in any month more cyprids attached to the panels during certain days than the daily figures show, the barnacle:cyprid ratio will give too low an estimate of the mortality; but such an error is not likely to be systematic, and would have to be evaluated separately.

Although it is abundantly clear that much of the mortality suffered by natural stands of barnacles is directly related to population density, much of it certainly is not. Predators, such as whelks and limpets, account for many deaths at all ages, and physical factors, including desiccation in summer and abrasion by boulders in winter, are also important. We are not yet able to dissect the barnacle life tables to expose the causes of death. It is enough for the purposes of this review to have pointed out: (1) the attraction of barnacle incrustations as objects for population research; and (2) the advantages of life table methods in their study.

COMPARISONS AND CONCLUSIONS

It is now apparent that, owing to the different ways in which data have been collected, all ecological life tables are not strictly comparable among themselves, and a summary graph containing survivorship curves for all the species considered would be misleading in the extreme. It is also true, though not so obvious, that within any one group of life tables, such as the "$d_x$ observed" group or the "$l_x$ observed" group, comparisons are also apt to lead us astray. For the various life tables so far constructed *take their origin at different biological ages.* Is it fair to compare a bird life table, beginning at early adult life, with the Dall sheep life table, which begins at birth, or with the life table of a sessile invertebrate, beginning at attachment or metamorphosis? Evidently not; birth itself is not an age of universal biological equivalence outside the placental mammals, and for a

broader view of comparative mortality the only safe point of reference would be the fertilized ovum.

This reservation should perhaps not be applied too literally. Human and insect survivorship curves have been compared in the past, and the comparison is instructive, despite the very different origins and statistical foundations of the life tables. It is possible to compare the survivorship of an insect such as *Drosophila*, beginning at sexual maturity, with that of a laboratory population of black widow spiders (Deevey and Deevey, 1945) which enter their life table at the antepenultimate instar when the sexes become distinguishable. The comparison, which of course is purely qualitative, suggests that organisms are born at different points on their survivorship curves, so to speak, and that heavy juvenile mortality may be carried over into later life as a neotenic character. This is the statistical aspect of that ancient proverb which Cicero quotes disparagingly, "grow old early if you would be old long."

The cognate suggestion has been made that altricial and praecocial birds should be examined in the light of this hypothesis. Unfortunately, such a comparison cannot yet be made. We now have life tables of a sort for several altricial species, (song sparrow, Turdidae, etc.) and for at least one markedly praecocial bird (the pheasant), but the data are lacking for those early ages at which the comparison might have some meaning.

If bird life tables cannot even be compared with one another except from adult ages onward, we can hardly make very enlightening comparisons between birds and other animals. The ecological information is deficient, to a variable degree it is true, but still deficient, for the early ages; and this is the segment of the life curve on which future investigators must concentrate their efforts. The most that can be said at present is that the more nearly complete natural life tables (Dall sheep, barnacle, rotifer) give no ground for supposing that ecological life tables are invariably diagonal, as is so often assumed *faute de mieux* in fisheries work. Increases and decreases in mortality rate must be expected at any age, as the laboratory populations also show.

Related to the paucity of data near the beginning of life is the remarkable absence, among the examples adduced, of life curves approaching Pearl's "Type III" distribution. Only the synthetic survivorship curve for the song sparrow calculated from the egg stage (Fig. 5) shows the pronounced dip in early life associated with this form. But Sette's data for the mackerel show that pelagic fishes actually fall here; the barnacle and the rotifer might also fall here if their life tables were complete, and ecologists will await with interest the construction of a life table for the oyster.

It is pertinent to inquire whether the ecological life tables throw any light on the relation between the different theoretical types of survivorship curve (Fig. 1). It is a well known property of human longevity that while the mean age at death shows extreme variation among different populations, ancient and modern, and has shown a marked increase in Europe and the United States in recent decades, the maximum life span is fixed (Dublin and Lotka, 1935; Pearl, 1946). In other words, the human survivorship curve is like a rubber band, fixed at points corresponding to birth and about the 115th year, and while medical science has succeeded in stretching the band more and more toward the upper side of Fig. 1, the termini have remained fixed as they were in Roman times.

If the maximum life span is fixed for all species by physiological considerations, as it probably is, the mean life span is not. Lack (1943b) points out that a young blackbird in nature can expect to live for but 8 per cent of its potential life span, compared to some 60 per cent for a juvenile human. Evidently there is much room for improvement in the expectation of life of species in the wild, to judge from the known longevity of some of them in captivity. As has been shown, birds as a group seem to have remarkably diagonal survivorship curves, the mortality being constant for a given bird with respect to age, and for all birds so far studied with respect to units of mean life span. This means that experience of life is of no use to a bird in avoiding death, although Farner (1945) raises the question whether the apparent diagonality may not be a result of insufficient data.

The case is quite otherwise with the Dall sheep, with its low mortality during middle life. This species seems to have evolved a mechanism for stretching its mean life span toward the maximum. Whether this has come about because of intimate demographic contact with a single important predator or for some other reason is a "puzzling question." Such an enhancement of survival during the years of maximum reproductive efficiency has important implications for the whole population problem, including the question of the nature of internally generated cycles; but on this matter little

more can be said than that the mathematical methods are available for a study of the relation between the fertility schedule and the death rate structure when the data come to hand (Leslie, 1945).

Bodenheimer (1938) has maintained that not only is the maximum life span fixed for a species, but that the potential mean longevity is the same as the maximum. On this view a species has a "physiological life table" of the negatively skew rectangular type, and a more diagonal or positively skew "ecological life table" which is the result of premature mortality. All such mortality is thus regarded as environmentally produced. This position is probably not tenable as a basis for a general theory of mortality, since there appears to be no reason why "endogenous senescence" (in Pearl's phrase) should be strictly confined to the end of the life span. Even in genetically homogeneous populations the members are not identical, and endogenous senescence must have a probability distribution which is not necessarily regular, though it may well be more so than that of "exogenous senescence." In any case, since we can not observe physiological survivorship except in an environment of some sort, Bodenheimer's conception would appear to be non-operational.

The question at issue resolves itself into the relation between the mean and the maximum life span. In theory there is a simple answer: the ratio of the maximum to the mean approaches 1.0 as a limit for Type I, approaches infinity for Type III, and its actual value for Type II depends on the level at which we permit the abscissa of Figure 1 to intersect the ordinate. If we decide to terminate the diagram when a cohort of 1000 individuals has been reduced to 1, a diagonal survivorship line will intersect the age axis at some point above 1.0, but if we start with 100,000 individuals the same line projected will give a higher maximum age for the last survivor. Reference to Figs. 2, 4, and 5 will make the matter plain, when it is realized that an age value of +100 per cent deviation from the mean corresponds to a maximum: mean ratio of 2.0, one of +500 per cent corresponds to a ratio of 6.0, etc. In all cases we have started with 1000 individuals, simply because the samples were of less than 1000 to begin with, and only three places at most can be significant. Had we larger samples available the maximum life span, as shown on the abscissas of Figs. 2, 4, and 5, would have been higher for a given mortality rate.

It should now be clear that we cannot yet formulate the relationship exactly. One stumbling block is that with a cohort of 1000 individuals the 1 per thousand level has lost all semblance of reliability: taking Fig. 4 as an illustration, we might well find that the last hundred birds in a cohort of 100,000 really have gained some benefit from their accumulated experience of life, and die at decreasing rates. This would mean that the true survivorship curve is concave. It is equally possible that these hypothetical survivors of a larger cohort would be found to be decrepit, and to die at greatly accelerated rates, giving a convexity to the tail of the survivorship curve.

The other obstacle to an exact formulation is that the mean length of life is calculated from different starting points in the cases before us, so that an observed relation between maximum and mean has no quantitative significance as a basis of comparison between species. Empirically, it will eventually be possible to divide animals into three groups, somewhat as follows: those in which the maximum length of life is between two and six times the mean may be called "thrifty" (the Dall sheep, rotifer, and barnacle might fall here, along with most of the populations studied in the laboratory); those in which the ratio lies between 6.0 and 15.0 (as perhaps in song birds) might be called "indifferent"; those which on the average realize less than one-fifteenth of their maximum life span might be called "prodigal." These limits would have to be arbitrarily defined by the age (in units of mean life span) attained by the oldest individual in a cohort of 1000. But such limits can not yet be specified, and the values assigned are pure guesses, based on data which we know to be inadequate, and intended simply for illustration.

So far we have confined our attention almost exclusively to the *form* of the life table, and have said very little about the *causes* of death other than to imply that they are suitable subjects for ecological investigation. Authors who have discussed the matter in some detail for particular cases have not reached very satisfactory general conclusions. Thus Ricker (1945) decides that "senile death is an everyday occurrence among bluegills and crappies," and Lack (1943a) says, "Who killed cock robin is, for the most part, still a mystery." Errington (1945, 1946) has argued energetically against the generally accepted view that predation is responsible for the maintenance of population size among vertebrates, believing that intraspecific competition demands more attention than it has received. Predation, in Errington's opinion, falls principally on the very young, the very old, and the diseased, i.e., on the insecure members of the population, who might otherwise have died in any event. Clearly, the task of constructing better life tables for natural populations, though an important prerequisite to the study of mortality, is not a substitute for such a study. Even so interesting a series of life tables as is available for *Balanus balanoides* proves to be unsatisfactory when it is realized that they all start at the same season, and the survivors are exposed to winter conditions at the same ages. What would happen to the survivorship curves if such animals were caused to be born out of season can only be found out by painstaking work. And until such questions, and many others, are answered, we will not be ready to establish a general theory of mortality.

> "Sed omnes una manet nox
> et calcanda semel via leti."

### SUMMARY

Materials for the study of the age distribution of mortality are available from several natural populations of animals. Attempts are made, in most instances for the first time, to condense this information into life tables, showing for each age interval the number of deaths, the number of survivors, the mortality rate, and the expectation of further life of members of an initial cohort of 1000 individuals. These life table functions, especially when age is expressed in terms of units of the mean life span rather than in years, months, or days, should afford the best basis for comparing populations of the same and of different species in respect to their order of dying. Unfortunately, the ecological information is of unequal value in the various cases, and only limited and tentative comparisons can be made.

According to the methods used in collecting the information, the species studied fall into three groups: (a) those in which the *age at death* ($d_x$) is known, with fair accuracy, at least beyond certain ages (Dall mountain sheep, the sessile rotifer *Floscularia conifera*, and several species of birds); (b) those in which the *number of survivors* ($l_x$) out of a definite initial number has been directly observed at frequent intervals (barnacles, song sparrow, pheasant, snowshoe rabbit); (c) those in which the *age structure* ($L_x$) of the population is observed at a specified time, and the age at death is inferred from the shrinkage between age classes (cormorant, many fish, fin whale). Information of type (b) is comparable to that obtainable from a laboratory experiment, provided only that the season of birth is sharply defined, and can be used without qualification for the construction of a life table. Information of types (a) and (c) can be so used only upon the assumption that the age structure of the population does not change with time.

Both in nature and in the laboratory, animals differ characteristically in their order of dying. When the mortality rate at all ages is constant, the survivorship ($l_x$) curve is diagonal on semi-logarithmic graph paper. Such a curve is found for many birds from adult stages onward; the mortality of adult birds is about 320 per thousand per hundred centiles of mean life span. If the constant age-specific mortality rate observed for the first few years of adult life is really maintained throughout life, the oldest bird in a cohort of 1000 lives 6.6 times as long as the average bird. Not all animals resemble birds in this respect, however, although many (e.g., fish) are assumed to do so. The Dall sheep, the rotifer, and possibly the barnacle are more like civilized man in that they seem to have evolved a mechanism for stretching the mean life span toward the maximum, so that the survivorship curve is convex. In these cases the maximum life span (among a sample of 1000) is only two or three times the mean. On the other hand there are undoubtedly species in which juvenile mortality is very heavy, but the few survivors to advanced ages die at reduced rates. This J-shaped or concave survivorship line, with the maximum longevity perhaps 15 or more times the mean, is presumed to characterize the oyster and other species, but it has not yet been formally recognized either in the laboratory or in nature. The closest approach to it, so far, is found when the survival of song sparrows is reckoned from the egg stage; but the mackerel will almost certainly provide an even better example.

Detailed comparisons between species cannot yet be made, partly because of the diverse statistical foundations of the life tables and partly because the data begin at different biological ages (birth, hatching, metamorphosis, sexual maturity, etc.) in the different cases. In all cases it is the youngest ages about which we know least, and ecologists should therefore concentrate their efforts on this segment of the life span of animals in nature.

The best examples of ecological life tables come from Hatton's work with the barnacle *Balanus balanoides*, which is a very favorable object for population research. By way of emphasizing the advantages of life table notation, Hatton's data are manipulated so as to show the relationship between longevity and population density. A theory of two-dimensional crowding by radially growing circular objects is first derived from geometric considerations, and it is then possible to relate the expectation of life ($e_x$) of a barnacle to a factor, called the *crowding coefficient*, which incorporates both the population density and the rate of growth. The number of barnacle populations available for study is limited, and Hatton's experiments were designed for a different purpose, but so far as the data go there is no evidence of an optimum density for survival of *B. balanoides*. Reasons are given for supposing that *Chthamalus stellatus* may prove to have such an optimum density.

#### ACKNOWLEDGMENTS

This article had its inception as part of a symposium, entitled "Life Tables and Their Application," held at Boston on December 27, 1943, under the joint auspices of the Ecological Society of America and the American Statistical Association. The present version has been completely reworked in the light of other contributions to the symposium. Remarks made at the meeting by Margaret Merrell, C. P. Winsor, and W. E. Ricker have been particularly helpful. Much has been learned also from later conversations with David Lack, G. E. Hutchinson, and Daniel Merriman. The author retains sole responsibility, however, for errors which may still remain.

## LIST OF LITERATURE

AUSTIN, O. L. 1942. The life span of the common tern (*Sterna hirundo*). *Bird-Banding*, 13: 159–176.

BARNABY, J. T. 1944. Fluctuations in abundance of red salmon, *Oncorhynchus nerka* (Walbaum) of the Karluk River, Alaska. *U. S. Fish & Wildlife Service, Fishery Bull.*, 50 (39): 235–295.

BERTRAM, G. C. L. 1940. The biology of the Weddell and Crabeater Seals, with a study of the comparative behaviour of the Pinnipedia. *Brit. Mus.*

(*Nat. Hist.*): *British Graham Land Expedition 1934–37, Sci. Rep.*, 1 (1): 139 pp., pls. 1–10.

BODENHEIMER, F. S. 1938. *Problems of animal ecology.* vi + 183 pp. Oxford Univ. Press, London.

DAVIS, M. B. 1945. The effect of population density on longevity in *Trogoderma versicolor* Creutz. ( = *T. inclusa* Lec.). *Ecology*, 26: 353–362.

DEEVEY, G. B., and E. S. DEEVEY. 1945. A life table for the black widow. *Trans. Conn. Acad. Arts Sci.*, 36: 115–134.

DUBLIN, L. I., and A. J. LOTKA. 1935. *Length of life. A study of the life table.* xxii + 400 pp. Ronald Press, New York.

EDMONDSON, W. T. 1945. Ecological studies of sessile Rotatoria, Part II. Dynamics of populations and social structures. *Ecol. Mon.*, 15: 141–172.

ERICKSON, M. M. 1938. Territory, annual cycle, and numbers in a population of wren-tits (*Chamaea fasciata*). *Univ. Calif. Pub. Zool.*, 42 (5): 247–334, pls. 9–14.

ERRINGTON, P. L. 1945. Some contributions of a fifteen-year local study of the northern bobwhite to a knowledge of population phenomena. *Ecol. Mon.*, 15: 1–34.

———. 1946. Predation and vertebrate populations. *Quart. Rev. Biol.*, 21: 144–177, 221–245.

ESCHMEYER, R. W. 1939. Analysis of the complete fish population from Howe Lake, Crawford County, Michigan. *Papers Mich. Acad. Sci. Arts Lett.*, 24 (II): 117–137.

FARNER, D. S. 1945. Age groups and longevity in the American robin. *Wilson Bull.*, 57: 56–74.

GEISER, S. W. 1923. Evidences of a differential death rate of the sexes among animals. *Amer. Midl. Nat.*, 8: 155–163.

———. 1924. The differential death-rate of the sexes among animals, with a suggested explanation. *Wash. Univ. Stud.*, 12: 73–96.

GREEN, R. G., and C. A. EVANS. 1940. Studies on a population cycle of snowshoe hares on the Lake Alexander area. I. Gross annual censuses, 1932–1939. *J. Wildl. Man.*, 4: 220–238. II. Mortality according to age groups and seasons. Ibid., 4: 267–278. III. Effect of reproduction and mortality of young hares on the cycle. Ibid., 4: 347–358.

HACKER, H. P., and H. S. PEARSON. 1946. The growth, survival, wandering, and variation of the long-tailed field mouse, *Apodemus sylvaticus*. II. Survival (By H. P. Hacker). *Biometrika*, 33: 333–361.

HATTON, H. 1938. Essais de bionomie explicative sur quelques espèces intercotidales d'algues et d'animaux. *Ann. Inst. Océanogr.*, 17: 241–348.

HODGE, W. B. 1857. On the rates of interest for the use of money in ancient and modern times. (Part I). *Assurance Mag. & J. Inst. Act.*, 6: 301–333.

JACKSON, C. H. N. 1936. Some new methods in the study of *Glossina morsitans*. *Proc. Zool. Soc. Lond.*, 1936: 811–896, pls. 1–12.

———. 1939. The analysis of an animal population. *J. Anim. Ecol.*, 8: 238–246.

JENSEN, A. J. C. 1939. On the laws of decrease in fish stocks. *Cons. Per. Intern. Explor. Mer, Rapp. Proc.-Verb.*, 110 (8): 85–96.

KORTLANDT, A. 1942. Levensloop, samenstelling en structuur der Nederlandse aalscholver bevolking. *Ardea*, 31: 175–280.

KRAAK, W. K., G. L. RINKEL, and J. HOOGERHEIDE. 1940. Oecologische bewerking van de Europese ringgegevens van de Kievit (*Vanellus vanellus* (L.) ). *Ardea*, 29: 151–175.

LACK, D. 1943a. *The life of the robin.* 200 pp. H. F. & G. Witherby, London.

———. 1943b. The age of the blackbird. *Brit. Birds*, 36: 166–175.

———. 1943c. The age of some more British birds. *Brit. Birds*, 36: 193–197, 214–221.

———. 1946. Do juvenile birds survive less well than adults? *Brit. Birds*, 39: 258–264.

LAURIE, A. H. 1937. The age of female blue whales and the effect of whaling on the stock. *Discov. Rep.*, 15: 223–284.

LEOPOLD, A., T. M. SPERRY, W. S. FEENEY, and J. S. CATENHUSEN. 1943. Population turnover on a Wisconsin pheasant refuge. *J. Wildl. Man.*, 7: 383–394.

LESLIE, P. H. 1945. On the use of matrices in certain population mathematics. *Biometrika*, 33: 183–212.

———, and R. M. RANSON. 1940. The mortality, fertility, and rate of natural increase of the vole (*Microtus agrestis*) as observed in the laboratory. *J. Anim. Ecol.*, 9: 27–52.

MACARTHUR, J. W., and W. H. T. BAILLIE. 1932. Sex differences in mortality in *Abraxas*-type species. *Quart. Rev. Biol.*, 7: 313–325.

MACDONELL, W. R. 1913. On the expectation of life in ancient Rome, and in the provinces of Hispania and Lusitania, and Africa. *Biometrika*, 9: 366–380.

MARSHALL, H. 1947. Longevity of the American herring gull. *Auk*, 64: 188–198.

MONTEROSSO, B. 1930. Studi cirripedologici, VI. Sul comportamento di "Chthamalus stellatus" in diverse condizioni sperimentali. *Atti. R. Accad. Naz. Lincei Rend.*, Ser. 6, *Cl. Sci. Fis. Mat. Nat.*, 11 (5): 501–505.

MOORE, H. B. 1934. The biology of *Balanus balanoides*. I. Growth rate and its relation to size, season, and tidal level. *J. Mar. Biol. Ass.*, n. s., 19: 851–868.

MOORE, H. B. 1935. A comparison of the biology of *Echinus esculentus* in different habitats. Part II. *J. Mar. Biol. Ass.*, n. s., 20: 109–128.

———, and J. A. KITCHING. 1939. The biology of *Chthamalus stellatus* (Poli). *J. Mar. Biol. Ass.*, n. s., 23: 521–541.

MURIE, A. 1944. *The wolves of Mount McKinley.* (Fauna of the National Parks of the U. S., Fauna Series No. 5, xx + 238 pp.) U. S. Dept. Int., Nat. Park Service, Washington.

NICE, M. M. 1937. Studies on the life history of the song sparrow. Vol. I. A population study of the song sparrow. *Trans. Linn. Soc. N. Y.*, 4: vi + 247 pp.

PAYNTER, R. A. (*in press*). The fate of Kent Island herring gulls. *Bird-Banding*, (in press).

PEARL, R. 1940. *Introduction to medical biometry and statistics.* 3rd ed. xv + 537 pp. W. B. Saunders, Philadelphia and London.

———. 1946. *Man the animal.* 128 pp. Principia Press, Bloomington.

———, and J. R. MINER. 1935. Experimental studies on the duration of life. XIV. The comparative mortality of certain lower organisms. *Quart. Rev. Biol.*, 10: 60–79.

———, ———, and S. L. PARKER. 1927. Experimental studies on the duration of life. XI. Density of population and life duration in *Drosophila. Amer. Nat.*, 61: 289–318.

———, T. PARK, and J. R. MINER. 1941. Experimental studies on the duration of life. XVI. Life tables for the flour beetle *Tribolium confusum* Duval. *Amer. Nat.*, 75: 5–19.

PRATT, D. M. 1943. Analysis of population development in *Daphnia* at different temperatures. *Biol. Bull.*, 85: 116–140.

RAITT, D. S. 1939. The rate of mortality of the haddock of the North Sea stock. *Cons. Perm. Intern. Explor. Mer, Rapp. Proc.-Verb.*, 110 (6): 65–79.

RICKER, W. E. 1940. Relation of "catch per unit effort" to abundance and rate of exploitation. *J. Fish. Res. Bd. Canada*, 5: 43–70.

———. 1944. Further notes on fishing mortality and effort. *Copeia*, 1944: 23–44.

———. 1945. Natural mortality among Indiana bluegill sunfish. *Ecology* 26: 111–121.

RUNNSTRÖM, S. 1925. Zur Biologie und Entwicklung von *Balanus balanoides* (Linné). *Bergens Mus. Aarbok* 1924–25, *Naturvid. Raekke*, (5). 46 pp.

RUSSELL, E. S. 1942. *The overfishing problem.* viii + 130 pp. Cambridge Univ. Press, Cambridge.

SETTE, O. E. 1943. Biology of the Atlantic mackerel (*Scomber scombrus*) of North America. Part I: Early life history, including the growth, drift, and mortality of the egg and larval populations. *U. S. Fish Wildl. Serv. Fish. Bull.*, 50 (38): 147–237.

THOMPSON, W. F., and F. H. BELL. 1934. Biological statistics of the Pacific halibut fishery. (2) Effect of changes in intensity upon total yield and yield per unit of gear. *Rep. Intern. Fish. Comm.*, 8: 49 pp.

TRENERRY, C. F. 1926. *The origin and early history of insurance, including the contract of bottomry.* xiv + 330 pp. P. S. King & Son, London.

WHEELER, J. F. G. 1934. On the stock of whales at South Georgia. *Discov. Rep.*, 9: 351–372.

# THE INTRINSIC RATE OF NATURAL INCREASE
# OF AN INSECT POPULATION

By L. C. BIRCH*, *Zoology Department, University of Sydney*

## CONTENTS

## 1. INTRODUCTION

The intrinsic rate of increase is a basic parameter which an ecologist may wish to establish for an insect population. We define it as the rate of increase per head under specified physical conditions, in an unlimited environment where the effects of increasing density do not need to be considered. The growth of such a population is by definition exponential. Many authors, including Malthus and Darwin, have been concerned with this and related concepts, but there has been no general agreement in recent times on definitions. Chapman (1931) referred to it as 'biotic potential', and although he does state in one place that biotic potential should in some way combine fecundity rate, sex ratio and survival rate, he never precisely defined this expression. Stanley (1946) discussed a somewhat similar concept which he called the 'environmental index'. This gives a measure of the relative suitability of different environments, but it does not give the actual rate of increase of the insect under these different conditions. An index for the possible rate of increase under different physical conditions would at the same time provide a measure of the relative suitability of different environments. Birch (1945 c) attempted to provide this in an index combining the total number of eggs laid, the survival rate of immature stages, the rate of development and the sex ratio. This was done when the author was unaware of the relevance of cognate studies in human demography. A sounder approach to insect populations based on demographic procedures is now suggested in this paper. The development of this branch of population mathematics is principally due to A. J. Lotka. From the point of view of the biologist, convenient summaries of his fundamental contributions to this subject will be found in Lotka (1925, Chapter 9; 1939 and 1945). A numerical example of the application of Lotka's methods in the case of a human population will be found in Dublin & Lotka (1925). The parameter which Lotka has developed for human populations, and which he has variously called the 'true' or 'inherent' or 'intrinsic' rate of natural increase, has obvious application to populations of animals besides the human species. The first determination of the intrinsic rate of increase of an animal other than man was made by Leslie & Ranson (1940). They calculated the 'true rate of natural increase' of the vole, *Microtus agrestis*, from age-specific rates of fecundity and mortality determined under laboratory conditions. With the use of matrices Leslie has extended these methods and, as an example, calculated the true rate of natural increase of the brown rat, *Rattus norvegicus* (Leslie, 1945). The author is much indebted to Mr Leslie for having drawn his attention to the possible application of actuarial procedures to insect populations. He has been completely dependent upon him for the methods of calculation used in this paper.

Before proceeding to discuss the reasons for the particular terminology adopted in this paper, it is necessary first to consider the true nature of the parameter with which we are concerned.

* This investigation was carried out at the Bureau of Animal Population, Oxford University, during the tenure of an overseas senior research scholarship from the Australian Science & Industry Endowment Fund.

## 2. BIOLOGICAL SIGNIFICANCE OF THE INTRINSIC RATE OF NATURAL INCREASE

The intrinsic rate of increase is best defined as the constant '$r$' in the differential equation for population increase in an unlimited environment,

$$dN/dt = rN,$$

or in the integrated form $N_t = N_0 e^{rt}$,

where $N_0 =$ number of animals at time zero,

$N_t =$ number of animals at time $t$,

$r \ \ =$ infinitesimal rate of increase.

The exponent $r$ is the difference between the birth-rate ($b$) and the death-rate ($d$) in the population ($r = b - d$). In some circumstances it may be more useful to know the finite rate of increase, i.e. the number of times the population multiplies in a unit of time. Thus, in a population which is increasing exponentially, if there are $N_t$ individuals at time $t$ then in one unit of time later the ratio

$$\frac{N_{t+1}}{N_t} = e^r$$
$$= \text{antilog}_e \, r = \lambda.$$

Hence the finite rate of increase ($\lambda$) is the natural antilogarithm of the intrinsic (infinitesimal) rate of increase.

Any statement about the rate of increase of a population is incomplete without reference to the age distribution of that population, unless every female in it happens to be producing offspring at the same rate at all ages, and at the same time is exposed to a chance of dying which is the same at all ages. In such an inconceivable population the age of the individuals obviously has no significance. In practice, a population has a certain age schedule both of fecundity and of mortality. Now a population with *constant* age schedules of fecundity and mortality, which is multiplying in an unlimited environment, will gradually assume a fixed age distribution known as the stable age distribution' (Lotka, 1925, p. 110). When this age distribution is established the population will increase at a rate $dN/dt = rN$. Thus the parameter $r$ refers to a population with a stable age distribution. The consideration of rates of increase in terms of the stable age distribution was one of the most important advances in vital statistics. In any other sort of population the rate of increase varies with time until a stable age distribution is assumed. There is, for example, no simple answer to the question: what is the rate of increase of $x$ newly emerged adult insects in an unlimited environment? The rate will vary with time as immature stages are produced until the population has a stable age distribution. The rate of increase in the first generation might be given, but that is a figure of limited value. On the other hand, the maximum rate that it can ever maintain over an indefinite period of time is given by the rate of increase in a population of stable age distribution. That rate is therefore the true intrinsic capacity of the organism to increase. Thompson (1931) rejected the use of the exponential formula in the study of insect populations in preference for a method of dealing with the rate of increase as a 'discontinuous phenomenon'. His paper should be consulted for the reasons why he considers a single index unsatisfactory in relation to the particular problems with which he was concerned.

If the 'biotic potential' of Chapman is to be given quantitative expression in a single index, the parameter $r$ would seem to be the best measure to adopt, since it gives the intrinsic capacity of the animal to increase in an unlimited environment.* But neither 'biotic potential' nor 'true rate of natural increase' can be regarded as satisfactory descriptive titles. The word 'potential' has physical connotations which are not particularly appropriate when applied to organisms. There is a sense in which it might be better used with reference to the environment rather than the organism. Contrary to what it seems to imply, the 'true rate of natural increase' does not describe the actual rate of increase of a population at a particular point in time, unless the age distribution of that population happens to be stable. But it does define the intrinsic capacity of that population, with its given regime of fecundity and mortality, to increase. This point is clearly made by Dublin & Lotka (1925). More recently, Lotka (1945) has dropped the use of 'true rate of natural increase' for the more precise 'intrinsic rate of natural increase'. It would seem desirable that students of populations should adopt the same terminology, irrespective of the animals concerned, and as 'intrinsic rate of natural increase' is more truly descriptive of the parameter $r$ than other alternatives, its use is adopted in this paper.

The intrinsic rate of increase of a population may be calculated from the age-specific fecundity† and survival rates observed under defined environmental conditions. For poikilothermic animals these rates vary with physical factors of the environment such as temperature and humidity. Furthermore, within any

---

* For a discussion of the relative merits of this and other parameters in human demography reference should be made to Lotka (1945).

† Fecundity rate is used to denote the rate at which eggs are laid by a female. Some eggs laid are infertile and so do not hatch. The percentage 'infertility' is included in the mortality rate of the egg stage. It is usual amongst entomologists to denote the percentage of fertile eggs as the 'fertility rate'. Demographers, on the other hand, use 'fertility rate' to denote the rate of live births. Since 'fertility rate' has this other usage in entomology the term 'fecundity rate' is used throughout this paper as synonymous with the 'fertility rate' of the demographers.

given combination of physical factors, the fecundity and survival rates will vary with the density of the animals. Hence it is possible to calculate an array of values of $r$ at different densities. But particular significance attaches to the value of $r$ when the fecundity and survival rates are maximal, i.e. when density is optimal, for this gives the maximum possible rate of increase *within* the defined physical conditions. *Between* the whole array of physical conditions in which the animal can survive there is a zone where fecundity and survival rates are greatest and where, therefore, the intrinsic rate of increase will be greatest too. The zone within which the intrinsic rate of increase is a maximum may be referred to as the optimum zone. This is an arbitrary use of the word optimum and it does not imply that it is always to the advantage of the animal to increase at the maximum possible rate. The maximum intrinsic rate of increase under given physical conditions has importance from two points of view. It has a theoretical value, since it is the parameter which necessarily enters many equations in population mathematics (cf. Lotka, 1925; Volterra, 1931; Gause, 1934; Crombie, 1945). It also has practical significance. The range of temperature and moisture within which the insect can multiply is defined most precisely by that range within which the parameter exceeds zero. This will define the maximum possible range. In nature the range of physical conditions within which the species may be found to multiply may be less, since it is possible that effects of density and interspecific competition may reduce this range, and also the range of the optimum zone. These considerations are, however, beyond the scope of this paper; some discussion of them will be found in a review paper by Crombie (1947).

There are some important differences in the orientation with which the demographer and the student of insect populations face their problems. In human populations the parameter $r$ varies in different civilizations and at different times in one civilization, depending upon customs, sanitation and other factors which alter mortality and fecundity rates. The maximum possible value of $r$ does not enter into most demographic studies. In a population which is growing logistically the initial rate of increase is theoretically the maximum intrinsic rate of increase, and this latter value can be determined indirectly by calculating the appropriate logistic curve. Lotka (1927) has done this for a human population and so arrived at an estimate of a physiological maximum for man. This has theoretical interest only. In insect populations, on the other hand, the maximum value for the intrinsic rate of increase does assume considerable theoretical and practical significance, as has already been pointed out. The entomologist can readily determine the maximum values and this is his

obvious starting-point. But the determination of $r$ at different stages in the population history of an insect, whether in an experimental population or in the field, offers many practical difficulties which have not yet been surmounted for any single species. The values which the entomologist has difficulty in determining are those which are most readily obtained for human populations. The crude birth-rates and crude death-rates of the population at specific stages in its history are precisely those indices with which the demographer works. His census data provides him with the actual age distribution which is something not known empirically for a single insect species. He can have a knowledge of age distribution even at inter-censal periods, and under civilized conditions he can also determine the age-specific rates of fecundity and mortality which were in operation during any particular year. In insect populations this is at present impossible; one can only keep a number of individuals under specified conditions and determine their age-specific rates of fecundity and survival, and from these data $r$ can be calculated.

The fact that populations in nature may not realize the maximum value of their intrinsic rate of natural increase, does not negate the utility of this parameter either from a theoretical or a practical point of view. Having determined this parameter, the next logical step is to find out the extent to which this rate of increase is realized in nature. It is conceivable that some species, such as those which infest stored wheat or flour, may increase exponentially when liberated in vast quantities of these foodstuffs. This would imply that the insects could move out of the area in which they were multiplying with sufficient speed to escape density effects and that they had no gregarious tendencies. An exponential rate of increase may also occur in temperate climates in some plant-feeding species which only multiply in a short period of the year in the spring. In seasons with abundant plant growth the insect population may be far from approaching any limitation in the resources of the environment before the onset of summer retards the rate of increase. The population counts of *Thrips imaginis* in some favourable seasons in South Australia suggest such a picture (Davidson & Andrewartha, 1948).

## 3. CALCULATION OF THE INTRINSIC RATE OF NATURAL INCREASE

### (a) Experimental data required

The calculation of $r$ is based on the female population; the primary data required being as follows:

(1) The female life table giving the probability at birth of being alive at age $x$. This is usually designated $l_x$ ($l_0 = 1$).

(2) The age-specific fecundity table giving the

mean number of female offspring produced in a unit of time by a female aged $x$. This is designated $m_x$.

In the calculation of the stable age distribution the age-specific survival rates ($l_x$) of both the immature stages and the reproductive stages are required. For the calculation of $r$ the life table of the adult and only the total survival of the immature stages (irrespective of age) are needed. In practice, the age-specific fecundity rates $m_x$ will be established for some convenient interval of age, such as a week. If $N$ eggs are laid per female alive between the ages $x$ to $x+1$ in the unit of time chosen, then $m_x$ simply equals $\frac{1}{2}N$ when sex ratio is unity. It is assumed that this value occurs at the mid-point of the age group.

A numerical example is worked out for the rice weevil *Calandra (Sitophilus) oryzae* (L.) living under optimum conditions (29° C. in wheat of 14 % moisture content). Data for the rates of development and survival of the immature stages, and the age-specific fecundity rates were obtained from Birch (1945 *a*, *b*). The life table of adult females has not been determined experimentally, only the mean length of adult life being known. However, an estimate was obtained for purposes of these calculations by adapting the known life table of *Tribolium confusum* Duval (Pearl, Park & Miner, 1941) to *Calandra oryzae*, making the necessary reduction in the time scale. Since the mean length of life of *Tribolium confusum* in this life table was 198 days and the mean length of life of *Calandra oryzae* at 29° was 84 days, one 'Calandra day' has been taken as equivalent to 2·35 'Tribolium days'. To this extent the example worked out is artificial, but, for reasons which will become evident later in the paper, it is unlikely that the error so introduced in the estimate of $r$ is of much significance.

Before proceeding to outline direct methods of estimating $r$ two other parameters must first be mentioned: the net reproduction rate and the mean length of a generation.

### (b) The net reproduction rate

This is the rate of multiplication in one generation (Lotka, 1945) and is best expressed as the ratio of total female births in two successive generations. This we shall call $R_0$ and so follow the symbolism of the demographers. $R_0$ is determined from age-specific fecundity and survival rates and is defined as

$$R_0 = \int_0^\infty l_x m_x \, dx,$$

where $l_x$ and $m_x$ are as already defined.

The method of calculating $R_0$ is set out in Table 1. The values of $l_x$ are taken at the mid-point of each age group and age is given from the time the egg is laid. Since the survival rate of the immature stages was 0·90 the life table of adults reckoned from 'birth',

i.e. oviposition, was the product: $l_x$ for adults × 0·90. Development from the egg to emergence of the adult from the grain lasts 28 days and 4·5 weeks is the mid-point of the first week of egg laying. The product $l_x m_x$ is obtained for each age group and the sum of these products $\Sigma l_x m_x$ is the value $R_0$. In this particular example $R_0 = 113·6$. Thus a population of *Calandra oryzae* at 29° will multiply 113·6 times *in each generation*.

Table 1. *Showing the life table (for oviposition span) age-specific fecundity rates and the method of calculating the net reproduction rate ($R_0$) for* Calandra oryzae *at 29° in wheat of* 14 % *moisture content. Sex ratio is equal*

| Pivotal age in weeks ($x$) | ($l_x$) | ($m_x$) | ($l_x m_x$) |
|---|---|---|---|
| 4·5 | 0·87 | 20·0 | 17·400 |
| 5·5 | 0·83 | 23·0 | 19·090 |
| 6·5 | 0·81 | 15·0 | 12·150 |
| 7·5 | 0·80 | 12·5 | 10·000 |
| 8·5 | 0·79 | 12·5 | 9·875 |
| 9·5 | 0·77 | 14·0 | 10·780 |
| 10·5 | 0·74 | 12·5 | 9·250 |
| 11·5 | 0·66 | 14·5 | 9·570 |
| 12·5 | 0·59 | 11·0 | 6·490 |
| 13·5 | 0·52 | 9·5 | 4·940 |
| 14·5 | 0·45 | 2·5 | 1·125 |
| 15·5 | 0·36 | 2·5 | 0·900 |
| 16·5 | 0·29 | 2·5 | 0·800 |
| 17·5 | 0·25 | 4·0 | 1·000 |
| 18·5 | 0·19 | 1·0 | 0·190 |

$$R_0 = 113·560$$

The comparison of two or more populations by means of their net reproduction rates may be quite misleading unless the mean lengths of the generations are the same. Two or more populations may have the same net reproduction rate but their intrinsic rates of increase may be quite different because of different lengths of their generations. Consider, for example, the effect of moving the $l_x m_x$ column in Table 1 up or down by a unit of age, $R_0$ remains the same but it is obvious that the generation times are now very different. For these reasons the parameter $R_0$ has limited value and it must always be considered in relation to the length of the generation ($T$).

### (c) The mean length of a generation

The relation between numbers and time in a population growing exponentially is given by

$$N_T = N_0 e^{rT}.$$

When $T =$ the mean length of a generation, then from the definition of net reproduction rate $N_T/N_0 = R_0$, hence

$$R_0 = e^{rT},$$

and

$$T = \frac{\log_e R_0}{r}.$$

It follows that an accurate estimate of the mean length of a generation cannot be obtained until the value of $r$ is known. For many purposes, however, an approximate estimate of $T$ which can be calculated independently of $r$ may be of use. Thus, although oviposition by the female is extended over a period of time, it may be considered as concentrated for each generation at one point of time, successive generations being spaced $T$ units apart (Dublin & Lotka, 1925). For approximate purposes therefore it may be defined as

$$T = \frac{\Sigma x l_x m_x}{\Sigma l_x m_x}.$$

We may thus consider the figures for the product $l_x m_x$ given in the last column of Table 1 as a frequency distribution of which the individual items are each concentrated at the mid-point of each age group. The mean of this distribution is the approximate value of $T$. In this particular example

$$T = \frac{943 \cdot 09}{113 \cdot 56} = 8 \cdot 3 \text{ weeks.}$$

If this were an accurate estimate of $T$ we could proceed to calculate the value of $r$ since, from the above equation relating $R_0$, $r$ and $T$, we have

$$r = \frac{\log_e R_0}{T}$$

$$= \frac{\log_e 113 \cdot 56}{8 \cdot 30} = 0 \cdot 57 \text{ per head per week.}$$

It will become evident in what follows that this is an underestimate of $r$ owing to the approximate estimate of $T$. The procedure does, however, serve to illustrate the nature of the parameter, and in some cases where $r$ is small it may be a sufficiently accurate means of calculation (cf. for example, Dublin & Lotka, 1925). We shall proceed in the next section to an accurate method for the calculation of $r$.

### (d) The calculation of 'r'

A population with constant age schedules of fecundity and mortality will gradually approach a fixed form of age distribution known as the stable age distribution (p. 16). Once this is established the population increases at a rate $dN/dt = rN$ and the value of $r$ may be calculated from the equation

$$\int_0^\infty e^{-rx} l_x m_x \, dx = 1.$$

For the derivation of this formula reference must be made to Lotka (1925) and the bibliography therein. The usual methods of calculation may be found in Dublin & Lotka (1925, Appendix) or Lotka (1939, p. 68 *et seq.*). For high values of $r$, these methods may not be particularly satisfactory (Leslie & Ranson, 1940; Leslie, 1945, Appendix), and the computations, moreover, become very tedious. Some approxima-

tions to the rigorous procedures are justified in so far as the determination of the primary data which enter the above formula is of course subject to considerable error, arising from the normal variation in the organisms and conditions to which they are subjected in the experiments. It was considered that an estimate of $r$, calculated to the second decimal place, was sufficient in these circumstances. The following approximate method was therefore adopted. It has the merit of being both simple and fast.

As an approximation we may write

$$\Sigma e^{-rx} l_x m_x = 1.$$

Here $x$ is taken to be the mid-point of each age group and the summation is carried out over all age groups for which $m_x > 0$. A number of trial values are now substituted in this equation, in each case calculating a series of values $e^{-rx}$ and multiplying them by the appropriate $l_x m_x$ values for each age group. By graphing these trial values of $r$ against the corresponding summation values of the left-hand side of the above expression, we may find the value of $r$ which will make $\Sigma e^{-rx} l_x m_x \to 1$.

The whole procedure is greatly simplified by the use of 4-figure tables for powers of $e$ (e.g. Milne-Thomson & Comrie 1944, Table 9). Since these tables only give the values of $e^{\pm x}$ at intervals of 0·01 in the argument $x$ up to $e^{\pm 6}$, it may be convenient to multiply both sides of the equation by a factor $e^k$ in order to work with powers of $e$ which lie in the more detailed parts of the table. Thus, in the present example, $k$ was taken as 7:

$$e^7 \Sigma e^{-rx} l_x m_x = e^7$$

$$\Sigma e^{7-rx} l_x m_x = 1097.$$

A value of $r$ was now sought which would make the left-hand side of this expression equal to 1097. The actual process of carrying out this simple computation is exemplified in Table 2. The summation of the expression is not carried beyond the age group centred at 13·5 because of the negligible contribution of the older age groups. It has already been mentioned that $r$ is an infinitesimal rate of increase not to be confused with a finite rate of increase $\lambda$ which equals antilog$_e$ $r$. In this particular example $r = 0 \cdot 76$ and $\lambda$ therefore has a value 2·14. In other words the population will multiply 2·14 times *per week*.

By reference to Table 2 it is clear that the relative weights with which the different age groups contribute to the value of $r$ are given by the values $l_x m_x e^{7-rx}$ at each age group. It is of particular interest to observe the relation between values at successive age intervals (Table 3). The value of $r$ is 56% accounted for by the first week of adult life. The first 2 weeks combined contribute 85% towards the final value and the first 3 weeks combined total 94%. The 13·5th week, on the other hand, contributes 0·02%. It should not be inferred that adults 13·5 weeks old are of no importance since their eggs will eventually give rise to adults in the productive age categories. The biological significance of Table 3 is that the intrinsic rate of increase is determined to a much greater extent by the rate of oviposition in the first couple of weeks of adult life than by the total number of eggs laid in the life span of the adult, even although only 27 % of the total number of eggs are laid in the first 2 weeks. With

Table 2. *Showing the method of calculating r for* Calandra oryzae *at 29° by trial and error substitutions in the expression* $\Sigma e^{7-rx}l_x m_x = 1097$

| Pivotal age group (x) | $l_x m_x$ | $r = 0.76$ | | $r = 0.77$ | |
|---|---|---|---|---|---|
| | | $7 - rx$ | $e^{7-rx}$ | $7 - rx$ | $e^{7-rx}$ |
| 4·5 | 17·400 | 3·58 | 35·87 | 3·53 | 34·12 |
| 5·5 | 19·090 | 2·82 | 16·78 | 2·76 | 15·80 |
| 6·5 | 12·150 | 2·06 | 7·846 | 1·99 | 7·316 |
| 7·5 | 10·000 | 1·30 | 3·669 | 1·22 | 3·387 |
| 8·5 | 9·875 | 0·54 | 1·716 | 0·45 | 1·5683 |
| 9·5 | 10·780 | −0·22 | 0·8025 | −0·32 | 0·7261 |
| 10·5 | 9·250 | −0·98 | 0·3753 | −1·09 | 0·3362 |
| 11·5 | 9·570 | −1·74 | 0·1755 | −1·86 | 0·1557 |
| 12·5 | 6·490 | −2·50 | 0·0821 | −2·62 | 0·0728 |
| 13·5 | 4·940 | −3·26 | 0·0384 | −3·39 | 0·0337 |

$$\sum_{4\cdot5}^{13\cdot5} e^{7-rx}l_x m_x = \quad 1108 \qquad 1047$$

*r* lies between 0·76 and 0·77 and by graphical interpretation = 0·762.

Table 3. *The contribution of each age group to the value of r when* $r = 0.76$

| Pivotal age group (x) | $l_x m_x e^{7-rx}$ | Percentage contribution of each age group |
|---|---|---|
| 4·5 | 624·1 | 56·33 |
| 5·5 | 320·3 | 28·91 |
| 6·5 | 95·3 | 8·60 |
| 7·5 | 36·7 | 3·31 |
| 8·5 | 17·0 | 1·53 |
| 9·5 | 8·7 | 0·78 |
| 10·5 | 3·5 | 0·32 |
| 11·5 | 1·7 | 0·15 |
| 12·5 | 0·5 | 0·05 |
| 13·5 | 0·2 | 0·02 |
| | 1108·0 | 100·00 |

each successive week, eggs laid make a lessened contribution to the value of *r*. In this particular case this can be expressed by stating that for each egg laid in the first week of adult life it would require 2·1 times as many in the second week to make the same contribution to the value of *r*, $(2 \cdot 1)^2$ in the third week and $(2 \cdot 1)^{n-1}$ in the *n*th week. The ratio 2·1 : 1 is the ratio between successive weighting values $e^{7-rx}$ (per egg) in Table 2. The importance of the first few weeks is further intensified by the fact that egg laying is at a maximum then. From these considerations it

follows that in determining oviposition rates experimentally, the rates in early adult life should be found with the greatest accuracy. Of corresponding importance is the accurate determination of the pivotal age for the first age category in which eggs are laid. In the example being cited an error of half a week causes an error of 8 % in the estimate of *r*.

The calculations were repeated ignoring the adult life table. The value of *r* was then 0·77. Since the imposition of an adult life table only makes a difference of 1 % in the value of *r* it is evident that the life table is of little importance in this example. This is due to the fact already noted that the major contribution to the value of *r* is made by adults in early life, and during early adult life survival rate is at a maximum. The life table may assume quite a different importance in a species with a different type of age schedule of fecundity or when the value of *r* is lower.

## 4. THE STABLE AGE DISTRIBUTION

With a knowledge of the intrinsic rate of increase and the life table it is possible to calculate the stable age distribution and the stable female birth-rate of the population. Thus if $c_x$ is the proportion of the stable population aged between *x* and $x + dx$, and *b* is the instantaneous birth-rate

$$c_x = be^{-rx}l_x,$$

and
$$1/b = \int_0^\infty e^{-rx}l_x dx.$$

For the usual methods of computation reference should be made again to Dublin & Lotka (1925). Mr Leslie has, however, pointed out to me another method of calculation which saves much of the numerical integration involved in the more usual methods. At the same time it is sufficiently accurate for our present purpose. If at time *t* we consider a stable population consisting of $N_t$ individuals, and if during the interval of time *t* to $t + 1$ there are $B_t$ female births, we may define a birth-rate

$$\beta = B_t/N_t.$$

Then if we define for the given life table $(l_x)$ the series of values $L_x$ by the relationship $L_x = \int_x^{x+1} l_x dx$ (the stationary or 'life table' age distribution of the actuary),* the proportion $(p_x)$ of individuals aged between *x* and $x + 1$ in the stable population is given by

$$p_x = \beta L_x e^{-r(x+1)},$$

$$1/\beta = \sum_{x=0}^{m} L_x e^{-r(x+1)},$$

where $x = m$ to $m + 1$ is the last age group considered in the complete life table age distribution. It will be noticed that the life table ($l_x$ values) for the complete

* For a discussion of $L_x$ see Dublin & Lotka (1936).

age span of the species are required for the computation of $p_x$ and $\beta$. But where $r$ is high it will be found that for the older age groups the terms $L_x e^{-r(x+1)}$ are so small and contribute so little to the value of $\beta$ that they can be neglected.

The calculations involved are quite simple and are illustrated in the following example for *Calandra oryzae* at 29° (Table 4). Actually, in the present example, instead of calculating the values of $L_x$, the values of $l_x$ were taken at the mid-points of each age group. This was considered sufficiently accurate in the present instance. It should also be pointed out that whereas only the total mortality of immature stages was required in the calculation of $r$, the age specific mortality of the immature stages is needed

Table 4. *Calculation of the stable age distribution of* Calandra oryzae *at* 29° *when* $r = 0.76$

| Age group (x) | $L_x$ | $e^{-r(x+1)}$ | $L_x e^{-r(x+1)}$ | Percentage distribution $100\beta L_x e^{-r(x+1)}$ | |
|---|---|---|---|---|---|
| 0— | 0·95 | 0·4677 | 0·4443150 | 54·740 | 95·5 % |
| 1— | 0·90 | 0·2187 | 0·1968300 | 24·249 | total |
| 2— | 0·90 | 0·10228 | 0·0920520 | 11·341 | immature |
| 3— | 0·90 | 0·04783 | 0·0430470 | 5·304 | stages |
| 4— | 0·87 | 0·02237 | 0·0194619 | 2·398 | |
| 5— | 0·83 | 0·01046 | 0·0086818 | 1·070 | |
| 6— | 0·81 | 0·00489 | 0·0039609 | 0·488 | |
| 7— | 0·80 | 0·002243 | 0·0017944 | 0·221 | |
| 8— | 0·79 | 0·001070 | 0·0008453 | 0·104 | 4·5 % |
| 9— | 0·77 | 0·000500 | 0·0003850 | 0·047 | total |
| 10— | 0·74 | 0·000239 | 0·0001769 | 0·022 | adults |
| 11— | 0·66 | 0·000110 | 0·0000726 | 0·009 | |
| 12— | 0·59 | 0·000051 | 0·0000301 | 0·004 | |
| 13— | 0·52 | 0·000024 | 0·0000125 | 0·002 | |
| 14— | 0·45 | 0·000011 | 0·0000050 | 0·001 | |

$$1/\beta = 0.8116704 \qquad 100.000$$

for the calculation of the stable age distribution. In this example the total mortality of the immature stages was 10 %—and 98 % of this mortality occurred in the first week of larval life (Birch, 1945 d). Hence the approximate value of $L_x$ for the mid-point of the first week will be 0·95 and thereafter 0·90 for successive weeks of the larval and pupal period (column 2, Table 4). The stable age distribution is shown in the fifth column of Table 4. This column simply expresses the fourth column of figures as percentages. It is of particular interest to note the high proportion of immature stages (95·5 %) in this theoretical population. This is associated with the high value of the intrinsic rate of natural increase. It emphasizes a point of practical importance in estimating the abundance of insects such as *C. oryzae* and other pests of stored products. The number of adults found in a sample of wheat may be quite a misleading representation of the true size of the

whole insect population. Methods of sampling are required which will take account of the immature stages hidden inside the grains, such, for example, as the 'carbon dioxide index' developed by Howe & Oxley (1944). The nature of this stable age distribution has a bearing on another practical problem. It provides further evidence to that developed from a practical approach (Birch, 1946) as to how it is possible for *C. oryzae* to cause heating in vast bulks of wheat, when only a small density of adult insects is observed. It is not an unreasonable supposition that the initial rate of increase of insects in bulks of wheat may approach the maximum intrinsic rate of increase and therefore that the age distribution may approach the stable form. Nothing, however, is known about the actual age distribution in nature at this stage of an infestation.

## 5. THE INSTANTANEOUS BIRTH-RATE AND DEATH-RATE

We have already defined a birth-rate $\beta$ by the expression

$$1/\beta = \sum_{x=0}^{m} L_x e^{-r(x+1)}.$$

This is not, however, the same as the instantaneous birth-rate $(b)$ where $r = b - d$. In personal communications Mr Leslie has provided me with the following relationship between these two birth-rates.

$$b = \frac{r\beta}{e^r - 1}.$$

Thus, in the example for *C. oryzae*, we have $1/\beta = 0.81167$ (Table 4), $r = 0.76$ and thus $b = 0.82$ and the difference between $r$ and $b$ is the instantaneous death-rate $(d) = 0.06$.

The instantaneous birth-rate and death-rate are widely used by students of human populations. The insect ecologist is more likely to find greater use for the finite rate of increase $\lambda$ (natural antilog$_e$).

## 6. THE EFFECT OF TEMPERATURE ON '$r$'

As an illustration of the way in which the value of $r$ varies with temperature and the corresponding changes in rate of development, survival and fecundity, an estimate of $r$ for *C. oryzae* has been made for two temperatures (23° and 33·5° C.) on either side of the optimum (29°). The span of adult life at 23° is about the same as at the optimum 29° and so the same life table has been applied. Even although the egg laying is more evenly distributed throughout adult life the life table makes little difference to the value of $r$. Furthermore, the first 2 weeks of adult life carry a weight of 59 % of the total weight of all age groups in the determination of the value of $r$. For every egg laid in the first week of adult life it would require 1·5 times as many eggs in the second week to make the same contribution to the value of $r$, and 2·3 times as many eggs in the third week to have the same effect. The relative weight of each week decreases less with successive weeks at 23° than at 29°. This is associated with the lower oviposition rates and the longer duration of the immature stages at 23°.

At 33·5° egg laying ceases after the fourth week of adult life, the mortality of adults during these 4 weeks is not high and so the estimate of $r$ obtained without a life table may not be very different from the true value.

Table 5. *Showing the values of* $l_x$, $m_x$ *and the estimate of* $r$ *for* Calandra oryzae *at 23° and 33·5°*

| 23° | | | 33·5° | | |
|---|---|---|---|---|---|
| Pivotal age in weeks (x) | $l_x$ | $m_x$ | Pivotal age in weeks (x) | $l_x$ | $m_x$ |
| 0·5 ⎫ | | | 0·5 ⎫ | | |
| · ⎪ Immature | 0·90 | — | · ⎪ Immature | 0·25 | — |
| · ⎬ stages | | | · ⎬ stages | | |
| · ⎪ | | | 8·5 ⎭ | | |
| 6·5 ⎭ | | | | | |
| 7·5 | 0·87 | 9·0 | 9·5 | 0·25 | 6·0 |
| 8·5 | 0·83 | 11·0 | 10·5 | 0·25 | 3·5 |
| 9·5 | 0·81 | 11·5 | 11·5 | 0·25 | 3·0 |
| 10·5 | 0·80 | 12·0 | 12·5 | 0·25 | 1·0 |
| 11·5 | 0·79 | 11·5 | | | |
| 12·5 | 0·77 | 13·0 | $r = 0.12$ per head per week | | |
| 13·5 | 0·74 | 11·5 | | | |
| 14·5 | 0·66 | 11·0 | | | |
| 15·5 | 0·60 | 10·0 | | | |
| 16·5 | 0·52 | 11·0 | | | |
| 17·5 | 0·45 | 12·5 | | | |
| 18·5 | 0·36 | 10·5 | | | |
| 19·5 | 0·29 | 11·5 | | | |
| 20·5 | 0·25 | 4·0 | | | |
| 21·5 | 0·19 | 2·0 | | | |

With adult life table    $r = 0.43$ per head per week.
Without adult life table $r = 0.44$    ,,      ,,

## 7. DISCUSSION

In order for a species to survive in a particular environment it may need to have evolved a certain minimum value for its intrinsic rate of natural increase. If its rate of increase is less than this it may succumb in the struggle for existence. It does not necessarily follow that the higher the intrinsic rate of increase the more successful will the species be. Evolution may operate to select species with an intrinsic rate of increase which is both large enough to enable them to compete successfully with other species and small enough to prevent a rate of multiplication which would exhaust the food supply in the environment. Whatever is the minimum necessary value of '$r$' it could be attained along more than one route,

since $r$ has a number of component variables; the length of development of the immature stages, the survival rate of the immature stages, the adult life table and the age-specific fecundity schedule. These components enter into the value of $r$ with various weights, and it is suggested in the discussion which follows that a knowledge of their relative contributions may provide a clue to the significance of the life patterns characteristic of different species. There is clearly a pattern in the seasonal environment too, which must be considered at the same time. A hot dry period, for example, may necessitate a prolonged egg stage. In an environment which has relatively uniform physical conditions all the year round, these complicating factors are at a minimum, e.g. a tropical forest or the micro-environment of a stack of wheat.

(1) Consider first the length of the immature stages (non-reproductive period) in relation to the span of egg laying and the age schedule of fecundity. The earlier an egg is laid in the life of the insect the greater is the contribution of that particular egg to the value of $r$. In illustration we may consider the age schedule of fecundity for *C. oryzae* at 29°. Since over 95 % of the value of $r$ is determined by the eggs laid in the first 4 weeks of adult life (Table 3) we can, for purposes of illustration, ignore the remaining period.

At 29° the immature stages of *C. oryzae* last 4 weeks and the maximum rate of egg laying is 46 eggs per week (Table 1). Now the same value of $r$ (0·76) is given in a number of imaginary life cycles by reducing the length of the immature stages along with a reduction in the rate of egg laying and alternatively by increasing both the length of the immature stages and the number of eggs laid (ordinary figures, Table 6). In Table 6 the age schedule of fecundity is kept proportionate in each case. In the extreme examples if the immature stages could develop in a week, an oviposition maximum of 5 eggs per week would give the same rate of increase as the imaginary insect which took 6 weeks to develop and had an oviposition maximum of 204 eggs per week. The imaginary life cycles have been calculated from the ratio (2·1:1) for successive weighting values ($e^{7-rx}$) in Table 2.

The question might now be asked, what determines the particular combination which the species happens to possess? In the specific example in question, if the larva took 6 weeks to develop the adult would need to lay 200 eggs per week. But it now becomes necessary to consider the behaviour pattern, for *C. oryzae* bores a hole in the grain of wheat for every egg which is laid. The whole process of boring and egg laying occupies about 1 hr. per egg. So that with this particular mode of behaviour 24 eggs per day would be an absolute maximum. There must of course also be some physiological limit to egg production. For a larger insect the physiological limit might be less restrictive provided that the size of the egg does not increase proportionately with the size of the insect. In considering this possibility, ecological considerations are important, for *C. oryzae* is adapted to complete its development within a grain of wheat and a size limit is set by the length of the grain. There is, in fact, a strain which is found in maize kernels in Australia and this is considerably larger than the so-called 'small strain' (Birch, 1944). Furthermore, the larger insect would probably require a longer time to complete development (which is actually the relationship observed between the small and large strains) and this would operate to reduce the value of $r$. In considering the possibilities in the opposite direction, there is obviously a limit below which the length of development could not be reduced any further. A species of smaller size could doubtless develop in a shorter time and on this merit might be a more successful mutation. But the question then arises whether a smaller species could command muscles and mandibles of sufficient strength to chew whole

The relative advantage of this type of fecundity schedule is less, the smaller the value of $r$. At 23° the value of $r$ for *C. oryzae* is 0·43 and the eggs laid in the first week of adult life are worth $(1·5)^{n-1}$ eggs in the $n$th week (compare this with the value of $(2·1)^{n-1}$ when $r=0·76$). The actual oviposition time curve at 23° has no distinct peak as at 29° (Tables 1 and 5).

There is a wide variation in the nature of the age schedule of fecundity amongst different species of insects with perhaps the tsetse fly and the lucerne flea illustrating contrasting extremes. Whereas tsetse flies (*Glossina*) deposit single larvae spaced at intervals of time, the 'lucerne flea' (*Smynthurus viridis*) deposits its eggs in one or two batches of as many as 120 at a time (Maclagan, 1932). The particular advantage of this mode of oviposition must be tremendous, and is probably responsible in part for the great abundance of this collembolan and possibly other members of the same order, which, as a whole, are among the most

Table 6. *Showing the actual relation between the length of the immature stages and the age schedule of fecundity for* Calandra oryzae *at 29° (black figures) and some theoretical possibilities which would give the same intrinsic rate of increase ($r=0·76$). The length of the immature stages is shown in the left of the table; figures in the body of the table are number of eggs per week*

| | | | | Pivotal age in weeks | | | | | | |
|---|---|---|---|---|---|---|---|---|---|---|
| 0·5 | 1·5 | 2·5 | 3·5 | 4·5 | 5·5 | 6·5 | 7·5 | 8·5 | 9·5 | Total |
| 1 week | 4 | 5 | 3 | 3 | — | — | — | — | — | 15 |
| 2 weeks | | 9 | 10 | 7 | 6 | — | — | — | — | 32 |
| 3 weeks | | | 19 | 22 | 14 | 12 | — | — | — | 67 |
| 4 weeks | | | | 40 | 46 | 30 | 25 | — | —· | 141 |
| 5 weeks | | | | | 84 | 97 | 63 | 53 | — | 297 |
| 6 weeks | | | | | | 117 | 204 | 132 | 111 | 564 |

grain. Grain-feeding species of beetles which are smaller than *C. oryzae* are in fact scavengers rather than feeders on sound grain. Thus it would seem that a balance is struck somewhere between the minimum time necessary for development and the maximum possible rate of egg laying, and this is conditioned by the behaviour pattern of the insect and the particular ecology of its environment.

For a maximum value of $r$ the optimum age schedule of fecundity is one which has an early maximum. In an imaginary schedule for *C. oryzae* a concentration of 71 eggs in the first week of egg laying would give the same value of $r$ (0·76) as 141 eggs distributed over 4 weeks.

*Age schedule of fecundity of* Calandra oryzae *at 29°*

| Weeks | 1 | 2 | 3 | 4 | Total |
|---|---|---|---|---|---|
| Actual | 40 | 46 | 30 | 25 | 141 |
| Imaginary | 71 | 0 | 0 | 0 | 71 |

abundant insects in nature. This is of course speculative and much more information is required before any generalizations can be made. Another interesting category are the social insects, since only one female of the population (in termites and the hive-bee) or a few (in social wasps) are reproductives. A theoretical consideration of the relative merits of one queen and many queens might throw more light on the evolution of these systems, especially as they relate to differences in behaviour.

The relation between the length of the pre-reproductive stages and the nature of the age-fecundity schedule is in part dependent upon the nature of the seasonal changes in the environment. Life histories may be timed so that the reproductive and feeding stages coincide with the least hostile season of the year. Diapause, aestivation and hibernation are some of the adaptations which ensure this. They have particular significance too in determining the age distribution of the initial population in the reproductive season. Consideration of this is left to a later section of the discussion.

(2) For the calculation of the maximum intrinsic rate of increase the life table of the species from deposition of the egg (or larva) to the end of egg-laying life in the adult must be known. The starting-point of this life table is thus the stage which corresponds to the point of 'birth'. Deevey (1947) has noted that the point of universal biological equivalence for animals is doubtless fertilization of the ovum. But, from the point of view of the number of animals in the population and for purposes of calculating $r$, a knowledge of pre-birth mortality is not required. For the calculation of $r$ the life table beyond the end of reproductive life has no significance, but a knowledge of age-specific post-reproductive survival until the point of death is needed, on the other hand, for the calculation of the stable age distribution and the instantaneous birth-rate. This is evident from a consideration of the method of calculation shown in Table 4. The post-reproductive life assumes negligible significance in this particular example, but its importance in such calculations increases as $r$ approaches a value of zero.

The relative importance of the survival pattern (i.e. the shape of the $l_x$ curve) in determining the value of $r$ is itself a function of $r$. When $r$ is small its value may be dependent to a significant extent on the oviposition in late adult life, when it is large it is mostly determined by the oviposition rates of adults in early adult life. When the intrinsic rate of increase is high and the life table of the adult follows the typical diagonal pattern (e.g. Pearl *et al.* 1941) with no high mortality in early adult life, consideration of the adult life table is of little importance in calculating $r$. This is because survival rate is high in the ages which contribute most to the value of $r$. In species which have a low intrinsic rate of increase the life table may assume more significance in determining the value of that rate of increase. More data are required before the importance of this point can be established. The pattern of survival which gives a maximum value of $r$ has its maxima in the pre-reproductive and early reproductive stages. A knowledge of total survival of the immature stages is of course essential in all cases. More attention might well be given by entomologists to securing life table data than has been given in the past. Without it no true picture of the intrinsic rate of increase can be obtained.

(3) There remains to be considered the age distribution of the population in relation to its capacity to increase in numbers. In a population in an unlimited environment the stable age distribution is the only one which gives an unvarying value of $r$. For this reason the stable age distribution is the only sound basis on which to make comparisons between different values for rates of increase (whether between different species or one species under different physical conditions). The actual age distribution of a population in nature may be quite different and its consideration is of importance in determining the initial advantage one form of distribution has over another. In an unlimited environment these initial differences in age composition are eventually ironed out. A population which initiates from a number of adults at the peak age of egg laying clearly has a higher initial rate of increase than one which starts from the same number in all different stages of development.

These considerations may be of most importance in temperate climates where there is a definite seasonal occurrence of active stages. The stage in which the insect overwinters or oversummers will determine the age distribution of the population which initiates the seasonal increase in the spring or in the autumn (whichever the case may be). The pea weevil, *Bruchus pisorum*, in California hibernates as an adult. With the first warm days in the spring the adults leave their overwintering quarters under bark and fly into the pea fields (Brindley, Chamberlin & Hinman, 1946). Following a meal of pollen they commence oviposition on the pea crops. This mode of initiating the spring population would be far more effective than one which started with the same number of insects in the egg stage. The overwintering adults begin their reproductive life at a much later age than the adults in the next generation. It would be of interest to know whether the age schedule of fecundity (taking the commencement of egg laying as zero age) is the same for both generations. This is a point which does not appear to have been investigated for insects which hibernate as adults. It is clearly of much importance in determining the intrinsic rate of increase of successive generations.

Overwintering as pupae must theoretically rank as the second most effective age distribution for initiating spring increase. Many species which overwinter as pupae would have a higher mortality if they overwintered as adults. The corn-ear worm, *Heliothis armigera*, for example, can hardly be conceived as overwintering as an adult moth in the North American corn belt. In the northern part of this belt even the pupae which are protected in the soil are unable to survive the winter. Recolonization evidently takes place each year from the warmer south (Haseman, 1931).

Overwintering in the egg stage (in hibernation or in diapause) is common in insects. Here again it is difficult to imagine the other stages of these orders as successfully hibernating. The grasshopper, *Austroicetes cruciata* (Andrewartha, 1944), and the majority of aphids are examples of this. A minority of aphid species are, however, able to overwinter as apterae by finding protection in leaf axils and similar niches (Theobald, 1926), some others are enabled to survive as adults by virtue of their symbiosis with ants (Cutright, 1925). The relatively vulnerable aphids find protection in the nests of ants. The ants not only carry them to their nests, but feed them during the winter months and with the return of spring plant them out on trees again!

Overwintering as nymphs or larvae is a rarer phenomenon except with species which can feed and grow at low temperatures and so are not hibernators. The active stages of the lucerne flea, *Smynthurus viridis*, for example, can be found in the winter in Australia (Davidson, 1934). The seasonal cycle of the reproducing population commences with the first rains in autumn; this population being initiated with oversummering eggs. The eggs are the only stage which are resistant to the dryness and high temperatures of the summer months. Species of insects with hardy adult stages like the weevil, *Otiorrhynchus cribricollis* (Andrewartha, 1933), aestivate as adults. An interesting case of a butterfly, *Melitaea phaeton*, aestivating as a quarter-grown larva at the base of its food plant is described by Hovanitz (1941).

The preceding examples illustrate how the age distributions of initiating populations vary in seasonal species. This depends on the nature of the overwintering or oversummering stage. The particular stage may have been selected in nature not only by virtue of its resistance to unfavourable physical conditions but also in relation to its merits in initiating rapid establishment of a population in the spring and autumn. The calculation of the initial and subsequent rates of increase of populations with these different types of age distribution is considerably more complicated than the calculation of intrinsic rates of increase for populations with stable age distributions. This problem is not dealt with in this paper and the reader is referred to Leslie (1945, p. 207 *et seq.*) for an outline of the principles involved in such calculations.

The length of the developmental stages, the age schedule of fecundity, the life table of the species and the age distribution of initiating populations present a pattern which has adaptive significance for the species. The analytic study of the intrinsic rate of increase of a species (as exemplified by *Calandra oryzae*) may throw light on the evolutionary significance of the life pattern of different species. Such a study must necessarily be related to the behaviour pattern of the insect and the type of environment it lives in. Nor can the importance of effects of density and competition be overlooked. These are, of course, studies in themselves beyond the scope of this paper.

concept for the study of insect populations. It is suggested that for the sake of uniformity of terminology in population biology and for precision of definition, that the term 'intrinsic rate of natural increase' might be considered more appropriate than an alternative term 'biotic-potential' which is more frequently used in relation to insect populations. The intrinsic rate of natural increase is defined as the exponent '$r$' in the exponential equation for population increase in an unlimited environment. The rate of increase of such a population is given by $dN/dt = rN$. The parameter $r$ refers to the rate of increase of a population with a certain fixed age distribution known as the stable age distribution. Both the intrinsic rate of natural increase and the stable age distribution may be calculated from the age-specific survival rates (life table) and age-specific fecundity rates. The methods of calculation are exemplified with data for the rice weevil, *Calandra oryzae* (L.), and some adapted from the flour beetle, *Tribolium confusum* Duval. It is shown in this example that the intrinsic rate of natural increase is determined to a much greater extent by the rate of oviposition in the first 2 weeks of adult life than by the total number of eggs laid in the entire life time. The oviposition rates in the first 2 weeks account for 85 % of the value of $r$ whereas only 27 % of the total number of eggs are laid in that time. With each successive week in the life of the adult, eggs laid make a lessened contribution to the value of $r$. The methods of calculation of $r$ provide a means of determining the extent to which the various components—the life table, the fecundity table and the length of the pre-reproductive stages—enter into the value of $r$. It is suggested that analyses of this sort may provide a clue to the life patterns characteristic of different species.

The importance of the age distribution of populations which initiate seasonal increase in the autumn and spring is discussed. These age distributions depend on the nature of the overwintering or oversummering stage. It is suggested that this particular stage, whether it be adult, larva, pupa or egg, has been selected by virtue not only of its resistance to the unfavourable season, but also in relation to its merits in initiating rapid establishment of a population in the succeeding season.

It is shown how the value of $r$ for *Calandra oryzae* varies with temperature. Four other parameters are also defined: the net reproduction rate, the mean length of a generation, the infinitesimal birth-rate and the infinitesimal death-rate. The methods of calculation of these parameters are also exemplified with data for *C. oryzae*.

## 8. SUMMARY

The parameter known as the intrinsic rate of natural increase, which was developed for demographic analyses by A. J. Lotka, is introduced as a useful

## 9. ACKNOWLEDGEMENTS

Grateful acknowledgement is made to the Director of the Bureau of Animal Population, Oxford University, Mr C. S. Elton, for the facilities of the Bureau which were placed at the author's disposal during his term there as a visiting worker. Mr Elton provided much encouragement during the investigation. It is a pleasure to acknowledge too the inspiration and help of Mr P. H. Leslie of the Bureau of Animal Popula-

tion. His direction was indispensable in all mathematical and actuarial aspects of the paper and his critical examination of the manuscript was much to its advantage.

## REFERENCES

**Andrewartha, H. G. (1933).** 'The bionomics of *Otiorrhynchus cribricollis* Gyll.' Bull. Ent. Res. 24: 373–84.

**Andrewartha, H. G. (1944).** 'The distribution of plagues of *Austroicetes cruciata* Sauss. (Acrididae) in relation to climate, vegetation and soil.' Trans. Roy. Soc. S. Aust. 68: 315–26.

**Birch, L. C. (1944).** 'Two strains of *Calandra oryzae* L. (Coleoptera).' Aust. J. Exp. Biol. Med. Sci. 22: 271–5.

**Birch, L. C. (1945a).** 'The influence of temperature on the development of the different stages of *Calandra oryzae* L. and *Rhizopertha dominica* Fab. (Coleoptera).' Aust. J. Exp. Biol. Med. Sci. 23: 29–35.

**Birch, L. C. (1945b).** 'The influence of temperature, humidity and density on the oviposition of the small strain of *Calandra oryzae* L. and *Rhizopertha dominica* Fab.' Aust. J. Exp. Biol. Med. Sci. 23: 197–203.

**Birch, L. C. (1945c).** 'The biotic potential of the small strain of *Calandra oryzae* and *Rhizopertha dominica*.' J. Anim. Ecol. 2: 125–7.

**Birch, L. C. (1945d).** 'The mortality of the immature stages of *Calandra oryzae* L. (small strain) and *Rhizopertha dominica* Fab. in wheat of different moisture contents.' Aust. J. Exp. Biol. Med. Sci. 23: 141–5.

**Birch, L. C. (1946).** 'The heating of wheat stored in bulk in Australia.' J. Aust. Inst. Agric. Sci. 12: 27–31.

**Brindley, T. A., Chamberlin, J. C. & Hinman, F. G. (1946).** 'The pea weevil and methods for its control.' U.S. Dept. Agric. Farmers' Bull. 1971: 1–24.

**Chapman, R. N. (1931).** 'Animal ecology with especial reference to insects.' New York.

**Crombie, A. C. (1945).** 'On competition between different species of graminivorous insects.' Proc. Roy. Soc. B, 132: 362–95.

**Crombie, A. C. (1947).** 'Interspecific competition.' J. Anim. Ecol. 16: 44–73.

**Cutright, C. R. (1925).** 'Subterranean aphids of Ohio.' Ohio Agric. Exp. Sta. Bull. 387: 175–238.

**Davidson, J. (1934).** 'The "lucerne flea" *Smynthurus viridis* L. (Collembola) in Australia.' Bull. Coun. Sci. Industr. Res. Aust. 79: 1–66.

**Davidson, J. & Andrewartha, H. G. (1948).** 'Annual trends in a natural population of *Thrips imaginis* Bagnall (Thysanoptera).' (In the Press.)

**Deevey, E. S. (1947).** 'Life tables for natural populations of animals.' Biometrics, 3: 59–60.

**Dublin, L. I. & Lotka, A. J. (1925).** 'On the true rate of natural increase as exemplified by the population of the United States, 1920.' J. Amer. Statist. Ass. 20: 305–39.

**Dublin, L. I. & Lotka, A. J. (1936).** 'Length of life.' New York.

**Gause, G. F. (1934).** 'The struggle for existence.' Baltimore.

**Haseman, L. (1931).** 'Outbreak of corn earworm in Missouri.' J. Econ. Ent. 24: 649–50.

**Hovanitz, W. (1941).** 'The selective value of aestivation and hibernation in a Californian butterfly.' Bull. Brooklyn Ent. Soc. 36: 133–6.

**Howe, R. W. & Oxley, T. A. (1944).** 'The use of carbon dioxide production as a measure of infestation of grain by insects.' Bull. Ent. Res. 35: 11–22.

**Leslie, P. H. (1945).** 'On the use of matrices in certain population mathematics.' Biometrika, 33: 183–212.

**Leslie, P. H. & Ranson, R. M. (1940).** 'The mortality, fertility and rate of natural increase of the vole (*Microtus agrestis*) as observed in the laboratory.' J. Anim. Ecol. 9: 27–52.

**Lotka, A. J. (1925).** 'Elements of physical biology.' Baltimore.

**Lotka, A. J. (1927).** 'The size of American families in the eighteenth century and the significance of the empirical constants in the Pearl-Reed law of population growth.' J. Amer. Statist. Ass. 22: 154–70.

**Lotka, A. J. (1939).** 'Théorie analytique des associations biologiques. Deuxième Partie. Analyse démographique avec application particulière à l'espèce humaine.' Actualités Sci. Industr. 780: 1–149.

**Lotka, A. J. (1945).** 'Population analysis as a chapter in the mathematical theory of evolution.' In LeGros Clark, W. E. & Medawar, P. B., 'Essays on Growth and Form', 355–85. Oxford.

**Maclagan, D. S. (1932).** 'An ecological study of the "lucerne flea" (*Smynthurus viridis*, Linn.)–I.' Bull. Ent. Res. 23: 101–90.

**Pearl, R., Park, T. & Miner, J. R. (1941).** 'Experimental studies on the duration of life. XVI. Life tables for the flour beetle *Tribolium confusum* Duval.' Amer. Nat. 75: 5–19.

**Stanley, J. (1946).** 'The environmental index, a new parameter as applied to *Tribolium*.' Ecology, 27: 303–14.

**Theobald, F. V. (1926).** 'The plant lice or the Aphididae of Great Britain.' Vol. 1. Ashford.

**Thompson, W. R. (1931).** 'On the reproduction of organisms with overlapping generations.' Bull. Ent. Res. 22: 147–72.

**Thomson, L. M. Milne- & Comrie, L. J. (1944).** 'Standard four-figure mathematical tables.' London.

**Volterra, V. (1931).** 'Leçons sur la théorie mathématique de la lutte pour la vie.' Paris.

# THE POPULATION CONSEQUENCES OF LIFE HISTORY PHENOMENA

By LAMONT C. COLE

*Department of Zoology, Cornell University*

### PREFACE

FEW branches of biology have attracted more analytical mathematical treatment than has the study of populations. Despite this, one may read in the most complete treatise of ecology yet published (Allee, et al., 1949, p. 271) that "theoretical population ecology has not advanced to a great degree in terms of its impact on ecological thinking." This unfortunate gap between the biologists and the mathematicians has elicited comments which need not be repeated in detail here (Allee, 1934; Gause, 1934; Allee et al., 1949, p. 386). The neglect of the analytical methods by biologists may be attributed in part to the tendency of writers in this field to concentrate on the analysis of human populations and in part to skepticism about the mathematical methods of analysis. Early analyses of population growth (Verhulst, 1838, 1845; Pearl and Reed, 1920) employed human populations as examples, although it is clear from other publications (e.g., Pearl and Miner, 1935; Pearl, 1937) that comparative and general population studies were the principal interest of some of these students. Similarly, the pioneer works of Lotka (1907b, 1910, 1925) were very general in conception but made their greatest impact in the field of demography (Dublin and Lotka, 1925; Dublin, Lotka, and Spiegelman, 1949). The skepticism expressed by biologists toward theoretical studies has ranged from antagonism (Salt, 1936) to approval given with the warning that "... for the sake of brevity and to avoid cumbersome expressions, variables are omitted and assumptions made in the mathematical analyses which are not justified by the biological data" (Allee, 1934). It may be unfortunate that warnings about mathematical oversimplification are especially pertinent in connection with the study of interactions between species (Ross, 1911; Lotka, 1920, 1925; Volterra, 1927, 1931; Nicholson and Bailey, 1935; Thompson, 1939), which is just that portion of the subject which has remained most closely associated with general ecology. Hence we have a situation in which the analytical theories which are recognized by ecologists deal with complex phenomena and are susceptible to cogent criticisms (e.g., Smith, 1952) while the simpler analysis of the ways in which differences between the life histories of species may result in different characteristics of their populations has remained relatively unexplored. It is the purpose of the present paper to consider some parts of this neglected branch of ecology which has been called "biodemography" by Hutchinson (1948).

It is possible, but often impracticable, to compute exactly the characteristics of the hypothetical future population obtained by assuming an unvarying pattern of the pertinent life history features which govern natality and mortality. It is often more practicable to employ approximate methods of computation of the type which have aroused skepticism among biologists. It will be shown that the two approaches can be reconciled and that for many cases of ecological interest they lead to identical conclusions. Some of these conclusions reached by the writer have appeared surprising when first encountered, and they seem to give a new perspective to life history studies. They also suggest that pertinent bits of information are frequently ignored in life history studies simply because their importance is not generally recognized.

The total life history pattern of a species has meaning in terms of its ability to survive, and ecologists should attempt to interpret these meanings. The following sections are intended primarily to indicate some of the possibilities in this direction. The writer wishes to express his gratitude to Professor Howard B. Adelmann for a critical reading of the manuscript of this paper, for suggesting numerous ways of clarifying the text and improving terminology, and for translating from the Latin parts of the text from Fibonacci (1202). Thanks are also due to Professors Robert J. Walker and Mark Kac who have been consulted about technical mathematical questions raised by the writer while considering various phases of this subject.

## INTRODUCTION

If it is to survive, every species must possess reproductive capacities sufficient to replace the existing species population by the time this population has disappeared. It is obvious that the ability of the ancestors of existing species to replace themselves has been sufficient to overcome all environmental exigencies which have been encountered and, therefore, that the physiological, morphological, and behavioral adaptations that enable offspring to be produced and to survive in sufficient numbers to insure the persistence of a species are of fundamental ecological interest.

On the other hand, it is conceivable that reproductive capacity might become so great as to be detrimental to a species. The many deleterious effects of overcrowding are well known. It also seems obvious that a species which diverts too large a proportion of its available energies into unnecessary, and therefore wasteful, reproduction would be at a disadvantage in competition with other species.

In this paper it will be regarded as axiomatic that the reproductive potentials of existing species are related to their requirements for survival; that any life history features affecting reproductive potential are subject to natural selection; and that such features observed in existing species should be considered adaptations, just as purely morphological or behavioral patterns are commonly so considered.

Some of the more striking life history phenomena have long been recognized as adaptations to special requirements. The great fecundity rather generally found in parasites and in many marine organisms is commonly regarded as an adaptation insuring the maintenance of a population under conditions where the probability is low that any particular individual will establish itself and reproduce successfully. Again, parthenogenesis obviously favors the rapid growth of a population because every member of a population reproducing in this fashion can be a reproductive female. In turning seasonally to parthenogenesis, organisms like cladocerans and aphids are responding in a highly adaptive way during a limited period of time when the environmental resources are sufficient to support a large population. Parthenogenesis, hermaphroditism, and purely asexual reproduction may clearly offer some advantages under conditions that restrict the probability of contacts between the sexes. Protandry, as exhibited, for example, by some marine molluscs, and various related phenomena where population density affects the sex ratio (Allee et al., 1949, p. 409) may be considered as compromise devices providing the advantages of biparental inheritance while maintaining an unbalanced sex ratio which makes most of the environmental resources available to reproductive females.

Reproductive potentialities may be related to the success of a species in still other ways. It was an essential part of Darwin's thesis that the production of excess offspring provided a field of heritable variations upon which environmental conditions could operate to select the most favorable combinations. A high degree of fecundity may also aid the dispersal of species. An extreme example of this is afforded by the ground pine, *Lycopodium* (Humphreys, 1929), whose light windborne spores may be scattered literally over the whole face of the earth and so make it likely that all favorable habitats will come to be occupied. Another adaptational interpretation of the overproduction of offspring postulates that the excessive production of young fish which are frequently cannibalistic is a form of maternal provisioning, the majority of the young serving merely as food for the few that ultimately mature.

Many additional examples of life history phenomena that have been regarded as adaptive could be cited. Here, however, we wish rather to call attention to the striking fact that in modern ecological literature there have been relatively few attempts to evaluate quantitatively the importance of specific features of life histories. The apparent mathematical complexity of the general problem is undoubtedly partly responsible for this. When the biologist attempts to compute from observed life history data the numbers of organisms of a particular type that can be produced in a given interval of time he may find it necessary to make assumptions which biologists in general would hesitate to accept. And even with these simplifying assumptions the computations may become so tedious as to make the labor involved seem unjustifiable in view of the seemingly academic interest of the result. In particular, such computations involve biological parameters which are not necessarily fixed characteristics of the species and which are not ordinarily expressible in convenient mathematical form. It is necessary to know the way in which the chance of dying (or of surviving) and the reproductive activities vary during the life span of an individual. These quantities are nicely summed up by the familiar life-table function, survivorship ($l_x$), which is defined as the probability of surviving from birth to some age $x$, and by the age-specific birth rate ($b_x$), which is defined as the mean number of offspring produced during the interval of age from age $x$ to age $x + 1$. The biologist immediately recognizes that these quantities vary with environmental conditions and that he cannot expect to obtain a realistic result if he must assume, for example, that the probability of surviving a day, a week, or a month, is the same for individuals born in the autumn as for those born in the spring. He also recognizes that the population consists of discrete units and that offspring are produced in batches (here called litters whether in plants or animals) rather than continuously; hence he necessarily regards with suspicion any formulation of the problem in terms of differential equations where these considerations are apparently ignored.

Actually a tremendous variability is observed in life history phenomena which could affect the growth of populations. Some organisms are semelparous, that is to say, they reproduce only once in a lifetime and in these semelparous forms reproduction may occur at the age of only 20 minutes in certain bacteria (Molisch, 1938), of a few hours in many protozoa, or of a few weeks or months in many insects. Many semelparous plants and animals are annuals; in other semelparous organisms reproduction may occur only after a number of years of maturation, for example, two or more years in dobson flies and Pacific salmon, and many years in "century plants" (*Agave*) and the periodic cicada or "17-year locust" (*Magicicada septendecim*). The number of potential offspring produced by semelparous individuals varies from two in the case of binary fission to the literally trillions ($2 \times 10^{13}$) of spores produced by a large puffball (*Calvatia gigantea*).

In iteroparous forms, that is to say, those which reproduce more than once in a lifetime, the period of maturation preceding the first production of prospective offspring may vary from as little as a few days in small crustaceans to over a century in the giant sequoia (U. S. Forest Service, 1948), and practically any intermediate value may be encountered. After the first reproduction has occurred in iteroparous organisms it may be repeated at various intervals—for example, daily (as in some tapeworms), semiannually, annually, biennially, or irregularly (as in man). As in semelparous organisms, the litter size of iteroparous forms may also vary greatly; here it may vary from one (as is usual, for example, in man, whales, bovines, and horses) to many thousands (as in various fishes, tapeworms, or trees). The litter size may be constant in a species, vary about some average, or change systematically with the age of the parent, in which case it may increase to some maximum (as in tapeworms) or climb to a maximum and then decline as in some cladocerans (Banta et al., 1939; Frank, 1952). Furthermore, individuals may live on after their reproduction has ceased completely, and this post-reproductive period may amount to more than one-half of the normal life span (Allee et al., 1949, p. 285).

There is similar variability in the potential longevity of individual organisms. Man, various turtles, and trees may survive more than a century, while, on the other hand, the life span of many other species is concluded in hours or days. Innumerable intermediate values of course occur.

Additional sources of variation (such as biased sex ratios and the occurrence of asexual reproduction in developmental stages so as to result in the production of many offspring from one egg or spore) force the conclusion that the number of theoretical combinations of observed life history phenomena must greatly exceed the number of known species of organisms. And if all these phenomena have potential adaptive importance the interpretation of the possible merits of the particular combination of features exhibited by a species presents a problem of apparent great complexity.

The usual mathematical approach to the problem of potential population growth is straightforward. It is assumed that the growth of a population at any instant of time is proportional to the size of the population at that instant. If $r$ is the factor of proportionality and $P_x$ represents the population size at any $x$ time this leads to the differential equation

$$\frac{dP}{dx} = rP \qquad (1)$$

which upon integration gives:

$$P_x = A e^{rx} \qquad (1')$$

where $A$ is a constant. This is an equation of continuous compound interest at the rate $r$ or of a geometric progression where the ratio between the sizes of the populations in two consecutive time intervals, say years, is $e^r$.

While formulas (1) and (1') represent only the usual starting point for mathematical discussions of population growth, they already exhibit points about which there has been, and still is, a great deal of controversy. Explicit statements to the effect that human populations potentially increase by geometric progression can be traced back at least to Capt. John Graunt (1662), who estimated that a human population tends to double itself every 64 years (which would correspond to $r = .0108$ in formula 1). This belief in geometric progression as the form of potential population increase was endorsed by numerous students prior to the great controversy initiated by Malthus in 1798 (see review by Stangeland, 1904). Among these early writers we may here note only Linnaeus (1743), who considered the problem of geometric increase in the progeny of an annual plant, and Benjamin Franklin (1751), who estimated that the population of "America" could double at least every 20 years (corresponding to $r = .035$), and who clearly regarded the geometric nature of potential population increase as a general organic phenomenon.

The great controversy over growth in human populations which was initiated by the publication in 1798 of Malthus' *Essay on Population* engendered numerous arguments regarding geometric progression as the potential form of population growth. This controversy is still alive and in much its original form, with the "Neo-Malthusian" position maintaining that potential population growth is indeed in the form of a geometric progression, whereas the capacity of the environment to absorb population is necessarily limited, and with their opponents denying both the geometric progression and the finite capacity of the environment. Essentially the modern arguments against the Malthusian thesis, although not presented in modern concise form, are to be found in the treatise by Sadler (1830) which, whatever its shortcomings from the modern point of view, contains in places (especially in the appendix to Book IV) a very remarkable pre-Darwinian statement of such ecological phenomena as food chains, species interactions, and the balance of numbers between predators and prey.

The entire problem of potential population growth and its relationship to the resources of the environment is clearly one of the fundamental problems of ecology, but one which has never been adequately summarized in a way to reconcile the mathematical approaches, such as those of Lotka (1925), Volterra (1927), Kuczynski (1932, 1935), Kostitzin (1939), and Rhodes (1940), and the purely biological approaches which have concentrated on life history features such as longevity, fecundity, fertility, and sex ratios. In the present paper we will consider the mathematical form of potential population growth and certain subsidiary phenomena and the way in which these are related to particular life history phenomena. It is hoped that this will bring to attention some of the possible adaptive values of observed life history phenomena and will lead ecologists to a greater consideration of population problems which are essentially ecological. Life history features do in fact control potential population growth, as Sadler recognized, but the quantitative relationships have still been so insufficiently elucidated that even today ecologists generally do not attempt to answer queries such as the following, written by Sadler in 1830 (Vol. 2, p. 318):

"For instance, how would those who have the folly to suppose that population in this country advances too fast by one per cent., so operate, had they even their wish, as to diminish the number of marriages by one in one hundred, or otherwise contract the fecundity of the existing number by about one twenty-fifth part of a birth each, or calculate, upon their own erroneous suppositions, the term of that postponement of marriage on which they insist so much, so as to produce this exact effect? The very idea is, in each instance, absurd to the last degree."

## FUNDAMENTAL CONSIDERATIONS

Sadler (1830) makes clear in numerous places his belief that ". . . the geometrical ratio of human increase is, nevertheless, in itself, an impossibility . . ." (Vol. 2, p. 68). However, when one examines his argument it is apparent that he is not actually opposing the principle that with fixed life history features populations would grow at compound interest, but rather is proposing the thesis that life history features change with population density, e.g., his fundamental thesis: "The prolificness of human beings, otherwise similarly circumstanced, varies inversely as their numbers" (Vol. 2, p. 252). Some of Sadler's computations assuming fixed ages at marriage and fecundity rates, in fact, lead to geometric progressions.

The modern conception of population growth regards the *potential* rate of increase as a more or less fixed species characteristic (cf. Chapman, 1935) governed by life history features; but it considers that this potential rate is ordinarily only partially realized, the "partial potential" characteristic of a particular situation being dependent on environmental conditions. Ecologists commonly associate this concept of "biotic potential" with the name of Chapman (1928, 1935), but actually the concept of populations as systems balanced between a potential ability to grow and an "environmental resistance" dates back at least to the Belgian statistician Quetelet (1835), who considered (p. 277) that potential population growth is a geometric progression, while the resistance to population growth (by analogy with a body falling through a viscous medium) varies as the square of the rate of growth. Only three years later Quetelet's student and colleague Verhulst (1838) set forth the thoroughly modern concept that potential population growth is a geometric progression corresponding to our formula (1'), and that the environmental resistance varies inversely with the unexploited opportunities for growth. By this conception, if $K$ represents the capacity of the environment or the ultimate size which the population can attain, the resistance to population growth increases as $K - P$, the amount of space

remaining to be occupied, decreases. As the simplest case Verhulst considered that the resistance is related in a linear manner to the remaining opportunities for growth and thus derived the familiar logistic function as a representation of population growth (for discussion see Allee et al., 1949).

The modern mathematical formulation of population growth, as given, for example, by Rhodes (1940), proceeds by expressing the environmental resistance as some function of population size, $f(P)$, and writing a differential equation of the type

$$\frac{dP}{dx} = rPf(P). \qquad (2)$$

By employing different functions for $f(P)$, any number of population growth laws may be derived and the mathematical connection between $P$ and $x$ determined, providing equation (2) can be integrated. Rhodes gives several examples of the procedure.

Formula (1'), the equation of the geometric progression representing population growth in an unlimited environment, represents the special case of formula (2) where the factor $f(P)$ is replaced by a constant, most conveniently by the constant value unity. By the foregoing interpretation it is clear that the constant $r$ must be regarded as a quantity of fundamental ecological significance. It is to be interpreted as the rate of true compound interest at which a population would grow if nothing impeded its growth and if the age-specific birth and death rates were to remain constant.

Quite recently a number of ecologists have recognized the importance of a knowledge of the value of $r$ for non-human populations and have computed its value for various species by employing empirical values of age-specific birth rates and survivorship (Leslie and Ranson, 1940; Birch, 1948; Leslie and Park, 1949; Mendes, 1949; Evans and Smith, 1952). While Chapman's term "biotic potential" would seem to have ecological merit as the name for this parameter $r$ it has been variously called by Lotka the "true," the "incipient," the "inherent," and the "intrinsic" rate of increase, and by Fisher (1930) the "Malthusian parameter" of population increase. Probably for the sake of stabilizing nomenclature it is advisable to follow the majority of recent writers and refer to $r$ as "the intrinsic rate of natural increase."

In the works of Dublin and Lotka (1925),

Kuczynski (1932), and Rhodes (1940) on human populations and in the papers mentioned above dealing with other species, the value of $r$ has typically been determined by some application of three fundamental equations developed by Lotka (1907a, b; Sharpe and Lotka, 1911). He showed that if the age-specific fecundity ($b_x$) and survivorship ($l_x$) remained constant, the population would in time assume a fixed or "stable" age distribution such that in any interval of age from $x$ to $x + dx$ there would be a fixed proportion ($c_x$) of the population. Once this stable age distribution is established the population would grow exponentially according to our formula (1') and with a birth rate per head, $\beta$. Then the following equations relate these quantities:

$$\int_0^\infty e^{-rx} l_x b_x \, dx = 1 \qquad (3)$$

$$\int_0^\infty e^{-rx} l_x \, dx = 1/\beta \qquad (4)$$

and

$$\beta e^{-rx} l_x = c_x. \qquad (5)$$

While the use of formulas (3), (4), and (5) to compute the value of $r$ often presents practical difficulties owing to the difficulty of approximating the functions $l_x$ and $b_x$ by a mathematical function, and also because the equations usually must be solved by iterative methods, it may fairly be stated that Lotka's pioneer work establishing these relationships provided the methods for interpreting the relationships between life history features and their population consequences.

However, the exceedingly important ecological questions of what potential advantages might be realized if a species were to alter its life history features have remained largely unexplored. Doubtless, as already noted, this is largely to be explained by a certain suspicion felt by biologists toward analyses such as those of Lotka, which seem to involve assumptions very remote from the realities of life histories as observed in the field and laboratories. A particularly pertinent statement of this point of view is that of Thompson (1931), who recognized the great practical need for methods of computing the rate of increase of natural populations of insects adhering to particular life history patterns but who insisted that the reproductive process must be dealt with as a discontinuous phenomenon rather than as a compound interest phenomenon such as that of formula (1'). His methods of computation were designed to give the exact number of individuals living in any particular time period and, while he recognized that the population growth can be expressed in an exponential form such as (1'), he rejected its use on these grounds:

"In the first place, the constant ($r$) cannot be determined until the growth of the population under certain definite conditions has been studied during a considerable period; in the second place, no intelligible significance can be attached to the constant after its value has been determined; in the third place, the growth of the population is considered in this formula to be at every moment proportional to the size of the population, which is not true except with large numbers and over long periods and cannot be safely taken as a basis for the examination of experimental data."

In the following sections of the present paper an effort will be made to reconcile these two divergent points of view and to show under what conditions Thompson's "discontinuous" approach and the continuous methods lead to identical results. Practical methods of computation can be founded on either scheme, and there are circumstances where one or the other offers distinct advantages. It is hoped that a theoretical approach to population phenomena proceeding from exact computational methods will clarify the meaning of some of the approximations made in deriving equations such as (3), (4), and (5) by continuous methods, and will stimulate students of ecology to a greater interest in the population consequences of life history phenomena.

Before proceeding to a discussion of potential population growth, one point which has sometimes caused confusion should be mentioned. This concerns the sex ratio and the relative proportions of different age classes in the growing population. Once stated, it is obvious that if a population is always growing, as are the populations in the models used for determining potential population growth, then each age and sex class must ultimately come to grow at exactly the same rate as every other class. If this were not the case the disproportion between any two classes would come to exceed all bounds; the fastest growing class would continue indefinitely to make up a larger and larger proportion of the total population. It is thus intuitively recognizable that with fixed life history features there must ultimately be a fixed sex ratio and a stable age distribution. In discussing potential population growth it is often convenient to confine our attention to females or even to a restricted age class, such as the annual births, while recognizing that the ultimate growth rate for such a restricted population segment must be identical to the rate for the entire population.

### SIMPLEST CASES OF POPULATION GROWTH

#### Non-overlapping generations

The simplest possible cases of population growth from the mathematical point of view are those in which reproduction takes place once in a lifetime and the parent organisms disappear by the time the new generation comes on the scene, so that there is no overlapping of generations. This situation occurs in the many plants and animals which are annuals, in those bacteria, unicellular algae, and protozoa where reproduction takes place by fission of one individual to form two or more daughter individuals, and in certain other forms. Thus in the century plants (*Agave*) the plant dies upon producing seeds at an age of four years or more, the Pacific salmon (*Oncorhynchus*) dies after spawning, which occurs at an age of two to eight years (two years in the pink salmon *O. gorbuscha*), and cicadas breed at the end of a long developmental period which lasts from two years (*Tibicen*) to 17 years in *Magicicada*. For many other insects with prolonged developmental stages such as neuropterans and mayflies potential population growth may be considered on the assumption that generations do not overlap.

In these cases, perhaps most typically illustrated in the case of annuals, the population living in any year or other time interval is simply the number of births which occurred at the beginning of that interval. Starting with one individual which is replaced by $b$ offspring each of which repeats the life history pattern of the parent, the population will grow in successive time intervals according to the series: $1, b, b^2, b^3, b^4, \cdots b^x$. Hence the number of "births," say $B_x$, at the beginning of any time interval, $T_x$, is simply $b^x$ which is identical with the population, $P_x$, in that interval of time. If the population starts from an initial number $P_0$ we have:

$$P_x = P_0 b^x \qquad (6)$$

which is obviously identical with the exponential formula (1'), $P_x = Ae^{rx}$, where the constant $A$ is precisely $P_0$, the initial population size, and $r = \ln b$; the intrinsic rate of increase is equal to the natural logarithm of the litter size.

If litter size varies among the reproductive individuals, with each litter size being characteristic of a fixed proportion of each generation, it is precisely correct to use the average litter size, say $\bar{b}$, in the computations, so that we have $r = \ln \bar{b}$. Furthermore, if not all of the offspring are viable, but only some proportion, say $l_1$, survive to reproduce, we shall have exactly $r = \ln \bar{b}^{l_1}$. Thus, mortality and variations in litter size do not complicate the interpretation of population growth in cases where the generations do not overlap. On the other hand, even in species which reproduce only once, if the generation length is not the same for all individuals, this will lead to overlapping generations, and the simple considerations which led to formula (6) will no longer apply. In other words, we can use an average figure for the litter size $b$ but not for the generation length $x$. It will be shown in the next section, however, that the more general formula (1') is still applicable.

In these simplest cases the assumption of a geometric progression as the potential form of population growth is obviously correct, and numerous authors have computed the fantastic numbers of offspring which could potentially result from such reproduction. For example, according to Thompson (1942), Linnaeus (1740?) pointed out that if only two seeds of an annual plant grew to maturity per year, a single individual could give rise to a million offspring in 20 years. (In all editions available to the present writer this interesting essay of Linnaeus' is dated 1743, and the number of offspring at the end of twenty years is stated by the curious and erroneous figure 91,296.) That is, $P_{20} = 2^{20} = e^{20 \ln 2} = 1,048,576$. Additional examples are given by Chapman (1935, p. 148).

Formulas (1') or (6) may, of course, also be used in an inverse manner to obtain the rate of multiplication when the rate of population growth is known. For the example given by Molisch (1938, p. 25), referring to diatoms reproducing by binary fission where the average population was observed to increase by a factor of 1.2 per day, we have $1.2 = e^{x \ln 2}$, where $x$ is the number of generations per day. Solving for $1/x$, the length of a generation, we obtain $1/x = \dfrac{\ln 2}{\ln 1.2} = \dfrac{.69315}{.18232} = 3.8$ days.

#### Overlapping generations

Interest in computing the number of offspring which would be produced by a species adhering to a constant reproductive schedule dates back at least to Leonardo Pisano ( = Fibonacci) who, in the year 1202, attempted to reintroduce into Europe the study of algebra, which had been neglected since the fall of Rome. One of the problems in his *Liber Abbaci* (pp. 283–84 of the 1857 edition) concerns a man who placed a pair of rabbits in an enclosure in order to discover how many pairs of rabbits would be produced in a year. Assuming that each pair of rabbits produces another pair in the first month and then reproduces once more, giving rise to a second pair of offspring in the second month, and assuming no mortality, Fibonacci showed that the number of pairs in each month would correspond to the series

$$1, 2, 3, 5, 8, 13, 21, 34, 55, \text{etc.},$$

where each number is the sum of the two preceding numbers. These "Fibonacci numbers" have a rather celebrated history in mathematics, biology, and art (Archibold, 1918; Thompson, 1942; Pierce, 1951) but our present concern with them is merely as a very early attempt to compute potential population growth.

Fibonacci derived his series simply by following through in words all of the population changes occurring from month to month. One with sufficient patience could, of course, apply the same procedure to more complicated cases and could introduce additional variables such as deductions for mortality. In fact, Sadler (1830, Book III) did make such computations for human populations. He was interested in discovering at what ages persons would have to marry and how often they would have to reproduce to give some of the rates of population doubling which had been postulated by Malthus (1798). To accomplish this, Sadler apparently employed the amazingly tedious procedure of constructing numerous tables corresponding to different assumptions until he found one which approximated the desired rate of doubling.

Although we must admire Sadler's diligence, anyone who undertakes such computations will find that it is not difficult to devise various ways of systematizing the procedure which will greatly reduce the labor of computation. By far the best of these methods known to the present writer is that of Thompson (1931), which was originally suggested to him by H. E. Soper.

In the Soper-Thompson approach a "generation law" $(G)$ is written embodying the fixed life history features which it is desired to consider. The symbol $T^x$ stands for the $x^{\text{th}}$ interval of time, and a generation law such as $G = 2T^1 + 2T^2$ would be read as "two offspring produced in the first time interval and two offspring produced in the second time interval." This particular generation law might, for example, be roughly applicable to some bird such as a cliff swallow, where a female produces about four eggs per year. Concentrating our attention on the female part of the population, we might wish to compute the rate of population growth which would result if each female had two female offspring upon attaining the age of one year and had two more female offspring at the age of two years. The fundamental feature of the Thompson method is the fact that the expression:

$$\frac{1}{1 - G} \tag{7}$$

is a generating function which gives the series of births occurring in successive time intervals. In the algebraic division the indices of the terms $T^1$, $T^2$, etc., are treated as ordinary exponents and the number of births occurring in any time interval $T^x$ is simply the coefficient of $T^x$ in the expansion of expression (7). Thus, for our example where $G = 2T^1 + 2T^2$ we obtain:

$$\frac{1}{1 - 2T^1 - 2T^2} = 1 + 2T^1 + 6T^2 +$$

$$16T^3 + 44T^4 + 120T^5 + 328T^6 + \cdots,$$

showing that one original female birth gives rise to 328 female offspring in the sixth year. The series could be continued indefinitely to obtain the number of births any number of years hence. However, in practice it is not necessary to continue the division. In the above series the coefficient of each term is simply twice the sum of the coefficients of the two preceding terms; hence the generation law gives us the rule for extending the series. $G = 2T^1 + 2T^2$ instructs us to obtain each new term of the series by taking twice the preceding term plus twice the second term back. In the case of the Fibonacci numbers we would have $G = T^1 + T^2$, telling us at once that each new term is the sum of the two preceding it.

From the birth series we can easily obtain the series enumerating the total population. If each individual lives for $\lambda$ years, the total population in $T^x$ will be the sum of $\lambda$ consecutive terms in the expansion of the generating function. Multiplying formula (7) by the length of life expressed in the form $1 + T^1 + T^2 + T^3 + \cdots + T^{\lambda-1}$ will give the population series. In our above example if we assume that each individual lives for three years, although, as before, it only reproduces in the first two, we obtain for the population

$$\frac{1 + T^1 + T^2}{1 - 2T^1 - 2T^2} = 1 + 3T^1 + 9T^2 +$$

$$24T^3 + 66T^4 + 180T^5 + 492T^6 + \cdots,$$

a series which still obeys the rule $G = 2T^1 + 2T^2$.

Thompson's method for obtaining the exact number of births and members of the population in successive time intervals is very general. As in the case of non-overlapping generations, the coefficients in the generation law may refer to average values for the age-specific fecundity. Also the length of the time intervals upon which the computations are based can be made arbitrarily short, so that it is easy to take into account variations in the age at which reproduction occurs. For the above example, time could have been measured in six-month periods rather than years so that the generation law would become $G = 2T^2 + 2T^4$, with the same results already obtained.

Furthermore, the factor of mortality can easily be included in the computations. For example, suppose that we wish to determine the rate of population growth for a species where the females have two female offspring when they reach the age of one, two more when they reach the age of two, and two more when they reach the age of three. Neglecting mortality, this would give us the generation law $G = 2T^1 + 2T^2 + 2T^3$. If we were further interested in the case where not all of the offspring survive for three years, the coefficients in the generation law need only be multiplied by the corresponding survivorship values. For example, if one-half of the individuals die between the ages of one and two, and one half of the remainder die before reaching the age of three we would have $l_1 = 1$, $l_2 = \frac{1}{2}$, $l_3 = \frac{1}{4}$, and the above generation law would be revised to $G = 2T^1 + T^2 + \frac{1}{2}T^3$. The future births per original individual would then be

$$\frac{1}{1 - G} = 1 + 2T^1 + 5T^2 + 25/2T^3 + 31T^4 +$$

$$151/2T^5 + \cdots.$$

Very generally, if the first reproduction for a species occurs at some age $\alpha$ and the last reproduction occurs at some age $\omega$, and letting $b_x$ and $l_x$ represent respectively the age-specific fecundity

and survivorship, we may write the generation law as:

$$G = l_\alpha b_\alpha T^\alpha + l_{\alpha+1} b_{\alpha+1} T^{\alpha+1} + \cdots$$

$$+ l_\omega b_\omega T^\omega = \sum_{x=\alpha}^{\omega} l_x b_x T^x. \tag{8}$$

Therefore, in the Thompson method we have a compact system of computation for obtaining the exact number of births and the exact population size at any future time, assuming that the significant life history features ($\alpha$, $\omega$, $l_x$, and $b_x$) do not change.

Not all of the possible applications of Thompson's method have been indicated above. For example, formula (7) may be used in an inverse manner so that it is theoretically possible to work back from a tabulation of births or population counts made in successive time intervals and discover the underlying generation law. Formulas (7) and (8), together with the procedure of multiplying the birth series by the length of life expressed as a sum of $T^x$ values, provide the nucleus of the system and offer the possibility of analyzing the potential population consequences of essentially any life-history phenomena. The system has the merit of treating the biological units and events as discontinuous variates, which, in fact, they almost always are. The members of populations are typically discrete units, and an event such as reproduction typically occurs at a point in time with no spreading out or overlapping between successive litters. While survivorship, $l_x$, as a population quantity, is most realistically regarded as continuously changing in time, the product $l_x b_x$ which enters our computations by way of formula (8) is typically discontinuous because of the discontinuous nature of $b_x$.

It is quite obvious that equations of continuous variation such as (1') are often much more convenient for purposes of computation than the series of values obtained by expanding (7). This is especially true in dealing with the life histories of species which have long reproductive lives. In writing a generation law for man by (8) we should have to take $\alpha$ at least as small as 15 years and $\omega$ at least as great as 40 years, since for the population as a whole reproduction occurs well outside of these extremes and it would certainly be unrealistic to regard $b_x$ as negligibly small anywhere between these limits. Thus there would be at least 25 terms in our generation law, and the computations would be extremely tedious. By selecting special cases

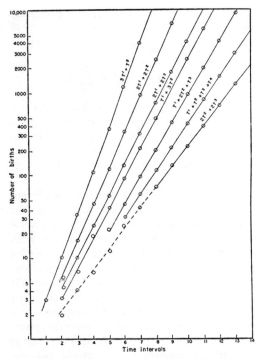

**FIG. 1. EXACT VALUES OF POPULATION GROWTH IN TERMS OF BIRTHS PER UNIT TIME UNDER SEVERAL GENERATION LAWS, WHEN EACH FEMALE HAS A TOTAL OF FOUR FEMALE OFFSPRING**

In each case it is assumed that a single female exists at time zero and produces her four progeny on or before her fourth birthday. The plotted points represent exact values as determined by Thompson's method. To the extent that the points for any generation law fall on a straight line in this logarithmic plot, they can be represented by the exponential growth formula (1′), and the slope of each line is a measure of the intrinsic rate of natural increase ($r$).

for study it is sometimes possible greatly to simplify the procedures. For example, if one is interested in the case where there is no mortality during the reproductive span of life and where the litter size is a constant, say $b$, the expression for the generation law (8) can be simplified to:

$$G = bT^\alpha + bT^{\alpha+1} + \cdots bT^\omega = \frac{bT^\alpha - bT^{\omega+1}}{1 - T}.$$

Since one can also write the length of life as

$$1 + T^1 + T^2 + \cdots + T^{\lambda-1} = \frac{1 - T^\lambda}{1 - T},$$

the generating function for the total population simplifies to

$$\frac{1 - T^\lambda}{1 - T - bT^\alpha + bT^{\omega+1}}.$$

This last formula is much more convenient for computations than one containing 25 terms or so in the denominator, but it applies only to a very special case and is much less convenient than formula (1′). Consequently, great interest attaches to these questions: can (1′) be used as a substitute for (7)? (i.e., does Thompson's method lead to a geometric progression?) and, if it is so used, can the constants, particularly $r$, be interpreted in terms of life-history features?

### THE GENERALIZATION OF THOMPSON'S METHOD

Fig. 1 shows the exact values, as determined by Thompson's method, of the birth series arising from several generation laws (life-history patterns) which have in common the feature that in each case every female produces a total of four female offspring in her lifetime and completes her reproductive life by the age of four "years." The number of births is plotted on a logarithmic scale, hence if it can be represented by formula (1′), $P = Ae^{rx}$ or, logarithmically, $\ln P = \ln A + rx$, the points should fall on a straight line with slope proportional to $r$. It is apparent from Fig. 1 that after the first few time intervals the points in each case are well represented by a straight line. Therefore, except in the very early stages, formula (1′) does give a good representation of potential population growth. The question remains, however, as to whether we can meet Thompson's objection to (1′) and attach any intelligible significance to the constants of the formula. From Fig. 1 it is obvious that the lines do not, if projected back to time 0, indicate exactly the single individual with which we started. Thus, in these cases the constant $A$ cannot be precisely $P_0$ as was the case with non-overlapping generations.

Before proceeding to interpret the constants of formula (1′) for the case of overlapping generations it will be well to notice one feature of Fig. 1 which is of biological interest. In the literature of natural history one frequently encounters references to the number of offspring which a female can produce per lifetime, with the implication that this is a significant life-history feature. The same implication is common in the literature dealing with various aspects of human biology, where great emphasis is placed on the analysis of total family size. From Fig. 1 it will be seen that this datum may be less significant from the standpoint of contributions to future population than is the age schedule upon which these offspring are

produced. Each life history shown in Fig. 1 represents a total production of four offspring within four years of birth, but the resulting rates of potential population growth are very different for the different schedules. It is clear that the cases of most rapid population growth are associated with a greater concentration of reproduction into the early life of the mother. This is intuitively reasonable because we are here dealing with a compound interest phenomenon and should expect greater yield in cases where "interest" begins to accumulate early. However, the writer feels that this phenomenon is too frequently overlooked in biological studies, possibly because of the difficulty of interpreting the phenomenon quantitatively.

In seeking to reconcile the continuous and discontinuous approaches to potential population growth, let us first note that Thompson's discontinuous method corresponds to an equation of finite differences. We have seen above that the generation law gives us a rule for indefinitely extending the series representing the population size or the number of births in successive time intervals by adding together some of the preceding terms multiplied by appropriate constants. If we let $f_{(x)}$ represent the coefficient of $T^x$ in the expansion of the generating function (7) and, for brevity, write in (8) $V_x = l_x b_x$, then our population series obeys the rule:

$$f_{(x)} = V_\alpha f_{(x-\alpha)} + V_{\alpha+1} f_{(x-\alpha-1)} + \cdots + V_\omega f_{(x-\omega)}, \qquad (9)$$

which may be written in the alternative form,

$$f_{(x+\omega)} - V_\alpha f_{(x+\omega-\alpha)} - V_{\alpha+1} f_{(x+\omega-\alpha-1)} - \cdots - V_\omega f_{(x)}, = 0. \qquad (10)$$

Thus for our "cliff swallow" example, where we had $G = 2T^1 + 2T^2$ we have

$$f_{(x)} = 2f_{(x-1)} + 2f_{(-2)} \text{ or,}$$
$$f_{(x+2)} - 2f_{(x+1)} - 2f_{(x)} = 0.$$

Formula (10) represents the simplest and best understood type of difference equation, a homogeneous linear difference equation with constant coefficients. It is outside the scope of the present paper to discuss the theory of such equations, which has been given, for example, by Jordan (1950). By the nature of our problem as summarized in formula (9), all of our $V_x$ values are either equal to zero or are positive real numbers and all of the signs of the coefficients in (9) are positive: features which considerably simplify

generalizations. By virtue of these facts it can be shown that there is always a "characteristic" algebraic equation corresponding to (10). This is obtained by writing $\rho^x$ for $f_{(x)}$ and dividing through by the $\rho$ value of smallest index. This gives

$$\rho^\omega - V_\alpha \rho^{\omega-\alpha} - V_{\alpha+1} \rho^{\omega-\alpha-1} \cdots - V_\omega = 0 \qquad (11)$$

an algebraic equation which has the roots $\rho_1$, $\rho_2$, etc.

The general solution of the corresponding difference equation (10) is

$$f_{(x)} = C_1 \rho_1^x + C_2 \rho_2^x + \cdots + C_n \rho_n^x \qquad (12)$$

where the $C$'s are constants to be determined by the initial conditions of the problem. Formula (12) is precisely equivalent to Thompson's method and is a general expression for the number of births or the population size in any future time interval.

As an example we may consider the case where $G = 2T^1 + 2T^2$. The difference equation, as already noted, is $f_{(x+2)} - 2f_{(x+1)} - 2f_{(x)} = 0$ and the characteristic algebraic equation is $\rho^2 - 2\rho - 2 = 0$ which is a quadratic equation with the roots $\rho_1 = 1 + \sqrt{3}$, and $\rho_2 = 1 - \sqrt{3}$. Hence the general solution is $f_{(x)} = C_1(1 + \sqrt{3})^x + C_2(1 - \sqrt{3})^x$. To determine the constants $C_1$ and $C_2$ we look at the beginning a of the seriesnd note that we have $f_{(0)} = 1$ and $f_{(1)} = 2$. Substituting these values in the general solution we obtain $C_1 = \dfrac{\sqrt{3} + 1}{2\sqrt{3}}$ and $C_2 = \dfrac{\sqrt{3} - 1}{2\sqrt{3}}$. Therefore, the general expression for the number of births in time interval $T^x$ is

$$f_{(x)} = \frac{\sqrt{3} + 1}{2\sqrt{3}}(1 + \sqrt{3})^x + \frac{\sqrt{3} - 1}{2\sqrt{3}}(1 - \sqrt{3})^x$$

which can be simplified to $f_{(x)} = \dfrac{\rho_1^{x+1} - \rho_2^{x+1}}{\sqrt{3}} = \rho_1^x + \rho_1^{x-1}\rho_2 + \cdots + \rho_2^x$.

In order to have the difference equation (12) correspond to the equation of exponential growth (1'), the ratio between populations in successive time intervals must assume a constant value giving

$$\frac{f_{(x+1)}}{f_{(x)}} = e^r. \qquad (13)$$

By the nature of our problem, as already noted, the potential population growth is always positive, so that any limit approached by the ratio $\dfrac{f_{(x+1)}}{f_{(x)}}$ must be a positive real number.

It is beyond the scope of the present paper to discuss the conditions, for difference equations in general, under which this ratio does approach as a limit the largest real root of the characteristic algebraic equation. (See, for example, Milne-Thompson, 1933, chap. 17). Dunkel (1925) refers to the homogeneous equation with real constant coefficients corresponding to our formulas (10) and (11). The algebraic equation (11) has a single positive root which cannot be exceeded in absolute value by any other root, real or complex. Using (12) to express the ratio between successive terms, we have

$$\frac{f_{(x+1)}}{f_{(x)}} = \frac{C_1 \rho_1^{x+1} + C_2 \rho_2^{x+1} + \cdots + C_n \rho_n^{x+1}}{C_1 \rho_1^{x} + C_2 \rho_2^{x} + \cdots + C_n \rho_n^{x}}. \quad (14)$$

If we let $\rho_1$ represent the root of (11) of greatest absolute value and divide both numerator and denominator of (14) by $C_1 \rho_1^x$ we obtain

$$\frac{f_{(x+1)}}{f_{(x)}} = \rho_1 \left[ \frac{1 + \frac{C_2}{C_1}\left(\frac{\rho_2}{\rho_1}\right)^{x+1} + \frac{C_3}{C_1}\left(\frac{\rho_3}{\rho_1}\right)^{x+1} + \cdots + \frac{C_n}{C_1}\left(\frac{\rho_n}{\rho_1}\right)^{x+1}}{1 + \frac{C_2}{C_1}\left(\frac{\rho_2}{\rho_1}\right)^{x} + \frac{C_3}{C_1}\left(\frac{\rho_3}{\rho_1}\right)^{x} + \cdots + \frac{C_n}{C_1}\left(\frac{\rho_n}{\rho_1}\right)^{x}} \right]. \quad (15)$$

The expressions in parentheses are all less than unity, on the assumption that $\rho_1$ is the largest root, and the entire expression in brackets approaches unity as $x$ increases. Consequently we have, for $x$ large

$$\frac{f_{(x+1)}}{f_{(x)}} \sim \rho_1 \sim e^r. \quad (16)$$

This then explains the shape of the potential birth and population series as illustrated in Fig. 1. In the very early stages population growth is irregular, because the expressions in (12) and (15) involving the negative and complex roots of (11) are still large enough to exert an appreciable influence. As $x$ increases, the influence of these other roots becomes negligible and the population grows exponentially, conforming to (16). In considering potential population growth we are concerned with the ultimate influence of life-history features, and the equation of geometric progression or compound interest does actually represent the form of potential population growth. We are interested only

in the single positive root of (11) for the purpose of determining the constant $r$, and this can readily be computed with any desired degree of precision by elementary algebraic methods.

Having established the relationship of formula (13) or (16), it is easy to reconcile Thompson's discontinuous approach to population growth with Lotka's continuous approach, as exemplified by formulas (3), (4), and (5).

Employing formula (9) we may write the ratio between populations in successive time intervals as

$$\frac{(f_{x+1})}{f_{(x)}} = V_\alpha \frac{f_{(x-\alpha+1)}}{f_{(x)}} + V_{\alpha+1} \frac{f_{(x-\alpha)}}{f_{(x)}} + \cdots + V_\omega \frac{f_{(x-\omega+1)}}{f_{(x)}}.$$

Substituting the relationship given by (13), this becomes

$$e^r = V_\alpha e^{-r(\alpha-1)} + V_{\alpha+1} e^{-r\alpha} + \cdots + V_\omega e^{-r(\omega-1)}, \text{ or}$$

$$1 = V_\alpha e^{-r\alpha} + V_{\alpha+1} e^{-r(\alpha+1)} + \cdots + V_\omega e^{-r\omega}.$$

Replacing $V_x$ by its equivalent, $l_x b_x$, this is

$$1 = \sum_{x=\alpha}^{\omega} e^{-rx} l_x b_x. \quad (17)$$

Formula (17) is the precise equivalent in terms of finite time intervals of Lotka's equation (3) for infinitesimal time intervals. In Lotka's equation, as in (17), the limits of integration in practice are $\alpha$ and $\omega$ since $b_x$ is zero outside of these limits. Formula (17) was in fact employed by Birch (1948) as an approximation to (3) in his method of determining $r$ for an insect population. The only approximation involved in our derivation of (17) is the excellent one expressed by formula (13); otherwise the formula corresponds to Thompson's exact computational methods. It is hoped that recognition of this fact will make some of the approaches of population mathematics appear more realistic from the biological point of view.

Formulas (4) and (5), originally due to Lotka, are also immediately derivable from the relationship (13). In any time interval, $T_x$, we may say that the population members aged 0 to 1 are simply the births in that interval, say $B_x$. The population members aged 1 to 2 are the survivors of the births in the previous interval, that is $l_1 B_{x-1}$, or employing (13), $l_1 B_x e^{-r}$. Quite generally, the population members aged between $z$ and $z + 1$ are the survivors from the birth $z$ intervals previous, or $l_z B_x e^{-rz}$. If $\lambda$ is the extreme length of life for any population members $(l_{\lambda+1} = 0)$ we have for the total population

$$P_x = B_x(1 + l_1 e^{-r} + l_2 e^{-2r} + \cdots$$

$$+ l_\lambda e^{-r\lambda} = B_x \sum_{z=0}^{\lambda} e^{-rz} l_x.$$

The birth rate per individual, $\beta$, is $B_x/P_x$, therefore,

$$1/\beta = \sum_{0}^{\lambda} e^{-rz} l_x \qquad (18)$$

which is the equivalent in finite time intervals of Lotka's equation (4). Also the proportion, $c_z$, of the population in the age range $z$ to $z + 1$ is $\dfrac{l_z B_x e^{-rz}}{P_x}$ which is simply,

$$c_z = \beta e^{-rz} l_z. \qquad (5)$$

### COMPUTATIONAL METHODS

In the following sections we will examine some of the population effects which are the consequences of particular life history patterns. Probably the most significant comparisons are those involving the effects of life-history features on the intrinsic rate of natural increase, $r$. Of course, any change in $r$ is accompanied by other effects, such as those on the age-structure and on the population birth-rate. However, the intrinsic rate of increase is a parameter of fundamental ecological importance. If a species is exposed to conditions which would favor the ability to outbreed competitors or where exceptional hazards limit the probability that an individual will become established, we might expect to find life-history adjustments tending to increase the value of $r$. Conversely, if a species has evolved life-history features of a type tending to hold down the intrinsic rate of increase, a fertile field of inquiry may be opened regarding the selective factors to which such a species is subject.

It is probably fairly obvious to anyone that in general a species might increase its biotic potential by increasing the number of offspring produced at a time (litter size), by reducing mortality at least until the end of active reproductive life, by reproducing oftener, by beginning reproduction at an earlier age, or by minimizing any wastage of environmental resources on sterile members of the population. Any biologist will at once recognize, however, that a great deal of evolution (an extreme case is the evolution of sterility in the social insects) has proceeded in precisely the wrong direction to increase biotic potential by some of these devices. Presumably, this can only mean that the optimum biotic potential is not always, or even commonly, the maximum that could conceivably be achieved by selecting for this ability alone. Comparative life-history studies appear to the writer to be fully as meaningful in evolutionary terms as are studies of comparative morphology or comparative physiology.

Although a great many empirical data on life histories have been accumulated, attempts to interpret these data comparatively have lagged far behind the corresponding efforts in morphology and physiology. The methods exhibited in the preceding parts of the present paper are adaptable for the quantitative interpretation of life history features and, while the number of conceivable life-history patterns is infinite, we propose to examine some of the cases which appear to possess particular ecological interest.

The life-history features with which we are concerned are the age at which reproduction begins $(\alpha)$, the litter size and frequency of reproduction (both summarized by a knowledge of the function $b_x$, which can also be computed so as to take account of the sex ratio), the maximum age at which reproduction occurs $(\omega)$, survivorship $(l_x)$, and maximum longevity $(\lambda)$. Corresponding to any given set of values for these quantities there is a definite value for the intrinsic rate of natural increase $(r)$ and a definite stable age distribution of the population $(c_x)$. In general, these population features will be altered by any alteration of the life-history features and we wish to examine some of these possible changes quantitatively.

The most efficient way of making the desired computations will vary from problem to problem. Thompson's method (formulas (7) and (8)), could be used to obtain exact population values arising from any life history, but the computations would in many cases be exceedingly laborious and would actually uield no more information about the ultimate course of population growth than would be obtained by solving (11) for the positive root.

In either case it will usually be most efficient to measure time in terms of the shortest interval between the pertinent life-history events with which we are concerned.

Except in very special cases, it is necessary to use iterative methods for obtaining the value of $r$ corresponding to particular life-history patterns. In most cases the solutions are quite rapidly obtained by employing a calculating machine and detailed tables of natural logarithms (e.g., Lowan, 1941) or of the exponential function (e.g., Newman, 1883). In the majority of the cases considered by the writer, the most efficient procedure has been to rewrite formula (17) in the form:

$$e^{r\alpha} = V_\alpha + V_{\alpha+1}e^{-r} + V_{\alpha+2}e^{-2r} + \cdots \\ + V_\omega e^{-r(\omega-\alpha)} \qquad (19)$$

and then to obtain the sum of the series on the right-hand side of (19) for different patterns of variation in the function $l_x b_x = V_x$. This method corresponds exactly to the discontinuous approach, granting only that potential population growth is a geometric progression, and it leads to relatively simple equations in a number of the cases of greatest ecological interest.

A more general approach from the standpoint of formal mathematics can be obtained by rewriting (3) in the form of a Stieltjes integral (Widder, 1940). We may define a maternity function $M(x)$ representing the average number of offspring which an individual will have produced by the time it has attained any age $x$, and such that its derivative with respect to time is $\left(V_x \dfrac{d}{dx} M(x) = V_x\right)$. We then have

$$\int_0^\infty e^{-rx} dM(x) = 1 \qquad (20)$$

which can represent cases where $V_{(x)}$ is either continuous or discontinuous because the integral vanishes for values where $V_x$ is discontinuous. When $V_x$ can be expressed as a function of time $(x)$, formula (20) is identical with (3) and the use of the Laplace transformation, a procedure of considerable importance in engineering and physical mathematics, makes it possible to avoid the numerical integration and express $V_x$ as a function of $r$. If $V_x$ is considered as a series of single impulses regularly spaced from $\alpha$ to $\omega$, equation (20) assumes the form (17). Laplace transformations for a number of functions are tabulated by Churchill (1944) and Widder (1947) and, no doubt, there

are cases where this procedure would lead to simpler iterative solutions than those obtained from equation (19). For the cases considered in the present paper, however, the solution of equation (19) generally leads to somewhat simpler results.

In dealing with any particular life-history pattern the computational method of choice may depend upon the types of features to be investigated. The pure numbers $\alpha$, $\omega$, and $\lambda$ typically offer no particular computational problems, as they are assigned different values, but this is not always the case with the functions $b_x$ and $l_x$.

In the cases considered by the writer the intervals between successive periods of reproduction have been considered to be equal. There is no particular difficulty in altering this assumption so as to consider cases where the frequency of reproduction varies with age, but regular spacing seems to be so much more usual in nature as well as representing a limiting case that it seems to merit first consideration. Litter size often does vary with the age of the parent organism, and this fact may introduce complexities into the behavior of the function $V_x$. In this case also, it appears that the ecologically most interesting cases are those in which the average litter size is a constant. Furthermore, as will become apparent in later sections, the first few litters produced by an organism so dominate its contribution to future population growth that later changes in litter size would have only very minor population consequences. In dealing with empirical data on human populations attempts have been made to express analytically the changes in $b_x$ with age [cf. "Tait's law" that fertility declines in a linear manner (Yule, 1906; Lotka, 1927)] but for the present we shall consider that $b_x$ assumes only the values zero and some constant, $b$.

The shape of the survivorship ($l_x$) curve is more difficult to deal with in a realistic manner. Pearl and Miner (1935) originated the classification of survivorship curves which is most employed for ecological purposes (cf. Deevey, 1947; Allee et al., 1949). The "physiological" survivorship curve is the limiting type in which each individual lives to some limit characteristic of the species and the age at death ($\lambda$) is regarded as a constant. In this case $l_x = 1$ when $x \leqslant \lambda$ and $l_x = 0$ when $x > \lambda$. This is the simplest case for computations, and actual cases are known which approach this type. Furthermore, there are other types of survivorship curves of ecological interest which may be treated in the same manner. In what Deevey (1947) calls Type III there is an extremely heavy early mortality with the few survivors tending to live out a "normal life span." For the computation of $r$ we are only concerned (cf. formula 19) with survivorship during the reproductive span of life, and it appears likely that "Type III" curves can be treated as constant throughout this age range without serious error. Another interesting type of survivorship curve which appears to be consistent with empirical data at least on some wild populations (cf. Jackson, 1939; Deevey, 1947; Ricker, 1948) is that in which a constant proportion of the population dies in each interval of age. This, of course, implies that life expectancy is independent of age, an assumption which cannot in general be considered realistic but which might apply to catastrophic causes of mortality. When this type of $l_x$ curve applies, the $V_x$ values will be in geometric progression and the right side of formula (19) can be summed as easily as in the case where $V_x$ is constant. This case is, therefore, easily dealt with.

The type of survivorship curve usually observed in actual cases is a reverse sigmoid curve, interpreted by Deevey as intermediate between the "physiological" type and the geometric progression. This can be interpreted in various ways as a "wearing-out" curve. Gompertz (1825) attempted to find an analytical form on the assumption that the ability of individuals to "resist destruction" decreases as a geometric progression with age. Elston (1923) has reviewed formulas proposed to represent human mortality; none of these has proved generally applicable, despite great complexity in some cases. Another approach is to assume that some sort of a "vital momentum" (Pearl, 1946) or ability to survive is distributed among the members of the population in the form of a bell-shaped or "normal" frequency distribution. This point of view is a familiar and controversial one in the recent literature on bio-assay problems (Finney, 1947, 1949; Berkson, 1944, 1951) and, at least to the extent that a bell-shaped curve can represent the empirical distribution of ages at death, a probit function or a logit function (Berkson, 1944) can be used to represent $l_x$.

In the present paper we are concerned primarily with the limiting cases or the *potential* meaning of life-history phenomena. Consequently the writer has chosen to deal with survivorship curves of the physiological type and thus to investigate the

ultimate effects of life-history phenomena for a species which is able to reduce mortality during the reproductive part of the life span to a negligible value. Our general conclusions will not be seriously altered even by rather startling drastic alterations of this assumption, and, in any case, our results will indicate the maximum gain which a species might realize by altering its life-history features.

Perhaps the most fundamental type of life-history pattern to be investigated in terms of population consequences is that in which the individuals are assumed to produce their first offspring at the age of $\alpha$ "years" with the mean litter size being a constant, $b$. A second litter is produced at age $\alpha + 1$ and an additional litter in each subsequent interval of age out to, and including, age $\omega$. The total number of litters produced per individual is then $n = \omega - \alpha + 1$.

We then have, from (19),

$$e^{r\alpha} = b(1 + e^{-r} + e^{-2r} + \cdots + e^{-r(\omega-\alpha)}).$$

The expression in parentheses is a geometric progression the sum of which is $\dfrac{1 - e^{-rn}}{1 - e^{-r}}$. Consequently, the general implicit equation for $r$ under these conditions may be written

$$1 = e^{-r} + be^{-r\alpha} - be^{-r(n+\alpha)} \qquad (21)$$

which may be solved by trial and error by employing a table of the descending exponential function.

Alternative formulas corresponding to (21) may be obtained by the use of the Laplace transformation. In the case where reproduction is considered to occur as a series of regularly spaced impulses, this approach leads to formula (21). Another approach is to consider that $V_x = 0$ when $x < \alpha$, $V_x = b$ when $\alpha \leq x \leq \omega$, and $V_x = 0$ when $x > \omega$. The Laplace transformation of a step-function is then employed, leading to the formula

$$\frac{be^{-r\alpha}}{r} - \frac{be^{-r(\omega+1)}}{r} = 1. \qquad (22)$$

Formula (22) and formula (21) would be identical under the condition that $r + e^{-r} = 1$, which is approximately true when $r$ is small. If one desires more nearly to reconcile the continuous and discontinuous approaches in this case, he may note that in formula (21) he is finding the area under a "staircase-shaped" curve with the first vertical step located at $x = \alpha$, whereas in formula (22) he is finding the area under a straight line paralleling the slope of the staircase. It is apparent that the two areas will be more nearly identical if the straight line is started about one-half unit of time earlier. If we substitute in (22) $\alpha - \frac{1}{2}$ for $\alpha$ and $\omega - \frac{1}{2}$ for $\omega$ we obtain a formula which gives results for practical purposes identical with those obtained from (21). The formulas are about equally laborious to solve, and the writer has employed (21) for the following computations because of its more obvious relationship to the exact computational methods.

### POSSIBLE VALUES OF REPEATED REPRODUCTION (ITEROPARITY)

One of the most significant of the possible classifications of life histories rests on the distinction between species which reproduce only once in a lifetime and those in which the individuals reproduce repeatedly. This being the case, it is very surprising that there seem to be no general terms to describe these two conditions. The writer proposes to employ the term semelparity to describe the condition of multiplying only once in a lifetime, whether such multiplication involves fission, sporulation, or the production of eggs, seeds, or live young. Thus nearly all annual plants and animals, as well as many protozoa, bacteria, insects, and some perennial forms such as century plants and the Pacific salmon, are semelparous species. The contrasting condition will be referred to as iteroparity. Iteroparous species include some, such as small rodents, where only two or three litters of young are produced in a lifetime, and also various trees and tapeworms where a single individual may produce thousands of litters. The distinction between annual and perennial plants is doubtless the most familiar dichotomy separating semelparous and iteroparous species, but general consideration of the possible importance of these two distinct reproductive habits illustrates some points of ecological and evolutionary interest. For purposes of illustration we shall first consider cases where the time interval between reproductive efforts is fixed at one year.

Many plants and animals are annuals. This is true, for example, of many of the higher fungi and seed plants, of insects, and even of a few vertebrates. One feels intuitively that natural selection should favor the perennial reproductive habit because an individual producing seeds or young annually over a period of several years obviously has the potential ability to produce many more offspring then is the case when reproduction occurs but once. It is, therefore, a matter of some interest to examine the effect of iteroparity on the intrinsic rate of natural increase in order to see if we can find an explanation for the fact that repeated reproduction is not more general.

Let us consider first the case of an annual plant (or animal) maturing in a single summer and dying in the fall at the time of reproduction. We have seen earlier (formula 16, seq.) that if $b$ is the number of offspring produced by such an annual the intrinsic rate of increase would be the natural logarithm of $b$. We wish to determine by how much this would be increased if the individual were to survive for some additional years, producing $b$ offspring each year. Obviously, an annual species with a litter size of one (or an average of one female per litter in sexual species) would merely be replacing current population and no growth would be possible (ln 1 = 0); therefore, when the litter size is one the species must necessarily be iteroparous.

The most extreme case of iteroparity, and the one exhibiting the absolute maximum gain which could be achieved by this means, would be the biologically unattainable case of a species with each individual producing $b$ offspring each year for all eternity and with no mortality. In this case we have $\alpha = 1$ "year" and, since $\omega$ is indefinitely large, the final term $be^{-r(\omega+1)}$ in equation (21) becomes zero. Thus we have

$$r = \ln(b + 1) \qquad (23)$$

which is to be contrasted with $r = \ln(b)$ for the case of an annual. *For an annual species, the absolute gain in intrinsic population growth which could be achieved by changing to the perennial reproductive habit would be exactly equivalent to adding one individual to the average litter size.* Of course, this gain might be appreciable for a species unable to increase its average litter size. The extreme gain from iteroparity for a species with a litter size of two would be (ln 3/ln 2) or an increase of about 58 per cent, for a species with a litter size of four the increase would be about 16 per cent, but for one producing 30 offspring in a single reproductive period the extreme gain would amount to less than one per cent. It seems probable that a change in life history which would add one to the litter size would be more likely to occur than a change permitting repeated reproduction, which in many cases would necessitate adjustments to survive several seasons of dormancy. It appears that for the usual annual plants and insects with their relatively high fecundity any selective pressure for perennial reproduction as a means of increasing biotic potential must be negligible.

The above conclusion, which appears surprising when first encountered, arouses curiosity as to why iteroparity exists at all. Perhaps some species are physiologically unable to increase their fecundity. This must, however, be unusual and we are led to investigate whether the situation would be different for a species with a prolonged period of development preceding reproduction. One thinks immediately of the giant Sequoias which require a century to mature and begin reproduction but which, once started, produce large numbers of seeds biennially for centuries.

In order to investigate this question we may again compare the intrinsic rate of increase for a single reproduction with that corresponding to an infinite number of reproductions. This procedure will, of course, tend to overestimate the possible

gain from iteroparity although it will set an upper limit, and the first few reproductive periods so dominate the situation that even for very modest litter sizes there is a negligible difference between the results of a very limited number of reproductive periods and an infinite number.

For $\alpha$ not necessarily equal to one, formula (21) gives

$$b = e^{r\alpha} - e^{r(\alpha-1)}, \qquad (24)$$

an implicit equation for $r$ which must be solved by iterative means.

Fig. 2 was constructed from formula (24) to show the relationship between the age at which reproduction begins ($\alpha$) and the litter size ($b$) in terms of the possible gain in intrinsic rate of increase which could be achieved by iteroparity. The ordinates represent the proportionate increase in the value of $r$ which could be achieved by changing from a single reproductive effort at age $\alpha$ to an infinite number at ages $\alpha$, $\alpha + 1$, $\alpha + 2$, etc. The curves all slope upward, indicating that species with long pre-reproductive periods could gain more

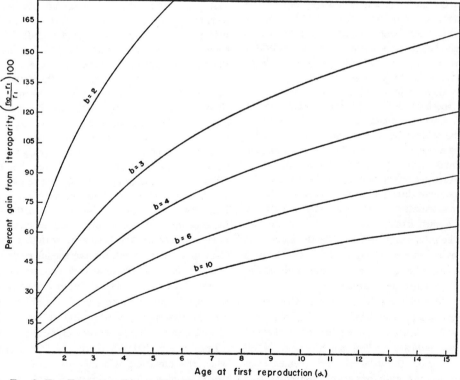

FIG. 2. THE EFFECTS OF LITTER SIZE ($b$) AND AGE AT MATURITY ($\alpha$) ON THE GAINS ATTAINABLE BY REPEATED REPRODUCTION

The litter size, $b$, is the number of female offspring per litter in the case of sexual species.

from iteroparity than forms which mature more rapidly. The tendency of the curves to flatten out with large values of $\alpha$, however, indicates that the advantages of repeated reproduction increase somewhat less rapidly as the pre-reproductive period is prolonged.

The relationship of iteroparity to litter size is clearly illustrated by Fig. 2. When the litter size is small, as shown by the curve for $b = 2$ (which would correspond to a litter of four individuals when the sex ratio is 1:1), iteroparity can yield important gains in biotic potential, and the possible gains are greater the longer maturity is delayed. The possible advantages diminish quite rapidly as litter size is increased, although it is clear that iteroparity as contrasted with a single reproductive effort would always add something to biotic potential.

Fig. 2 suggests that for semelparous species with large litters there would be very slight selective pressure in favor of adopting the iteroparous habit, and that for iteroparous species with large litters there would be little selection against loss of the iteroparous habit, especially in forms which mature rapidly. On the other hand, in a species which is established as iteroparous there would be slight selection for increasing fecundity or if litter size is relatively large, even against loss of fecundity. This perhaps explains the notoriously low level of viability among the seeds of many trees.

From these considerations it is obvious that when a species could benefit by an increase in the intrinsic rate of natural increase, this advantage might be achieved either by increasing fecundity in a single reproductive period or by adopting the iteroparous habit. A selective advantage would accrue to a mutation altering the life history in either of these directions, and it is an interesting field for speculation as to which type of mutation might be most likely to occur. In this connection it may be interesting to determine the amount of increase in litter size which, for a semelparous species, would be equivalent to retaining the initial litter size but becoming iteroparous.

From (6) we have seen that the intrinsic rate of increase for a semelparous species is defined by $e^{r\alpha} = b$. We wish to find an equivalence factor $(E)$ which will indicate by how much $b$ must be increased to make the value of $r$ for a semelparous species equal to that in formula (21) referring to an iteroparous species. By neglecting the last term in (21) so as to consider the most extreme case of

iteroparity and substituting $Eb = e^{r\alpha}$, we obtain

$$E = \frac{1}{1 - e^{-r}} = \frac{e^{r\alpha}}{b} \qquad (25)$$

where the value of $r$ must be obtained by solving equation (21). When $E$ is plotted against $\alpha$ for various values of $b$, as shown in Fig. 3, the resulting curves are essentially straight lines.

Fig. 3 illustrates some interesting points bearing on the life histories of organisms, such as tapeworms and many trees, which are iteroparous in addition to producing large litters. From the arrangement of Fig. 2 one might suspect that the iteroparous habit would provide very little advantage to a species that could produce a thousand or so offspring in a single litter, but Fig. 3 indicates that the selective value of iteroparity may be greatly increased when the pre-reproductive part of the life span is prolonged.

A mature tapeworm may produce daily a number of eggs on the order of 100,000 and may continue this for years (Allee et al., 1949, p. 272; Hyman, 1951). With so large a litter size one wonders if iteroparity in this case may not represent something other than an adaptation for increasing biotic potential. Perhaps the probability that a tapeworm egg (or a *Sequoia* seed) will become established may be increased by distributing the eggs more widely in time and space, and this could conceivably be the reason for the iteroparous habit. No definite answer to this problem is possible at present, but Fig. 3 indicates that a knowledge of the length of the life cycle from egg to egg is an essential datum for considering the question. In at least some tapeworms a larva may grow into a mature worm and reproduce at an age of 30 days (Wardle and McLeod, 1952). If this represented the length of the entire life cycle, then Fig. 3 indicates, assuming $b = 100,000$, that a threefold increase in litter size would be the equivalent of indefinite iteroparity. However, with the larval stage in a separate host, the average life cycle must be much longer. If the total cycle requires as much as 100 days, Fig. 3 shows that it would require almost an eight-fold increase in litter size (a single reproductive effort producing 790,167 offspring) to yield the same biotic potential as iteroparity with a litter size of 100,000. Obviously, it is possible, when the life cycle is sufficiently prolonged, to reach a point where any attainable increase in litter size would be less advantageous for potential population growth than a change to the iteroparous

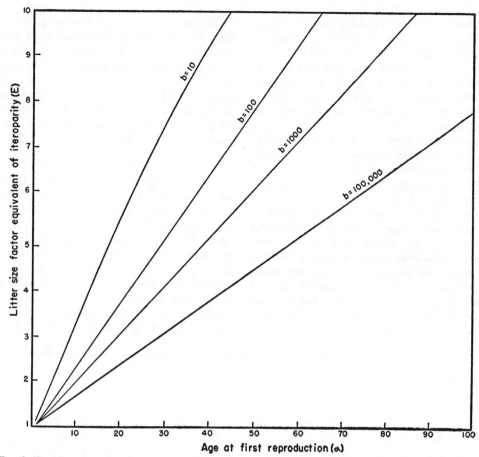

Fig. 3. The Changes in Litter Size which would be Required to Achieve in a Single Reproduction the Same Intrinsic Rate of Increase that would Result from Indefinite Iteroparity

*b* represents the litter size for an iteroparous species and the ordinate scale (*E*) represents the factor by which *b* would have to be multiplied to attain the same intrinsic rate of increase when each female produces only one litter in her lifetime.

habit. Hence a selective pressure can operate in favor of iteroparity even when the litter size is large. It is clear from Fig. 3, noting the greater slope of the lines representing smaller litter sizes, that in these cases the point will be reached more quickly at which the potential gains from iteroparity outweigh those attainable by increasing the litter size.

Man has a life cycle which is rather unusual in that it combines a long pre-reproductive period with a very small litter size; the very conditions under which iteroparity should be most advantageous. Everyone is, of course, aware that multiple births occur in man but with such a low frequency in the population that they are of negligible importance in population phenomena. It is also rather generally accepted that there is a hereditary basis for the production of multiple births. The question

arises as to why increased litter size should not become more common simply as a result of increased contributions to subsequent population resulting from the increase in biotic potential associated with large litters. It should be of interest, therefore, to determine how large a litter would have to be produced in a single reproductive effort to provide an intrinsic rate of increase equal to that resulting from three or more single births.

In the case of man we may rather confidently accept the value $b = \frac{1}{2}$ to signify that the average number of female offspring produced per human birth, and which will ultimately mature, is one-half. Accepting this value means that a mother must on the average produce two "litters" merely to replace herself (to give $r = 0$), so we shall examine the intrinsic rate of increase only for cases where $n$, the total number of births, is greater than two. To examine the maximum gain attainable by iteroparity we assume that successive births are spaced one year apart and obtain the value of $r$ from formula (21), employing different values of $n$ and $\alpha$. It is easily seen that the necessary litter size, say $b'$, to give the same value of $r$ by means of a single reproductive effort at age $\alpha$, would be precisely $e^{r\alpha}$.

The value of $r$ from formula (21) corresponding to three annual births beginning at age 12 is .0312. At the other extreme, if the first of the three births occurs at age 30 we obtain $r = .0131$. The corresponding values of $e^{r\alpha} = b'$ are successively 1.41 and 1.48. Under these conditions *it would require essentially a three-fold increase in litter size to achieve in one reproductive effort the same biotic potential as that obtained from three successive births.* The same conclusion is obtained when we consider larger numbers of births. In the case of man very little could be gained by increasing the litter size by any reasonable amount and it is probable that the biological risk involved in producing multiple

births is more than sufficient to outweigh the very slight gain in biotic potential which could be obtained by this means. This would not be the case if the pre-reproductive period was drastically shortened, so we see that even in the case of man there is an interaction of life-history phenomena such that the importance of any conceivable change can only be evaluated through consideration of the total life-history pattern.

### THE EFFECT OF TOTAL PROGENY NUMBER

In the preceding section we compared the two possible means by which an increase in total progeny number might lead to an increase in biotic potential. Our general conclusion was that the relative importance of changes in litter size and changes in the number of litters produced depends upon the rate of maturation. For species which mature early a modest change in litter size might be the equivalent of drastic changes in litter number but the possible value of iteroparity increases as the pre-reproductive part of the life span

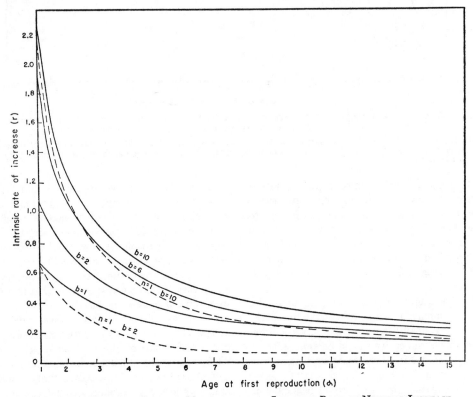

FIG. 4. THE EFFECT OF DELAYED MATURITY ON THE INTRINSIC RATE OF NATURAL INCREASE

The two broken lines represent semelparous species. The solid lines represent indefinitely iteroparous species where each female, after producing her first litter of size $b$, produces another similar litter in every succeeding time interval.

is lengthened. The importance of discovering the age at which reproduction begins has commonly been overlooked by students of natural history, hence it appears worthwhile to explore the matter further by examining the actual values of the intrinsic rate of natural increase corresponding to specified patterns of reproduction.

Fig. 4 was constructed from formula (21) to show, for several litter sizes, how the intrinsic rate of increase, $r$, is affected by lengthening the pre-reproductive period, $\alpha$. Both semelparous ($n = 1$) and indefinitely iteroparous ($n = \infty$) species are illustrated. The striking feature of Fig. 4 is the way in which the lines representing different litter sizes converge as $\alpha$ increases. This occurs whether there is a single reproduction per lifetime or an infinite number, hence it is a general phenomenon. This supplements our earlier conclusions by suggesting that in species where reproductive maturity is delayed there should be relatively slight selection pressure for increased litter size. Here we are referring, of course, to the effective litter size or number of offspring which are capable of maturing. In cases where early mortality is very high, as is known to be the case with many fishes, it might require a tremendous increase in fecundity to produce a very small increase in effective litter size, and such increases might not be very important from the population standpoint. For example, a semelparous species reproducing at age 20 and with an effective litter size of 10 would have, $r = 0.120$. A ten-fold increase in litter size, to $b = 100$, would give $r = 0.231$ or an increase in biotic potential of 92 per cent. Another ten-fold increase to $b = 1000$ would give $r = 0.345$, or a gain of 50 per cent. The diminishing returns attainable by increasing litter size are obvious. For an iteroparous species reproducing first at age 20 and thereafter in each subsequent time interval, the increase in effective litter size from 10 to 100 would give only a 50 per cent increase in biotic potential and a further ten-fold increase in litter size would increase $r$ by only another 35 per cent. In late-maturing species the litter size must be great enough to make it highly probable that *some* of the progeny will mature, but any further increases in fecundity will yield rapidly diminishing returns.

It is also clear from Fig. 4 that for any fixed litter size the biotic potential could be increased by shortening the period of maturation. Any specified amount of decrease in the pre-reproductive period will, however, be most effective for species where this part of the life span is already short.

Fig. 5 illustrates the way in which the two factors of length of the pre-reproductive part of the life span ($\alpha$) and the number of offspring produced interact to determine the intrinsic rate of natural increase. These values were also computed from formula (21), in this case considering the litter size, $b$, as a constant with the value one-half. The figure then applies to species which, like man, produce one offspring at a time and where one-half of these offspring are females. Under these conditions it obviously requires two births just to replace the parents, but the population consequences of producing more than two offspring per lifetime vary tremendously with the age at which reproduction begins.

The female of the extinct passenger pigeon presumably produced her first brood consisting of a single egg at the age of one year. From the steep slope of the line representing $\alpha = 1$ in Fig. 5 it is clear that, beyond the minimum of two eggs per average female, several additional eggs produced in successive years would each add very appreciably to the value of $r$. Accordingly, a relatively slight reduction of the life expectancy for such a species might greatly reduce the biotic potential. The flattening out of the curves in Fig. 5 again illustrates the fact that each litter contributes less to potential population growth than the one preceding it. However, in a case such as that of the passenger pigeon even the seventh and eighth annual "litters" would add appreciable increments to the value of $r$.

Fig. 5 also shows that as the age at maturity increases the possible gains in biotic potential attainable by producing many offspring rapidly diminish. When $\alpha = 3$, as in the economically important fur-seal, each pup contributes much less to biotic potential than was the case for the eggs of the passenger pigeon. Nevertheless, it is apparent from the figure that if the life expectancy for females should be reduced to seven or eight years (corresponding to the fifth or sixth pup), or less, the species would be in a vulnerable position. The curve is steep in this portion of the graph and relatively slight changes in average longevity could produce disproportionately large population effects.

The lowest curves in Fig. 5 represent ages at maturity falling within the possible range for man. The curves come close together as $\alpha$ increases, so that in this range a change of a year or two in the age at which reproduction begins is less significant than in the case of a species that matures more

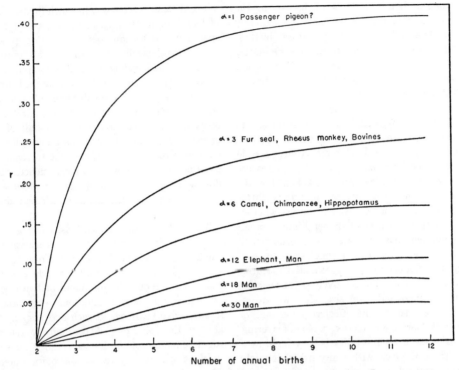

FIG. 5. THE EFFECTS OF PROGENY NUMBER ON THE INTRINSIC RATE OF NATURAL INCREASE WHEN THE LITTER SIZE IS ONE ($b = \frac{1}{2}$)

The ordinate scale shows the intrinsic rate of increase for species which produce an average of one-half female offspring per litter. For any given total progeny number, the intrinsic rate ($r$) is seen to be greatly affected by the age ($\alpha$) at which the first offspring is produced.

rapidly. Furthermore, the curves flatten out rapidly so that families which are very large by ordinary standards actually contribute little more to potential population growth or to future population than do families of quite moderate size. As an explicit illustration consider the intrinsic rate of increase which would result if, on the average, human females produced their first offspring at the age of 20 and had a total of five children spaced at one-year intervals. In this case we would have $r = 0.042$. If, on the other hand, we assume that, instead of producing only five children, the females could live forever producing a child each year we would obtain $r = 0.0887$. Under these conditions we conclude that in terms of biotic potential five children are almost one-half (actually 47 per cent) the equivalent of an infinite number. With larger values of $\alpha$ the effect of very large families would be even further reduced. From these considerations the writer feels that human biologists, as well as other natural historians, often overemphasize the importance of total number of progeny while underestimating the significance of the age at which reproduction begins. It is impossible to conclude that one segment of the population is contributing more to future population than is some other segment without examining the total life-history pattern. Age at marriage could, in studying human populations, be a more significant datum than total family size.

The foregoing discussion suggests that a species such as man which is characterized by a long period of maturation and a small litter size can exhibit considerable variability in the details of its life history without greatly affecting the intrinsic rate of natural increase. The population consequences to be anticipated if the average age at which reproduction begins were to be altered by a few years or if the average number of progeny per female were slightly altered are much less striking than is the case for many other species. This implies that the intrinsic rate of increase should be relatively constant over the range of possible variations in the life-history features for man.

Such a conclusion would seem to be of both practical and theoretical interest and to merit closer examination.

The intrinsic rate of increase for man would be the rate of compound interest at which a human population, unrestrained by environmental resistance, would grow. We have already noted that Franklin (1751) estimated that a human population could double in 20 years and that this would correspond to $r = .035$. Malthus (1798) estimated that an unrestrained human population such as that of the United States at that time could double in 25 years. Malthus' estimate corresponds to $r = .0277$ which is remarkably close to the value of $r = .0287$ obtained by Lotka (1927) using much more refined methods for estimating the rate of increase prevailing in 1790 in the United States. Pearl and Reed (1920) fitted a logistic curve to the population figures for the United States, and their equation gives the value $r = .03134$. Additional examples of estimates based on empirical data could be given, but these are sufficient to suggest that the value of the intrinsic rate of increase for man is not far from 0.03.

Fig. 6 was constructed from formula (21) in order to examine the question whether or not the life-history features of man would actually lead us to anticipate the approximate value, $r = 0.03$. Fig. 6 suggests rather definitely that the value $r = 0.02$ is too low, since it falls well below the obvious reproductive capabilities of humans. If females, on the average, had their first child at the age of 12 years (which is possible, cf. Pearl, 1930, p. 223) it would require an average of 2.6 surviving annual births per female to correspond to the rate $r = .02$. This curve is quite flat, so that if the first birth was delayed until the age of 20 years, which seems to be roughly the beginning of the semi-decade of maximum human fertility (Pearl, 1939), three annual births would still be adequate to give $r = .02$. Even if the first birth is delayed until the age of 28 years, this intrinsic rate of increase calls

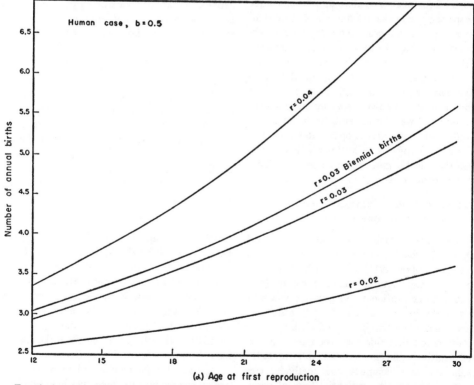

FIG. 6. AVERAGE REPRODUCTIVE PERFORMANCES REQUIRED TO GIVE SPECIFIED VALUES OF $r$, THE INTRINSIC RATE OF NATURAL INCREASE, IN HUMAN POPULATIONS

Assuming the average number of female offspring per human birth to be one-half ($b = 0.5$), this graph shows the extent to which total progeny number would have to be altered to maintain a specified intrinsic rate of increase while shifting the age at which reproduction begins. The figure also makes it possible to estimate the intrinsic rate of increase for a population when the average reproductive performance per female is known.

for an average progeny number of only 3.5. Clearly, man can easily exceed this average level of performance. On the other hand, the value $r = .04$ seems to require reproductive performance which would be astonishingly high as an average condition. If the first birth occurred when the mother was aged 13 years, an average of 3.5 children per female would suffice to give $r = .04$. However, the curve turns upward and if the first birth was delayed until the age of 20 it would require an average of 4.8 children to obtain this value. A delay of one more year, to the age of 21 for the first child, would increase the necessary mean progeny number to 5.0, while six children would be necessary if the first birth came when the mother was 25 years old. This intrinsic rate of increase then seems to call for exceptional rather than average reproductive performance, and the writer believes that Fig. 6 would lead us to expect that the intrinsic rate of increase for man lies between the limits .02 and .04 and might be estimated at about .03. Of course, the figure makes no allowance for mortality or for spacing the births at intervals of more than one year, so in actual cases the reproductive performance would have to be somewhat greater than indicated. The interval between births, however, is less critical than might be anticipated. The reproductive performances necessary to give $r = .03$ are shown both for one-year spacing and for two-year spacing between births and, to the writer, at least, either of these curves appears to represent a more reasonable picture of average human reproduction than do the cases representing the higher and lower intrinsic rates of increase.

### THE POPULATION BIRTH-RATE AS A CONSEQUENCE OF LIFE-HISTORY PHENOMENA

We have noted earlier formulas (4) and (5) which were originally derived by Lotka (1907a, b; Sharpe and Lotka, 1911) and which show that when life-history features remain constant from generation to generation the population will ultimately settle down to a "fixed" or "stable" age distribution and will exhibit a fixed birth rate. We have also noted that this conclusion could be expected intuitively and can be obtained (formula 18) from discontinuous computational methods, once it is established that the potential form of population growth is a geometric progression. These potential consequences appear to provide the best justification for studying the life histories of various species, yet when such studies are conducted

it is common practice not to attempt any interpretation in terms of population phenomena.

It is evident from formulas (3), (4), and (5) that the birth rate and the stable age distribution are tied together with the intrinsic rate of increase and that any extensive discussion of the way in which changes in life-history features would affect these population features might repeat many of the points already covered. Consequently, we shall here note very briefly the relationships between life-history features and the resultant phenomena of birth rates and age structure.

If we consider a "closed" population, which changes in size only through the processes of birth and death, it is apparent that the intrinsic rate of increase, $r$, in formula (1), $\dfrac{dP}{dx} = rP$, must represent the difference between the instantaneous birth rate and the instantaneous death rate. In practice, however, we are more interested in a finite rate of population change. If we employ formula (1') to express the rate of population growth and consider that the changes result entirely from the birth rate ($BR$) and the death rate ($DR$), we obtain:

$$BR - DR = \frac{P_{x+1} - P_x}{P_x} = e^r - 1. \quad (26)$$

A birth rate, $\beta$, appropriate to this approach has already been defined by formula (18). However, because we are dealing with finite time intervals the $B_x$ births regarded as occurring at the beginning of some time interval, $T_x$, should properly be credited to the $P_{x-1}$ individuals living in the previous time interval. The birth rate would, therefore, be:

$$BR = e^r \beta. \quad (27)$$

On the other hand, the death rate should properly be the ratio of the $D_x$ deaths in interval $T_x$ to the total population exposed to the risk of death; that is $D_x/P_x$. Hence the simple relationship of formulas (5) and (26) can be misleading, especially when there is a rapid population turnover. For example, the birth rate $\beta$ in Lotka's formula (5) is by definition identical with $c_0$, the fraction of the population aged between zero and one. Consequently $\beta$ can never exceed unity no matter how many offspring are on the average produced per individual during a time interval.

In practical population problems the crude birth rate is often observed and employed as a criterion of the state of the population. This practice can be misleading, especially in comparing species which differ widely in their life-history features. It would be redundant to undertake a detailed analysis of the way in which life-history phenomena affect the crude birth rate because, as is evident from formulas (5), (26), and (27), any change which affects the value of $r$ also affects the population birth-rate. However, the birth rate is subject to additional influences and these may be briefly examined.

The methods used in computing the value of $r$ (formulas 17, 21, and 22) have involved survivorship only out to the age $\omega$ at which reproduction ceases. In species having a post-reproductive part of the life span, the crude birth rate corresponding to a given value of $r$ will be reduced simply because post-reproductive individuals accumulate and are counted as part of the population on which the computations are based. It is clear, therefore, that

any increase in longevity ($\lambda$) which is not accompanied by an increase in $\omega$ will tend to lower the observed birth rate; conversely, the birth rate must affect the age structure of the population.

If the maximum longevity for a species is $\lambda$, a continued birth rate of $1/\lambda$ would just suffice to leave a replacement behind at the time each individual dies. Hence $1/\lambda$ represents an absolute minimum for a steady birth rate which is capable of maintaining the population. For example, if it were possible to keep every human female alive for 100 years a birth rate as low as 0.01 or 10 births per thousand population per annum (assuming $\frac{1}{2}$ of the offspring to be females), could theoretically suffice for population maintenance. However, for human females the value of $\omega$ is not much beyond 40 years; in general, if a female has not produced a replacement by the age of 40 she is not going to do so. The latter consideration might lead one to

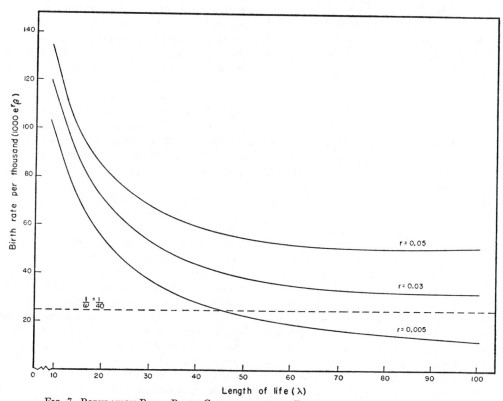

FIG. 7. POPULATION BIRTH RATES CORRESPONDING TO DIFFERENT LIFE HISTORY PATTERNS

The figure shows that the intrinsic rate of natural increase ($r$), the birth rate, and mean longevity ($\lambda$) are all interdependent. The broken line represents the minimum birth rate which would maintain a population if females did not survive beyond the age of 40 "years," which is here used as an estimate of the normal age ($\omega$) at which reproduction is concluded. As longevity is increased, slow population growth becomes possible even when birth rates fall below $1/\omega$. Such low birth rates, however, have sometimes caused unwarranted concern about excessive population increase when abnormal conditions have temporarily reduced the death rate so that there is a large excess of births over deaths.

designate as a minimum maintenance birth rate the value $1/\omega$, or 0.025 in the case of man. But it is clear from the foregoing sections that offspring produced prior to the time that a female reaches the age of 40 will already have begun to "accumulate interest" before the mother can reach the age of 100. The compound interest nature of potential population growth complicates the relationship between birth rate and life-history phenomena and makes it conceivable that populations of species where $\lambda > \omega$ could even continue to grow while exhibiting birth rates lower than $1/\omega$.

No end of interesting combinations of birth rates, death rates, and life-history phenomena might merit consideration, but a single simple example will be selected here to illustrate the general relationship between changing longevity and population birth-rates. If we assume, as before, a physiological type of survivorship such that each individual that is born lives to attain its $\lambda$th birthday but dies before reaching the age of $\lambda + 1$, we can sum the right-hand side of formula (19) as a geometric progression and combine this with formula (27) to obtain the following expression for the population birth rate ($BR$):

$$BR = e^r\beta = \frac{e^r - 1}{1 - e^{-r\lambda}}. \qquad (28)$$

Formula (28) shows, as would be expected, that as longevity ($\lambda$) is increased, with the other life-history features remaining unchanged, the birth rate will fall and approach as a limit the value $e^r - 1$, which is in accord with (26) when the death rate is set equal to zero.

Fig. 7 was constructed from formula (28) to illustrate the interrelations between $BR$, $r$, and $\lambda$ within a range of values of life history features roughly applicable to man. The condition for a stationary population would, of course, correspond to $r = 0$, while all positive values of $r$ correspond to growing populations. $r$ must become negative when the birth rate falls below $1/\lambda$, and it will be noted that the birth rates below about 20 per thousand which are sometimes observed in human populations (see tabulation in Allee et al., 1949, p. 288) must, unless they represent abnormal temporary phenomena, correspond to populations with very low potential growth rates. The curve for $r = .005$, in fact, does not differ greatly from $1/\lambda$. The curves in Fig. 7 flatten out rapidly for large values of $\lambda$, so that drastic and generally unattainable increases in longevity would be re-

quired to make such low birth rates compatible with appreciable population growth.

Looking at these relationships from a different point of view, Fig. 7 shows that a reduction in longevity, such as might result from reducing the life expectancy of game animals, can be expected to result in an increased birth rate even if the intrinsic rate of increase is unchanged. It does not seem worthwhile at present to attempt a quantitative estimate of these relationships because the assumption of a physiological type of survivorship curve is probably not even approximately true for game animals. When more realistic estimates of survivorship are available, however, the type of relationship illustrated in Fig. 7 may assume practical importance.

### THE STABLE AGE DISTRIBUTION

The age structure of a population often is a matter of considerable practical concern. In economically valuable species such as timber, game animals, and commercial fishes certain age classes are more valuable than others, and it would be desirable to increase the proportion of the most valuable age classes in a population. Similarly, certain age classes of noxious organisms may be more destructive than others and the relative numbers of these destructive individuals will be governed by life-history phenomena which may conceivably be subject to alteration by control measures. In human populations, also, it is sometimes a matter of concern that the proportion of the population falling within the age limits most suitable for physical labor and military service seems to be below optimum. An article in the New York *Times* for September 24, 1950, headed "population shift in France traced—Study finds too many aged and very young in relation to total of workers" illustrates the potential importance of a knowledge of the age structure of populations.

The mathematical basis for relating the age structure of a population to life-history features was established in Lotka's first paper on population analysis (1907); and in the same year Sundbärg (1907) reached the conclusion that a human population reveals its condition (tendency to grow or decline) through its age structure. These important conclusions have not been sufficiently noted by ecologists. When the mortality factors affecting a population are altered either through natural environmental changes or through human exploitation or attempts at control there will in general result a change in the age structure of the population, and this may be observable even before changes in population size or in birth rates provide evidence of the consequences of the changed mortality factors. The subject of age structure is a large and difficult one because the various combinations of life-history features, birth rates, death rates, and age structure are analogous to a multi-dimensional figure where a change imposed in any one feature induces changes in all of the others. The subject has been considered most in connection with human populations, and some empirical generalizations have been obtained which may profitably be examined by means of the computational methods we have been employing. For the purpose of illustrating the general character of the relationships involved, one species will serve as well as another.

For illustrative purposes we may proceed as in the preceding sections and consider the stable age distribution for cases where survivorship is of the physiological type. Letting $c_x$ represent the fraction of the population aged between $x$ and $x + 1$, we may employ formulas (5) and (28) directly to obtain, for $x < \lambda$:

$$c_x = \frac{e^{-rx}(1 - e^r)}{1 - e^{-r\lambda}}. \tag{29}$$

From formula (29) it is apparent that if the extreme longevity for a population is altered without changing the intrinsic rate of increase, the effect on the age structure will be of a very simple type. An increase in longevity from $\lambda_1$ to $\lambda_2$ will simply reduce the proportion of the population in each age category below $\lambda_1$ by the constant proportion $\frac{1 - e^{-r\lambda_1}}{1 - e^{-r\lambda_2}}$. Consequently, the effect will be most noticeable on the youngest age classes, because these are the largest classes.

Changes in the value of $r$ affect the stable age distribution in a more complex way than do changes in $\lambda$, although the general result of increasing the value of $r$ will be to increase the proportion of young in the population, with a corresponding decrease in the proportion of older individuals. Fig. 8 illustrates this effect for three values of $r$,

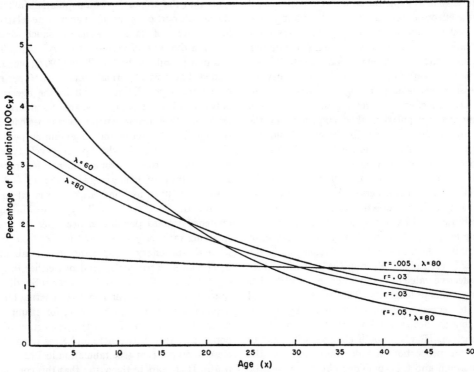

FIG. 8. THE STABLE AGE DISTRIBUTION, OR PROPORTION OF THE POPULATION FALLING WITHIN EACH INTERVAL OF AGE, IS SHOWN HERE AS A FUNCTION OF THE INTRINSIC RATE OF INCREASE ($r$) AND THE LENGTH OF LIFE ($\lambda$)

These relationships have important ecological correlaries. See text for a discussion relating these to the "optimum yield" problem.

assuming that λ in formula (29) remains constant at 80 "years."

The way in which population age-structure is affected by changes in the value of $r$ and λ, as illustrated by formula (29) and Fig. 8, permits some qualitative conclusions which are of interest in connection with the "optimum yield problem" (for discussion, see Allee et al., 1949, p. 377). If man (or some other species) begins exploitation of a previously unexploited population, the age structure will be affected in a definite manner. An obvious result of increased predation will be to decrease the average longevity, corresponding to a decrease in λ. We have seen earlier (Fig. 7) that this will ordinarily have the effect of increasing the population birth rate, and Fig. 8 and formula (29) show that another effect will be to increase the proportion of young in the population, the very youngest age classes being most affected. However, the increased mortality may also affect the value of $r$. If the population is initially in equilibrium with the capacity of its environment, its total life history pattern will be adjusted to the effective value, $r = 0$. If exploitation is not too intense, it has the effect of making additional environmental resources available to the surviving members of the population and thus of stimulating population increase; the population "compensates" (see Errington, 1946) for the increased mortality by increasing the value of $r$. Fig. 8 shows that this will have the effect of increasing the proportion of young in the population, thus supplementing the effect of exploitation on λ. On the other hand, the increase in $r$ will have the effect of reducing the proportion of aged individuals in opposition to the effect of reduced λ which is to increase all of the age classes which still persist. It seems clear that the most obvious population consequence of such exploitation will be to increase the proportion of young members of the population. If predation or exploitation becomes still more intense, as in the case of "overfishing" (Russell, 1942), it will reduce the effective value of $r$, and, of course, still further reduce average longevity. The decrease in $r$ will tend to decrease the proportion of young individuals, but the decrease in λ will tend to increase this proportion. However, both changes will tend to raise the proportion of older individuals in the population, and this combined effect can then be expected to be the most obvious corollary of over-fishing. These conclusions, of course, greatly over-simplify a complex phenomenon. In order to make quantitative estimates of these effects it would be necessary to have detailed information about the life-history features, especially survivorship under the conditions of increased predation. Nevertheless, these qualitative conclusions show the type of effect to be expected when populations are subjected to increased predation, and they suggest that observations of the changes in the age structure of populations may provide valuable evidence of over-exploitation, or, from the opposite point of view, of the effectiveness of control measures. Bodenheimer (1938) comments on the fact that ecologists have neglected this important subject.

From Fig. 8 it will be noticed that changes in life-history features produce their greatest effects on the extreme age classes, whereas the curves representing different patterns are close together in the "middle" age range. The same phenomenon is evident, for example, in a graph (Fig. 27) reproduced by Dublin, Lotka, and Spiegelman (1949) from Lotka (1931) to show the age structure of human populations corresponding to stationary, increasing, and decreasing populations. This suggests that the proportion of a population falling in the middle portion of the life span may be relatively independent of factors which produce drastic shifts in the ratio of very old to very young. This was first postulated by Sundbärg (1907), who concluded that it was "normal" for about 50 per cent of a human population to fall in the age range between 15 years and 50 years. Sundbärg distinguishes three primary population types based on the age distribution of the remaining 50 per cent of the population. In the "progressive" type of population there is a strong tendency for increase and the ratio of young (aged under 15) to old (aged over 50) is, by Sundbärg's criteria, about 40 to 10. In the "regressive" type, exhibiting a tendency toward population decrease, the corresponding ratio of young to old is about 20 to 30, while a "stationary" type with the ratio about 33 to 17 shows no particular tendency either to grow or to decrease. When first encountered Sundbärg's conclusion appears surprising, but in actual human populations differing as radically, for example, as those of Sweden and India, the proportion of the population aged between 15 and 50 is remarkably close to 50 per cent (see tabulation in Pearl, 1946, p. 78). It appears to the writer that this conclusion should be of great interest to students of human populations. The age class between 15 and 50 years includes the bulk of the workers and persons of military age, and Sundbärg's conclusion implies that the size of this class relative to the remainder of the population must be determined by life-history features which cannot readily be deliberately controlled.

For other species also, the life span may be meaningfully divided into three primary age classes, pre-reproductive (aged 0 to $\alpha$), reproductive (aged $\alpha$ to $\omega$), and post-reproductive (aged $\omega$ to $\lambda$), which differ considerably in their biological significance. If we continue with our assumption of physiological survivorship we can obtain the relative sizes of these three age classes directly from formula (29), and Sundbärg's generalization offers an interesting empirical pattern with which to compare our results. For the relative sizes of the three fundamental age classes formula (29) gives:

$$
\begin{aligned}
\text{Pre-reproductive} &= \frac{1 - e^{-r\alpha}}{1 - e^{-r\lambda}} \\[2mm]
\text{Reproductive} &= \frac{e^{-r\alpha} - e^{-r\omega}}{1 - e^{-r\lambda}} \\[2mm]
\text{Post-reproductive} &= \frac{e^{-r\omega} - e^{-r\lambda}}{1 - e^{-r\lambda}}
\end{aligned}
\right\} \quad (30)
$$

By putting $\alpha = 15$ and $\omega = 50$, we may examine the relationship between $r$ and $\lambda$ for Sundbärg's primary population types.

The generalization that about 50 per cent of a human population normally falls in the age range from 15 to 50 is in accord with formulas (30). When $r = .03$ the value of $\lambda$ to give a stable age distribution with just 50 per cent in the middle age range would be 59 years, but an increase in longevity to 85 years would only reduce this class to 45 per cent of the population. The same general conclusion applies when $r$ is small. The values $r = .005$ and $\lambda = 63$ years correspond to 55 per cent aged 15 to 50 years, and $\lambda$ would have to be increased to 81 years to reduce this to 45 per cent. It appears that over the usual range of values of human longevity and potential population growth Sundbärg's generalization is very good. This is shown graphically in Fig. 9. It is noteworthy that when the length of life is about 70 years, Sundbärg's generalization holds over a wide range of values of $r$. In other words, this ratio of "middle-aged" to total population is quite insensitive to changes in other life history features.

Figure 9 illustrates Sundbärg's population criteria for values of $r > 0$. It is clear that the

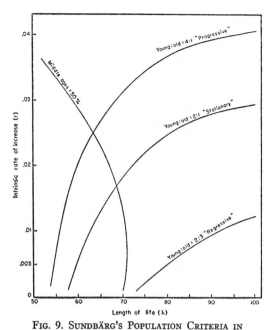

Fig. 9. Sundbärg's Population Criteria in Relation to Life-History Features

The "middle age" range here consists of individuals aged 15 years to 50 years.

"regressive" type of population structure is not consistent with populations possessing a strong tendency to increase and, in fact, for usual longevity figures, will ordinarily correspond to decreasing populations ($r < 0$). On the other hand, the "progressive" type of structure does correspond to large values of $r$ even when $\lambda$ is not particularly large. The "stationary" type of population structure is less well defined. Any population for which the life-history features correspond to $r > 0$ will tend to grow, and the ratio of two "old" to one "young" can correspond to a large value of $r$ when $\lambda$ is large. The value of $r$ is, of course, independent of the length of the post-reproductive part of the life span, whereas the age structure is not. For any given value of $r$, which is determined by the life-history features of individuals aged below $\omega$, the effect of an increase in longevity will be to decrease the proportion of young and, to a lesser extent, the proportion of reproductive members of the population.

At first glance, the type of interactions shown in Fig. 9 might suggest that if the age structure of a population were artificially shifted in the "regressive" direction, for example, through migration or improvements in public health, there would result a reduction in the value of $r$. This, however, is not the case, since $r$ is completely determined by life-history events occurring before age $\omega$. Sharpe and Lotka (1911) showed that a characteristic of the "stable" age distribution is the fact that it will become reestablished after temporary displacements. However, practical problems arise in analyzing actual populations because phenomena such as birth rates and death rates may give a very misleading picture of population trends when the age structure is displaced from the stable type and has not yet had time to reestablish a stable age distribution. From Fig. 7 we have noted that in human populations birth rates on the order of 20 per thousand per annum would in general be little more than sufficient to maintain a population. But if the age distribution is displaced from the stable type in the direction of increased frequency of young individuals, the death rate may be temporarily reduced, so that there is a great excess of births over deaths and the population can grow temporarily even if the age-specific birth rates are too low to maintain the population permanently at a constant size. Under these conditions the population is "aging," and in human populations this phenomenon has a number of interesting and important corollaries (see Dublin, Lotka, and Spiegelman, 1949). Fisher (1930) has considered the problem in a more general sense, noting that the apparent value of $r$ given by formula (3) will be incorrect when the age structure is displaced. Fisher suggests the possibility of measuring population size not in terms of the number of individuals present but in terms of "reproductive value," where the "value" of an individual represents his remaining potentialities for contributing to the ancestry of future generations. Some such approach has great potential value for ecological studies of natural populations, but its possibilities in this direction seem not yet to have been explored.

### EMPIRICAL APPLICATIONS

In the preceding sections we have been concerned with the influence of specific life-history patterns on the characteristics of populations. In order to examine these effects we have made simplifying assumptions by regarding some of the life-history features as fixed in a certain way while we examined the results of varying other features. While this procedure oversimplifies the biological situation as it exists in actual populations, the writer regards it as a sound way of investigating the meaning of life-history features. The same general attitude may be traced back to Robert Wallace (1753) in his book which profoundly influenced Malthus. Wallace pointed out that "mankind do not actually propagate according to the rules in our tables, or any other constant rule ..." but he emphasized that tables of potential population growth are still valuable because they permit us to evaluate the influences restraining population growth.

Wallace, then, was a pioneer in appreciating the potential value of comparisons between empirical and theoretical population phenomena. In modern actuarial practice, population data are subjected to involved mathematical treatments which are sometimes considered to represent biological laws and at other times to be merely empirical equations, but which, in any case, are known to yield results of practical value. In the words of Elston (1923, p. 68):

"... it seems to me that even though there be governing causes of mortality that may result in a true law of mortality, any group of lives studied is so heterogeneous, due to differences in occupation, climate, sanitary conditions, race, physical characteristics, etc., that any formula must in practice be considered to be merely a generalization of what is actually happening."

The number of different combinations of life-history features of the type we have been discussing is essentially infinite, and it is out of the question to make detailed examinations of any great proportion of these from the theoretical standpoint. However, we have seen that certain population features, such as the prevailing age distribution and the intrinsic rate of increase, summarize a great deal of information about the potentialities of the population and its relationship to its particular and immediate environment. As mentioned earlier, the recent ecological literature demonstrates that ecologists are becoming interested in determining such features as the intrinsic rate of increase for non-human populations. These computations may have practical value in dealing with valuable or noxious species, and they possess great theoretical interest for ecologists. For example, the logistic equation has been widely employed to represent population growth in a variety of organisms (Allee et al., 1949; Pearl, 1927); and it has also been attacked (Yule, 1925; and succeeding discussion, Gray, 1929; Hogben, 1931; Smith, 1952), on the grounds that it is too versatile and can be made to fit empirical data that might arise from entirely different "laws" of population growth. This criticism is, of course, directed at the fact that the curve-fitter has three arbitrary constants at his disposal in seeking to obtain a good fit. One of these constants is $r$, the intrinsic rate of increase. The grounds for accepting or rejecting the logistic equation as a law of population growth (or for seeking some other law) would be greatly strengthened if the value of $r$ was computed directly from observed life-history features and independently of the data on population size.

The computational methods employed in the preceding sections suggest several possible ways of computing the value of $r$ from empirical life-history data. The usual procedure for such computations has been a tedious one based on formula (3) (see Lotka's appendix to Dublin and Lotka, 1925), although Birch (1948) employed formula (17) as an approximation to (3) for his computations. The methods discussed in the preceding sections suggest that a logical procedure for obtaining an empirical value of $r$ would be to observe age-specific birth rates and survivorship under the environmental conditions of interest, and from these to write a "generation law" so that formula (11) can be employed. The single positive root of (11) is $e^r$ and this can be estimated to any desired degree of accuracy without great difficulty even for species where the reproductive life is prolonged. When one is actually solving equation (11) it is strikingly brought to one's attention that the final terms representing reproduction in later life are relatively unimportant in influencing the value of $r$. This once again reinforces our conclusion that reproduction in early life is of overwhelming importance from the population standpoint, and should be much more carefully observed in field and laboratory studies than has usually been the case.

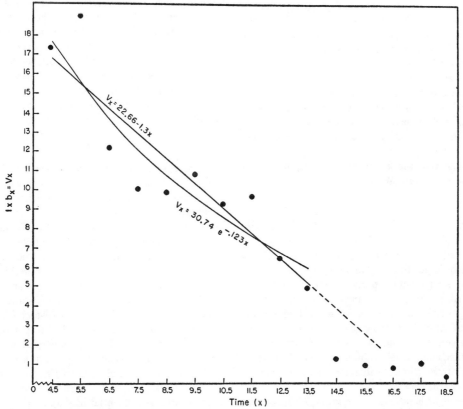

FIG. 10. A STRAIGHT LINE AND AN EXPONENTIAL FUNCTION FITTED TO THE DATA OF BIRCH (1948)

These data are suitable only for illustrating computational methods. Birch observed the age-specific fecundity rates ($b_x$) for the rice weevil *Calandra oryzae* living under constant conditions of temperature and moisture. He did not observe survivorship ($l_x$) but carried over the shape of the survivorship curve from the flour beetle *Tribolium confusum*. The black dots represent the product $l_x b_x$.

An alternative approach for obtaining empirical values of $r$ consists of fitting the $V_x$ ($= l_x b_x$) values with mathematical curves of types which make it possible either to obtain the sum of the series on the right-hand side of equation (19) or to employ Laplace transformations to solve equations (3) or (20) by simple iterative methods. Different formulas could be fitted to different sections of the $V_x$ curve, and, when good fits can be obtained with combinations of straight lines, step-functions, exponential functions, and other simple formulas, this procedure will often lead to easy ways of solving for $r$. As a very simple example of this procedure we may consider the data of Birch (1948), for which he employed formula (17) and, by computations which are given in detail in his paper, obtained the value $r = 0.762$.

The $V_x$ data employed by Birch are shown graphically in Fig. 10 by means of the black dots. The two curves, a straight line and a simple exponential function, were fitted by the method of least squares to the values up to $x = 13.5$. Neither of the functions gives an extremely good fit to the observed data, but, on the other hand, one may question whether the irregularities in the empirical data are not partly artifacts which should be smoothed out when one is attempting to estimate the value of $r$ for a species. In any case, it appears worthwhile to compare Birch's value of $r = .762$ with that obtained by use of the empirically fitted curves.

Using first the exponential curve, if we set $V_x = K e^{ax}$, formula (19) may be written in the form:

$$K e^{\alpha(a-r)} = \frac{1 - e^{a-r}}{1 - e^{n(a-r)}}. \qquad (31)$$

When reproduction occurs several times, so that $n$ is fairly large, the denominator in equation (31) becomes for practical purposes unity and may be ignored. In this case we have $\alpha = 4.5$, $K = 30.74$, $a = -.123$, and $n = 9$, so we will ignore the denominator. The equation is easily solved by iterative means, using a table of the exponential function, and the value obtained is $r = .758$, which differs from Birch's value by about one-half of one per cent.

The right-hand side of equation (19) can also be summed for the linear case where $V_x = a + bx$, but in this case the Laplace transformation employed with formula (3) yields a slightly simpler equation:

$$\frac{ar + b}{r^2} = e^{r\alpha}. \qquad (32)$$

Putting $a = 22.66$, $\alpha = 4.5$, and $b = -1.3$ in equation (32), and solving by iterative means we obtain $r = .742$, which differs from Birch's value by nearly three per cent, although this seems to be good agreement in view of the crude approximations employed.

In many practical applications dealing with natural and experimental populations some approximation to the value of $r$ such as those presented above may be all that can be justified by the accuracy of the data. The estimate of $r$ could undoubtedly be improved by fitting different portions of the $V_x$ curve with different functions. Another refinement suggested by observations presented earlier in this paper would be to fit the empirical curves by a method which would give greater weight to the earlier points which have more influence on the value of $r$ than do the later points. Any detailed discussion of these empirical applications would be out of place in the context of the present paper. The writer, however, anticipates that ecologists will in the future devote more attention to the interrelations of life-history features and population phenomena, and it is to be hoped that some of the approaches which have been indicated will accelerate trends in this direction.

SUMMARY

Living species exhibit a great diversity of patterns of such life-history features as total fecundity, maximum longevity, and statistical age schedules of reproduction and death. Corresponding to every possible such pattern of life-history phenomena there is a definitely determined set of population consequences which would ultimately result from adherence to the specified life history. The birth rate, the death rate, and the age composition of the population, as well as its ability to grow, are consequences of the life-history features of the individual organisms. These population phenomena may be related in numerous ways to the ability of the species to survive in a changed physical environment or in competition with other species. Hence it is to be expected that natural selection will be influential in shaping life-history patterns to correspond to efficient populations.

Viewed in this way, comparative studies of life histories appear to be fully as meaningful as studies of comparative morphology, comparative psychology, or comparative physiology. The former type of study has, however, been neglected from the evolutionary point of view, apparently because the adaptive values of life-history differences are almost entirely quantitative. The recent ecological literature does show a trend toward the increasing application of demographic analysis to non-human populations, but the opposite approach of deducing demographic consequences from life-history features has been relatively neglected. The present paper is presented with the hope that this situation can be changed. In other fields of comparative biology it is usual to examine individual characteristics and to regard these as possible adaptations, and the writer believes that life-history characteristics may also be profitably examined in this way.

It is possible by more or less laborious methods to compute the exact size and composition of the population which at any future time would be produced by any given initial population when the life-history pattern of the individual organisms is regarded as fixed. Thus it is possible to make an exact evaluation of the results of changing any life-history feature, and the value of this type of analysis may be apparent to those biologists who distrust the usual demographic procedures.

Starting with exact computational methods, it has been shown that early population growth may exhibit irregularities or cyclic components which are identifiable with negative or complex roots of an algebraic equation, but that these components vanish in time so that potential population growth is ultimately a geometric progression. Having established this fact, it is shown that the exact computational methods and the more convenient approximate methods lead to identical conclusions when considered over the long time scale which is of interest in adaptational and evolutionary considerations.

Some life-history patterns of ecological interest are examined and compared by means of relatively simple formulas derived from a consideration of the form of potential population growth. The results have bearing on the possible adaptive value of genetically induced changes of life-history features. It is suggested that this type of approach may add to the value of life-history studies and that an awareness of the possible meanings of empirical life-history data may aid in planning such studies by insuring that all pertinent information will be recorded. One of the most striking points revealed by this study is the fact that the age at which reproduction begins is one of the most significant characteristics of a species, although it is a datum which is all too frequently not recorded in the literature of natural history.

The number of conceivable life-history patterns is essentially infinite, if we judge by the possible combinations of the individual features that have been observed. Every existing pattern may be presumed to have survival value under certain environmental conditions, and the writer concludes that the study of these adaptive values represents one of the most neglected aspects of biology.

## LIST OF LITERATURE

ALLEE, W. C. 1934. Recent studies in mass physiology. *Biol. Rev.*, 9: 1–48.

——, A. E. EMERSON, O. PARK, T. PARK, and K. P. SCHMIDT. 1949. *Principles of Animal Ecology.* Saunders, Philadelphia.

ARCHIBOLD, R. C. 1918. A Fibonacci series. *Amer. math. Monthly*, 25: 235–238.

BANTA, A. M., T. R. WOOD, L. A. BROWN, and L. INGLE. 1939. Studies on the physiology, genetics, and evolution of some Cladocera. *Publ. Carneg. Inst.*, 39.

BERKSON, J. 1944. Application of the logistic function to bio-assay. *J. Amer. statist. Ass.*, 39: 357–365.

——. 1951. Why I prefer logits to probits. *Biometrics*, 7: 327–329.

BIRCH, L. C. 1948. The intrinsic rate of natural increase of an insect population. *J. Anim. Ecol.*, 17: 15–26.

BODENHEIMER, F. S. 1938. *Problems of Animal Ecology.* Oxford Univ. Press, London.

CHAPMAN, R. N. 1928. The quantitative analysis of environmental factors. *Ecology*, 9: 111–122.

——. 1938. *Animal Ecology.* McGraw-Hill, New York.

CHURCHILL, R. V. 1944. *Modern Operational Mathematics in Engineering.* McGraw-Hill, New York.

DEEVEY, E. S., JR. 1947. Life tables for natural populations of animals. *Quart. Rev. Biol.*, 22: 283–314.

DUBLIN, L. I., and A. J. LOTKA. 1925. On the true rate of natural increase as exemplified by the population of the United States, 1920. *J. Amer. statist. Ass.*, 20: 305–339.

——, ——, and M. SPIEGELMAN. 1949. *Length of Life. A Study of the Life Table*, rev. ed. Ronald Press, New York.

DUNKEL, O. 1925. Solutions of a probability difference equation. *Amer. math. Monthly*, 32: 354–370.

ELSTON, J. S. 1923. Survey of mathematical formulas that have been used to express a law of mortality. *Rec. Amer. Inst. Actuar.*, 12: 66–95.

ERRINGTON, P. L. 1946. Predation and vertebrate populations. *Quart. Rev. Biol.*, 21: 144–177, 221–245.

EVANS, F. C., and F. E. SMITH. 1952. The intrinsic rate of natural increase for the human louse, *Pediculus humanus* L. *Amer. Nat.*, 86: 299–310.

FIBONACCI, L. (1857). *Liber Abbaci di Leonardo Pisano publicati da Baldasarre Boncompagni.* Tipografia delle Scienze mathematiche e fisiche, Roma.

FINNEY, D. J. 1947. The principles of biological assay. *J. R. statist. Soc.*, 109: 46–91.

——. 1949. The choice of a response metameter in bio-assay. *Biometrics*, 5: 261–272.

FISHER, R. A. 1930. *The Genetical Theory of Natural Selection.* Oxford Univ. Press, London.

FRANK, P. W. 1952. A laboratory study of intraspecies and interspecies competition in *Daphnia pulicaria* (Forbes) and *Simocephalus vetulus* O. F. Müller. *Physiol. Zool.*, 25: 178–204.

FRANKLIN, B. 1751. Observations concerning the increase of mankind and the peopling of countries. In *The Works of Benjamin Franklin*, ed. by J. Sparks, 1836, Vol. 2: 311–321. Hilliard, Grey, Boston.

GAUSE, G. F. 1934. *The Struggle for Existence.* Williams & Wilkins, Baltimore.

GOMPERTZ, B. 1825. On the nature of the function expressive of the law of human mortality. *Phil. Trans.*, 36: 513–585.

GRAUNT, J. 1662. *Natural and Political Observations Mentioned in a Following Index and Made upon the Bills of Mortality....* Printed by T. Roycroft, London.

GRAY, J. 1929. The kinetics of growth. *Brit. J. exp. Biol.*, 6: 248–274.

HOGBEN, L. 1931. Some biological aspects of the population problem. *Biol. Rev.*, 6: 163–180.

HUMPHREYS, W. J. 1929. *Physics of the Air*, 2nd ed. McGraw-Hill, New York.

HUTCHINSON, G. E. 1948. Circular causal systems in ecology. *Ann. N. Y. Acad. Sci.*, 50: 221–248.

HYMAN, L. H. 1951. *The Invertebrates. Vol. 2. Platyhelminthes and Rhynchocoela. The Acoelomate Bilateria.* McGraw-Hill, New York.

JACKSON, C. H. N. 1939. The analysis of an animal population. *J. Anim. Ecol.*, 8: 238–246.

JORDAN, C. 1950. *Calculus of Finite Differences*, 2nd ed. Chelsea, New York.

KOSTITZIN, V. A. 1939. *Mathematical Biology.* Harrap, London.

KUCZYNSKI, R. R. 1932. *Fertility and Reproduction.* Falcon Press, New York.

——. 1935. *The Measurement of Population Growth.* Sidgwick & Jackson, London.

LESLIE, P. H., and R. M. RANSON. 1940. The mortality, fertility, and rate of natural increase of the vole (*Microtus agrestis*) as observed in the laboratory. *J. Anim. Ecol.*, 9: 27–52.

——, and T. PARK. 1949. The intrinsic rate of natural increase of *Tribolium castaneum* Herbst. *Ecology*, 30: 469–477.

LINNAEUS, C. 1743. Oratio de telluris habitabilis. In *Amoenitates Academicae seu Dissertationes Variae....* Editio tertia curante J. C. D. Schrebero, 1787, Vol. 2: 430–457. J. J. Palm, Erlangae.

LOTKA, A. J. 1907a. Relation between birth rates and death rates. *Science*, 26: 21–22.

——. 1907b. Studies on the mode of growth of material aggregates. *Amer. J. Sci.*, 24: 119–216.

——. 1910. Contributions to the theory of periodic reactions. *J. phys. Chem.*, 14: 271–274.

——. 1925. *Elements of Physical Biology.* Williams & Wilkins, Baltimore.

——. 1927. The size of American families in the eighteenth century and the significance of the empirical constants in the Pearl-Reed law of population growth. *J. Amer. statist. Ass.*, 22: 154–170.

——. 1931. The structure of a growing population. *Human Biol.*, 3: 459–493.

——. 1934. *Théorie Analytique des Associations Biologiques.* Hermann, Paris.

LOWAN, A. N., Technical director. 1941. *Table of Natural Logarithms.* 4 vols. Federal Works Agency, Works Projects Administration for the City of New York. Rept. of Official Project No. 15-2-97-33.

MALTHUS, T. R. 1798. *An Essay on the Principle of Population as it Affects the Future Improvement of Society, with Remarks on the Speculations of Mr. Godwin, M. Condorcet, and Other Writers.* Printed for J. Johnson in St. Paul's Churchyard, London.

MENDES, L. O. 1949. Determinação do potencial biotico da "broca do café"—*Hypothenemus hampei* (Ferr.)—e consideracões sôbre o crescimento de sua população. *Ann. Acad. bras. Sci.*, 21: 275–290.

MILNE-THOMPSON, L. M. 1933. *The Calculus of Finite Differences.* Macmillan, London.

MOLISCH, H. 1938. *The Longevity of Plants.* E. H. Fulling, Lancaster Press, Lancaster, Pa.

NEWMAN, F. W. 1883. Table of the descending exponential function to twelve or fourteen places of decimals. *Trans. Camb. phil. Soc.*, 13: 145–241.

NICHOLSON, A. J., and V. A. BAILEY. 1935. The balance of animal populations. Part I. *Proc. zool. Soc. Lond.*, 1935: 551–598.

PEARL, R. 1925. *The Biology of Population Growth.* Knopf, New York.

——. 1930. *Introduction to Medical Biometry and Statistics*, 2nd ed. Saunders, Philadelphia.

——. 1937. On biological principles affecting populations: human and other. *Amer. Nat.*, 71: 50–68.

——. 1939. *The Natural History of Population.* Oxford Univ. Press, London.

——. 1946. *Man the Animal.* Principia Press, Bloomington, Ind.

——, and L. J. REED. 1920. On the rate of growth of the population of the United States since 1790 and its mathematical representation. *Proc. natl. Acad. Sci. Wash.*, 6: 275–288.

——, and J. R. MINER. 1935. Experimental studies on the duration of life, XIV. The comparative mortality of certain lower organisms. *Quart. Rev. Biol.*, 10: 60–79.

PIERCE, J. C. 1951. The Fibonacci series. *Sci. Monthly*, 73: 224–228.

QUETELET, A. 1835. *Sur l'Homme et le Développment de ses Facultés ou Essai de Physique Sociale.* Bachelier, Imprimeur-Libraire, Paris.

RHODES, E. C. 1940. Population mathematics. *J. R. statist. Soc.*, 103: 61–89, 218–245, 362–387.

RICKER, W. E. 1948. *Methods of Estimating Vital Statistics of Fish Populations.* Indiana Univ. Pubs. Sci. Ser., 15, Bloomington.

ROSS, R. 1911. *The Prevention of Malaria*, 2nd ed. Dutton, New York.

RUSSELL, E. S. 1942. *The Overfishing Problem.* Cambridge Univ. Press, Cambridge.

SADLER, M. T. 1830. *The Law of Population: A Treatise, in Six Books; in Disproof of the Superfecundity of Human Beings, and Developing the Real Principle of their Increase.* Murray, London.

SALT, G. 1936. Experimental studies in insect parasitism. IV. The effect of superparasitism on populations of *Trichogramma evanescens*. *Brit. J. exp. Biol.*, 13: 363–375.

SHARPE, F. R., and A. J. LOTKA. 1911. A problem in age distribution. *Phil. Mag.*, 21: 435–438.

SMITH, F. E. 1952. Experimental methods in population dynamics, a critique. *Ecology*, 33: 441–450.

STANGELAND, C. E. 1904. *Pre-Malthusian Doctrines of Population; a Study in the History of Economic Theory.* Columbia Univ. Stud. Hist. Econ. pub. Law, Vol. 21, no. 3.

SUNDBÄRG, A. G. 1907. *Bevölkerungsstatistik Schwedens 1750–1900.* P. A. Norstedt and Söner, Stockholm.

THOMPSON, D'ARCY W. 1942. *On Growth and Form*, new ed. Cambridge Univ. Press, Cambridge.

THOMPSON, W. R. 1931. On the reproduction of organisms with overlapping generations. *Bull. ent. Res.*, 22: 147–172.

——. 1939. Biological control and the theories of the interactions of populations. *Parasitology*, 31: 299–388.

U. S. Forest Service. 1948. The woody-plant seed manual. *Misc. Publ. U. S. Dep. Agric.*, No. 654.

VERHULST, P. F. 1838. Notice sur la loi que la population suit dans son accroisissement. *Corresp. math. phys., A. Quetelet*, 10: 113–121.

——. 1845. Recherches mathématiques sur la loi d'accroissement de la population. *Mém. Acad. R. Belg.*, 18: 1–38.

VOLTERRA, V. 1927. Variazioni e fluttuazioni del numero d'individui in specie animali conviventi. *Mem. Accad. Lincei*, 324 (ser. sesta). Vol. 2.

——. 1931. Variation and fluctuations of the number of individuals in animal species living together. In *Animal Ecology* (Chapman, R. N.). McGraw-Hill, New York.

WALLACE, R. 1753. *A Dissertation on the Numbers of Mankind in Antient and Modern Times: in which the Superior Populousness of Antiquity is Maintained.* Printed for G. Hamilton and J. Balfour, Edinburgh.

WARDLE, R. A., and J. A. McLEOD. 1952. *The Zoology of Tapeworms.* Univ. of Minnesota Press, Minneapolis.

WIDDER, D. V. 1940. *The Laplace Transform.* Princeton Univ. Press, Princeton.

——. 1947. *Advanced Calculus.* Prentice-Hall, New York.

YULE, G. U. 1906. On the changes in the marriage- and birth-rates in England and Wales during the past half century; with an inquiry as to their probable causes. *J. R. statist. Soc.*, 69: 88–132.

——. 1925. The growth of population and the factors which control it. *J. Roy. statist. Soc.*, 88: 1–58 (related discussions, pp. 58–90).

# AN EXPERIMENTAL APPROACH TO THE DYNAMICS OF A NATURAL POPULATION OF *DAPHNIA GALEATA MENDOTAE*

Donald James Hall

*Department of Entomology and Limnology, Cornell University, Ithaca, New York*

## Introduction

In general, populations have been studied either in the laboratory under experimental conditions with environmental variables controlled, or in their natural habitat where variables are uncontrolled. In laboratory investigations the analyses are often powerful and yield knowledge of the fundamentals of population growth but are limited to specific conditions seldom found in nature. In field studies, analyses are limited to correlations of population phenomena with environmental variables and frequently involve large errors in estimates of the inferred rates.

The apparent paradox of many field and laboratory population studies can be reconciled in part by manipulating laboratory populations in such a manner that information appropriate to an analysis of the natural population is obtained. To manipulate experimental populations properly, some a priori knowledge of influential variables in the natural population is necessary.

This study is directed to combining an experimental approach with a field description. The purpose of such an analysis is to predict natural population growth of *Daphnia*, and, consequently, to focus attention on the factors which control it.

Because of the difficulties encountered in determining population rate processes and the role of underlying environmental variables, predictive models of population growth have been limited to controlled laboratory populations or unusual natural situations with relatively constant environmental conditions. Predictive schemes applied to natural populations are more likely to succeed the more information they utilize; but such models become hopelessly complicated, requiring vast amounts of empirical information. It is not yet clear whether simple models, requiring relatively little information, can adequately predict population growth in natural situations. However, comparison of a model with the observed population growth focuses attention upon the kinds and amounts of information absolutely essential for prediction. Inappropriate models may prove valuable by emphasizing the effect of disregarding important variables.

Few investigations of this sort have been attempted on plankton populations. Elster (1954) in studying the population dynamics of the copepod, *Eudiaptomus gracilis,* utilized the ratio of eggs-to-females to obtain a reproductive index for the population. By determining the developmental rate of eggs at different temperatures he was able to estimate the increase of the population. Edmondson (1960) applied the experimental-field approach to several rotifer populations, placing great emphasis on the eggs-to-female ratio as a useful tool for determining the birth rates of populations. A model based on birth alone was then used to predict population growth and size.

Although not concerned with zooplankton populations, 2 other studies are pertinent because the approaches are similar. Reynoldson (1961) made a quantitative population study of the triclad *Dugesia lugubris.* Laboratory experiments allowed Reynoldson to assess the effects of temperature and food on the reproduction of *Dugesia,* and to conclude that population growth was often food limited. Subsequent field experiments strengthened his conclusion. Morris (1959) in a study of 2 spruce-defoliating insects constructed a predictive model based on a single key factor. The incidence of parasitism in a larval stage of a given generation of defoliators could be used to predict the density of the next generation. This approach proved quite successful, in both a predictive and analytic sense.

*Daphnia* was selected for the present study because much is known of its biology and population attributes (Banta, Wood, Brown, and Ingle 1939; Slobodkin 1954; Edmondson 1955; Frank, Boll, and Kelly 1957). *Daphnia* reproduces parthenogenetically and at frequent intervals, is easily maintained under laboratory conditions, and is usually an important constituent of the zooplankton in lakes and ponds.

The decision on what variables to include was influenced by several sources. Previous investigations of *Daphnia* as well as pilot studies of *Daphnia galeata mendotae* indicate that food and temperature strongly influence population growth rate. Other variables, such as alkalinity, dissolved gases, and light, either tend to remain relatively constant in the zone of the lakes inhabited by *Daphnia* or seem to be of little importance. Predation undoubtedly affects growth rate in many *Daphnia* populations. This variable is intentionally ignored in this study because the necessary labor of estimating predation rates was prohibitive. The difference between observed and predicted population growth, if carefully evaluated, can indicate the extent of predation upon the *Daphnia* population.

Laboratory experiments were performed to determine rate functions of *Daphnia* under controlled conditions and to obtain relevant descriptive population data so that rates could be inferred from similar data on natural populations.

The experiments deal with the effects of food and temperature upon reproduction, development, individual growth, and survival. The choice of experimental temperature conditions was determined by the range of environmental temperatures throughout the year in the natural habitat. Food levels were selected high enough to permit nearly maximal growth, and low enough (it was hoped) to include the range of food levels existing in the lake. The population of *Daphnia galeata mendotae* in Base Line Lake, Michigan, was selected for study because of its dominant position in the zooplankton, and because of the relatively simple morphometric features of the lake.

## Materials and Methods

### Laboratory Experiments

*Daphnia* were raised individually from the newborn state in "old-fashion" glasses containing 150 $m^3$ medium (surface area: 30 $cm^2$; depth: 7 cm) at $25 \pm 0.5$, $20 \pm 1$, and $11 \pm 1°C$.

Three different food levels or concentrations were used at each temperature. Animal responses

TABLE I. Instantaneous rates of population increase (r) of *Daphnia galeata mendotae* with associated standard errors at 3 temperatures and 3 food levels

| Temperature (°C) | Food level (Klett units) | r |
|---|---|---|
| 25 | 16 | $0.51 \pm 0.006$ |
| | 1 | $0.46 \pm 0.013$ |
| | 1/4 | $0.36 \pm 0.015$ |
| 20 | 16 | $0.33 \pm 0.016$ |
| | 1 | $0.30 \pm 0.002$ |
| | 1/4 | $0.23 \pm 0.002$ |
| 11 | 16 | $0.12 \pm 0.006$ |
| | 1 | $0.10 \pm 0.003$ |
| | 1/4 | $0.07 \pm 0.005$ |

were so uniform that samples of only a few individually raised *Daphnia* yield a very small sampling error to the population rate of increase data (Table I). With 2 exceptions at 11°C, the sample size for each experimental condition was 10. In addition to these 9 experimental conditions 21 *Daphnia* were grown at $5 \pm 1°C$.

Before the experiments *Daphnia* were maintained for several generations at the experimental conditions to account for effects of acclimatization and conditioning to food level.

Food consisted of mixed green algae (*Chlorella, Ankistrodesmus,* and other small species) grown at room temperature in large aquaria exposed to natural as well as fluorescent light. No attempt was made to provide pure or uni-algal sources of food. Consequently, some bacteria and detritus were also included, but at all times the algae represented the major food source. The aquaria contained fish and snails. Food rations were passed through a #25 silk bolting cloth in order to remove undesirable large material. At each feeding the optical density of a sample of the algal culture was measured with a Klett-Summerson photometer equipped with a #42 blue filter. The sample was then centrifuged for 15 min at 3,500 rpm in a clinical centrifuge, after which the optical density of the supernatant liquid was measured. The difference in readings was considered the optical density of centrifugable (and, hence, probably filterable) material. Tap water, conditioned for about one week in large aerated aquaria containing various plants and invertebrates, was passed through an HA Millipore filter and used to dilute the stock algae to 3 concentrations representing 16, 1, and 1/4 Klett units. Sixteen Klett units equal approximately one million algal cells per $cm^3$. The relationship of optical density of cells to cell count over this range of Klett units appears to be linear. This procedure of quantifying the food resulted in uniform responses as reflected by the uniform brood size of daphnids reared at any given food level in the laboratory during the course of 2 years. This food suspension was then brought to the experimental temperature. The medium was changed daily for the 20 and 25° conditions, bidaily for the 11°, and every 4 days for the 5° conditions.

*Daphnia* were examined at every change of medium. Molting rate was determined by the frequency of appearance of cast skins. The maximum carapace length of the cast skin was the criterion used to measure size. The duration of egg development and duration of adult instar are nearly identical. *Daphnia* carry eggs in their brood chamber which are released as fully developed young during the molting process, at which time a new batch of eggs enters the brood chamber. Reproduction was measured as the number of newborn present at each change of medium. Calculations of the instantaneous rates of increase (r) were made by combining age-specific survival ($l_x$) and age-specific birth rates ($m_x$) following the technique of Evans and Smith (1952). Once data for the rate of increase were complete, experiments were terminated even though not all daphnids were dead.

### Field Data

Morphometric information was obtained from the contour map of Base Line Lake published by the Institute for Fisheries Research, Michigan Department of Conservation. Temperature conditions were measured with a Whitney resistance thermometer. Water samples were taken periodically and analyzed for oxygen content according to the PKA modification of the Winkler method. A pigmy Gurley current meter was used to estimate current velocities of the river at the outlet of the lake. Current profiles were then constructed from which flow rates were calculated. Two such estimates were made, one during spring high water and another in midsummer. Stomach analyses were made of fish collected in April 1961 from Base Line Lake.

A #6 mesh, 12-in. diameter plankton net equipped with a Clarke-Bumpus flow meter served as the quantitative sampler. It possessed no closing device, however. Calibration of this instrument indicated that one revolution represents 33.4 liters of water through a range of towing speeds from one to 4 knots. A #6 mesh net retains the smallest *Daphnia galeata mendotae* but allows most of the phytoplankton and much of the zooplankton to pass through, thus facilitating the counting procedure. Collections were made from a rowboat moving at a speed of from one to 2

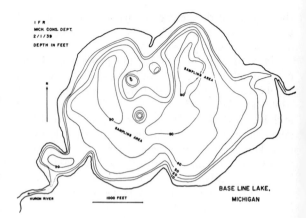

Fig. 1. Contour map of Base Line Lake, Michigan.

knots. With few exceptions, samples were not taken on windy days. The sampling procedure consisted of making long oblique tows through each of 3 strata: upper, middle, and deep. This ensured a stratified but extensive sampling of the population. The meter of water immediately overlying the lake bottom was not sampled. The vertical depth of the tows was calculated, using an angle measurer attached to the tow line. Occasionally in homothermous periods a complete oblique tow (from top to bottom of the lake) was made, while during the winter months vertical hauls were taken under the ice.

The 1960 samples were taken in duplicate at one station. The 1961 samples were taken in duplicate but from opposite sides of the lake (Fig. 1). Samples were also taken at the inlet and outlet of the lake. Each sample represented the contents of 2,000 liters or more of water, excepting those taken in the winter. Thirty-five collections were made during the period from July 1960 to July 1961. *Daphnia* samples were immediately preserved in 95% alcohol. Formalin or less concentrated alcohol caused carapaces to balloon with the consequence that appreciable numbers of eggs fell out of the brood chambers, and it became difficult to assess carapace length.

Samples were too large (about one liter) for complete analysis. After thoroughly mixing the sample, 2 ml subsamples were taken and counted in their entirety until at least 100 *Daphnia* had been counted. Subsamples were placed in a narrow rectangular counting chamber and examined under a dissecting microscope equipped with an ocular micrometer. The maximum carapace length and brood size of each specimen of *Daphnia galeata mendotae* were recorded. Other daphnids were noted if found.

The following equation was used to obtain the density estimate of *Daphnia* in each stratum:

$$\frac{\#\ Daphnia}{100\ \text{liters}} = \frac{\text{average}\ \#\ Daphnia\ \text{in subsample} \times \#\ \text{subsamples in concentrate}}{\#\ \text{revolutions of flow meter} \times 33.4\ \text{liters}} \times 100$$

The density for the total water column was obtained by taking an average of the upper, middle, and lower strata density estimates, weighted according to the thickness of the strata.

Identification and classification of *Daphnia* follow the monograph of Brooks (1957).

### Results

#### Laboratory Studies

Survivorship and fecundity tables were constructed from the age-specific survival ($l_x$) and reproductive rates ($m_x$) under 9 experimental conditions. These tables are then combined into an $l_x m_x$ column which is used to solve the following equation for r, the instantaneous rate of population increase:

$$\Sigma\ l_x m_x e^{-rx} = 1.00$$

Birch (1948) gives an excellent discussion of the calculation of r. Since survival through the juvenile and early adult stages is nearly perfect, mortality has little effect on the estimates of r. Consequently, only fecundity tables are presented in Appendix A; $l_x$ values are 1.00 throughout. This treatment permits quantitative evaluation of the effects of food and temperature on the population rate of increase. Population rates of increase (r per day) for each food level are plotted in Figure 2 as a function of temperature. For the chosen conditions, temperature shows a much greater effect upon r than does food level. Obviously, low enough food levels would also have a profound effect upon r. It is clear by inspection of the range of r values (r = 0.07 to r = 0.51) that any reference to the rate of increase of a

TABLE II. Temperature effects upon duration of instar, egg development, and the ratio of duration of juvenile period to duration of adult instar for *Daphnia galeata mendotae*

| Temperature | Duration of instar or duration of egg development | Duration of juvenile period / Duration of adult instar |
|---|---|---|
| °C | Days | |
| 25 | 2.0 | 3.0 (6/2) |
| 20 | 2.6 | 2.9 (7.5/2.6) |
| 15 | 4.5 | |
| 13 | 6.0 | |
| 11 | 8.0 | 3.0 (24/8) |
| 9 | 10.8 | |
| 8 | 12.3 | |
| 7 | 14.2 | |
| 5 | 18.0 | |
| 4 | 20.2 | |
| 2 | ? | |

population should be accompanied by a statement of the environmental conditions under which the value was determined.

#### Temperature

Temperature affects the frequency of molting and hence the frequency with which young are produced (Table II). Reproduction occurs every 2.0 days at 25°C; every 2.6 days at 20°C; and every 8.0 days at 11°C. A single adult at 5°C gave birth to young 18 days after producing the eggs.

For each temperature condition the food level had no observable effect upon the frequency of molting and reproduction. Under conditions of near-starvation, however, Banta, Wood, Brown, and Ingle (1939) have demonstrated that the frequency of molting and reproduction is somewhat reduced.

The duration of egg development is identical to the duration of the adult instars at the food levels used. The ratios of the juvenile periods (time from birth to reproductive maturity of instar V) to the duration of adult instars seem temperature-independent (Table II).

Growth is discontinuous in *Daphnia,* for size increases only during and immediately following ecdysis. The amount of growth at each ecdysis does not seem to be dependent upon temperature.

The median lifespan of *Daphnia* is 30 days at 25°C; 60-80 days at 20°C; and about 150 days at 11°C. *Daphnia* grown at 5°C showed no mortality over a 2-month period. These survival estimates suggest that the physiological mortality rate is quite low, probably less than 3% per day

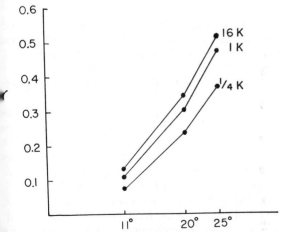

Fig. 2. Instantaneous rates of population increase (r) in relation to temperature (°C) and Klett units of food (K).

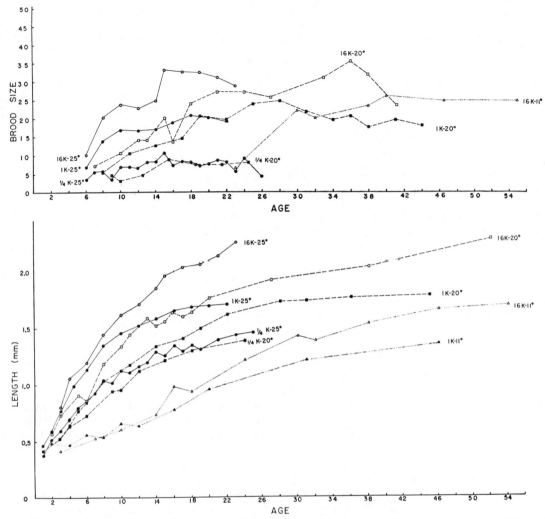

Fɪɢ. 3. Upper figure: mean brood size in relation to age (days) under different temperature (°C) and food conditions (Klett units). Lower figure: mean length in relation to age (days) under different temperature (°C) and food conditions (Klett units).

throughout the year. The survival curves were incomplete, but indicate the near-rectangular shape reported for *Daphnia* by Frank, Boll, and Kelly (1957) and Banta, Wood, Brown, and Ingle (1939).

### Food

Food level affects reproduction through the number of young per brood (Fig. 3). This effect may appear to be slightly temperature-dependent. When a difference in average brood size does occur for a given food level, the larger size is always associated with a higher temperature. Two features of these experiments might have some bearing on the results. First, at higher temperatures food levels might have been effectively higher than at lower temperatures because the algae seemed to remain suspended better in the warmer water. Second, had the experiments been carried out for the same number of instars, the curves representing brood size at lower temperatures might have reached the same heights as the curves representing brood size at higher temperatures.

Food level also affects the amount of growth per instar (Fig. 3). Adult stages are affected more by different food levels than are juvenile stages. This effect may appear slightly temperature-dependent, but the 2 reservations mentioned in connection with reproduction apply here also.

Since food level strongly affects both brood size and body size, the relation of brood size to body size (Fig. 4) in daphnids is a poor criterion for inferring food level. *Daphnia* from the different food levels show similar trends, although low food

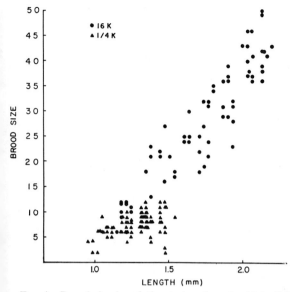

Fig. 4. Brood size in relation to length under high (16 Klett units) and low (¼ Klett unit) food levels at 25°C.

animals remain at the lower end of the distribution.

Although numerous age and size categories are usually present in any natural population, the maximum length and brood size attained by *Daphnia* is apparently determined by the abundance of food. Therefore, an estimate of natural food conditions might be obtained by matching maximum length and brood size from field data to experimentally determined length and brood maxima obtained under specified food levels. Applying this criterion to the collection from Base Line Lake indicates a natural food level of about ¼ Klett unit for much of the year. This technique may prove useful in analyses of other zooplankton populations.

Different food levels did not affect the median

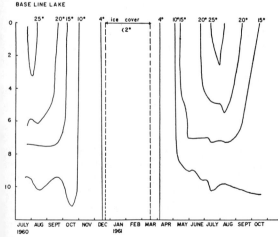

Fig. 5. Base Line Lake isotherms (°C) in 1960-1961.

life span. Banta, Wood, Brown, and Ingle (1939) report that extremely low food levels (near-starvation) increase median longevity.

The separability of the effects of food and temperature greatly facilitates the application of these data to the field collections. Temperature alone may be utilized to predict frequency of molting and reproduction, duration of egg development, and physiological life span. Food level may be inferred from the largest carapace sizes and brood sizes encountered.

### Field Studies

#### Limnological measurements

Base Line Lake in southeastern Michigan (T. 1S.—R. 5E.—Sec. 5, 6; T. 1N.—R. 5E.—Sec. 31, 32) is the last downstream member of a chain of lakes connected by the Huron River. The lake is oval in outline and generally steep-sided, forming a relatively uniform basin ¾ mile long by ½ mile wide (Fig. 1). About 70% of the surface area of the lake overlies water of greater than 8 m depth.

TABLE III. Estimates of volume outflow, lake volume, and flushing rates of Base Line Lake, 1961

| VOLUME OUTFLOW | |
|---|---|
| Spring | $1.07 \times 10^6$ m³ / day |
| Midsummer | $1.63 \times 10^5$ m³ / day |

| LAKE VOLUME | |
|---|---|
| Spring | $8.73 \times 10^6$ m³ |
| Midsummer | $8.10 \times 10^6$ m³ (total lake) |
| | $5.67 \times 10^6$ m³ (epilimnion only) |

| FLUSHING RATES | |
|---|---|
| Spring | 12.3% / day |
| Midsummer | 3.0% / day (epilimnion only) |

Shoal areas are covered with fine marl and are generally devoid of aquatic vegetation. Base Line Lake is a hard-water lake (average surface total alkalinity 155 ppm). Temperature conditions are shown in Figure 5. Stratification occurs from May into October and again from December into March. Oxygen depletion occurred in the hypolimnion in both summers but not during the winter. By June 25, 1961, oxygen concentration was reduced to 1.0 ppm in the hypolimnion; on July 12, 1961, less than 0.10 ppm remained. The effect of summer depletion on *Daphnia* is to reduce the habitable zone of the lake to the epilimnion and thermocline. Prevailing winds are westerly. Circulation patterns within the lake seem to be primarily wind-determined, although the effect of the river flowing through the lake may be considerable during periods of high water.

Table III indicates the volume outflow from the

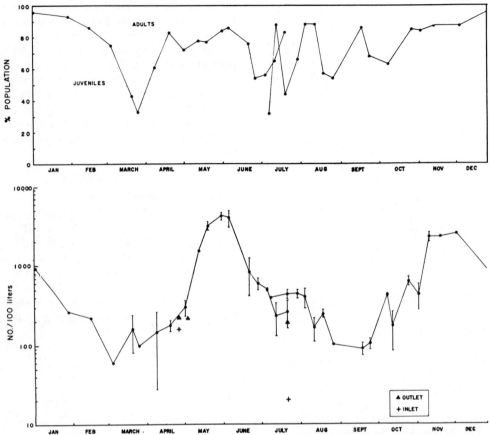

Fig. 6. Upper figure: per cent juveniles and adults in the population. Lower figure: population size
(# *Daphnia galeata mendotae* / 100 liters) in 1960-1961. Vertical bars represent standard deviations.

lake at spring high-water level and at summer low-water level. The volume outflow per day is compared with the lake volume yielding a turnover or flushing rate. During May the flushing rate was 12% of the total lake per day. By midsummer the rate had decreased to 3% of the epilimnion per day or 2% of the total lake per day. It is assumed that the outflow rate equals the inflow rate, which is true if the lake level does not fluctuate violently. An annual fluctuation in lake volume of ±3.7%, based on extremes in lake level, lends support to this argument.

### Population Attributes

#### Population size

Population size of *Daphnia galeata mendotae* throughout the course of a year is indicated in Figure 6. The values given are densities (numbers/100 liters) rather than estimates of total population size. Since the densities were determined as an average for all depths, the only assumption involved in converting densities to total numbers is that the densities apply to all parts of the lake. Samples were taken in duplicate, which

should be considered the minimum allowable for population studies. However, samples were very large when compared to most sampling procedures utilizing plankton traps or Clarke-Bumpus samplers. The average coefficient of variability of the population for the pairs of samples is 17.3%, which is relatively low as far as field studies go. Subsamples represented a very small fraction of the total sample (1/200 or less). If any subsample has an equal (but very small) probability of including a given daphnid from the concentrate, then the distribution of the daphnids in the concentrate may be considered a Poisson distribution in which the variance is equal to the mean. Comparing the variance to the mean from samples taken in spring, summer, and fall yields a chi-square value with a probability of 0.10-0.250. The conclusion is that the method of mixing the concentrate ensured randomness, and that the subsampling error was random. The average coefficient of variability associated with subsampling is 18.5%.

Two population maxima occurred; one in late spring, the 2d in late fall. The maximum densities were 4331/100 liters and 2556/100 liters, respec tively. During the summer months population density gradually decreased from about 400/100 liters in July to 100/100 liters in September. A large number of *Daphnia galeata mendotae* were present throughout the winter. The minimum density of 60/100 liters occurred in early March just as reproduction was commencing.

Exceedingly few individuals were observed to carry ephippia. All ephippia obtained from bottom samples proved to be *Daphnia pulex*. A few males were observed in fall and spring. *Daphnia galeata mendotae* apparently overwinters largely in the free-swimming stage in Base Line Lake. No reproduction occurred between January 1 and March 4. The water temperature was less than 2°C during the period. Although reproduction occurred in the laboratory at 5°C, it is possible that at 2°C reproduction is prevented. Such a low temperature may also alter the mortality rate.

The vertical distribution of the population seemed dependent upon the temperature stratification of the lake. Under homothermous conditions nearly equal densities of *Daphnia* occurred in the upper, middle, and deep strata. As soon as the lake began to stratify, however, the majority of the daphnids were found in the upper and middle strata. Densities during summer were 10 times greater in the upper stratum than they were in the deep stratum. Lack of oxygen precludes the permanent existence of *Daphnia* in the hypolimnion, and thus few, if any, *Daphnia* would be expected from the deep stratum. Their occurrence in samples from this stratum may be a sampling artifact, since the sampler lacked a closing device. This would bias the density estimates, but the bias would be quite small because the time spent in ascending through the upper and middle strata is very short compared with the time spent in the deep stratum. Another explanation may be that the deep samples frequently included the lower limits of the thermocline where daphnids could live.

Diurnal vertical migration of *Daphnia galeata mendotae* is probably confined to the epilimnion and the thermocline. Attempts to demonstrate vertical migration showed no pattern whatsoever. If vertical migration does occur, it probably does not markedly change the daily temperature environment of the population as a whole. McNaught and Hasler (1961) believe that this species migrates vertically through one m or less of water in Lake Mendota, Wisconsin.

*Reproduction*

The average brood size (ratio of eggs to mature *Daphnia*) served as a population reproductive index. The criterion of reproductive maturity is

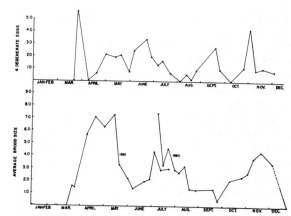

Fɪɢ. 7. Upper figure: per cent degenerate eggs in the population. Lower figure: average brood size (average number of eggs per adult).

somewhat arbitrary, since no morphological distinction can be made between mature and immature *Daphnia* unless the adults are reproductive. Carapace length at the onset of reproduction (instar V) was determined under various food and temperature conditions. The range of such lengths was from 0.97 mm to 1.25 mm. All shorter lengths occurred at low food levels. Since it appears that the natural population also experienced a low food level, the size at maturity was arbitrarily set at 0.97 mm. At a high food level this would include many of the last juvenile instars, but would nevertheless yield a very high average brood size.

Average brood sizes are plotted in Figure 7. Three distinct peaks occur. The spring and fall brood size maxima immediately precede the two population density maxima. The summer increase in brood size is not accompanied by an increase in daphnids. The average brood size ranged from 2.0 to 4.0 eggs throughout most of the reproductive season. The largest average brood size was 7.5 eggs.

The per cent reproductive adult females was usually high, especially during peak egg production, but dropped to 50% or less after the spring and summer reproductive peaks and immediately after the onset of reproduction in March. If degenerate broods were also included the per cent would be higher.

Degenerate eggs were frequently observed in the brood chambers of *Daphnia* taken from Base Line Lake. These eggs were a dark gray-brown color and often appeared to be disintegrating. Normal eggs appeared blue-green or yellow-green in color and were of a firm, less fragile texture. Degenerate eggs were excluded from the calculation of average brood size. The percentage degenerate eggs in relation to the total eggs present is shown in Figure 7. There is no suggestion of any relationship with normal brood size. The frequency of entire broods appearing degenerate was greater than the frequency of only a fraction of the brood appearing degenerate, whereas under laboratory conditions the few degenerate eggs observed occurred singly.

The stage of development of the eggs in the brood chamber was also noted. Three stages were defined: the egg stage (no segmentation), first embryo stage (segmentation, but no eyespot), and 2d embryo stage (possession of an eyespot). This classification is similar to Edmondson's (1955). Although the 3 stages are not of identical duration, the relative frequency of their occurrence may still be used to evaluate the question of reproductive periodicity. All 3 stages were present in roughly equal numbers in all samples, indicating that no diurnal periodicity in reproduction occurs under natural conditions. This observation permits reproduction to be treated as a continuous function of the population.

*Size structure*

Knowledge of the age and size structure of metazoan populations is necessary to analyze properly population growth (Slobodkin 1954). *Daphnia* exhibit no age-specific characters, making it difficult to describe the age structure of the population. A method of estimating the age structure of a population would be to determine, under laboratory conditions, the length of *Daphnia* grown under a variety of experimental conditions, and then to apply the appropriate length-age relationship to the observed field size distribution. The validity of such an estimate depends upon how well the laboratory-determined length-age relationship can be applied.

In this study an attempt was made to estimate the instar structure of the population (later, using temperature data from the laboratory, ages of immature instars will be estimated). The ranges of lengths of instars grown in the laboratory were used to construct a series of size categories, which, when applied in the field samples, probably represent distinct instars at least for the immature period. Once maturity is reached the individual growth rate (increases in length per molt) decreases and becomes more strongly dependent upon food level. Thus, it becomes increasingly difficult to assign an individual to a specific instar. The size structure is therefore based upon 4 immature instars and 3 mature "categories." Figure 6 represents the frequency distribution of adults and juveniles throughout one year. The increase in the proportion of adults from January through March was caused by the absence of reproduction

coupled with the slow maturation of the existing immature daphnids. However, as reproduction commenced in late March the population size structure shifted rapidly until by mid-April less than 20% of the *Daphnia* were mature. For 2 months the proportion of mature daphnids remained at this level with only minor fluctuations. This period coincides with the spring period of rapid population growth. By mid-June the proportion of adults began to increase, reaching 46% of the population before again decreasing to the 20% level. A series of 3 rather violent fluctuations in all size categories occurred during the summer and early fall. Each increase in percentage of adults was followed by a decrease to the 10 to 20% level. In October a 4th such decrease occurred, but this time the proportion of adults reached the 15% level and remained there for more than a month. This last period of stable age structure coincides with the fall period of rapid population growth.

Population size structure in relation to depth showed little variation among the upper, middle, and lower strata. The juveniles were slightly more frequent in the upper and middle strata in the summer. Because most of the population was located in the epilimnion (upper and middle strata), the small differences of size frequency categories in relation to depth are considered unimportant. The population size structure was similar at all depths in spring and fall. The size structure of samples taken at the outlet at spring high water was very similar to the size structure of the population in the lake. The size structure of outlet samples taken in midsummer was composed entirely of juveniles and did not correspond to the size structure of the lake population.

*Population losses*

Observations on the abundance and feeding habits of several predators indicate that *Leptodora* (a cladoceran), *Chaoborus* (phantom midge

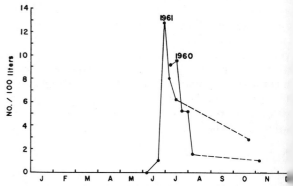

Fig. 8. Population size of *Leptodora* (# / 100 liters) in 1960-1961.

larva), and fish prey upon *Daphnia*. Population density was estimated for *Leptodora* only. *Leptodora* appears in June and reaches peak numbers in July (Fig. 8). Andrews (1949) reports a similar seasonal abundance of *Leptodora* in Lake Erie, but with a 2d minor peak of males in October. *Chaoborus* appear in the upper waters only at night, spending the day in or just above the bottom of the lake. Stomach analyses of adult cisco (*Leucichthys artedi*) and crappies (*Pomoxis nigromaculatus*) taken from Base Line Lake indicate that these fish feed extensively on large *Daphnia pulex* in early spring, but not upon the smaller adults of *Daphnia galeata mendotae*.

Another population loss is caused by the Huron River. This loss may be considered the net effect of passive immigration and emigration of *Daphnia*. Once carried out of the lake, *Daphnia* are lost to the system and soon die (Chandler 1939). The net loss of the population was determined by subtracting the density of *Daphnia* in the river immediately below the lake from the density in the river immediately above the lake. During late April and early May the high flushing rate of the lakes was accompanied by considerable but nearly identical immigration and emigration (Fig. 6). The net loss was low (perhaps as high as 3% of the population per day). During midsummer the low flushing rate of the lake was accompanied by lower immigration and emigration rates. The net loss was one per cent of population per day. These estimates indicate that the river flowing through Base Line Lake exerts a relatively constant and small source of mortality.

*Other zooplankton populations*

Four other species of *Daphnia* were found in Base Line Lake: *Daphnia pulex, D. retrocurva, D. ambigua,* and *D. longiremis.* Only the first 2 species ever reached appreciable numbers. *D. pulex* reaches a peak abundance in spring after which numbers become sparse. At no time was *D. pulex* more abundant than *D. galeata mendotae.* During summer *D. pulex* is found only in the colder regions of the lake, i.e., the thermocline, where it is the dominant daphnid. The fact that this species does not appear in the warmer epilimnion, and often possesses considerable haemoglobin which is an adaptation to enable it to withstand low oxygen concentration (Fox 1948), would indicate that this species occupies a restricted habitat during much of the year. *D. retrocurva* appeared in the plankton only after the lake had warmed to 20°C. Population size of this species increased during July and early August, and, by late August, this species became the most abundant cladoceran. On September 24, 1960, *D.*

*retrocurva* occurred at a density of 730/100 liters in the epilimnion compared to a density of about 175/100 liters of *D. galeata mendotae.* By late October *D. galeata mendotae* again dominated other cladocera. Indeed, during spring and fall maxima, this species was far more abundant than any species of copepod. *Cyclops* is the predominant copepod. *Diaptomus* is present also. *Bosmina* appears as an important member of the zooplankton during the colder months.

## PREDICTIONS

A first-order prediction of *Daphnia* population growth may now be attempted utilizing much of the information obtained from the field and laboratory observations. Such a prediction will indicate if important variables have been overlooked in the population analysis, and may prove a valuable means of gaining insight into this biological system.

Two related kinds of predictions are made: predicted rates of increase and predicted population size or density.

*Population growth rate*

The rate of increase of the population may be estimated if the birth, death, emigration and immigration rates are known. Although no animal reproduces continuously, many do reproduce frequently enough so that the instantaneous growth equation,

$$(1) \qquad N_t = N_0 e^{rt}$$

is a close approximation to natural population growth. $N_0$ and $N_t$ denote initial population size and size t time units later; e is the base of natural logarithms; t represents time units; and r denotes the instantaneous rate of increase and is determined by the 4 rates mentioned above.

If the effects of death, emigration, and immigration are ignored, the growth equation becomes,

$$N_t = N_0 e^{bt}$$

in which b is the instantaneous rate. Although the symbols r, b, and d (instantaneous death rate) have been defined under stable age conditions (see Lotka 1925), they may be applied to populations without a stable age distribution as well. The only distinction is that under stable age conditions r, b, and d remain constant; whereas under a continually changing age distribution the instantaneous rates will change accordingly. The instantaneous birth rate, b, may be estimated if the finite birth rate, B is known:

$$b = \ln (1 + B)$$

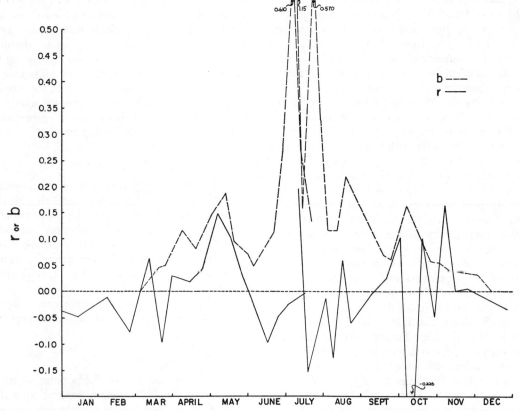

FIG. 9. Observed (r) and estimated (b) instantaneous rates of population increase of *Daphnia galeata mendotae* in Base Line Lake.

The finite birth rate is defined as the number of newborn occurring during an interval of time divided by the number of animals already existing:

(2)
$$B = \frac{\text{number of newborn (during interval t to } t+1)}{\text{population size at t}}$$

The problem then is to predict the number of newborn during any interval of time. Four kinds of information are used for this prediction: the population size ($N_o$); the number of adults ($N_A$); the average brood size of adults ($\bar{E}$); and the rate of development of the eggs expressed as the fraction of development accomplished per day ($1/D$). The finite birth rate or number of newborn per individual per day is given by the equation:

$$(3) \qquad B = \frac{N_A \cdot \bar{E} \cdot 1/D}{N_o}$$

The values of $N_A$, $\bar{E}$, and $N_o$ are estimated from a sample of the natural population. In order to determine $1/D$, the temperature at which the eggs develop must be known. Table II indicates values of D for various temperatures. The lengths of

TABLE IV. Average temperatures (°C) during different periods of the year in the upper, middle, and lower strata of Base Line Lake

| Periods | Strata | | |
|---|---|---|---|
| | Upper | Middle | Deep |
| 1960 | | | |
| July-Aug. | 25 | 20 | 15 |
| Sept. | 20 | 20 | 15 |
| Oct. | 13 | 13 | 11 |
| Nov. | 7 | 7 | 7 |
| 1961 | | | |
| Jan.-March | 2 | 2 | 2 |
| 1/2 March | 4 | 4 | 4 |
| April | 6 | 6 | 6 |
| 1/2 May | 11 | 11 | 8 |
| 1/2 May | 15 | 15 | 9 |
| June | 20 | 15 | 9 |
| July | 25 | 15 | 11 |

time required for development (D) at 25, 20, 11 and 5°C were determined under constant laboratory conditions. The remainder of the values were obtained by curvilinear interpolation, but no y logarithmic interpolation, since $Q_{10}$ changed considerably throughout this temperature range. Table IV indicates the estimated average temperatures for the 3 strata of Base Line Lake for various months of the year. These average temperatures were determined from the annual temperature profile of Base Line Lake (Fig. 5). During periods of rapid temperature changes in Base Line Lake the averages were based on shorter periods. When the 3 strata differed in average temperatures, 3 separate values of b were calculated from which a weighted average of the 3 was determined. The calculated values of b for the 28 dates are plotted in Figure 9.

Successive pairs of points from Figure 6 yield values of $N_o$ and $N_t$, from which an average r for each time period can be calculated.

From equation (1):

$$(4) \qquad r = \frac{l_n N_t - l_n N_o}{t}$$

The 32 points of r in Figure 9 were calculated in this manner.

The properties of b include a lower limit of zero whenever reproduction ceases). Rapid shifts in the age structure of the population as well as sampling errors produce large changes in the value of b. The lower limit of r is—∞. Values of b should always exceed values of r, since $r = b - d$. Population rate of increase based on b alone is, except for 2 periods of time, always higher than the observed rate of increase.

Despite fluctuations in b and r definite trends in the 2 sets of points are apparent. During spring and fall months r and b values are both positive and nearly equal. Maximum values of b are attained in the summer months, whereas r is negative during this period indicating a population decrease. During the winter b is zero, and r is negative.

Obviously, the curve of r is related to the population numbers from which it was derived. The maximal densities of spring and fall are preceded by maximal r values whereas the minimal summer and winter densities are preceded by minimal r values. The seasonal curve for b is very different. Values of b reach a single large peak during the summer months rather than 2 peaks in spring and fall.

Comparison of birth rates and rates of population change show that in spring and fall, predation, natural death, and net loss to the Huron River are not important variables affecting population growth. Average total population losses of 3.9 and 5.6% per day for April-May and October-November respectively were determined by subtracting r from b during these periods. During

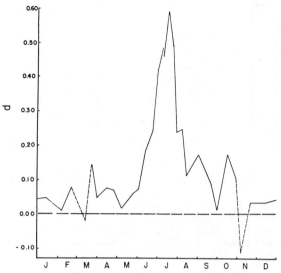

Fig. 10. Estimated instantaneous death rate (d) of *Daphnia galeata mendotae* in Base Line Lake obtained by subtracting r from b in Fig. 9.

the winter a 4.4% loss per day occurs, which probably reflects natural death and loss to the river alone. From mid-June through mid-September the very large difference between r and b indicates that the total population loss is very high (Fig. 10). An average total loss of 28.5% per day was determined by subtracting r from b during July and early August.

Since the net loss to the population due to the river system is 3% per day or less in the spring and 1% in the summer (0.03 and 0.01 daphnids lost per daphnid per day respectively), the effect of animals entering and leaving the population in this manner is small and reasonably constant. Physiological mortality as discussed above is probably low also. Predation then would seem to be the cause of the negative population growth rate throughout most of the summer.

A 2d method of estimating the loss rate is to construct survivorship curves for the population from the size distributions for various periods of the year. A survivorship curve yields the rate of survival (or conversely the death rate) if plotted as a semilogarithmic graph. Knowledge of the age structure and growth rate of the population is necessary to construct a survivorship curve from field data. Laboratory data on the length-age relationship under different food and temperature conditions were here employed to estimate the age and instar of *Daphnia* taken from the natural population. If population size remains unchanged for a length of time greater than one generation period, then the survival curve will become identical or nearly identical to the stable age distribution curve. To obtain a survival curve when the

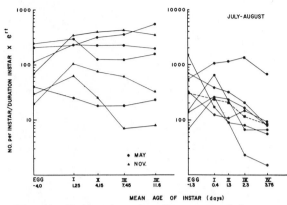

FIG. 11. Estimated survivorship curves relating numbers (# per instar / duration of instar X $e^{rt}$) to age (days) for May, November, and July-August. Average survivorship in July-August is represented by the dotted line.

population is changing size, the number of animals in each age category of the age distribution must be multiplied by a correction factor which is based upon the population rate of change and the age of the animal. This method should work providing the rate of population change is known and remains relatively constant over a length of time greater than the generation period.

Figure 11 represents survival curves estimated by the above technique for May, July-August, and November. These periods were chosen because population rate of change was relatively constant (Fig. 6). On the abscissa are plotted the mean ages of the eggs and estimated instars I-IV. The numbers of daphnids within each of these categories was determined by (1) dividing the number of individuals existing as eggs, instar I, etc., by the duration of the category (to adjust for different instar durations), and (2) multiplying this by the finite rate of population change over the time period between birth (t = o) and mean age of category. In the case of eggs, negative time units were employed since the eggs had not entered the population yet. This procedure adjusts the numbers in each category so that they represent the estimated survival in time of a population of the size that exists at t = o. The slope of the line indicates the survival rate since a logarithmic scale was used to plot numbers. A horizontal line indicates perfect survival. It is interesting to note that during May survival appears to be complete; in other words, the death rate is negligible. The survivorship curves for November indicate much the same thing, although not so clearly. In both cases sampling error may produce an apparent increase in numbers with age, which is unrealistic, but the average horizontal trend is obvious. During July and August the curves are no longer

horizontal. Their negative slopes reflect a high death rate. The average summer survivorship curve indicates a death rate of 0.259 daphnids per daphnid per day. Since net immigration-emigration effects indicate a loss of 0.01 daphnids per daphnid per day and the physiological death rate amounts to no more than 3% per day, the conclusion is again reached that predation is the most important factor controlling population size in the summer.

The average summer survivorship curve indicates a reasonably constant loss rate for all age categories. This suggests that predation viewed for the entire period is not age-specific.

## Population size

Population size was predicted for 4 intervals: May 1-May 19, June 5-June 28, July 8-August 4, and September 21-November 10. The rate of increase, r, was estimated for one generation period by estimating the number of *Daphnia* that would be produced during the period that it took for a newborn *Daphnia* present at t = o to mature. Thus mature daphnids present at the beginning of each interval were assumed to produce young throughout the entire interval at a rate dependent upon the average brood size and developmental rate 1/D. Daphnids in the last immature instar at the onset of the period were treated in the same manner except the number of "reproductive days" in the period for these animals was shortened by the time it took to reach the mature instar. All subsequent immature instars were treated in the same manner with the number of reproductive days decreased by how many days short of maturity they were. The estimated duration of immature instars at various temperatures was determined from the laboratory experiments. The total number of *Daphnia* born during this generation period was added to the initial number to obtain a predicted population size for the end of the generation period. The instantaneous rate of increase was then determined by solving equation (4), in which t equals the number of days from birth to maturity at the given temperature. The 4 values of r were then utilized to solve for predicted population size at the end of each of the 4 intervals of prediction.

If but one generation occurred during the interval (owing to a low temperature or the shortness of the interval) then the estimated population size would be a good estimate of the expected population size based upon birth rate alone. However, if several generations occurred during the interval, then the r associated with the initial population size structure would be insensitive to changes in size structure occurring during the in

TABLE V. Observed population size compared to estimated population size of *Daphnia galeata mendotae* at the end of 4 intervals

| Time interval | Population size (#/100 liters) | |
| --- | --- | --- |
| | Observed | Estimated |
| May 1-May 19 | 3,225 | 2,661 |
| June 5-June 28 | 607 | 114,723 |
| July 8-August 4 | 413 | 8,745,000 |
| Sept. 24-Nov. 10 | 2,337 | 3,663 |

terval. It is impossible to assume that the initial size structure would not change during some of these intervals (Fig. 6); therefore, this method must be criticized for this shortcoming. However, population size estimated in this manner (Table V) indicates much the same thing as the estimate of population growth did when compared to the observed population growth.

The estimated population size of 2,661 *Daphnia*/100 liters is similar to the observed population size of 3,225 *Daphnia*/100 liters present at the end of the interval May 1-May 19. The estimated population size of 3,663 *Daphnia*/100 liters is also similar to the observed population size of 2,337 *Daphnia*/100 liters present at the end of the interval from September 24-November 10. However, the 144,723 *Daphnia*/100 liters estimated from June 5-June 28 is far greater than the observed population of 607 *Daphnia*/100 liters. An even greater discrepancy exists at the end of the period of July 8-August 4 when the estimated population is 8,745,000 *Daphnia*/100 liters compared to observed 413 *Daphnia*/100 liters.

## DISCUSSION

The population growth model based on birth rate alone is an adequate expression of population growth of *Daphnia galeata mendotae* in Base Line Lake during spring and fall, but is inadequate during the summer. Predation seems to be a key variable affecting the population throughout the summer.

Population losses during the summer, estimated by determining the average difference between the expected and observed population growth (b-r) for this period, amount to 28.5% of the population per day. This estimate is remarkably similar to the loss rate of 25.9% of the population per day obtained from the estimated survivorship curves for the same period.

Although both estimates make use of the parameter r, the effect of r in correcting the numbers in each age category in the construction of the survivorship curves is small. The 2 estimates of population loss may be considered virtually

independent, since they utilize mainly different information in different ways. Confidence in the reality of such a high population loss rate is increased by the agreement of the estimates.

An average predation rate of just over 25% of the population per day when the population is decreasing very slowly implies that the population turnover time is about every 4 days during July and early August. The turnover rate applies to biomass as well as numbers since the slope of the average summer survival curve is nearly constant (Fig. 11). This appears to be an exceptionally high turnover rate for a microcrustacean population. Stross *et al.* (1961) estimated the turnover time of *Daphnia longispina* in a lime-treated lake to be 2.1 weeks, whereas the estimated turnover time of a *Daphnia pulex* population in the untreated control lake was 4.6 weeks. The slightly lower average temperature of these lakes in comparison to Base Line Lake would, in itself, increase the population turnover time.

Under laboratory conditions *Daphnia galeata mendotae* exhibits a maximal rate of increase of 0.51 at 25°C. If we assume that predation rates would be proportional to the age frequency classes (i.e., predation does not change the age distribution), the theoretical minimum turnover time for *Daphnia* would be slightly less than 1.5 days. This is the length of time necessary to double population size calculated from the exponential growth equation (1).

Temperatures frequently reach 25°C in the surface waters of lakes but not for long periods of time. Food levels in natural habitats rarely, if ever, reach the levels associated with a maximal rate of increase. Even at the lowest laboratory food level, which is approximately the same as that of the lake, the maximum rate of increase is 0.36. Thus, a higher predation rate than that estimated (0.25) is possible, although the daphnids might risk extinction.

The turnover rate of once every 4 days observed in *Daphnia galeata mendotae* indicates that practically all the biomass produced by this population is passed on rapidly to the next trophic level. Since this species is a major component of the zooplankton, it must play a major role in the food chain of the lake during the summer. The role of *Daphnia galeata mendotae* as food would be much less important in spring and fall, since predation appears to be negligible at these times.

The bimodal curve representing population size of *Daphnia galeata mendotae* throughout a period of one year (Fig. 6) is typical of many zooplankton populations. This pattern of population growth is generally interpreted as a reflection of a food-limited system, in which phytoplankton become abundant as the result of increased nutrients following spring and fall mixing of the lake. The zooplankton respond to this increased food level by an increase in numbers until the food supply is essentially exhausted. A decline in numbers results from the shortage of food. In summer the phytoplankton (mainly blue-green and filamentous green algae) may be abundant but are considered unavailable as food for the zooplankton, resulting in low zooplankton densities. In winter phytoplankton growth is limited so that food is again a limiting factor in the growth of zooplankton populations.

The bimodal population curve of *Daphnia galeata mendotae* in this study is not simply the result of a food-limited system. This conclusion stems from considerations of reproductive potential and age-size structure of the *Daphnia* population.

The carrying capacity of the environment in terms of food is not reached during the summer because considerable energy is still available for the production of eggs. A very low average brood size is expected in an equilibrium population (which has reached the carrying capacity of the environment in terms of food supply), for at equilibrium only one egg, on the average, will be produced by each daphnid, and yet the life expectancy of daphnids includes several adult instars. Slobodkin (1954) has observed that equilibrium laboratory populations of *Daphnia* exhibit very little egg production. The average brood size in his equilibrium populations was less than 0.5 eggs/adult.

On one date only (September 24, 1960) did the average brood size fall below 1.0 egg/adult in Base Line Lake. During July and early August the average brood size ranged between 2 and 5 eggs per adult, which is much too large a brood size to be associated with a completely food-limited population.

The population growth rate in spring and fall is initially slowed by a decrease in reproduction indicating lower food levels, but only low enough to reduce the rate of increase and not to cause the rapid decline in population size that was observed in late May and early June.

Thus population size in summer is probably regulated more by predation pressure than by the scarcity of food. The predators are removing the center portion out of what otherwise would be a unimodal population curve. Without predation *Daphnia* would become food limited, but at a considerably higher population density.

Other zooplankton populations may show the same bimodal population curve as a result of similar heavy predation pressures in the summer

months. Nelson and Edmondson (1955) report that following the fertilization of Bare Lake, Alaska, the phytoplankton increased rapidly in density. This was followed by increased reproduction of the zooplankton (especially rotifers), but the size of the zooplankton population increased very little. The interpretation is that most of the increased growth of zooplankton populations was immediately consumed by the next trophic level (Nelson 1958).

In a study of *Daphnia retrocurva* in Bantam Lake, Connecticut, Brooks (1946) reports a population maximum of 3,650 *Daphnia*/100 liters in late spring. The density rapidly decreased thereafter, reaching 340 *Daphnia*/100 liters by July 9, and remained at this level for more than one month. The average brood size (mean number of eggs/adult) increased from less than 1.0 in mid-June to 2.5 on July 21. The mean water temperature during this period was 20°C. The similarity of his observations to those of the present study is striking. Again, the interpretation is that the rapid population growth in the spring is initially slowed by a food shortage, but the population size is drastically reduced by predation during the summer. Brooks did not estimate predation rates, however.

Stross *et al.* (1961) report a rapid increase in population size of *Daphnia longispina* in July. Average brood size exceeded 1.0 egg/adult during most of the period of population increase. However, before the population maximum was reached the brood size dropped to about 0.2 eggs/adult and remained at this size for 2 weeks while the population density decreased by a factor of 10. In this case food scarcity may have played a larger role in the control of population size than in the other studies discussed, although predation would still have to play a major role to account for the observed rate of decrease of population size.

A population with constant age-specific survival and reproductive rates will eventually reach a stable age distribution (Lotka 1931). Slobodkin (1954) found that a stable age-size population structure is not achieved in laboratory populations of *Daphnia* because of time lags inherent in the populations. In natural populations a stable age distribution is unlikely because the age-specific survival and reproductive rates change in association with changing environmental conditions.

The high, relatively constant proportions of juveniles in the spring and fall are certainly reflective of a population growing under relatively stable conditions. However, these periods are followed by a rapid shift toward an adult-dominated population indicative of lowered reproduction and/or selection predation upon the juveniles These interpretations are borne out by observation of the brood size and estimates of population loss (Figs. 7 and 9).

The role of fungal diseases and other parasites conceivably could contribute greatly to the high summer loss rate. However, extensive examinations of field collections during the summer indicated no visibly parasitized *Daphnia*.

Applying developmental rates obtained from but a few clones of *Daphnia* to the entire natural population assumes that no significant genetic variability of developmental rate exists. The validity of this assumption has not been examined.

The frequent occurrence of degenerate eggs in the natural population (Fig. 7) was unexpected from the results of the laboratory studies. Brooks (1946) reports a similar finding in a natural population of *Daphnia retocurva*. He suggests that egg degeneration is caused by inadequate nutrition. He also postulates that brood size is indicative of nutritional level. However, a comparison of brood size and frequency of degenerate eggs in both his and the present investigations indicates that these 2 criteria of nutritional level are inconsistent. Laboratory studies show that brood size is a reflection of the amount of food or energy available. Degenerate eggs may reflect a specific nutritional deficiency, a change in food level, temporary anoxia, or other conditions.

Causal analyses of natural population growth have frequently been attempted using the correlation approach. Although correlations are valuable in indicating the degree of relationship between variables, their biological significance is often difficult to evaluate. Hazelwood and Parker (1961) examined the effect of various environmental factors upon population size of *Daphnia* and *Diaptomus* (Copepoda). Their approach was based entirely upon correlations of several factors with population size. Accurate population estimates are essential if correlations are to be meaningful. Their analyses are based upon single samples at one depth at one station, and, may thus confound distributional variation with population density. Considerable distributional variation was, in fact, borne out by a single series of samples taken August 13, 1959, from different parts of the lake. Little, if any, experimental evidence was obtained about the effects of variables upon population parameters which would have permitted a stronger analysis of the system.

To perform adequate analyses of natural populations, experimental approaches must be utilized. In the present study the effects of different food and temperature conditions upon various attributes of *Daphnia* were found to be important. The range of laboratory temperatures tested was probably adequate to discern the effects on *Daph-*

*nia* of the ambient temperature conditions throughout the year. The laboratory food levels extended to much higher levels than those occurring in Base Line Lake. Testing the effects of food levels lower than $\frac{1}{4}$ Klett unit would have improved the present study.

Reduction of the complexity of natural population systems to a minimal number of variables is needed before any generalities can be made about the operation of such systems. The birth rate model is a beginning in this direction. Its value does not lie so much in the actual prediction of population growth (in the sense of forecasting), for the model requires empirical information about the population during the interval of prediction. Instead, the model is valuable in testing the effects upon population growth of omitting all but a few variables.

Where the model fails to predict growth rates adequately, attention is then focused upon those variables which seem most influential. An experimental analysis of these suspect variables in both the laboratory and the field will provide further insight into the dynamics of the system. Because reproduction appears to be so labile in most zooplankton populations, the birth rate model may prove of widespread use.

## Summary

The dynamics of the population of *Daphnia galeata mendotae* in Base Line Lake, Michigan, were analyzed by combining field and laboratory studies. Life-table and fecundity-table experiments were performed at 25, 20, and 11°C. Three food levels were tested at each temperature. Daily or bidaily observations enabled determination of the frequency of molting, duration of egg development, number of newborn per day, individual growth rate, and median life span.

Calculated population rates of increase, r, ranged from 0.07 to 0.51. Temperature influences r more strongly than food level does under the conditions examined. The effects of food and temperature are separable, thereby facilitating the application of experimental data to the field collection. Frequency of molting and reproduction, duration of egg development, and physiological life span are influenced principally by temperature. Growth per instar, maximum carapace length, and brood size are influenced principally by food.

The population in Base Line Lake was sampled for one year. All samples were examined permitting the estimation of population density, size structure, and average brood size. Population density shows a bimodal annual curve with maximal number in late spring and fall. Average brood size shows a trimodal annual curve. Two peaks in brood size precede and apparently cause the density maxima, whereas the 3d peak occurs in midsummer and is not followed by an increased population size. Average brood size ranged between 2 and 4 eggs per brood during most of the reproductive season. Population loss rates caused by the Huron River are relatively constant and small (3% and 1% population loss/day in spring and summer).

Population rates of increase based on birth rate alone, b, are estimated and compared with observed rates of increase, r. In spring, fall, and winter the small differences between b and r (3.9, 5.6, and 4.4% per day respectively) are accounted for by physiological mortality and river loss. Average summer population loss rate of 28% per day seems primarily due to predation. Summer survival curves estimated from field data indicate an average loss rate of 25% per day.

The summer population turnover rate of both numbers and biomass is estimated to be once every 4 days. *Daphnia galeata mendotae* plays an important role in the food chain of the lake during the summer. Population size does not appear to be solely determined by food. Predation pressure prevents the population from being large in the summer.

The birth rate model focuses attention upon the effect of ignoring important variables and should prove valuable in analyzing other zooplankton populations.

### Acknowledgments

The author wishes to acknowledge the advice and encouragement of Dr. Frederick E. Smith, Department of Zoology, University of Michigan. Also, appreciation goes to the Horace H. Rackham, School of Graduate Studies, University of Michigan, which awarded the author a scholarship and fellowships during this study.

### Literature Cited

Andrews, T. F. 1949. The life history, distribution, growth and abundance of *Leptodora kindtii* (Focke) in western Lake Erie. Abstracts of Doctoral Dissertations, 57. Ohio State University Press.

Banta, A. M., T. R. Wood, L. A. Brown, and L. Ingle. 1939. Studies on the physiology, genetics, and evolution of some Cladocera. Carnegie Inst. Wash., Dept. Genetics, Paper no. 39. 285 pp.

Birch, L. C. 1948. The intrinsic rate of natural increase of an insect population. Jour. Anim. Ecol. 17: 15-26.

Brooks, J. L. 1946. Cyclomorphosis in *Daphnia*. I. An analysis of *D. retrocurva* and *D. galeata*. Ecol. Monog. 16: 409-447.

———. 1957. The systematics of North American *Daphnia*. Mem. Conn. Acad. Arts & Sci. 13. 180 pp.

Chandler, D. C. 1939. Plankton entering the Huron River from Portage and Base Line lakes, Michigan. Trans. Am. Micro. Soc. 58: 24-41.

Edmondson, W. T. 1955. The seasonal life history of *Daphnia* in an arctic lake. Ecology 36: 439-455.

———. 1960. Reproductive rates of rotifers in natural populations. Mem. Inst. Ital. Idrobiol. 12: 21-77.

Elster, H. J. 1954. Über die Populationsdynamik von *Eudiaptomus gracilis* Sara und *Heterocope borealis* Fischer im Bodensee-Obersee. Arch. für Hydrobiol., Suppl. 20: 546-614.

Evans, F. C., and F. E. Smith. 1952. The intrinsic rate of natural increase for the human louse, *Pediculus humanus* L. Amer. Nat. 86: 299-310.

Fox, H. M. 1948. *Daphnia* hemoglobin. Roy. Soc. London Proc. Ser. B., 135: 195-212.

Frank, P. W. 1960. Prediction of population growth form in *Daphnia pulex* cultures. Amer. Nat. 94: 357-372.

———, C. D. Boll, and R. W. Kelly. 1957. Vital statistics of laboratory cultures of *Daphnia pulex* De Geer as related to density. Physiol. Zool. 30: 287-305. .

Hazelwood, D. H., and R. A. Parker. 1961. Population dynamics of some freshwater zooplankton. Ecology 42: 266-273.

Lotka, A. J. 1925. Elements of physical biology. Baltimore: Williams and Wilkins. 460 pp.

———. 1931. The structure of a growing population. Human Biol. 3: 459-493.

McNaught, D. C., and A. D. Hasler. 1961. Surface schooling and feeding behavior in the white bass, *Roccus chrysops* (Rafinesque), in Lake Mendota. Limnol. and Oceanogr. 6: 53-60.

Morris, R. F. 1959. Single-factor analysis in population dynamics. Ecology 40: 580-588.

Nelson, P. R. 1958. Relationship between rate of photosynthesis and growth of juvenile red salmon. Science 128: 205-206.

Nelson, P. R., and W. T. Edmondson. 1955. Limnological effects of fertilizing Bare Lake, Alaska. U.S. Fish and Wildlife Service Fishery Bull. no. 102, 56: 415-436.

Reynoldson, T. B. 1961. A quantitative study of the population biology of *Dugesia lugubris* (O. Schmidt) (Turbellaria, Tricladida). Oikos 12: 111-125.

Slobodkin, L. B. 1954. Population dynamics in *Daphnia obtusa* Kurz. Ecol. Monog. 24: 69-88.

Stross, R. G., J. C. Neess, and A. D. Hasler. 1961. Turnover time and production of the planktonic crustacea in limed and reference portion of a bog lake. Ecology 42: 237-244.

## APPENDIX A

Age-specific reproduction of *Daphnia galeata mendotae* under 9 different conditions of food and temperature expressed as total number of offspring per day. The values of N remain unchanged with respect to age in these tables.

| Age (days) | Food levels (Klett units) | | |
|---|---|---|---|
| | 1/4 (N=12) | 1 (N=10) | 16 (N=10) |
| TEMPERATURE: 25°C | | | |
| 6.0 | 31 | 75 | 100 |
| 7.0 | 33 | 0 | 0 |
| 8.0 | 27 | 138 | 202 |
| 9.0 | 18 | 0 | 0 |
| 10.0 | 46 | 168 | 237 |
| 11.0 | 48 | 0 | 0 |
| 12.0 | 33 | 166 | 227 |
| 13.0 | 41 | 0 | 0 |
| 14.0 | 58 | 153 | 248 |
| 15.0 | 42 | 0 | 229 |
| 16.0 | 57 | 170 | 36 |
| 17.0 | 33 | 0 | 260 |
| 18.0 | 40 | 185 | 0 |
| 19.0 | 28 | 0 | 258 |
| 20.0 | 38 | 161 | 0 |
| 21.0 | 0 | 0 | 248 |
| 22.0 | | 152 | |

| Age (days) | TEMPERATURE: 20°C | | |
|---|---|---|---|
| | (N=8) | (N=9) | (N=10) |
| 7.5 | 0 | 0 | 28 |
| 8.5 | 0 | 36 | 6 |
| 9.5 | 8 | 0 | 8 |
| 10.5 | 13 | 12 | 86 |
| 11.5 | 3 | 56 | 42 |
| 12.5 | 22 | 12 | 98 |
| 13.5 | 14 | 7 | 24 |
| 14.5 | 1 | 66 | 80 |
| 15.5 | 45 | 14 | 64 |
| 16.5 | 25 | 8 | 25 |
| 17.5 | 0 | 82 | 171 |
| 18.5 | 45 | 15 | 43 |
| 19.5 | 13 | 117 | 33 |
| 20.5 | 0 | 18 | 193 |
| 21.5 | 21 | 36 | 18 |
| 22.5 | 8 | 98 | 48 |
| 23.5 | 5 | 31 | 141 |
| 24.5 | 14 | 18 | 21 |
| 25.5 | 8 | 92 | 46 |
| 26.5 | 21 | 39 | 129 |
| 27.5 | 0 | | |
| 28.5 | 0 | | |
| 29.5 | 9 | | |
| 30.5 | | | |

| Age (days) | TEMPERATURE: 11°C | | |
|---|---|---|---|
| | (N=2) | (N=5) | (N=9) |
| 22 | 0 | 5 | 13 |
| 24 | 0 | 7 | 44 |
| 26 | 0 | 7 | 4 |
| 28 | 0 | 7 | 0 |
| 30 | 8 | 11 | 88 |
| 32 | 0 | 25 | 80 |
| 34 | 0 | 0 | 0 |
| 36 | 0 | 20 | 0 |
| 38 | 10 | 11 | 140 |
| 40 | 0 | 21 | 52 |
| 42 | 0 | 0 | 16 |
| 44 | 0 | 21 | 0 |
| 46 | 11 | 12 | 156 |
| 48 | 0 | 20 | 41 |
| 50 | | | 0 |
| 52 | | | 0 |
| 54 | | | 182 |

## APPENDIX B

*Daphnia galeata mendotae,* Base Line Lake, 1960-1961

| Date | (1)[a] Stratum | (2) $N_o$ | (3) $N_A$ | (4) $\overline{E}$ | (5) 1/D | (6) b | (7) r observed |
|---|---|---|---|---|---|---|---|
| 8 July 1960 | U | 667 | 395 | 7.3 | 0.50 | 1.15 | |
| | M | 341 | 290 | 7.8 | 0.39 | 1.27 | |
| | D | 107 | 88 | 6.8 | 0.22 | 0.81 | |
| (8) Weighted average | | $N_o{}^a$:401 | | $\overline{E}$:7.4 | | b:1.15 | 0.20 |
| 14 July 1960 | U | 1492 | 146 | 3.0 | 0.50 | 0.14 | |
| | M | 2255 | 333 | 3.5 | 0.39 | 0.18 | |
| | D | 194 | 14 | 2.8 | 0.22 | 0.04 | |
| (8) | | $N_o$:1313 | | $\overline{E}$:3.3 | | b:0.16 | 0.15 |
| 21 July 1960 | U | 497 | 95 | 4.6 | 0.50 | 0.37 | |
| | M | 750 | 571 | 4.7 | 0.39 | 0.87 | |
| | D | 94 | 76 | 4.0 | 0.22 | 0.54 | |
| (8) | | $N_o$:447 | | $\overline{E}$:4.6 | | b:0.66 | 0.00 |
| 29 July 1960 | U | 778 | 52 | 0.5 | 0.50 | 0.02 | |
| | M | 722 | 459 | 3.9 | 0.39 | 0.67 | |
| | D | 77 | 31 | 3.1 | 0.22 | 0.25 | |
| (8) | | $N_o$:450 | | $\overline{E}$:2.9 | | b:0.33 | 0.01 |
| 4 Aug. 1960 | U | 458 | 0 | 0 | 0.50 | 0.00 | |
| | M | 693 | 142 | 2.6 | 0.39 | 0.19 | |
| | D | 89 | 19 | 3.3 | 0.22 | 0.15 | |
| (8) | | $N_o$:413 | | $\overline{E}$:2.7 | | b:0.12 | 0.13 |
| 11 Aug. 1960 | U | 245 | 5 | 2.0 | 0.50 | 0.02 | |
| | M | 217 | 35 | 3.8 | 0.39 | 0.21 | |
| | D | 39 | 16 | 2.3 | 0.22 | 0.19 | |
| (8) | | $N_o$:167 | | $\overline{E}$:3.2 | | b:0.12 | 0.06 |
| 18 Aug. 1960 | U | 265 | 118 | 1.8 | 0.50 | 0.34 | |
| | M | 400 | 154 | 1.1 | 0.39 | 0.15 | |
| | D | 85 | 57 | 1.3 | 0.22 | 0.18 | |
| (8) | | $N_o$:250 | | $\overline{E}$:1.4 | | b:0.22 | 0.06 |
| 26 Aug. 1960 | (8) | $N_o$:103 | | | | | 0.01 |
| 18 Sept. 1960 | | 128 | 17 | 1.4 | 0.39 | 0.07 | |
| | (8) | $N_o$: 91 | | | | | 0.03 |
| 24 Sept. 1960 | | 143 | 45 | 0.5 | 0.39 | 0.06 | |
| | (8) | $N_o$:106 | | | | | 0.10 |
| 8 Oct. 1960 | U | 827 | 283 | 2.3 | 0.22 | 0.16 | |
| | M | 322 | 162 | 2.2 | 0.22 | 0.22 | |
| | D | 155 | 49 | 1.3 | 0.17 | 0.07 | |
| (8) | | $N_o$:434 | | $\overline{E}$:2.1 | | b:0.16 | 0.23 |
| 25 Oct. 1960 | | 647 | 97 | 2.4 | 0.17 | 0.06 | |
| | (8) | $N_o$:647 | | | | | 0.05 |
| 2 Nov. 1960 | | 438 | 70 | 2.7 | 0.13 | 0.05 | |
| | (8) | $N_o$:438 | | | | | 0.16 |
| 10 Nov. 1960 | | 2337 | 304 | 3.4 | 0.09 | 0.04 | |
| | (8) | $N_o$:2337 | | | | | 0.00 |
| 19 Nov. 1960 | (8) | $N_o$:2348 | | | | | 0.01 |

## APPENDIX B (Continued)

| Date | (1)[a] Stratum | (2) No | (3) NA | (4) Ē | (5) 1/D | (6) b | (7) r observed |
|---|---|---|---|---|---|---|---|
| 3 Dec. 1960 | | 2256 | 332 | 3.5 | 0.07 | 0.03 | |
| | (8) | No:2256 | | | | | 0.03 |
| 1 Jan. 1961 | | | | | | | |
| | (8) | No:941 | | | | | 0.05 |
| 28 Jan. 1961 | | | | | | | |
| | (8) | No:264 | | | | | 0.01 |
| 15 Feb. 1961 | | | | | | | |
| | (8) | No:222 | | | | | 0.08 |
| 4 Mar. 1961 | | | | | | | |
| | (8) | No: 60 | | | | | 0.06 |
| 20 Mar. 1961 | | 162 | 92 | 1.6 | 0.05 | 0.05 | |
| | (8) | No:162 | | | | | 0.10 |
| 25 Mar. 1961 | | 99 | 66 | 1.5 | 0.05 | 0.05 | |
| | (8) | No: 99 | | | | | 0.03 |
| 8 Apr. 1961 | | 152 | 58 | 5.7 | 0.05 | 0.11 | |
| | (8) | No:148 | | | | | 0.02 |
| 19 Apr. 1961 | | 180 | 31 | 7.1 | 0.07 | 0.08 | |
| | (8) | No:180 | | | | | 0.04 |
| 1 May 1961 | | 307 | 84 | 6.2 | 0.09 | 0.15 | |
| | (8) | No:307 | | | | | 0.15 |
| 12 May 1961 | | 1576 | 342 | 7.6 | 0.13 | 0.19 | |
| | (8) | No:1576 | | | | | 0.10 |
| 19 May 1961 | | 3225 | 744 | 3.4 | 0.13 | 0.10 | |
| | (8) | No:3225 | | | | | 0.03 |

| Date | (1)[a] Stratum | (2) No | (3) NA | (4) F | (5) 1/D | (6) b | (7) r observed |
|---|---|---|---|---|---|---|---|
| 30 May 1961 | U&M | 11597 | 1939 | 2.2 | 0.22 | 0.08 | |
| | D | 1728 | 242 | 2.0 | 0.09 | 0.03 | |
| | (8) | No:4331 | | | | b:0.07 | 0.01 |
| 5 June 1961 | U | 9177 | 1379 | 0.9 | 0.39 | 0.05 | |
| | M | 2478 | 426 | 1.4 | 0.22 | 0.06 | |
| | D | 667 | 80 | 1.5 | 0.09 | 0.02 | |
| | (8) | No:4124 | | | | b:0.05 | 0.10 |
| 21 June 1961 | U | 1664 | 306 | 2.0 | 0.39 | 0.13 | |
| | M | 776 | 213 | 1.8 | 0.22 | 0.10 | |
| | D | 198 | 44 | 1.5 | 0.09 | 0.03 | |
| | (8) | No:854 | | | | b:0.11 | 0.05 |
| 28 June 1961 | U | 1204 | 511 | 2.3 | 0.39 | 0.32 | |
| | M | 524 | 237 | 2.4 | 0.22 | 0.22 | |
| | D | 170 | 77 | 2.7 | 0.09 | 0.11 | |
| | (8) | No:607 | | | | b:0.27 | 0.03 |
| 5 July 1961 | U | 1275 | 562 | 4.8 | 0.50 | 0.72 | |
| | M | 229 | 106 | 3.4 | 0.22 | 0.30 | |
| | D | 150 | 46 | 3.9 | 0.13 | 0.14 | |
| | (8) | No:510 | | | | b:0.61 | |
| 12 July 1961 | U | 709 | 166 | 2.1 | 0.50 | .022 | |
| | M | 184 | 141 | 3.8 | 0.22 | 0.50 | |
| | (8) | No:238 | | | | b:0.28 | 0.04 |
| 21 July 1961 | U | 831 | 81 | 2.5 | 0.50 | 0.12 | |
| | M | 114 | 45 | 2.5 | 0.22 | 0.20 | |
| | D | 129 | 59 | 3.8 | 0.13 | 0.20 | |
| | (8) | No:268 | | | | b:0.13 | |

[a] (1) Upper, middle, and lower strata of lake; (2) total population size (total/100 liters); (3) total adults (adults/100 liters); (4) average brood size; (5) developmental rate of eggs which is the reciprocal of duration of egg development from Table II; (6) instantaneous birth rate $b = \ln(1+B)$; (7) observed instantaneous rate of population increase from equation (1); (8) weighted average of $N_o$, $\overline{E}$, and $b$ for the entire water column.

# EXPERIMENTAL METHODS IN POPULATION DYNAMICS:
## A CRITIQUE

FREDERICK E. SMITH

*Department of Zoology, University of Michigan, Ann Arbor, Michigan*

## INTRODUCTION

Until very recently, deterministic theory has been the source of mathematical models for population dynamics. Simple equations have been proposed as suitable representations of sigmoid growth, competition, predation, etc., and these have been fitted to various data. The studies of Gause (1934) epitomize this field.

Stochastic theory provides a kind of model that expresses, not only the general sequence of events, but also the inherent variability of the system. While the deterministic function may represent the "pure" curve of maximum likelihood, the stochastic function permits an evaluation of the actual, observed curve, regardless of its irregularities. Since this ability to handle chance variations and their sequential effects during dynamic processes is relatively new, one must conclude that its future effect upon the approach to population dynamics will be one of progressive increase.

As the theoretical approach is shifting its base, it would be well to look closely to the experimental methods that are in use. The intent of such a critique is two-fold: to determine what has actually been accomplished by such methods, as opposed to what is supposed to have been accomplished, and to launch the newer theoretical approach upon a somewhat better methodology.

Only a few aspects of the experimental techniques are discussed, serving to emphasize phenomena that may well be extended to other aspects. Those discussed fall into the following sections: the mechanisms of culture, the responses of the population, certain properties of deterministic theories, and the application of theories to data. It is the methods that are criticized; such criticisms as occur on the usefulness of particular theories are more or less incidental.

While this paper represents the views of one individual, its existence is very much a result of discussions with E. S. Deevey, G. A. Riley, L. B. Slobodkin, D. W. Calhoun, and especially with G. E. Hutchinson, all at Yale University. Later developments reflect the influence of many others in several places.

## THE EXPERIMENTAL ENVIRONMENT

Experiments in population dynamics are accomplished in cultures, and associated with these cultures are specific environments. One advantage of an experiment over field studies is the possibility of simplifying the environment through appropriate manipulation of the culture.

The culture can be treated in many ways, producing various qualitative effects in the environment and hence upon the population. If the experiment is designed as a test of some theory, the manipulations should be such as to simulate the conditions implied by the theory. Thus, if one were to test the

Reproduced with permission from Ecology, 33: 441-450, 1952. Published by the Ecological Society of America and The Duke University Press, Durham, North Carolina.

predation theory of Lotka (1925) and Volterra (1928), the environment would have to be such that the growth of the prey were in no way inhibited by prey density.

Surprisingly little attention has been paid to the possibility that a given theory, under investigation, defines certain properties for the experiment. In an attempt to emphasize such relationships, a very crude system of classification is given for several culture techniques that may be used in the laboratory. To these will be related the corresponding environments, and the latter will be associated with particular theories.

From the standpoint of ease of interpretation, the simplest culture technique is the *unlimited* culture. Either the population is continually so rarefied or the culture is so rapidly enriched that the organisms never suffer any inhibitive effects upon each other, at least not during the course of study.

Among culture techniques that have limited capacities for growth, the *unrenewed* culture is most frequently used, especially in bacteriology and protozoology. The culture is innoculated, and the subsequent history of the population is recorded. Nothing is added or subtracted by the experimenter.

A variant of this technique is the *periodically renewed* culture. At regular intervals, either the entire population is transferred to a new culture (as is done with flour beetles) or the culture is given booster shots of concentrated medium (as has been done with protozoa).

A still further refinement is the *continuously renewed* culture. The intervals between renewals are so small as to be ineffective, and the system can be treated as though fresh medium is being flushed through at a constant rate all of the time.

While these are but a few techniques, they are simple, and adequate for the present purpose.

Associated with each culture, and determined by the particular factors that are limiting, is a corresponding environment. In the unlimited culture, of course, since nothing is limiting, the environment is of the same type, an unlimited environment.

If the limiting factor is an expendable component of the medium, such as sugar or amino acid, the environment will follow the pattern of the culture.

If the limiting factor is non-expendable, such as space, the environment will in all cases follow the continuously renewed pattern, since the factor is resupplied automatically by the death of individuals. If spatial organization is involved, however, the rhythmic disturbance of the periodically renewed environment may produce a significant effect.

If the limiting factor is a freely diffusable substance like oxygen or carbon dioxide, again the system will in all cases regulate toward the continuously renewed pattern.

If the limiting factor is a noxious metabolite, the environment will follow the pattern of the culture, except that adding booster shots accomplishes little, and this type of culture will be modified toward the unrenewed type.

While these are but a few possibilities, they are enough to indicate some patterns that may occur. Combinations of limiting factors will complicate these patterns, so that, for example, it is not unlikely for an unrenewed culture to be temporarily regulated toward a continuously renewed environment by the supply of oxygen, only to revert to type later as the food is exhausted.

If we now examine some of the published theories, the implied environmental types (extrinsic to the interspecies relation when two populations are involved) are as follows:

1. Unlimited environment: exponential growth (Malthus 1798), predation (Lotka 1925; Volterra 1928), and the host-parasite relation

(Nicholson and Bailey 1935; Thompson 1939).

2. Unrenewed environment: sigmoid growth (Klem 1933).
3. Periodically renewed environment: none.
4. Continuously renewed environment: sigmoid growth (Verhulst 1838; Pearl and Reed 1920; Gompertz and Wilson, both in Wilson 1934) and indirect competition (Volterra 1928; Gause 1934).

In experiments on exponential growth, the culture has usually been so manipulated as to provide the proper environment. This is not known to be so for any of the experiments on predation; in those of Gause (1934, 1935) and of Gause, Smaragdova, and Witt (1936) the prey definitely reached densities that inhibited their own rate of growth. The same is true for most of the experiments on the host-parasite relation. Only one, an experiment by DeBach and Smith (1947), specifically eliminated self-inhibition in the growth of the prey population.

Klem's theory of sigmoid growth was developed for his experiments on yeast. The event appears to be unique, since no one else has applied a theory of growth in an unrenewed environment to data from an unrenewed environment.

While no theories have been developed to include the rhythmic effects of periodic renewal, many experiments have been recorded in which such effects probably existed. This would apply especially to studies of flour insects.

No ecological experiment has been conducted in a continuously renewed culture, although such techniques can be adapted from the work of Novick and Szilard (1950) or of Myers and Clark (1944). No experimental environment has ever been proved to be continuously renewed. While the chances are very good that in some experiments the unrenewed or periodically renewed culture technique that was used was modified by the limiting factors toward a continuously renewed type, this cannot be said with assurance for any particular case.

In summary, from the point of view that an experiment should simulate the conditions of the theory to which it is compared, very few of the published comparisons are known to be suitable. It is known for only one experiment on sigmoid growth (in which the theory did not fit the data well), one experiment on the host-parasite relation (in which the fit of theory to data is fair), and for many experiments on exponential growth. All of the remaining comparisons are open to question.

## The Experimental Population

While theories developed in population dynamics are admittedly oversimplified, a general awareness of this in experimental terms seems to be deficient. For, again, if the data are to be used as a "test" of a theory, they should be derived from an appropriate ecological system.

An almost universal simplification in theories is that the unit of the population, the organism, always bears the same relation to the environment. While this is never true, if the distribution of (qualitative) variations among the units is always similar, the approximation is satisfactory.

But stability or constancy of such properties as size-distribution, age-distribution, sex-ratio, etc. is surprisingly rare. Even in the most simple case of population dynamics, exponential growth, marked changes in the population during a recorded phase of such growth are frequent. Demonstrations of such changes are relatively infrequent, since more than one measure of the population has to be taken if a change is to be discerned.

Hershey (1938) demonstrated that, during the period that the cell count was increasing along a good exponential curve, the rate of nitrogen uptake in the population was increasing along a different curve, having a rate function at least 30% smaller. Obviously some character of the population was changing with time; the organism did not stay the same.

The most striking demonstration of this phenomenon was found by Richards (1932) in yeast. During the thirty hours of exponential increase in cell count, the percentage of budding cells increased steadily from 10 to 25, the percentage of moribund cells fell exponentially from 7 to 1, and the surface-volume ratio increased from about 2.9 to 3.4. Richards remarked that the sigmoid growth of yeast was too complicated for comparison to "formulae with arbitrary constants which over simplify the various influences that determine the extent of natural unlimited growth of the cells"; this remark applies equally well to the exponential phase of growth.

Finally, it is a commonplace in bacteriology that cell-count curves and colorimetric curves do not agree.

The conclusion from these demonstrations is that, although the culture is mechanically of the proper type, insufficient time is allowed for the population to adjust to exponential growth. Before the population is able to "settle down," it becomes crowded and passes into plateau. This may be avoided (Hershey 1939) by subculturing from very young cultures. Effectively the period of exponential growth is prolonged, and a steady state of population characteristics is able to develop. In an adjusted culture, all estimates of the growth rate (number, total volume, nitrogen uptake, etc.) must be the same. Most of the published observations of exponential growth are probably inaccurate estimates of the "true" rate of increase.

The concept of unchanging population characteristics in sigmoid growth or in other ecological relations is absurd. This has been recognised, and such "simple" organisms as yeast, protozoa, and bacteria have been used with the assumption that, here, at least, qualitative changes are minimal. It would now appear that such an assumption is unwarranted. The reactions of yeast to environmental stress, as recorded by Richards (1932), are fully as complicated from a mathematical point of view as those of any higher organism.

It is unfortunate that just those species which culture easily (yeast, flour insects, fruit flies, etc.) come from naturally unstable environments. Their complex adaptabilities, which facilitate culture, are precisely what complicate the population experiment. A simpler system would be one using species (not necessarily simple) from stable, uniform environments—species that usually are difficult to culture. Another possible solution is to present the traditional laboratory species with totally new limiting factors, and gamble that the population response will be relatively simple.

It is possible that in some experiments physiological adaptation to stress has combined with an unsuitable environmental type to produce a deceptive result. This is especially likely in comparisons of sigmoid growth with the Verhulst-Pearl theory. In many yeasts and bacteria, as growth proceeds in the unrenewed culture, the population shifts progressively to an inactive state. In an unrenewed environment one would expect the upper part of the sigmoid curve to be small, since it is curtailed by a falling capacity in the culture. After the peak of growth the population, if it could not adapt, would fall, perhaps along a negative exponential. But in these cases, the sum of inactive and active cells enlarges the upper portion of the growth curve and postpones the fall almost indefinitely.

While the result may be described closely by the mathematical form of the Verhulst-Pearl logistic, such a description is not useful. Either the combination of two errors has produced a fortuitous result, or their interaction is regulated by a process as yet unsuspected. In either case the theory does not describe the underlying biology.

Other complications that may be introduced by the organisms cannot be treated lightly. These include environmental conditioning, changes in the age structure of the population, and mutation with a complete replacement of the population (as occurs frequently in the chemostat of Novick and Szilard 1950). Whatever the specific complications, they must be reconciled in any comparison of theory and experiment.

## PROPERTIES OF DETERMINISTIC THEORIES

Any equation in population dynamics has specific properties, properties which are obvious to the mathematician, but which seem to have escaped any degree of experimental application. Many of these properties are useful, in that some of them may show immediately that the theory has limitations, while others may provide tools for study. These properties will be discussed by examples.

The theory of Verhulst (1838) and Pearl and Reed (1920) has the following form:

$$\frac{dN}{dt} = rN\left(1 - \frac{N}{K}\right)$$

where $N$ = population size,

$t$ = time,
$r$ = intrinsic (net, maximum, exponential) rate of increase,
$K$ = saturation level or plateau,

expressing the rate of change of the population $(dN)$ with respect to change in time $(dt)$. The equation can also be written as the average rate of change for the individual $(dN/N)$ with respect to the change in time:

$$\frac{dN}{Ndt} = r\left(1 - \frac{N}{K}\right).$$

In this latter form, the average growth rate is seen to be a linear function of the degree of saturation $(N/K)$. Thus, when this ratio is nearly zero, the growth rate is maximal $(r)$, when it is one-half, the growth rate is one-half, and when the system is just saturated, the growth rate is zero.

In unrenewed environments, and in competitive and predative relationships, the possibility of a population level exceeding the current saturation level must be considered. In the Verhulst-Pearl theory, the linear relation continues; when the system is twice saturated, the growth rate is minus $r$, when it is ten times saturated, the rate is minus $9r$. Thus, the rate of decrease is not a limited function. Lotka (1925) indicated that this property may not be suitable for some situations.

The Verhulst-Pearl theory stands up under this kind of analysis better than most. In the Gompertz theory (Wilson 1934), the equation can be stated:

$$\frac{dN}{dt} = rN \log_e\left(\frac{K}{N}\right)$$

or:

$$\frac{dN}{Ndt} = r \log_e\left(\frac{K}{N}\right).$$

This equation has the same limitation as the Verhulst-Pearl theory, setting no limit to the rate of decrease. It has the more serious fault, however, of setting no limit to the rate of increase. When the ratio, $N/K$, is small, the rate of growth approaches infinity. It is only between about one-third saturation (where $\log_e K/N$ is 1.0) and full saturation (where $\log_e K/N$ is 0.0) that the constants of the equation can be interpreted biologically.

As a final example, the predation equations of Lotka (1925) and Volterra (1928) are:

$$\frac{dN_1}{dt} = r_1 N_1 - k_1 N_1 N_2$$

$$\frac{dN_2}{dt} = k_2 N_1 N_2 - d_2 N_2$$

where  $N_1$ = prey population,
 $N_2$ = predator population,
 $r_1$ = intrinsic rate of increase for the prey,
 $d_2$ = exponential death rate of the predators,
 $k_1, k_2$ = predation constants.

If the predation constants are taken as simple, as they were in the development of an intrinsic cyclic relation, some of the properties are as follows:

$$\frac{dN_1}{N_1 dt} = r_1 - k_1 N_2,$$

$$\frac{dN_2}{N_2 dt} = k_2 N_1 - d_2.$$

1. Neither species enters in its own average growth function; hence, neither ever inhibits its own growth; the environment extrinsic to the relation is unlimited.
2. Prey density has no effect upon the likelihood of a prey being eaten; there is no safety in numbers.
3. Predator density has no effect upon the likelihood of a predator catching a prey; there is no competition for food.
4. The predators have an unlimited rate of increase.

While (1) can be arranged mechanically, and (2) may be true if the predators are certain filter-feeders, (3) and especially (4) are biologically unknown. These simple interpretations of the predation constants must be considered useless. To do so at once invalidates the predation "laws" of Volterra and the regular intrinsic cyclic relation developed by both Lotka and Volterra.

A more complex interpretation of the predation constants is that:

$$k_1 = a + bN_1 + cN_2 + \ldots$$

$$k_2 = a' + b'N_1 + c'N_2 + \ldots$$

defining each as a power series (Lotka 1925). If we consider only the second function, $k_2$, it is evident that a power series is most inept for its purpose.

For the growth function of the predators to be satisfactory, the average rate of growth $(dN_2/N_2 dt)$ must rise to some asymptote $(r_2)$ as the prey are made more numerous. To describe such a curve by a power series that will handle all values of prey up to infinity, an infinite number of terms and constants are needed. Even to handle the numbers of prey that are likely to develop in an experiment requires several terms of the series. Furthermore, the function fails markedly should the prey density exceed that expected and allowed for. The use of exponential functions, as suggested by Gause (1934), offers a much higher efficiency in terms of the number of constants that would be required to describe this relation.

So far in this section only the deficiencies of theories have been emphasized. The second use of such an analysis of equations is to develop experimental tools. These will be discussed at the end of the following section.

## The Application of Theories to Data

Actually, little can be said in favor of the fitting of deterministic theoretical curves to empirical data. The technique, as a means of "testing" theories, is indefensible on at least three independent counts:

(1) Judgment has to be subjective. Deviations from the best-fit curve always occur, and statistical methods for evaluating these deviations are lacking.

(2) The prior probability of the method is high. This aspect of probability is too often ignored; regardless of the calculated probability of a particular fit, if it is likely to be good before the fit is made, the test itself is inefficient. The method is uncritical; while it may exclude extreme misfits, it fails to discriminate among a host of similar but basically different situations.

Kavanagh and Richards (1934), among others, demonstrated that a variety of theoretical curves could be fitted to the same data on sigmoid growth, and with equal felicity. An even more powerful criticism of this weak method is the fact that the theory of Verhulst and Pearl, for example, has been accepted as a satisfactory fit to a remarkably heterogeneous set of ecological situations. The heterogeneity emphasizes, not the generality of the theory, as is usually assumed, but the weak method of application. The problems discussed in the preceeding sections have not caused difficulty in the past because the established method of fitting theories is not powerful enough to discriminate them.

This weakness is related to the number of constants fitted in the process of comparing a curve to data. With more than two such constants, the prior probability of a "nice" fit (a subjective term to match the subjective basis of judgment) is already high, and with more than four constants to be fitted to one population curve it is hardly necessary to make the comparison.

(3) The method centers attention on the whole rather than on the parts. A direct result has been a general satisfaction with the wholes, without the realization that at least some of the parts in the comparison are not of the right kind. If the overall fit is "nice," a prejudice is established against a rejection of the comparison through some particular fault.

The best fit of a theory to data has been said to be that of the Verhulst-Pearl theory to the growth curve of a yeast culture (Allee *et al*. 1949). The data were gathered by Carlson (1913), and the fit was made by Pearl (1930). In spite of this belief, the culture was unrenewed, the limiting factors were probably at first the food supply (sugar) and the waste accumulation, shifting later to the lower usefulness of the wastes as foods and the re-use of material from burst cells; the culture ended by converting to resting cells!

These three arguments are an unfortunate combination. A high prior probability leaves one at a loss in subjective judgement; the usual standards are not adequately strict. The lack of objective evaluation in whole comparisons, which has been accepted as a necessary evil, has forestalled any degree of partial analysis, in which objective methods are indeed possible. The lack of partial analyses has in turn promoted the habit of fitting all constants, whether some can be calculated independently or not, thus pushing the prior probability to its maximum.

For the comparison of whole theories to the history of a culture, the developing field of stochastic processes offers the only reasonable approach.

But whole comparisons may not be the best way to test theories. The danger still remains that the whole need not be the sum of the right parts. Rigorous testing of the separate aspects of the theories would not only simplify the mathematics, but would eliminate, at least to some degree, this last criticism.

In the Verhulst-Pearl theory, two basic concepts are combined. One is that the exponential rate of growth has a maximum $(r)$, and the other is that the degree of saturation $(N/K)$ is a linear depressant of the rate of growth $(dN/Ndt)$.

The first concept is well supported and established. To measure it in a particular case, however, may be difficult. If there is to be any assurance of its accuracy it should be obtained from at least two kinds of measures in the growing population. Such estimates can be made "deterministic," in the sense that the average of many observations of a constant will approach its deterministic value. Furthermore, the empirical range of error would, with a suitable distribution, provide a means of probability evaluation. The two measures can be tested for the absence of trend and for agreement with each other.

The second concept has never been analysed. Rate curves derived from growth curves are not adequate, since they contain the same stochastic processes as the original data. But the problem can be handled in a different way. In the equation:

$$\frac{dN}{Ndt} = r\left(1 - \frac{N}{K}\right) = r - \frac{r}{K}(N)$$

a graph of the rate of change ($dN/Ndt$) plotted against the population size ($N$) shows a straight line, with a $y$-intercept of $r$, and $x$-intercept of $K$, and a slope of $-r/K$.

Points for this graph could be obtained from a modified chemostat. Keeping the composition of the inflow constant, its rate (the washing-out rate, $V/W$) can be set at various levels between $r$ and zero. At $r$, the system will be unstable, but for any rate of flow less than this the population will increase until its growth rate is density-depressed to the rate of flow ($dN/Ndt = V/W$). At each level of this flow, after the system comes to a steady state, a series of observations can be made on the population size ($N$). The data can then be put through the standard statistical test (again, if a suitable distribution is found) to determine whether the regression of population size ($N$) upon the rate of growth ($dN/Ndt$) is linear. This would be a first test of the basic principle of the theory.

Needless to say, this method will apply to other theories of sigmoid growth. In the Gompertz curve, the linear plot becomes:

$$\frac{dN}{Ndt} = r \log_e K - r \log_e N.$$

The procedure can be turned about, to use the methods of partial analysis as a means of finding simple functions for theories. If, for example, none of the functions in established theories worked,

a search with the aid of these partial systems may produce suitable relationships. Any experimental technique which will produce a steady state should yield information that can be used in deterministic theory.

The Lotka-Volterra predation theory indicates that:

1. A plot of $dN_1/N_1dt$ against $N_2$ is a straight line, with a $y$-intercept of $r_1$ and a slope of $-1/k_1$.
2. A plot of $dN_2/N_2dt$ against $N_1$ is a straight line, with a $y$-intercept of $-d_2$ and a slope of $1/k_2$.
3. $dN_1/N_1dt$, for one value of $N_2$, is constant for all values of $N_1$.
4. $dN_2/N_2dt$, for one value of $N_1$, is constant for all values of $N_2$.

Even these partial analyses, however, are not foolproof. Straight lines are easier to obtain than most people believe. If the data conform to a straight line "except at one end," or if they conform to two straight lines with a "break" in the middle, a linear relation is probably absent. Furthermore, small deviations toward one end of a curve may reflect large discrepancies in the dynamic processes of growth. For the faith that is put into population theories, the experimental examination will have to be rigorous.

## DISCUSSION

The preceding sections point to one conclusion: very little in this field of population dynamics is beyond the hypothetical stage. With the possible exception of the concept of exponential growth, it is a misuse of terms to refer to any of the interpretations as "theories." Almost all of the evidence used in support of various interpretations is, at best, inconclusive.

Yet, the field has provided a considerable fund of interesting material, enough to have profound effects upon allied areas. Perhaps, more than anything else, this influence urges an intense and cautious re-examination of our concepts.

The degree of acceptance of such concepts as, for examples, the Verhulst-Pearl logistic and the Lotka-Volterra equations, is astonishing.

Concepts do not appear easily. Although logic teaches that an infinite number of curves can be fitted to data on sigmoid growth, very few such equations have been set down, and of these only two, the Verhulst-Pearl and the Klem equations, have been expressed adequately in ecological terms. We have only one well-known theory of predation, one of competition, and two or three for parasitism. Sparse as it may be, this collection is the accumulated work of many people for many years.

Hence, even though the present stock of concepts is but a collection of hypotheses, it is a valuable collection. It contains what must be considered progress of the most difficult kind. For the future, also, the continued development of hypothetical relationships will be useful; the armchair is still a necessary piece of equipment.

The experimental side of population dynamics is in a different situation. In spite of the many curves recorded, the many fits made, the work will have to be largely discounted as evidence in support of any particular theories. A repetition of all of it, with more appropriate and more carefully detailed designs, will have to be initiated.

Regardless of the use to be made of stochastic processes, deterministic theory will continue to play a major role. It is a way of thinking; inevitably one considers, not the sequential range of values, but the most likely course of events. Most important, thinking in deterministic terms is a way of producing concepts.

## SUMMARY

The methods for experimental verification of deterministic theories in population dynamics are criticized from several points of view.

The mechanism of control in the culture should conform to the conditions implied in the theory. This is often not the case; the most notable instance of disagreement concerns the Verhulst-Pearl logistic, which has never been supported by an experiment known to be made in an appropriate environment. Several kinds of culture control are classified.

The reactions of the population should be limited to those provided in the theory. Most equations are admittedly simplified, but such an admission should be coupled with a much more successful restriction to simplified responses by the organisms. Many laboratory species are highly complex in their reactions to environmental control; physiological adaptation is especially common. A simple response is probably unrelated to evolutionary complexity. Two possible means of finding ideally simple reactions are indicated.

Theoretical equations are manipulated to show various of their properties. The method is useful as a means of "*a priori*" evaluation of equations, especially of their limitations. It is also useful as a means of discovering more simple but vital aspects of theories for specific analysis.

The common method of fitting deterministic curves to data is criticized from three points of view, any one of which raises a serious objection. One solution to the problem in the use of stochastic theory is mentioned, but methods are also discussed for the application of sound experimental techniques to deterministic theory.

The general conclusion is that we have a useful and valuable stockpile of concepts, but that up to the present little of the experimental work is at all conclusive. Most of the ideas in this field should be regarded as hypotheses, not theories.

## REFERENCES

Allee, W. C., A. E. Emerson, O. Park, T. Park, and K. P. Schmidt. 1949. Principles of animal ecology. Phila. and London: Saunders.

De Bach, P., and H. S. Smith. 1947. Effects of parasite population density on the rate of change of host and parasite populations. Ecology, 28: 290–298.

Carlson, T. 1913. Über Geschwindigkeit und Grösse der Hefevermehrung in Würze. Biochem. Ztschr., 57: 313–334.

Gause, G. F. 1934. The struggle for existence. Baltimore: Williams & Wilkins.

——. 1935. Vérifications expérimentales de la théorie mathématique de la lutte pour la vie. Actual. Sci. Industr., 277: 1–61.

Gause, G. F., N. P. Smaragdova, and A. A. Witt. 1936. Further studies of interaction between predators and prey. J. Anim. Ecol., 5: 1–18.

Hershey, A. D. 1938. Factors limiting bacterial growth. II. Growth without lag in Bacterium coli cultures. Proc. Soc. Exp. Biol. Med., 38: 127–128.

——. 1939. Factors limiting bacterial growth. IV. The age of the parent culture and the rate of growth of transplants in Escherichia coli. J. Bact., 37: 285–299.

Kavanagh, A. J., and O. W. Richards. 1934. The autocatalytic growth curve. Amer. Nat., 68: 54–59.

Klem, Alf. 1933. On the growth of populations of yeast. Norske Vetensk.-Akad., Oslo, Hvalrådets Skrifter, 7: 55–91.

Lotka, A. J. 1925. Elements of physical biology. Baltimore: Williams & Wilkins.

Malthus, T. R. 1798. An essay on the principle of population. London.

Myers, J., and L. B. Clark. 1944. Culture conditions and the development of the photosynthetic mechanism. II. An apparatus for the continuous culture of Chlorella. J. Gen. Physiol., 28: 103–112.

Novick, A., and L. Szilard. 1950. Experiments with the chemostat on spontaneous mutations of bacteria. Proc. Nat. Acad. Sci., 36: 708–719.

Nicholson, A. J., and V. A. Bailey. 1935. The balance of animal populations. Part I. Proc. Zool. Soc. London, 1935, Part III: 551–598.

Pearl, Raymond. 1930. The biology of population growth. New York: Knopf.

Pearl, Raymond, and L. J. Reed. 1920. On the rate of growth of the population of the United States since 1790 and its mathematical representation. Proc. Nat. Acad. Sci., 6: 275.

Richards, O. W. 1932. The second cycle and subsequent growth of a population of yeast. Archiv Protistenkunde, 78: 263–301.

Thompson, W. R. 1939. Biological control and the theories of the interaction of populations. Parasitology, 31: 299–388.

Verhulst, P. F. 1838. Notice sur la loi que la population suit dans son accroissement. Corr. Math. et Phys., 10: 113.

Volterra, Vito. 1928. Variations and fluctuations of the number of individuals in animal species living together. J. du Conseil intern. pour l'explor. de la mer III vol. I, reprinted in: Animal Ecology, by R. N. Chapman, McGraw-Hill, New York, 1931.

Wilson, E. B. 1934. Mathematics of growth. Cold Spring Harbor Symp. on Quant. Biol., 2: 199–202.

# PART III

# RELATIONSHIPS BETWEEN SPECIES: COMPETITION AND PREDATION

# THE INFLUENCE OF INTERSPECIFIC COMPETITION AND OTHER FACTORS ON THE DISTRIBUTION OF THE BARNACLE *CHTHAMALUS STELLATUS*

Joseph H. Connell

*Department of Biology, University of California, Santa Barbara, Goleta, California*

## Introduction

Most of the evidence for the occurrence of interspecific competition in animals has been gained from laboratory populations. Because of the small amount of direct evidence for its occurrence in nature, competition has sometimes been assigned a minor role in determining the composition of animal communities.

Indirect evidence exists, however, which suggests that competition may sometimes be responsible for the distribution of animals in nature. The range of distribution of a species may be decreased in the presence of another species with similar requirements (Beauchamp and Ullyott 1932, Endean, Kenny and Stephenson 1956). Uniform distribution is space is usually attributed to intraspecies competition (Holme 1950, Clark and Evans 1954). When animals with similar requirements, such as 2 or more closely related species, are found coexisting in the same area, careful analysis usually indicates that they are not actually competing with each other (Lack 1954, MacArthur 1958).

In the course of an investigation of the animals of an intertidal rocky shore I noticed that the adults of 2 species of barnacles occupied 2 separate horizontal zones with a small area of overlap, whereas the young of the species from the upper zone were found in much of the lower zone. The upper species, *Chthamalus stellatus* (Poli) thus settled but did not survive in the lower zone. It seemed probable that this species was eliminated by the lower one, *Balanus balanoides* (L), in a struggle for a common requisite which was in short supply. In the rocky intertidal region, space for attachment and growth is often extremely limited. This paper is an account of some observations and experiments designed to test the hypothesis that the absence in the lower zone of adults of *Chthamalus* was due to interspecific competition with *Balanus* for space. Other factors which may have influenced the distribution were also studied. The study was made at Millport, Isle of Cumbrae, Scotland.

I would like to thank Prof. C. M. Yonge and the staff of the Marine Station, Millport, for their help, discussions and encouragement during the course of this work. Thanks are due to the following for their critical reading of the manuscript: C. S. Elton, P. W. Frank, G. Hardin, N. G. Hairston, E. Orias, T. Park and his students, and my wife.

### Distribution of the species of barnacles

The upper species, *Chthamalus stellatus,* has its center of distribution in the Mediterranean; it reaches its northern limit in the Shetland Islands, north of Scotland. At Millport, adults of this species occur between the levels of mean high water of neap and spring tides (M.H.W.N and M.H.W.S.: see Figure 5 and Table I) In southwest England and Ireland, adult *Chtham-*

Reproduced with permission from Ecology, 42:710-723, 1961. Published by Duke University Press.

*alus* occur at moderate population densities throughout the intertidal zone, more abundantly when *Balanus balanoides* is sparse or absent (Southward and Crisp 1954, 1956). At Millport the larvae settle from the plankton onto the shore mainly in September and October; some additional settlement may occur until December. The settlement is most abundant between M.H.W.S. and mean tide level (M.T.L.), in patches of rock surface left bare as a result of the mortality of *Balanus*, limpets, and other sedentary organisms. Few of the *Chthamalus* that settle below M.H. W.N. survive, so that adults are found only occasionally at these levels.

*Balanus balanoides* is a boreal-arctic species, reaching its southern limit in northern Spain. At Millport it occupies almost the entire intertidal region, from mean low water of spring tides (M.L.W.S.) up to the region between M.H.W.N. and M.H.W.S. Above M.H.W.N. it occurs intermingled with *Chthamalus* for a short distance. *Balanus* settles on the shore in April and May, often in very dense concentrations (see Table IV).

The main purpose of this study was to determine the cause of death of those *Chthamalus* that settled below M.H.W.N. A study which was being carried on at this time had revealed that physical conditions, competition for space, and predation by the snail *Thais lapillus* L. were among the most important causes of mortality of *Balanus balanoides*. Therefore, the observations and experiments in the present study were designed to detect the effects of these factors on the survival of *Chthamalus*.

## METHODS

Intertidal barnacles are very nearly ideal for the study of survival under natural conditions. Their sessile habit allows direct observation of the survival of individuals in a group whose positions have been mapped. Their small size and dense concentrations on rocks exposed at intervals make experimentation feasible. In addition, they may be handled and transplanted without injury on pieces of rock, since their opercular plates remain closed when exposed to air.

The experimental area was located on the Isle of Cumbrae in the Firth of Clyde, Scotland. Farland Point, where the study was made, comprises the southeast tip of the island; it is exposed to moderate wave action. The shore rock consists mainly of old red sandstone, arranged in a series of ridges, from 2 to 6 ft high, oriented at right angles to the shoreline. A more detailed description is given by Connell (1961). The

other barnacle species present were *Balanus crenatus* Brug and *Verruca stroemia* (O. F. Muller), both found in small numbers only at and below M.L.W.S.

To measure the survival of *Chthamalus*, the positions of all individuals in a patch were mapped. Any barnacles which were empty or missing at the next examination of this patch must have died in the interval, since emigration is impossible. The mapping was done by placing thin glass plates (lantern slide cover glasses, $10.7 \times 8.2$ cm, area 87.7 cm$^2$) over a patch of barnacles and marking the position of each *Chthamalus* on it with glass-marking ink. The positions of the corners of the plate were marked by drilling small holes in the rock. Observations made in subsequent censuses were noted on a paper copy of the glass map.

The study areas were chosen by searching for patches of *Chthamalus* below M.H.W.N. in a stretch of shore about 50 ft long. When 8 patches had been found, no more were looked for. The only basis for rejection of an area in this search was that it contained fewer than 50 *Chthamalus* in an area of about 1/10 m$^2$. Each numbered area consisted of one or more glass maps located in the 1/10 m$^2$. They were mapped in March and April, 1954, before the main settlement of *Balanus* began in late April.

Very few *Chthamalus* were found to have settled below mid-tide level. Therefore pieces of rock bearing *Chthamalus* were removed from levels above M.H.W.N. and transplanted to and below M.T.L. A hole was drilled through each piece; it was then fastened to the rock by a stainless steel screw driven into a plastic screw anchor fitted into a hole drilled into the rock. A hole 1/4" in diameter and 1" deep was found to be satisfactory. The screw could be removed and replaced repeatedly and only one stone was lost in the entire period.

For censusing, the stones were removed during a low tide period, brought to the laboratory for examination, and returned before the tide rose again. The locations and arrangements of each area are given in Table I; the transplanted stones are represented by areas 11 to 15.

The effect of competition for space on the survival of *Chthamalus* was studied in the following manner: After the settlement of *Balanus* had stopped in early June, having reached densities of 49/cm$^2$ on the experimental areas (Table I) a census of the surviving *Chthamalus* was made on each area (see Figure 1). Each map was then divided so that about half of the number of

TABLE I. Description of experimental areas*

| Area no. | Height in ft from M.T.L. | % of time submerged | Chthamalus, autumn 1953 settlement | | All barnacles, undisturbed portion | Remarks |
|---|---|---|---|---|---|---|
| | | | Undisturbed portion | Portion without Balanus | | |
| MHWS.............. | +4.9 | 4 | — | — | — | — |
| 1.................. | +4.2 | 9 | 2.2 | — | 19.2 | Vertical, partly protected |
| 2.................. | +3.5 | 16 | 5.2 | 4.2 | — | Vertical, wave beaten |
| MHWN.............. | +3.1 | 21 | — | — | -- | — |
| 3a............... | +2.2 | 30 | 0.6 | 0.6 | 30.9 | Horizontal, wave beaten |
| 3b............... | " | " | 0.5 | 0.7 | 29.2 | " " " |
| 4................. | +1.4 | 38 | 1.9 | 0.6 | — | 30° to vertical, partly protected |
| 5................. | +1.4 | " | 2.4 | 1.2 | — | " " " " " |
| 6................. | +1.0 | 42 | 1.1 | 1.9 | 38.2 | Horizontal, top of a boulder, partly protected |
| 7a............... | +0.7 | 44 | 1.3 | 2.0 | 49.3 | Vertical, protected |
| 7b............... | " | " | 2.3 | 2.0 | 51.7 | " " |
| 11a.............. | 0.0 | 50 | 1.0 | 0.6 | 32.0 | Vertical, protected |
| 11b.............. | " | " | 0.2 | 0.3 | — | " " |
| 12a.............. | 0.0 | 100 | 1.2 | 1.2 | 18.8 | Horizontal, immersed in tide pool |
| 12b.............. | " | 100 | 0.8 | 0.9 | — | " " " " " |
| 13a.............. | −1.0 | 58 | 4.9 | 4.1 | 29.5 | Vertical, wave beaten |
| 13b.............. | " | " | 3.1 | 2.4 | — | " " " |
| 14a.............. | −2.5 | 71 | 0.7 | 1.1 | — | 45° angle, wave beaten |
| 14b.............. | " | " | 1.0 | 1.0 | — | " " " " |
| MLWN.............. | −3.0 | 77 | — | — | -- | — |
| MLWS.............. | −5.1 | 96 | — | — | - . | — |
| 15................ | +1.0 | 42 | 32.0 | — | -- | ⎧Chthamalus of autumn, 1954 set- |
| 7b................ | +0.7 | 44 | 5.5 | 3.7 | -- | ⎩tlement; densities of Oct., 1954. |

* The letter "a" following an area number indicates that this area was enclosed by a cage; "b" refers to a closely adjacent area which was not enclosed. All areas faced either east or south except 7a and 7b, which faced north.

Chthamalus were in each portion. One portion was chosen (by flipping a coin), and those Balanus which were touching or immediately surrounding each Chthamalus were carefully removed with a needle; the other portion was left untouched. In this way it was possible to measure the effect on the survival of Chthamalus both of intraspecific competition alone and of competition with Balanus. It was not possible to have the numbers or population densities of Chthamalus exactly equal on the 2 portions of each area. This was due to the fact that, since Chthamalus often occurred in groups, the Balanus had to be removed from around all the members of a group to ensure that no crowding by Balanus occurred. The densities of Chthamalus were very low, however, so that the slight differences in density between the 2 portions of each area can probably be disregarded; intraspecific crowding was very seldom observed. Censuses of the Chthamalus were made at intervals of 4-6 weeks during the next year; notes were made at each census of factors such as crowding, undercutting or smothering which had taken place since the last examination. When necessary, Balanus which had grown until they threatened to touch the Chthamalus were removed in later examinations.

To study the effects of different degrees of immersion, the areas were located throughout the tidal range, either in situ or on transplanted stones, as shown in Table I. Area 1 had been under observation for 1½ years previously. The effects of different degrees of wave shock could not be studied adequately in such a small area

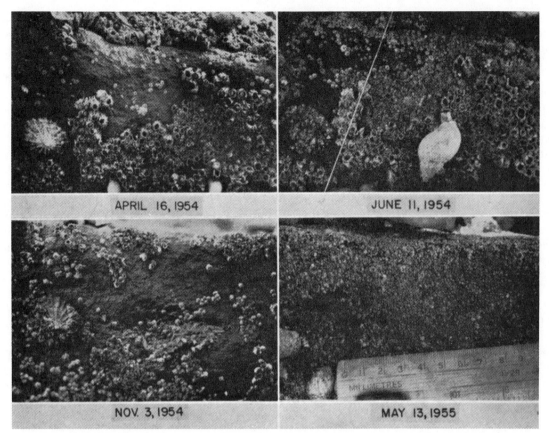

APRIL 16, 1954

JUNE 11, 1954

NOV. 3, 1954

MAY 13, 1955

Fig. 1. Area 7b. In the first photograph the large barnacles are *Balanus,* the small ones scattered in the bare patch, *Chthamalus.* The white line on the second photograph divides the undisturbed portion (right) from the portion from which *Balanus* were removed (left). A limpet, *Patella vulgata,* occurs on the left, and predatory snails, *Thais lapillus,* are visible.

of shore but such differences as existed are listed in Table I.

The effects of the predatory snail, *Thais lapillus,* (synonymous with *Nucella* or *Purpura,* Clench 1947), were studied as follows: Cages of stainless steel wire netting, 8 meshes per inch, were attached over some of the areas. This mesh has an open area of 60% and previous work (Connell 1961) had shown that it did not inhibit growth or survival of the barnacles. The cages were about 4 × 6 inches, the roof was about an inch above the barnacles and the sides were fitted to the irregularities of the rock. They were held in place in the same manner as the transplanted stones. The transplanted stones were attached in pairs, one of each pair being enclosed in a cage (Table I).

These cages were effective in excluding all but the smallest *Thais.* Occasionally small *Thais,* ½ to 1 cm in length, entered the cages through gaps at the line of juncture of netting and rock surface. In the concurrent study of *Balanus* (Con-

nell 1961), small *Thais* were estimated to have occurred inside the cages about 3% of the time.

All the areas and stones were established before the settlement of *Balanus* began in late April, 1954. Thus the *Chthamalus* which had settled naturally on the shore were then of the 1953 year class and all about 7 months old. Some *Chthamalus* which settled in the autumn of 1954 were followed until the study was ended in June, 1955. In addition some adults which, judging from their large size and the great erosion of their shells, must have settled in 1952 or earlier, were present on the transplanted stones. Thus records were made of at least 3 year-classes of *Chthamalus.*

## Results

### The effects of physical factors

In Figures 2 and 3, the dashed line indicates the survival of *Chthamalus* growing without contact with *Balanus.* The suffix "a" indicates that the area was protected from *Thais* by a cage.

In the absence of *Balanus* and *Thais,* and protected by the cages from damage by water-borne objects, the survival of *Chthamalus* was good at all levels. For those which had settled normally on the shore (Fig. 2), the poorest survival was on the lowest area, 7a. On the transplanted stones (Fig. 3, area 12), constant immersion in a tide pool resulted in the poorest survival. The reasons for the trend toward slightly greater mortality as the degree of immersion increased are unknown. The amount of attached algae on the stones in the tide pool was much greater than on the other areas. This may have reduced the flow of water and food or have interfered directly with feeding movements. Another possible indirect effect of increased immersion is the increase in predation by the snail, *Thais lapillus,* at lower levels.

*Chthamalus* is tolerant of a much greater degree of immersion than it normally encounters. This is shown by the survival for a year on area 12 in a tide pool, together with the findings of Fischer (1928) and Barnes (1956a), who found that *Chthamalus* withstood submersion for 12 and 22 months, respectively. Its absence below M.T.L. can probably be ascribed either to a lack of initial settlement or to poor survival of newly settled larvae. Lewis and Powell (1960) have suggested that the survival of *Chthamalus* may be favored by increased light or warmth during emersion in its early life on the shore. These conditions would tend to occur higher on the shore in Scotland than in southern England.

The effects of wave action on the survival of *Chthamalus* are difficult to assess. Like the degree of immersion, the effects of wave action may act indirectly. The areas 7 and 12, where relatively poor survival was found, were also the areas of least wave action. Although *Chthamalus* is usually abundant on wave beaten areas and absent from sheltered bays in Scotland, Lewis and Powell (1960) have shown that in certain sheltered bays it may be very abundant. Hatton (1938) found that in northern France, settlement and growth rates were greater in wave-beaten areas at M.T.L., but, at M.H.W.N., greater in sheltered areas.

At the upper shore margins of distribution *Chthamalus* evidently can exist higher than *Balanus* mainly as a result of its greater tolerance to heat and/or desiccation. The evidence for this was gained during the spring of 1955. Records from a tide and wave guage operating at this time about one-half mile north of the study area showed that a period of neap tides had coincided with an unusual period of warm calm weather in April so that for several days no water, not even waves, reached the level of Area 1. In the period

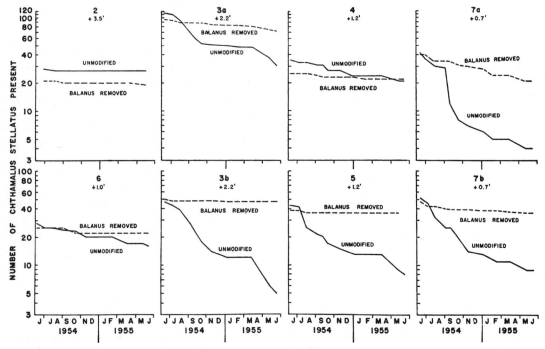

FIG. 2. Survivorship curves of *Chthamalus stellatus* which had settled naturally on the shore in the autumn of 1953. Areas designated "a" were protected from predation by cages. In each area the survival of *Chthamalus* growing without contact with *Balanus* is compared to that in the undisturbed area. For each area the vertical distance in feet from M.T.L. is shown.

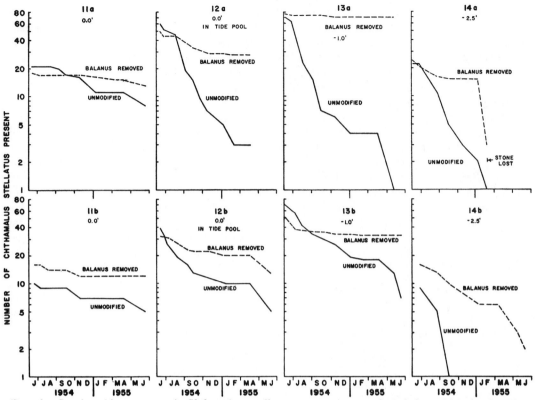

FIG. 3. Survivorship curves of *Chthamalus stellatus* on stones transplanted from high levels. These had settled in the autumn of 1953; the arrangement is the same as that of Figure 2.

between the censuses of February and May, *Balanus* aged one year suffered a mortality of 92%, those 2 years and older, 51%. Over the same period the mortality of *Chthamalus* aged 7 months was 62%, those 1½ years and older, 2%. Records of the survival of *Balanus* at several levels below this showed that only those *Balanus* in the top quarter of the intertidal region suffered high mortality during this time (Connell 1961).

*Competition for space*

At each census notes were made for individual barnacles of any crowding which had occurred since the last census. Thus when one barnacle started to grow up over another this fact was noted and at the next census 4-6 weeks later the progress of this process was noted. In this way a detailed description was built up of these gradually occurring events.

Intraspecific competition leading to mortality in *Chthamalus* was a rare event. For areas 2 to 7, on the portions from which *Balanus* had been removed, 167 deaths were recorded in a year. Of these, only 6 could be ascribed to crowding between individuals of *Chthamalus*. On the undisturbed portions no such crowding was

observed. This accords with Hatton's (1938) observation that he never saw crowding between individuals of *Chthamalus* as contrasted to its frequent occurrence between individuals of *Balanus*.

Interspecific competition between *Balanus* and *Chthamalus* was, on the other hand, a most important cause of death of *Chthamalus*. This is shown both by the direct observations of the process of crowding at each census and by the differences between the survival curves of *Chthamalus* with and without *Balanus*. From the periodic observations it was noted that after the first month on the undisturbed portions of areas 3 to 7 about 10% of the *Chthamalus* were being covered as *Balanus* grew over them; about 3% were being undercut and lifted by growing *Balanus;* a few had died without crowding. By the end of the 2nd month about 20% of the *Chthamalus* were either wholly or partly covered by *Balanus;* about 4% had been undercut; others were surrounded by tall *Balanus*. These processes continued at a lower rate in the autumn and almost ceased during the later winter. In the spring *Balanus* resumed growth and more crowding was observed.

**162**

In Table II, these observations are summarized for the undistributed portions of all the areas. Above M.T.L., the *Balanus* tended to overgrow the *Chthamalus,* whereas at the lower levels, undercutting was more common. This same trend was evident within each group of areas, undercutting being more prevalent on area 7 than on area 3, for example. The faster growth of *Balanus* at lower levels (Hatton 1938, Barnes and Powell 1953) may have resulted in more undercutting. When *Chthamalus* was completely covered by *Balanus* it was recorded as dead; even though death may not have occurred immediately, the buried barnacle was obviously not a functioning member of the population.

TABLE II. The causes of mortality of *Chthamalus stellatus* of the 1953 year group on the undisturbed portions of each area

| Area no. | Height in ft from M.T.L. | No. at start | No. of deaths in the next year | Percentage of Deaths Resulting From: | | | |
|---|---|---|---|---|---|---|---|
| | | | | Smothering by *Balanus* | Undercutting by *Balanus* | Other crowding by *Balanus* | Unknown causes |
| 2......... | +3.5 | 28 | 1 | 0 | 0 | 0 | 100 |
| 3a........ | +2.2 | 111 | 81 | 61 | 6 | 10 | 23 |
| 3b........ | " | 47 | 42 | 57 | 5 | 2 | 36 |
| 4......... | +1.4 | 34 | 14 | 21 | 14 | 0 | 65 |
| 5......... | +1.4 | 43 | 35 | 11 | 11 | 3 | 75 |
| 6......... | +1.0 | 27 | 11 | 9 | 0 | 0 | 91 |
| 7a........ | +0.7 | 42 | 38 | 21 | 16 | 53 | 10 |
| 7b........ | " | 51 | 42 | 24 | 10 | 10 | 56 |
| 11a........ | 0.0 | 21 | 13 | 54 | 8 | 0 | 38 |
| 11b........ | " | 10 | 5 | 40 | 0 | 0 | 60 |
| 12a........ | 0.0 | 60 | 57 | 19 | 33 | 7 | 41 |
| 12b........ | " | 39 | 34 | 9 | 18 | 3 | 70 |
| 13a........ | -1.0 | 71 | 70 | 19 | 24 | 3 | 54 |
| 13b........ | " | 69 | 62 | 18 | 8 | 3 | 71 |
| 14a........ | -2.5 | 22 | 21 | 24 | 42 | 10 | 24 |
| 14b........ | " | 9 | 9 | 0 | 0 | 0 | 100 |
| Total, 2- 7.. | — | 383 | 264 | 37 | 9 | 16 | 38 |
| Total, 11-14.. | — | 301 | 271 | 19 | 21 | 4 | 56 |

In Table II under the term "other crowding" have been placed all instances where *Chthamalus* were crushed laterally between 2 or more *Balanus,* or where *Chthamalus* disappeared in an interval during which a dense population of *Balanus* grew rapidly. For example, in area 7a the *Balanus,* which were at the high population density of 48 per cm², had no room to expand except upward and the barnacles very quickly grew into the form of tall cylinders or cones with the diameter of the opercular opening greater than

that of the base. It was obvious that extreme crowding occurred under these circumstances, but the exact cause of the mortality of the *Chthamalus* caught in this crush was difficult to ascertain.

In comparing the survival curves of Figs. 2 and 3 within each area it is evident that *Chthamalus* kept free of *Balanus* survived better than those in the adjacent undisturbed areas on all but areas 2 and 14a. Area 2 was in the zone where adults of *Balanus* and *Chthamalus* were normally mixed; at this high level *Balanus* evidently has no influence on the survival of *Chthamalus.* On Stone 14a, the survival of *Chthamalus* without *Balanus* was much better until January when a starfish, *Asterias rubens* L., entered the cage and ate the barnacles.

Much variation occurred on the other 14 areas. When the *Chthamalus* growing without contact with *Balanus* are compared with those on the adjacent undisturbed portion of the area, the survival was very much better on 10 areas and moderately better on 4. In all areas, some *Chthamalus* in the undisturbed portions escaped severe crowding. Sometimes no *Balanus* happened to settle close to a *Chthamalus,* or sometimes those which did died soon after settlement. In some instances, *Chthamalus* which were being undercut by *Balanus* attached themselves to the *Balanus* and so survived. Some *Chthamalus* were partly covered by *Balanus* but still survived. It seems probable that in the 4 areas, nos. 4, 6, 11a, and 11b, where *Chthamalus* survived well in the presence of *Balanus,* a higher proportion of the *Chthamalus* escaped death in one of these ways.

The fate of very young *Chthamalus* which settled in the autumn of 1954 was followed in detail in 2 instances, on stone 15 and area 7b. The *Chthamalus* on stone 15 had settled in an irregular space surrounded by large *Balanus.* Most of the mortality occurred around the edges of the space as the *Balanus* undercut and lifted the small *Chthamalus* nearby. The following is a tabulation of all the deaths of young *Chthamalus* between Sept. 30, 1954 and Feb. 14, 1955, on Stone 15, with the associated situations:

| | |
|---|---|
| Lifted by *Balanus* | : 29 |
| Crushed by *Balanus* | : 4 |
| Smothered by *Balanus* and *Chthamalus* | : 2 |
| Crushed between *Balanus and Chthamalus* | : 1 |
| Lifted by *Chthamalus* | : 1 |
| Crushed between two other *Chthamalus* | : 1 |
| Unknown | : 3 |

This list shows that crowding of newly settled *Chthamalus* by older *Balanus* in the autumn mainly takes the form of undercutting, rather than of smothering as was the case in the spring. The reason for this difference is probably that the *Chthamalus* are more firmly attached in the spring so that the fast growing young *Balanus* grow up over them when they make contact. In the autumn the reverse is the case, the *Balanus* being firmly attached, the *Chthamalus* weakly so.

Although the settlement of *Chthamalus* on Stone 15 in the autumn of 1954 was very dense, 32/cm², so that most of them were touching another, only 2 of the 41 deaths were caused by intraspecific crowding among the *Chthamalus*. This is in accord with the findings from the 1953 settlement of *Chthamalus*.

The mortality rates for the young *Chthamalus* on area 7b showed seasonal variations. Between October 10, 1954 and May 15, 1955 the relative mortality rate per day $\times$ 100 was 0.14 on the undisturbed area and 0.13 where *Balanus* had been removed. Over the next month, the rate increased to 1.49 on the undisturbed area and 0.22 where *Balanus* was absent. Thus the increase in mortality of young *Chthamalus* in late spring was also associated with the presence of *Balanus*.

Some of the stones transplanted from high to low levels in the spring of 1954 bore adult *Chthamalus*. On 3 stones, records were kept of the survival of these adults, which had settled in the autumn of 1952 or in previous years and were at least 20 months old at the start of the experiment. Their mortality is shown in Table III; it was always much greater when *Balanus* was not removed. On 2 of the 3 stones this mortality rate was almost as high as that of the younger group. These results suggest that any *Chthamalus* that managed to survive the competition for space with *Balanus* during the first year would probably be eliminated in the 2nd year.

Censuses of *Balanus* were not made on the experimental areas. However, on many other areas in the same stretch of shore the survival of *Balanus* was being studied during the same period (Connell 1961). In Table IV some mortality rates measured in that study are listed; the *Balanus* were members of the 1954 settlement at population densities and shore levels similar to those of the present study. The mortality rates of *Balanus* were about the same as those of *Chthamalus* in similar situations except at the highest level, area 1, where *Balanus* suffered much greater mortality than *Chthamalus*. Much of this mortality was caused by intraspecific crowding at all levels below area 1.

TABLE III. Comparison of the mortality rates of young and older *Chthamalus stellatus* on transplanted stones

| Stone No. | Shore level | Treatment | Number of *Chthamalus* present in June, 1954 | | % mortality over one year (or for 6 months for 14a) of *Chthamalus* | |
|---|---|---|---|---|---|---|
| | | | 1953 year group | 1952 or older year groups | 1953 year group | 1952 or older year groups |
| 13b | 1.0 ft below MTL | *Balanus* removed | 51 | 3 | 35 | 0 |
| | | Undisturbed | 69 | 16 | 90 | 31 |
| 12a | MTL, in a tide pool, caged | *Balanus* removed | 50 | 41 | 44 | 37 |
| | | Undisturbed | 60 | 31 | 95 | 71 |
| 14a | 2.5 ft below MTL, caged | *Balanus* removed | 25 | 45 | 40 | 36 |
| | | Undisturbed | 22 | 8 | 86 | 75 |

TABLE IV. Comparison of annual mortality rates of *Chthamalus stellatus* and *Balanus balanoides**

| Area no. | *Chthamalus stellatus*, autumn 1953 settlement | | |
|---|---|---|---|
| | Height in ft from M.T.L. | Population density: no./cm² June, 1954 | % mortality in the next year |
| 1............... | +4.2 | 21 | 17 |
| 3a............... | +2.2 | 31 | 72 |
| 3b............... | " | 29 | 89 |
| 6............... | +1.0 | 38 | 41 |
| 7a............... | +0.7 | 49 | 90 |
| 7b............... | " | 52 | 82 |
| 11a............... | 0.0 | 32 | 62 |
| 13a............... | −1.0 | 29 | 99 |
| 12a............... | (tide pool) | 19 | 95 |
| | *Balanus balanoides*, spring 1954 settlement | | |
| 1 (top).......... | +4.2 | 21 | 99 |
| 1:Middle Cage 1.. | +2.1 | 85 | 92 |
| 1:Middle Cage 2.. | " | 25 | 77 |
| 1:Low Cage 1.... | +1.5 | 26 | 88 |
| Stone 1.......... | −0.9 | 26 | 86 |
| Stone 2.......... | " | 68 | 94 |

* Population density includes both species. The mortality rates of *Chthamalus* refer to those on the undisturbed portions of each area. The data and area designations for *Balanus* were taken from Connell (1961); the present area 1 is the same as that designated 1 (top) in that paper.

In the observations made at each census it appeared that *Balanus* was growing faster than *Chthamalus*. Measurements of growth rates of the 2 species were made from photographs of the areas taken in June and November, 1954. Barnacles growing free of contact with each other were measured; the results are given in Table V. The growth rate of *Balanus* was greater than that of *Chthamalus* in the experimental areas; this agrees with the findings of Hatton (1938) on the shore in France and of Barnes (1956a) for continual submergence on a raft at Millport.

TABLE V. Growth rates of *Chthamalus stellatus* and *Balanus balanoides*. Measurements were made of uncrowded individuals on photographs of areas 3a, 3b and 7b. Those of *Chthamalus* were made on the same individuals on both dates; of *Balanus*, representative samples were chosen

| | CHTHAMALUS | | BALANUS | |
| --- | --- | --- | --- | --- |
| | No. measured | Average size, mm. | No. measured | Average size, mm. |
| June 11, 1954................ | 25 | 2.49 | 39 | 1.87 |
| November 3, 1954.............. | 25 | 4.24 | 27 | 4.83 |
| Average size in the interval....... | | 3.36 | | 3.35 |
| Absolute growth rate per day x 100 | | 1.21 | | 2.04 |

After a year of crowding the average population densities of *Balanus* and *Chthamalus* remained in the same relative proportion as they had been at the start, since the mortality rates were about the same. However, because of its faster growth, *Balanus* occupied a relatively greater area and, presumably, possessed a greater biomass relative to that of *Chthamalus* after a year.

The faster growth of *Balanus* probably accounts for the manner in which *Chthamalus* were crowded by *Balanus*. It also accounts for the sinuosity of the survival curves of *Chthamalus* growing in contact with *Balanus*. The mortality rate of these *Chthamalus*, as indicated by the slope of the curves in Figs. 2 and 3, was greatest in summer, decreased in winter and increased again in spring. The survival curves of *Chthamalus* growing without contact with *Balanus* do not show these seasonal variations which, therefore, cannot be the result of the direct action of physical factors such as temperature, wave action or rain.

Seasonal variations in growth rate of *Balanus* correspond to these changes in mortality rate of *Chthamalus*. In Figure 4 the growth of *Balanus* throughout the year as studied on an intertidal panel at Millport by Barnes and Powell (1953), is compared to the survival of *Chthamalus* at about the same intertidal level in the present study. The increased mortality of *Chthamalus* was found to occur in the same seasons as the increases in the growth rate of *Balanus*. The correlation was tested using the Spearman rank correlation coefficient. The absolute increase in diameter of *Balanus* in each month, read from the curve of growth, was compared to the percentage mortality of *Chthamalus* in the same month. For the 13 months in which data for *Chthamalus* was available, the correlation was highly significant, P = .01.

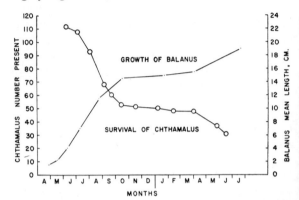

FIG. 4. A comparison of the seasonal changes in the growth of *Balanus balanoides* and in the survival of *Chthamalus stellatus* being crowded by *Balanus*. The growth of *Balanus* was that of panel 3, Barnes and Powell (1953), just above M.T.L. on Keppel Pier, Millport, during 1951-52. The *Chthamalus* were on area 3a of the present study, one-half mile south of Keppell Pier, during 1954-55.

From all these observations it appears that the poor survival of *Chthamalus* below M.H.W.N. is a result mainly of crowding by dense populations of faster growing *Balanus*.

At the end of the experiment in June, 1955, the surviving *Chthamalus* were collected from 5 of the areas. As shown in Table VI, the average size was greater in the *Chthamalus* which had grown free of contact with *Balanus;* in every case the difference was significant (P < .01, Mann-Whitney U. test, Siegel 1956). The survivors on the undisturbed areas were often misshapen, in some cases as a result of being lifted on to the side of an undercutting *Balanus*. Thus the smaller size of these barnacles may have been due to disturbances in the normal pattern of growth while they were being crowded.

These *Chthamalus* were examined for the presence of developing larvae in their mantle cavities. As shown in Table VI, in every area the proportion of the uncrowded *Chthamalus* with larvae was equal to or more often slightly greater than on the crowded areas. The reason for this may be related to the smaller size of the crowded *Chthamalus*. It is not due to separation, since *Chthamalus* can self-fertilize (Barnes and Crisp

TABLE VI. The effect of crowding on the size and presence of larvae in *Chthamalus stellatus,* collected in June, 1955

| Area | Treatment | Level, feet above MTL | Number of Chthamalus | DIAMETER IN MM Average | DIAMETER IN MM Range | % of individuals which had larvae in mantle cavity |
|------|-----------|------|------|------|------|------|
| 3a...... | Undisturbed | 2.2 | 18 | 3.5 | 2.7-4.6 | 61 |
| "...... | *Balanus* removed | " | 50 | 4.1 | 3.0-5.5 | 65 |
| 4...... | Undisturbed | 1.4 | 16 | 2.3 | 1.8 3.2 | 81 |
| "...... | *Balanus* removed | " | 37 | 3.7 | 2.5-5 1 | 100 |
| 5...... | Undisturbed | 1.4 | 7 | 3.3 | 2.8-3.7 | 70 |
| "...... | *Balanus* removed | " | 13 | 4.0 | 3.5-4.5 | 100 |
| 6...... | Undisturbed | 1.0 | 13 | 2.8 | 2.1-3.9 | 100 |
| "...... | *Balanus* removed | " | 14 | 4.1 | 3.0-5.2 | 100 |
| 7a & b.. | Undisturbed | 0.7 | 10 | 3.5 | 2.7-4.5 | 70 |
| " .. | *Balanus* removed | " | 23 | 4.3 | 3.0-6.3 | 81 |

TABLE VII. The effect of predation by *Thais lapillus* on the annual mortality rate of *Chthamalus stellatus* in the experimental areas*

| Area | Height in ft from M.T.L. | % mortality of Chthamalus over a year (The initial numbers are given in parentheses) a: Protected from predation by a cage With Balanus | Without Balanus | Difference | b: Unprotected, open to predation With Balanus | Without Balanus | Difference |
|------|------|------|------|------|------|------|------|
| Area 3.. | +2.2 | 73 (112) | 25 (96) | 48 | 89 (47) | 6 (50) | 83 |
| Area 7.. | +0.7 | 90 ( 42) | 47 (40) | 43 | 82 (51) | 23 (47) | 59 |
| Area 11.. | 0 | 62 ( 21) | 28 (18) | 34 | 50 (10) | 25 (16) | 25 |
| Area 12 . | 0† | 100 ( 60) | 53 (50) | 47 | 87 (39) | 59 (32) | 28 |
| Area 13.. | −1.0 | 98 ( 72) | 9 (77) | 89 | 90 (69) | 35 (51) | 55 |

*The records for 12a extend over only 10 months; for purposes of comparison the mortality rate for 12a has been multiplied by 1.2.
†Tide pool.

1956). Moore (1935) and Barnes (1953) have shown that the number of larvae in an individual of *Balanus balanoides* increases with increase in volume of the parent. Comparison of the cube of the diameter, which is proportional to the volume, of *Chthamalus* with and without *Balanus* shows that the volume may be decreased to ¼ normal size when crowding occurs. Assuming that the relation between larval numbers and volume in *Chthamalus* is similar to that of *Balanus,* a decrease in both frequency of occurrence and abundance of larvae in *Chthamalus* results from competition with *Balanus.* Thus the process described in this paper satisfies both aspects of interspecific competition as defined by Elton and Miller (1954): "in which one species affects the population of another by a process of interference, i.e., by reducing the reproductive efficiency or increasing the mortality of its competitor."

### The effect of predation by Thais

Cages which excluded *Thais* had been attached on 6 areas (indicated by the letter "a" following the number of the area). Area 14 was not included in the following analysis since many starfish were observed feeding on the barnacles at this level; one entered the cage in January, 1955, and ate most of the barnacles.

*Thais* were common in this locality, feeding on barnacles and mussels, and reaching average population densities of 200/m² below M.T.L. (Connell 1961). The mortality rates for *Chthamalus* in cages and on adjacent areas outside cages (indicated by the letter "b" after the number) are shown on Table VII.

If the mortality rates of *Chthamalus* growing without contact with *Balanus* are compared in and out of the cages, it can be seen that at the upper levels mortality is greater inside the cages,

at lower levels greater outside. Densities of *Thais* tend to be greater at and below M.T.L. so that this trend in the mortality rates of *Chthamalus* may be ascribed to an increase in predation by *Thais* at lower levels.

Mortality of *Chthamalus* in the absence of *Balanus* was appreciably greater outside than inside the cage only on area 13. In the other 4 areas it seems evident that few *Chthamalus* were being eaten by *Thais.* In a concurrent study of the behavior of *Thais* in feeding on *Balanus balanoides,* it was found that *Thais* selected the larger individuals as prey (Connell 1961). Since *Balanus* after a few month's growth was usually larger than *Chthamalus,* it might be expected that *Thais* would feed on *Balanus* in preference to *Chthamalus.* In a later study (unpublished) made at Santa Barbara, California, *Thais emarginata* Deshayes were enclosed in cages on the shore with mixed populations of *Balanus glandula* Darwin and *Chthamalus fissus* Darwin. These species were each of the same size range as the corresponding species at Millport. It was found that *Thais emarginata* fed on *Balanus glandula* in preference to *Chthamalus fissus.*

As has been indicated, much of the mortality of *Chthamalus* growing naturally intermingled with *Balanus* was a result of direct crowding by *Balanus.* It therefore seemed reasonable to take the difference between the mortality rates of *Chthamalus* with and without *Balanus* as an index of the degree of competition between the species. This difference was calculated for each area and is included in Table VII. If these differences are compared between each pair of adjacent areas in and out of a cage, it appears that the difference, and therefore the degree of competition, was greater outside the cages at the upper shore levels and less outside the cages at the lower levels.

Thus as predation increased at lower levels, the degree of competition decreased. This result would have been expected if *Thais* had fed upon *Balanus* in preference to *Chthamalus*. The general effect of predation by *Thais* seems to have been to lessen the interspecific competition below M.T.L.

## DISCUSSION

"Although animal communities appear qualitatively to be constructed as if competition were regulating their structure, even in the best studied cases there are nearly always difficulties and unexplored possibilities" (Hutchinson 1957).

In the present study direct observations at intervals showed that competition was occurring under natural conditions. In addition, the evidence is strong that the observed competition with *Balanus* was the principal factor determining the local distribution of *Chthamalus*. *Chthamalus* thrived at lower levels when it was not growing in contact with *Balanus*.

However, there remain unexplored possibilities. The elimination of *Chthamalus* requires a dense population of *Balanus*, yet the settlement of *Balanus* varied from year to year. At Millport, the settlement density of *Balanus balanoides* was measured for 9 years between 1944 and 1958 (Barnes 1956b, Connell 1961). Settlement was light in 2 years, 1946 and 1958. In the 3 seasons of *Balanus* settlement studied in detail, 1953-55, there was a vast oversupply of larvae ready for settlement. It thus seems probable that most of the *Chthamalus* which survived in a year of poor settlement of *Balanus* would be killed in competition with a normal settlement the following year. A succession of years with poor settlements of *Balanus* is a possible, but improbable occurrence at Millport, judging from the past record. A very light settlement is probably the result of a chance combination of unfavorable weather circumstances during the planktonic period (Barnes 1956b). Also, after a light settlement, survival on the shore is improved, owing principally to the reduction in intraspecific crowding (Connell 1961); this would tend to favor a normal settlement the following year, since barnacles are stimulated to settle by the presence of members of their own species already attached on the surface (Knight-Jones 1953).

The fate of those *Chthamalus* which had survived a year on the undisturbed areas is not known since the experiment ended at that time. It is probable, however, that most of them would have been eliminated within 6 months; the mortality rate had increased in the spring (Figs. 2 and 3), and these survivors were often misshapen and smaller than those which had not been crowded (Table VI). Adults on the transplanted stones had suffered high mortality in the previous year (Table III).

Another difficulty was that *Chthamalus* was rarely found to have settled below mid tide level at Millport. The reasons for this are unknown; it survived well if transplanted below this level, in the absence of *Balanus*. In other areas of the British Isles (in southwest England and Ireland, for example) it occurs below mid tide level.

The possibility that *Chthamalus* might affect *Balanus* deleteriously remains to be considered. It is unlikely that *Chthamalus* could cause much mortality of *Balanus* by direct crowding; its growth is much slower, and crowding between individuals of *Chthamalus* seldom resulted in death. A dense population of *Chthamalus* might deprive larvae of *Balanus* of space for settlement. Also, *Chthamalus* might feed on the planktonic larvae of *Balanus;* however, this would occur in March and April when both the sea water temperature and rate of cirral activity (presumably correlated with feeding activity), would be near their minima (Southward 1955).

The indication from the caging experiments that predation decreased interspecific competition suggests that the action of such additional factors tends to reduce the intensity of such interactions in natural conditions. An additional suggestion in this regard may be made concerning parasitism. Crisp (1960) found that the growth rate of *Balanus balanoides* was decreased if individuals were infected with the isopod parasite *Hemioniscus balani* (Spence Bate). In Britain this parasite has not been reported from *Chthamalus stellatus*. Thus if this parasite were present, both the growth rate of *Balanus*, and its ability to eliminate *Chthamalus* would be decreased, with a corresponding lessening of the degree of competition between the species.

### The causes of zonation

The evidence presented in this paper indicates that the lower limit of the intertidal zone of *Chthamalus stellatus* at Millport was determined by interspecific competition for space with *Balanus balanoides*. *Balanus*, by virtue of its greater population density and faster growth, eliminated most of the *Chthamalus* by directing crowding.

At the upper limits of the zones of these species no interaction was observed. *Chthamalus* evidently can exist higher on the shore than *Balanus* mainly as a result of its greater tolerance to heat and/or desiccation.

The upper limits of most intertidal animals are probably determined by physical factors such as these. Since growth rates usually decrease with increasing height on the shore, it would be less likely that a sessile species occupying a higher zone could, by competition for space, prevent a lower one from extending upwards. Likewise, there has been, as far as the author is aware, no study made which shows that predation by land species determines the upper limit of an intertidal animal. In one of the most thorough of such studies, Drinnan (1957) indicated that intense predation by birds accounted for an annual mortality of 22% of cockles (*Cardium edule* L.) in sand flats where their total mortality was 74% per year.

In regard to the lower limits of an animal's zone, it is evident that physical factors may act directly to determine this boundary. For example, some active amphipods from the upper levels of sandy beaches die if kept submerged. However, evidence is accumulating that the lower limits of distribution of intertidal animals are determined mainly by biotic factors.

Connell (1961) found that the shorter length of life of *Balanus balanoides* at low shore levels could be accounted for by selective predation by *Thais lapillus* and increased intraspecific competition for space. The results of the experiments in the present study confirm the suggestions of other authors that lower limits may be due to interspecific competition for space. Knox (1954) suggested that competition determined the distribution of 2 species of barnacles in New Zealand. Endean, Kenny and Stephenson (1956) gave indirect evidence that competition with a colonial polychaete worm, (*Galeolaria*) may have determined the lower limit of a barnacle (*Tetraclita*) in Queensland, Australia. In turn the lower limit of *Galeolaria* appeared to be determined by competition with a tunicate, *Pyura,* or with dense algal mats.

With regard to the 2 species of barnacles in the present paper, some interesting observations have been made concerning changes in their abundance in Britain. Moore (1936) found that in southwest England in 1934, *Chthamalus stellatus* was most dense at M.H.W.N., decreasing in numbers toward M.T.L. while *Balanus balanoides* increased in numbers below M.H.W.N. At the same localities in 1951, Southward and Crisp (1954) found that *Balanus* had almost disappeared and that *Chthamalus* had increased both above and below M.H.W.N. *Chthamalus* had not reached the former densities of *Balanus* except

at one locality, Brixham. After 1951, *Balanus* began to return in numbers, although by 1954 it had not reached the densities of 1934; *Chthamalus* had declined, but again not to its former densities (Southward and Crisp 1956).

Since *Chthamalus* increased in abundance at the lower levels vacated by *Balanus,* it may previously have been excluded by competition with *Balanus.* The growth rate of *Balanus* is greater than *Chthamalus* both north and south (Hatton 1938) of this location, so that *Balanus* would be likely to win in competition with *Chthamalus.* However, changes in other environmental factors such as temperature may have influenced the abundance of these species in a reciprocal manner. In its return to southwest England after 1951, the maximum density of settlement of *Balanus* was 12 per $cm^2$; competition of the degree observed at Millport would not be expected to occur at this density. At a higher population density, *Balanus* in southern England would probably eliminate *Chthamalus* at low shore levels in the same manner as it did at Millport.

In Loch Sween, on the Argyll Peninsula, Scotland, Lewis and Powell (1960) have described an unusual pattern of zonation of *Chthamalus stellatus.* On the outer coast of the Argyll Peninsula *Chthamalus* has a distribution similar to that at Millport. In the more sheltered waters of Loch Sween, however, *Chthamalus* occurs from above M.H.W.S. to about M.T.L., judging the distribution by its relationship to other organisms. *Balanus balanoides* is scarce above M.T.L. in Loch Sween, so that there appears to be no possibility of competition with *Chthamalus,* such as that occurring at Millport, between the levels of M.T.L. and M.H.W.N.

In Figure 5 an attempt has been made to summarize the distribution of adults and newly settled larvae in relation to the main factors which appear to determine this distribution. For *Balanus* the estimates were based on the findings of a previous study (Connell 1961); intraspecific competition was severe at the lower levels during the first year, after which predation increased in importance. With *Chthamalus,* it appears that avoidance of settlement or early mortality of those larvae which settled at levels below M.T.L., and elimination by competition with *Balanus* of those which settled between M.T.L. and M.H.W.N., were the principal causes for the absence of adults below M.H.W.N. at Millport. This distribution appears to be typical for much of western Scotland.

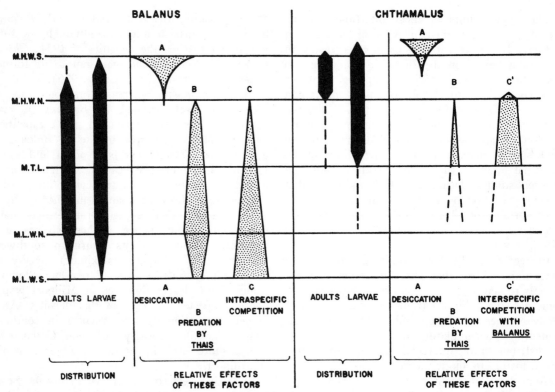

BALANUS                                              CHTHAMALUS

Fig. 5. The intertidal distribution of adults and newly settled larvae of *Balanus balanoides* and *Chthamalus stellatus* at Millport, with a diagrammatic representation of the relative effects of the principal limiting factors.

## Summary

Adults of *Chthamalus stellatus* occur in the marine intertidal in a zone above that of another barnacle, *Balanus balanoides*. Young *Chthamalus* settle in the *Balanus* zone but evidently seldom survive, since few adults are found there.

The survival of *Chthamalus* which had settled at various levels in the *Balanus* zone was followed for a year by successive censuses of mapped individuals. Some *Chthamalus* were kept free of contact with *Balanus*. These survived very well at all intertidal levels, indicating that increased time of submergence was not the factor responsible for elimination of *Chthamalus* at low shore levels. Comparison of the survival of unprotected populations with others, protected by enclosure in cages from predation by the snail, *Thais lapillus*, showed that *Thais* was not greatly affecting the survival of *Chthamalus*.

Comparison of the survival of undisturbed populations of *Chthamalus* with those kept free of contact with *Balanus* indicated that *Balanus* could cause great mortality of *Chthamalus*. *Balanus* settled in greater population densities and grew faster than *Chthamalus*. Direct observations at each census showed that *Balanus* smothered,

undercut, or crushed the *Chthamalus*; the greate[st] mortality of *Chthamalus* occurred during th[e] seasons of most rapid growth of *Balanus*. Eve[n] older *Chthamalus* transplanted to low levels we[re] killed by *Balanus* in this way. Predation b[y] *Thais* tended to decrease the severity of th[e] interspecific competition.

Survivors of *Chthamalus* after a year of crowd[ing] by *Balanus* were smaller than uncrowde[d] ones. Since smaller barnacles produce fewer off[spring], competition tended to reduce reproductiv[e] efficiency in addition to increasing mortality.

Mortality as a result of intraspecies competitio[n] for space between individuals of *Chthamalus* wa[s] only rarely observed.

The evidence of this and other studies indicate[s] that the lower limit of distribution of intertid[al] organisms is mainly determined by the action [of] biotic factors such as competition for space [or] predation. The upper limit is probably more ofte[n] set by physical factors.

References

Barnes, H. 1953. Size variations in the cyprids [of] some common barnacles. J. Mar. Biol. Ass. U. K. 3[2]: 297-304.

———. 1956a. The growth rate of *Chthamalus stellatus* (Poli). J. Mar. Biol. Ass. U. K. **35**: 355-361.

———. 1956b. *Balanus balanoides* (L.) in the Firth of Clyde: The development and annual variation of the larval population, and the causative factors. J. Anim. Ecol. **25**: 72-84.

——— and H. T. Powell. 1953. The growth of *Balanus balanoides* (L.) and *B. crenatus* Brug. under varying conditions of submersion. J. Mar. Biol. Ass. U. K. **32**: 107-128.

——— and D. J. Crisp. 1956. Evidence of self-fertilization in certain species of barnacles. J. Mar. Biol. Ass. U. K. **35**: 631-639.

Beauchamp, R. S. A. and P. Ullyott. 1932. Competitive relationships between certain species of freshwater Triclads. J. Ecol. **20**: 200-208.

Clark, P. J. and F. C. Evans. 1954. Distance to nearest neighbor as a measure of spatial relationships in populations. Ecology **35**: 445-453.

Clench, W. J. 1947. The genera *Purpura* and *Thais* in the western Atlantic. Johnsonia **2**, No. 23: 61-92.

Connell, J. H. 1961. The effects of competition, predation by *Thais lapillus,* and other factors on natural populations of the barnacle, *Balanus balanoides.* Ecol. Mon. **31**: 61-104.

Crisp, D. J. 1960. Factors influencing growth-rate in *Balanus balanoides.* J. Anim. Ecol. **29**: 95-116.

Drinnan, R. E. 1957. The winter feeding of the oyster-catcher (*Haematopus ostralegus*) on the edible cockle (*Cardium edule*). J. Anim. Ecol. **26**: 441-469.

Elton, Charles and R. S. Miller. 1954. The ecological survey of animal communities: with a practical scheme of classifying habitats by structural characters. J. Ecol. **42**: 460-496.

Endean, R., R. Kenny and W. Stephenson. 1956. The ecology and distribution of intertidal organisms on the rocky shores of the Queensland mainland. Aust. J. mar. freshw. Res. **7**: 88-146.

Fischer, E. 1928. Sur la distribution geographique de quelques organismes de rocher, le long des cotes de la Manche. Trav. Lab. Mus. Hist. Nat. St.-Servan **2**: 1-16.

Hatton, H. 1938. Essais de bionomie explicative sur quelques especes intercotidales d'algues et d'animaux. Ann. Inst. Oceanogr. Monaco **17**: 241-348.

Holme, N. A. 1950. Population-dispersion in *Tellina tenuis* Da Costa. J. Mar. Biol. Ass. U. K. **29**: 267-280.

Hutchinson, G. E. 1957. Concluding remarks. Cold Spring Harbor Symposium on Quant. Biol. **22**: 415-427.

Knight-Jones, E. W. 1953. Laboratory experiments on gregariousness during setting in *Balanus balanoides* and other barnacles. J. Exp. Biol. **30**: 584-598.

Knox, G. A. 1954. The intertidal flora and fauna of the Chatham Islands. Nature Lond. **174**: 871-873.

Lack, D. 1954. The natural regulation of animal numbers. Oxford, Clarendon Press.

Lewis, J. R. and H. T. Powell. 1960. Aspects of the intertidal ecology of rocky shores in Argyll, Scotland. I. General description of the area. II. The distribution of *Chthamalus stellatus* and *Balanus balanoides* in Kintyre. Trans. Roy. Soc. Edin. **64**: 45-100.

MacArthur, R. H. 1958. Population ecology of some warblers of northeastern coniferous forests. Ecology **39**: 599-619.

Moore, H. B. 1935. The biology of *Balnus balanoides.* III. The soft parts. J. Mar. Biol. Ass. U. K. **20**: 263-277.

———. 1936. The biology of *Balanus balanoides.* V. Distribution in the Plymouth area. J. Mar. Biol. Ass. U. K. **20**: 701-716.

Siegel, S. 1956. Nonparametric statistics. New York, McGraw Hill.

Southward, A. J. 1955. On the behavior of barnacles. I. The relation of cirral and other activities to temperature. J. Mar. Biol. Ass. U. K. **34**: 403-422.

——— and D. J. Crisp. 1954. Recent changes in the distribution of the intertidal barnacles *Chthamalus stellatus* Poli and *Balanus balanoides* L. in the British Isles. J. Anim. Ecol. **23**: 163-177.

———. 1956. Fluctuations in the distribution and abundance of intertidal barnacles. J. Mar. Biol. Ass. U. K. **35**: 211-229.

# POPULATION ECOLOGY OF SOME WARBLERS OF NORTHEASTERN CONIFEROUS FORESTS[1]

## Robert H. MacArthur
### *Department of Zoology, University of Pennsylvania*

## Introduction

Five species of warbler, Cape May (*Dendroica tigrina*), myrtle (*D. coronata*), black-throated green (*D. virens*), blackburnian (*D. fusca*), and bay-breasted (*D. castanea*), are sometimes found together in the breeding season in relatively homogeneous mature boreal forests. These species are congeneric, have roughly similar sizes and shapes, and all are mainly insectivorous. They are so similar in general ecological preference, at least during years of abundant food supply, that ecologists studying them have concluded that any differences in the species' requirements must be quite obscure (Kendeigh, 1947; Stewart and Aldrich, 1952). Thus it appeared that these species might provide an interesting exception to the general rule that species either are limited by different factors or differ in habitat or range (Lack, 1954). Accordingly, this study was undertaken with the aim of determining the factors controlling the species' bundances and preventing all but one from being exterminated by competition.

## Logical Nature of Population Control

Animal populations may be regulated by two types of events. The first type occurs (but need not exert its effect) independently of the density of the population. Examples are catastrophes

[1] A Dissertation Presented to the Faculty of the Graduate School of Yale University in Candidacy for the Degree of Doctor of Philosophy, 1957.

such as storms, severe winters, some predation, and some disease. The second type of event depends upon the density of the population for both its occurrence and strength. Examples are shortages of food and nesting holes. Both types seem to be important for all well-studied species. The first kind will be called density independent and the second density dependent. This is slightly different from the usual definitions of these terms which require the effects upon the population and not the occurrence to be density independent or dependent (Andrewartha and Birch 1954).

When density dependent events play a major role in regulating abundance, interspecific relations are also important, for the presence of an individual of another species may have some of the effects of an individual of the original density dependent species. This is clearly illustrated by the generalized habitats of the few species of passerine birds of Bermuda contrasted with their specialized habitats in continental North America where many additional species are also present (Bourne 1957).

If the species' requirements are sufficiently similar, the proposition of Volterra (1926) and Gause (1934), first enunciated by Grinnell (1922), suggests that only one will be able to persist, so that the existence of one species may even control the presence or absence of another. Because of this proposition it has become customary for ecologists to look for differences in food or habitat of related species; such differences, if found, are then cited as the reason competition is not eliminating all but one of the species. Unfortunately, however, differences in food and space requirements are neither always necessary nor always sufficient to prevent competition and permit coexistence. Actually, to permit coexistence it seems necessary that each species, when very abundant, should inhibit its own further increase more than it inhibits the other's. This is illustrated in Figure 1. In this figure, the populations of the two species form the coordinates so that any point in the plane represents a population for each species. Each shaded area covers the points (*i.e.*, the sets of combined populations of the species) in which the species corresponding to the shading can increase, within a given environment. Thus, in the doubly-shaded area both species increase and in the unshaded area both species decrease. The arrows, representing the direction of population change, must then be as shown in the figure for these regions. In order that a stable equilibrium of the two species should exist, the arrows in the singly shaded regions obviously must also be as in the figure; an interchange of the species represented by the shading would reverse the directions of these arrows resulting in a situation in which only one species could persist. Thus, for stability, the boundaries of the shaded zones of increase must have the relative slope illustrated in the figure with each species inhibiting its own further increase more than the other's. The easiest way for this to happen would be to have each species' population limited by a slightly different factor. It is these different limiting factors which are the principal problem in an investigation of multispecific animal populations regulated by density dependent events.

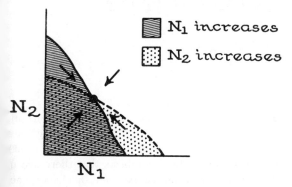

Fig. 1. The necessary conditions for a stable equilibrium of two species. The coordinate axes represent the populations of the species.

An example which has not received sufficient attention is competition in a heterogeneous en-

vironment. As has often been pointed out (Kluijver and Tinbergen 1953, Lack 1955, Hinde 1956) birds may emigrate or disperse from the most suitable areas where reproduction is successful into marginal habitats. Consider such a species which will be called A. Let B be a species that lives only in the area that is marginal for species A. Now, even if in an unlimited environment of this type, species B would eliminate species A by competition, in the heterogeneous environment species B may be eliminated from its own preferred habitat. For, if there is sufficient dispersal by species A, it may maintain, partly by immigration, such a high population in the marginal habitat that species B is forced to decrease. This process is probably very important in considering the environmental distributions of birds and implies that small areas of habitat typical for one species may not contain that species.

The study of limiting factors in nature is very difficult because ideally it requires changing the amount of the factor alone and observing whether this change affects the size of the population. Theoretically, if more than one factor changes, the analysis can still be performed, but in practice, if more changes of known nature occur, more of an unknown nature usually also occur. Limiting factors have been studied in two ways. The best way is artificially to modify single factors in the environment, observing the effect upon the birds. MacKenzie (1946) reviews some experiments of this type. The most notable was the increase from zero to abundant of pied flycatchers (*Muscicapa hypoleuca*) when nest boxes were introduced in the Forest of Dean. This showed conclusively that lack of nesting sites had limited the population. Such simple modifications are not always feasible. For instance, changing the food supply of an insectivorous bird is nearly impossible. The most feasible approach in such a case is to compare the bird populations in two regions which differ in the abundance of the factor being considered. Ideally, the two regions should differ only in this respect, but this is very improbable. A good example of this method of study is the work of Breckenridge (1956) which showed that the least flycatchers (*Empidonax minimus*) were more abundant in a given wood wherever the wood was more open.

The present study of the factors limiting warblers was conducted by the second approach. This is slightly less accurate than the first method, but permits studying more factors and requires less time. There are actually four parts to the study. First, it is shown that density dependent events play a large role in controlling the populations of the species. Second, a discussion of the general ecology of the species (food, feeding zones, feeding behavior, territoriality, predators, and mortality) is presented. The observations were made in the summers of 1956 and 1957. Third, the habits of the different species in different seasons are compared to see what aspects of the general ecology are invariant and hence characteristic of the species. Some observations on the species' morphology are discussed in the light of these characteristics. This was the project of the fall and winter of 1956 and the spring of 1957. Finally, a wood-to-wood comparison of species abundances, relative to the important constituents of their niches as determined in the earlier stages, is presented. This work was done in the summers of 1956 and 1957.

### DENSITY DEPENDENCE

It is the aim of this section to demonstrate that the five species of warbler are primarily regulated by density dependent events, that is, that they increase when rare and decrease when common (relative to the supply of a limiting factor). The strongest argument for this is the correlation of abundances with limiting factors discussed later. However, to avoid any risk of circularity, an independent partial demonstration will now be given.

If density independent events do not occur randomly but have a periodic recurrence, then a population controlled by these events could undergo a regular oscillation nearly indistinguishable in form from that of a population regulated by density dependent events. The distinction can be made, however, by observing the effect of the presence of an ecologically similar species. Here it will first be shown that increases and decreases are not random; then an argument will be given which renders the density independent explanation improbable.

If increases, I, and decreases, D, occur randomly, the sequence of observed I's and D's would have random order. A run of I's (or D's) is a sequence (perhaps consisting of one element) of adjacent I's (or D's) which cannot be lengthened; *i.e.*, the total number of runs is always one greater than the number of changes from I to D or D to I. If more runs of I's or D's are observed than would be expected in a random sequence, then an increase makes the following change more likely to be a decrease and conversely. This is what would be expected on the hypothesis of density dependent events.

There have been very few extensive censuses of any of the five species of warbler that are studied here. The longest are reproduced below

from the data of Smith (1953) in Vermont, Williams (1950) in Ohio, and Cruickshank (1956) in Maine. The populations of myrtle, black-throated green, and blackburnian are listed; only those species are mentioned that are consistently present.

*Myrtle*
| Maine | 7 | 5 | 7 | 7 | 6 | 7 | 8 | 10 | 9 | 8 | 10 | 10 | 10 |
|   |   | 8 | 10 | 7 | 10 |   |   |   |   |   |   |   |   |

*Black-throated green*
| Ohio | 3 | 3 | 5 | 3 | 4 | 3 | 2 | 4 | 0 | 1 | – | 3 | 3 |
|   |   | 3 | 4 | 3 | 3 | 4 | 3 |   |   |   |   |   |   |
| Vermont | 7 | 7 | 7 | 6 | 8 | 5 | 6 | 6 | 7 | 8 | 8 | 6 | 8 |
|   |   | 8 | 3 | 6 | 3 |   |   |   |   |   |   |   |   |
| Maine | 8 | 9 | 11 | 10 | 10 | 10 | 11 | 11 | 11 | 10 | 11 | 9 | 8 |
|   |   | 9 | 8 | 9 |   |   |   |   |   |   |   |   |   |

*Blackburnian*
| Vermont | 11 | 11 | 10 | 7 | 8 | 7 | 7 | 10 | 10 | 8 | 5 | 6 | 3 |
|   |   | 3 | 6 | 6 | 5 |   |   |   |   |   |   |   |   |
| Maine | 2 | 4 | 3 | 3 | 5 | 5 | 7 | 5 | 6 | 5 | 7 | 5 | 5 |
|   |   | 7 | 6 | 6 | 3 |   |   |   |   |   |   |   |   |

The increases, I, and decreases, D, of these censuses, in order are as follows:

*Myrtle*
D I D I I I D D I D I D I

*Black-throated green*
I D I D D I D I I I I D I D
D I D I I I D I D I D
I I D I D I D D I D I

*Blackburnian*
D D I D I D D I D I D
I D I I D I D I D I D D

In this form the data from different censuses are perfectly compatible and, since censuses end or begin with I or D in no particular pattern, all the censuses for a given species may be attached:

*Myrtle*
D I D I I I D D I D I D I  (10)

*Black-throated green*
I D I D D I D I I I I D I D D I D

I I I D I D I D I I D I  (27)

D I D D I D I

*Blackburnian*
D D I D I D D I D I D I D I I D I

D I D I D D  (19)

Here the groups of letters underlined are runs and the number of runs is totalled in parentheses. From the tables of Swed and Eisenhart (1943), testing the one-sided hypothesis that there are no more runs than would be expected by chance, each of these shows a significantly large number of runs (the first less than 5% significance, the others less than 2.5%). That is, each species tends to decrease following an increase and to increase following a decrease, proving population control not random. The mean periods of these fluctuations can easily be computed. For a run of increases followed by a run of decreases constitutes one oscillation. Thus, the periods of the oscillations of the three species are $13/5 = 2.6$, $70/27 = 2.6$, and $46/19 = 2.4$ years respectively. These fluctuations would require an unknown environmental cycle of period approximately 2.5 years if a regularly recurring density independent event were controlling the populations. Thus, from these data alone, it seems very probable that the three species (myrtle, black-throated green, blackburnian) are primarily regulated by density dependent events.

A species may be regulated by density dependent events and yet undergo dramatic changes in populations due to changes in the limiting factor itself. In this case tests by the theory of runs, used above, are likely to be useless. However, if a correlation can be made of the population with the environmental factor undergoing change, then not only can density dependence, *i. e.* existence of a limiting factor, be established, but also the nature of the limiting factor. For, if an increase in one environmental variable can be established, an experiment of the first type described above has been performed. That is, the habitat has been modified in one factor and a resulting change in bird population has been observed. Therefore, because the population changes, that one factor has been limiting.

This is apparently what happens in populations of Cape May and bay-breasted warblers. Kendeigh (1947), examining older material, established the fact that these species are abundant when there is an outbreak of *Choristoneura fumiferana* (Clem.), the spruce budworm. More recent information confirms this. To correlate with the fact (Greenbank 1956) that there have been continuously high budworm populations since 1909, there is the statement of Forbush (1929) that the Cape May warbler became more common about 1909, and the statement of Bond (pers. comm.) that the winter range of the species has been increasing in size. An outbreak of spruce budworms started in northern Maine in the late 1940's, and Stewart and Aldrich (1951) and Hensley and Cope (1951) studied the birds during 1950 and 1951. Cape May and bay-breasted warblers were among the commonest birds present, as in the earlier outbreaks, although both species were formerly not common in Maine (Knight 1908). The outbreak has continued through New Brunswick, where current bird studies (Cheshire 1954) indicate that bay-breasted is again the commonest bird, although

for unknown reasons the Cape May has not been observed.

In conclusion, it appears that all five species are primarily regulated by density dependent events, and that a limiting factor is food supply for bay-breasted and Cape May warblers.

## GENERAL ECOLOGY

The density dependence tentatively concluded above implies that the presence of individuals of a species makes the environment less suitable for other individuals of that species. It would also be expected then that the presence of individuals of one species may make the environment less suitable for individuals of a different species. This is called interspecific competition. As mentioned above, this seems to mean that two sympatric species will have their populations limited by different factors so that each species inhibits its own population growth more than it inhibits that of the others. The factors inseparably bound to a species' persistence in a region are, then, its relation to other species and the presence of food, proper feeding zone, shelter from weather, and nesting sites (Andrewartha and Birch 1954, Grinnell 1914). In this section these factors as observed during the breeding season of the five species of warbler will be discussed.

The summer of 1956 was devoted to observations upon the four species, myrtle, black-throated green, blackburnian, and bay-breasted warblers, on their nesting grounds. The principal area studied was a 9.4 acre plot of mature white spruce (*Picea glauca*) on Bass Harbor Head, Mt. Desert Island, Hancock County, Maine. On 7 July 1956 the site of observations was changed to the town of Marlboro in Windham County, Vermont, where a red spruce (*P. rubens*) woodlot of comparable structure was studied. In the summer of 1957 more plots were studied. From 30 May until 5 June, eighteen plots of balsam fir (*Abies balsamea*), black spruce (*P. mariana*), and white spruce near Cross Lake, Long Lake, and Mud Lake in the vicinity of Guerette in Aroostook County, Maine, were studied. The remainder of the breeding season was spent on Mt. Desert Island, Maine, where five plots were censused. These will be described later.

### Feeding Habits

Although food might be the factor for which birds compete, evidence presented later shows that differences in type of food between these closely related species result from differences in feeding behavior and position and that each species eats what food is obtainable within the characteristic feeding zone and by the characteristic manner of feeding. For this reason, differences between the species' feeding positions and behavior have been observed in detail.

For the purpose of describing the birds' feeding zone, the number of seconds each observed bird spent in each of 16 zones was recorded. (In the summer of 1956 the seconds were counted by saying "thousand and one, thousand and two, . . ." all subsequent timing was done by stop watch. When the stop watch became available, an attempt was made to calibrate the counted seconds. It was found that each counted second was approximately 1.25 true seconds.) The zones varied with height and position on branch as shown in Figure 2. The height zones were ten foot units measured from the top of the tree. Each branch could be divided into three zones, one of bare or lichen-covered base (B), a middle zone of old needles (M), and a terminal zone of new (less than 1.5 years old) needles or buds (T). Thus a measurement in zone T3 was an observation between 20 and 30 feet from the top of the tree and in the terminal part of the branch. Since most of the trees were 50 to 60 feet tall, a rough idea of the height above the ground can also be obtained from the measurements.

There are certain difficulties concerning these measurements. Since the forest was very dense, certain types of behavior rendered birds invisible. This resulted in all species being observed slightly disproportionately in the open zones of the trees. To combat this difficulty each bird was observed for as long as possible so that a brief excursion into an open but not often-frequented zone would be compensated for by the remaining part of the observation. I believe there is no serious error in this respect. Furthermore, the comparative aspect is independent of this error. A different difficulty arises from measurements of time spent in each zone. The error due to counting should not affect results which are comparative in nature. If a bird sits very still or sings, it might spend a large amount of time in one zone without actually requiring that zone for feeding. To alleviate this trouble, a record of activity, when not feeding, was kept. Because of these difficulties, non-parametric statistics have been used throughout the analysis of the study to avoid any *a priori* assumptions about distributions. One difficulty is of a different nature; because of the density of the vegetation and the activity of the warblers a large number of hours of watching result in disappointingly few seconds of worthwhile observations.

The results of these observations are illustrated in Figures 2-6 in which the species' feeding zones are indicated on diagrammatic spruce trees. While

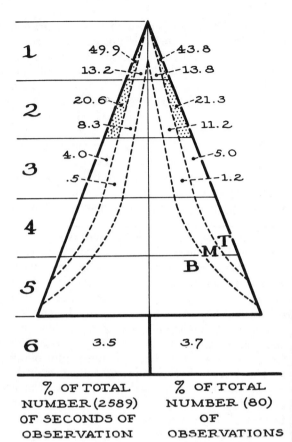

% OF TOTAL NUMBER (2589) OF SECONDS OF OBSERVATION

% OF TOTAL NUMBER (80) OF OBSERVATIONS

Fig. 2. Cape May warbler feeding position. The zones of most concentrated activity are shaded until at least 50% of the activity is in the stippled zones.

the base zone is always proximal to the trunk of the tree, as shown, the T zone surrounds the M, and is exterior to it but not always distal. For each species observed, the feeding zone is illustrated. The left side of each illustration is the percentage of the number of seconds of observations of the species in each zone. On the right hand side the percentage of the total number of times the species was observed in each zone is entered. The stippled area gives roughly the area in which the species is most likely to be found. More specifically, the zone with the highest percentage is stippled, then the zone with the second highest percentage, and so on until at least fifty percent of the observations or time lie within the stippled zone.

Early in the investigation it became apparent that there were differences between the species feeding habits other than those of feeding zone. Subjectively, the black-throated green appeared "nervous," the bay-breasted slow and "deliberate." In an attempt to make these observations objective the following measurements were taken on feeding birds. When a bird landed after a flight, a cou

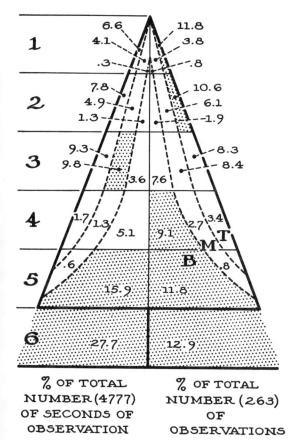

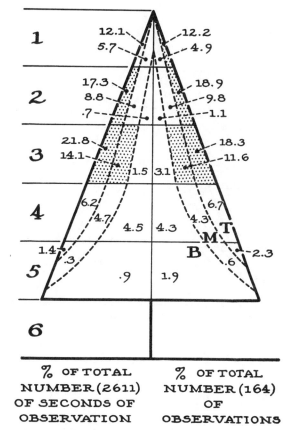

FIG. 3. Myrtle warbler feeding position. The zones of most concentrated activity are shaded until at least 50% of the activity is in the stippled zones.

FIG. 4. Black-throated green warbler feeding position. The zones of most concentrated activity are shaded until at least 50% of the activity is in the stippled zones.

of seconds was begun and continued until the bird was lost from sight. The total number of flights (visible uses of the wing) during this period was recorded so that the mean interval between uses of the wing could be computed.

The results for 1956 are shown in Table I. The results for 1957 are shown in Table II. Except for the Cape May fewer observations were taken than in 1956.

By means of the sign test (Wilson, 1952), treating each observation irrespective of the number of flights as a single estimate of mean interval between flights, a test of the difference in activity can be performed. These data are summarized in the following inequality, where $\underset{<}{95}$ is interpreted to mean "has smaller mean interval between flights, with 95% certainty."

their time searching in the foliage for food, some appear to crawl along branches and others to hop across branches. To measure this the following procedure was adopted. All motions of a bird from place to place in a tree were resolved into components in three independent directions. The natural directions to use were vertical, radial, and tangential. When an observation was made in which all the motion was visible, the number of feet the bird moved in each of the three directions was noted. A surprising degree of diversity was discovered in this way as is shown in Figure 7. Here, making use of the fact that the sum of the three perpendicular distances from an interior point to the sides of an equilateral triangle is independent of the position of the point, the proportion of motion in each direction is recorded within a triangle. Thus the Cape May

$$\text{Black-throated green} \quad \underset{<}{95} \left\{ \begin{array}{l} \text{Blackburnian} \\ \text{Myrtle} \end{array} \right\} \quad \underset{<}{99} \left\{ \begin{array}{l} \text{Cape May} \\ \text{Bay-breasted} \end{array} \right\}$$

The differences in feeding behavior of the warblers can be studied in another way. For, while all the species spend a substantial part of

moves predominantly in a vertical direction, black-throated green and myrtle in a tangential direction, bay-breasted and blackburnian in a radial direc-

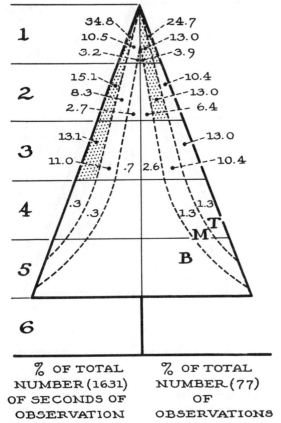

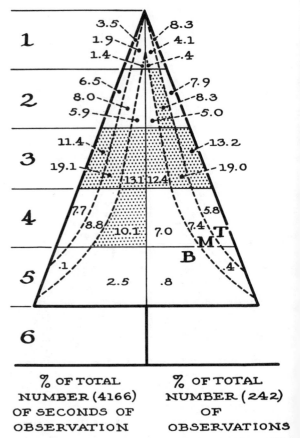

| % OF TOTAL NUMBER (1631) OF SECONDS OF OBSERVATION | % OF TOTAL NUMBER (77) OF OBSERVATIONS |
|---|---|

FIG. 5. Blackburnian warbler feeding position. The zones of most concentrated activity are shaded until at least 50% of the activity is in the stippled zones.

| % OF TOTAL NUMBER (4166) OF SECONDS OF OBSERVATION | % OF TOTAL NUMBER (242) OF OBSERVATIONS |
|---|---|

FIG. 6. Bay-breasted warbler feeding position. The zones of most concentrated activity are shaded until at least 50% of the activity is in the stippled zones.

tion. To give a nonparametric test of the significance of these differences Table III is required.

Each motion was classified according to the direction in which the bird moved farthest. Thus, in 47 bay-breasted warbler observations of this type, the bird moved predominantly in a radial direction 32 times. Applying a $\chi^2$ test to these, bay-breasted and blackburnian are not different but all others are significantly (P<.01) different from one another and from bay-breasted and blackburnian.

There is one further quantitative comparison which can be made between species, providing additional evidence that during normal feeding behavior the species could become exposed to different types of food. During those observations of 1957 in which the bird was never lost from sight, occurrence of long flights, hawking, or hovering was recorded. A flight was called long if it went between different trees and was greater than an estimated 25 feet. Hawking is distinguished from hovering by the fact that in hawking a moving prey individual is sought in the air, while in hovering a nearly stationary prey individual is sought amid the foliage. This information is summarized in Table IV.

Both Cape May and myrtle hawk and undertake long flights significantly more often than any of the other species. Black-throated green hovers significantly more often than the others.

At this point it is possible to summarize differences in the species' feeding behavior in the breeding season. Unfortunately, there are very few original descriptions in the literature for comparison. The widely known writings of William Brewster (Griscom 1938), Ora Knight (1908) and S. C. Kendeigh (1947) include the best observations that have been published. Based upon the observations reported by these authors, the other scattered published observations, and the observations made during this study, the following comparison of the species' feeding behavior seem warranted.

Cape May Warbler. The foregoing data show that this species feeds more consistently near the top of the tree than any species expect blackburnian, from which it differs principally in typ

TABLE I. The number of intervals between flights (I) recorded in 1956 and the total number of seconds (S) of observation counted

| | Myrtle | | Black-throated green | | Blackburnian | | Bay-breasted | |
|---|---|---|---|---|---|---|---|---|
| | I | S | I | S | I | S | I | S |
| | 1 | 40 | 4 | 45 | 1 | 5 | 5 | 55 |
| | 4 | 32 | 8 | 20 | 13 | 77 | 3 | 22 |
| | 4 | 13 | 6 | 60 | 2 | 11 | 2 | 33 |
| | 4 | 17 | 5 | 35 | 5 | 18 | 1 | 7 |
| | 2 | 10 | 5 | 23 | 5 | 24 | 3 | 37 |
| | 1 | 10 | 3 | 7 | 3 | 16 | 2 | 20 |
| | 5 | 25 | 9 | 35 | 3 | 18 | 1 | 7 |
| | 5 | 10 | 8 | 25 | 3 | 15 | 4 | 10 |
| | 5 | 11 | 1 | 12 | 4 | 11 | 11 | 60 |
| | 6 | 30 | 7 | 20 | 3 | 12 | 5 | 41 |
| | 3 | 10 | 7 | 39 | 4 | 46 | 3 | 50 |
| | 1 | 5 | 13 | 25 | 2 | 26 | 1 | 17 |
| | 13 | 68 | 5 | 10 | | | 1 | 3 |
| | 1 | 5 | 5 | 12 | | | 1 | 49 |
| | 1 | 7 | 2 | 37 | | | 4 | 42 |
| | 4 | 26 | | | | | 5 | 60 |
| | | | | | | | 5 | 35 |
| | | | | | | | 5 | 26 |
| | | | | | | | 3 | 14 |
| | | | | | | | 4 | 38 |
| | | | | | | | 3 | 14 |
| | | | | | | | 1 | 11 |
| | | | | | | | 3 | 22 |
| | | | | | | | 2 | 29 |
| Total......... | 60 | 319 | 88 | 405 | 48 | 279 | 78 | 702 |
| Total Adjusted to True seconds | 60 | 399 | 88 | 506 | 48 | 349 | 78 | 876 |

TABLE II. Intervals between flights and seconds of observation in 1957

| | Cape May | | Myrtle | | Black-throated green | | Blackburnian | | Bay-breasted | |
|---|---|---|---|---|---|---|---|---|---|---|
| | I | S | I | S | I | S | I | S | I | S |
| | 3 | 47 | 4 | 18 | 3 | 18 | 1 | 22 | 7 | 110 |
| | 12 | 35 | 1 | 62 | 5 | 22 | 3 | 22 | 2 | 115 |
| | 5 | 50 | 5 | 47 | 6 | 47 | 9 | 110 | 1 | 18 |
| | 2 | 15 | 3 | 17 | 13 | 89 | 7 | 26 | 1 | 22 |
| | 1 | 15 | 1 | 5 | 23 | 40 | 3 | 8 | 2 | 19 |
| | 1 | 45 | 12 | 86 | | | | | 2 | 47 |
| | 1 | 20 | | | | | | | 3 | 27 |
| | 4 | 29 | | | | | | | 8 | 112 |
| | 11 | 129 | | | | | | | 7 | 46 |
| | 6 | 47 | | | | | | | | |
| | 1 | 15 | | | | | | | | |
| | 4 | 50 | | | | | | | | |
| | 3 | 20 | | | | | | | | |
| | 21 | 122 | | | | | | | | |
| | 1 | 12 | | | | | | | | |
| | 1 | 34 | | | | | | | | |
| | 4 | 20 | | | | | | | | |
| | 10 | 79 | | | | | | | | |
| Total................ | 91 | 782 | 26 | 235 | 47 | 184 | 24 | 188 | 33 | 576 |
| Adjusted 1956 Total... | | | 60 | 399 | 88 | 506 | 48 | 349 | 78 | 876 |
| Grand Total......... | 91 | 782 | 86 | 644 | 125 | 690 | 72 | 537 | 111 | 1392 |
| Mean Interval Between flights............. | | 8.59 | | 7.48 | | 5.52 | | 7.47 | | 12.53 |

TABLE III. Number of times each species was observed to move predominantly in a particular direction. (Numbers ending in .5 result from ties)

| Species | Radial | Tangential | Vertical | Total |
|---|---|---|---|---|
| Cape May....... | 5.5 | 1.5 | 25 | 32 |
| Myrtle.......... | 4.5 | 11.5 | 9 | 25 |
| Black-throated green........ | 4 | 21 | 5 | 30 |
| Blackburnian.... | 11 | 1 | 3 | 15 |
| Bay-breasted.... | 32 | 7 | 8 | 47 |

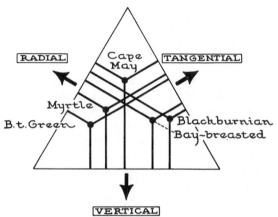

FIG. 7. Components of Motion. From the dot representing a species, lines are drawn to the sides of the triangle. The lengths of these lines are proportional to the total distance which the species moved in radial, tangential, and vertical directions, respectively.

TABLE IV. Classification of the flights observed for each species

| Species | Long Flights | Hawking | Hovering | No. of Observ. |
|---|---|---|---|---|
| Cape May......... | 35 | 12 | 0 | 53 |
| Myrtle............ | 25 | 9 | 0 | 62 |
| Black-throated green.......... | 1 | 0 | 7 | 42 |
| Blackburnian...... | 0 | 1 | 0 | 35 |
| Bay-breasted...... | 4 | 2 | 2 | 57 |

Applying $\chi^2$ tests to pairs of species, the following conclusions emerge.

of feeding action. It not only hawks far more often than the blackburnian, but also moves vertically rather than radially in the tree, causing its feeding zone to be more restricted to the outer shell of the tree. Myrtle warblers when feeding in the tips of the trees nearly duplicate the feeding behavior of the Cape May. During rainy, windy, and cold weather Cape Mays were not found in the tree tops, but were instead foraging in the low willows (*Salix* sp.) and pin cherries (*Prunus pensylvanica*). Here they often fed among the flowers, for which their semitubular tongue (Gardner 1925) may be advantageous.

Because of this species' irregular breeding distribution, both in space and time, and its former rarity, there are very few published descriptions of its feeding behavior. Knight (1908), although he lived in Maine, had never seen one. Brewster (Griscom 1938) wrote that:

"It keeps invariably near the tops of the highest trees whence it occasionally darts out after passing insects. . . . In rainy or dark weather they came in numbers from the woods to feed among the thickets of low firs and spruces in the pastures. Here they spent much of their time hanging head downward at the extremity of the branches, often continuing in this position for nearly a minute at a time. They seemed to be picking minute insects from under the surface of the fir needles. They also resorted to a thicket of blossoming plum trees directly under the window, where we were always sure of finding several of them."

He also said that it was more active than the bay-breasted. Bond (1937) stated that all feeding was done more than twenty feet above the ground. Kendeigh (1947) said males tend to sing about seven feet from the tops of the trees, and that feeding is done at the same level. He also mentions that the birds sometimes hawk after passing insects. The rainy weather observations indicate behavior very much like that of winter and migration to be discussed later.

Myrtle Warbler. This species seems to have the most varied feeding habits of any species. Although it moves slightly more in a tangential direction than any except black-throated green, it is probably more correct to think of the myrtle as having the most nearly equal components (radial, tangential, and vertical) of any species. This is shown by its most nearly central location in Figure 7. It is also seen to have the most widely distributed feeding zone, although the ground feeding was nearly, but not completely, restricted to the gathering of emerging Tipulids for newly hatched young. Sometimes a substantial amount of this is hawking for flying insects; at other times it is largely by rapid peering (Grinnell 1921) amid the thick foliage near the tree tops. Myrtle, along with Cape May, makes a much higher proportion of flights to other trees than do the other species, often flying from one side of its territory to the other with no apparent provocation. The other three species tend to search one tree rather thoroughly before moving on. Further evidence of the plasticity of the myrtle warbler's feeding habits will be presented when the other seasons are considered. Grinnell and Storer (1924) stated that the Audubon's warbler (which often hybridizes with the myrtle and with it froms a superspecies (Mayr 1950)) also feeds in peripheral foliage and does a greater amount of hawking than other species. Kendeigh (1947) said that

birds fed from ground to tops of trees, and also that two males covered two and four acres respectively in only a few minutes. Knight (1908) said "Many of the adult insects are taken on the wing, the warblers taking short springs and flights into the air for this purpose. The young for the first few days are fed on the softer sorts of insects secured by the parents, and later their fare is like that of the parents in every way."

Black-throated Green Warbler. Compared to the myrtle warbler this species is quite restricted in feeding habits. As seen in Figure 4, it tends to frequent the dense parts of the branches and the new buds, especially at mid elevations in the tree. Most of its motion is in a tangential direction, keeping the bird in foliage of a nearly constant type. It has the shortest interval between flights of any of the five species and thus appears the most active. Almost all feeding seems to be by the method of rapid peering, necessitating the frequent use of the wings which the observations indicate. The foliage on a white spruce is a thick, dense mat at the end of the branch, changing to bare branch rather more sharply than in the red spruce. The black-throated greens characteristically hop about very actively upon these mats, often, like the other species, looking down among the needles, and just as often, unlike the myrtle and bay-breasted, peering up into the next mat of foliage above. When food is located above, the bird springs into the air and hovers under the branch with its bill at the point whence the food is being extracted. While other species occasionally feed in this fashion, it is typical only of the black-throated green. After searching one branch, the black-throated green generally flies tangentially to an adjacent branch in the same tree or a neighboring one and continues the search. Only rarely, during feeding does it make long flights. While it occasionally hawks for flying insects (missing a substantial proportion), this is not a typical behavior and the birds seldom sit motionless watching for flying insects in true hawking behavior. During its feeding, this species is very noisy, chipping almost incessantly, and, if it is a male and if it is early in the season, singing frequently. The other species are very quiet. A portion of this behavior can be confirmed from the literature. Knight (1908) said "Only rarely do they take their prey in the air, preferring to diligently seek it out among the branches and foliage" and Stanwood (Ber 1953) said "The bird is quick in its movement but often spends periods of some length on one tree." Like the myrtle, this species enlarges its feeding zone while gathering food for its young. This is similar to the results of Betts (195 ndicating that the young tits eat different food from the adults.

Blackburnian Warbler. This species generally feeds high in the trees but is otherwise more or less intermediate between black-throated green and bay-breasted in its feeding behavior. This is true both of its flight frequency and its preferred feeding position on the limb (Figure 5). It is also intermediate in its method of hunting, usually moving out from the base to the tip of the branches looking down in the fashion of the bay-breasted and occasionally hopping about rapidly upon the mat of foliage at the branch tips looking both up and down for insects and even hovering occasionally. They seem to use the method of rapid peering, only occasionally hawking after a flying insect. As further evidence, Knight (1908) wrote "As a rule they feed by passing from limb to limb and examining the foliage and limbs of trees, more seldom catching anything in the air." Kendeigh (1945) said "It belongs to the treetops, singing and feeding at heights of 35 to 75 feet from the ground."

Bay-breasted Warbler. The usual feeding habits of this species are the most restricted of any of the species studied. All of the observations in the T1 zone and most in the T2 zone refer to singing males. This species uses its wings considerably less often than the other species, although it still appears to use the method of rapid peering in its hunting since it moves nearly continuously. These motions are, however, predominantly radial and seldom require the use of wings. The bird regularly works from the licheny base of the branches well out to the tip, although the largest part of the time is spent in the shady interior of the tree. It frequently stays in the same tree for long periods of time. This species very rarely hovers in the black-throated green fashion, and appears much less nimble in its actions about the tips of the branches, usually staying away from those buds which are at the edge of the mat of foliage. When it does feed at the edge of the mat, it is nearly always by hanging down rather than peering up. Other observers have emphasized the slowness. Brewster (Griscom 1938) called this warbler "slow and sluggish," and Kendeigh (1947) said "The birds do not move around much, but may sing and feed for long periods in the same tree." Forbush (1929) stated that it spends most of its time "moving about deliberately, after the manner of vireos."

### Food

Two species may eat different food for only three reasons: 1. They may feed in different places

or different times of day; 2. They may feed in such a manner as to find different foods; 3. They may accept different kinds of food from among those to which they are exposed. (Of course, a combination of these reasons is also possible.)

In the previous section it was shown that the warblers feed in different places and in a different manner, thus probably being exposed to different foods for the first and second reasons mentioned above. It is the aim of this section to show that the five warbler species have only small differences of the third kind. Theoretically, such differences, unaccompanied by morphological adaptations, would be disadvantageous, for, lacking the adaptations required to give greater efficiency in food collecting, and suffering a reduction in the number of acceptible food species, a bird would obtain food at a lesser rate. When the necessary adaptations are present, they usually consist of quite marked differences in bill structure such as those reported by Huxley (1942), Lack (1947), and Amadon (1950). As Table V shows, the mean bill measurements in millimeters of the five species of warbler considered in this study are quite similar. Twelve specimens of each species from the Peabody Museum of Natural History at Yale University were measured for each of the means given.

TABLE V. Mean dimensions of the bills of 12 specimens of each species

| Species | Bill Length | Height at Nares | Width at Nares | Width 2.5mm from tip |
|---|---|---|---|---|
| Cape May | 12.82 | 2.85 | 2.93 | 0.96 |
| Myrtle | 12.47 | 3.26 | 2.12 | 1.33 |
| Black-throated green | 12.58 | 3.38 | 3.15 | 1.34 |
| Blackburnian | 12.97 | 3.24 | 3.36 | 1.17 |
| Bay-breasted | 13.04 | 3.69 | 3.58 | 1.43 |

The Cape May alone has a noticeably different bill, it being more slender, especially at the tip. This bill houses a semi-tubular tongue as mentioned above, which is unique in the genus. These may be useful adaptations for their rainy weather flower feeding, but would seem ill-adapted for the characteristic flycatching of the breeding season (Gardner 1925). It is doubtless useful in other seasons, as will be discussed later. Aside from the Cape May, all other species differ in bill measurement by only a small fraction of a millimeter. Thus, for theoretical reasons, no pronounced differences of the third kind would be expected. Empirically, there is evidence to support this belief.

McAtee (1932) reported upon the analysis of eighty thousand bird stomachs, in an effort to disprove mimicry. Although his results were not conclusive, he claimed that insects appeared in bird stomachs about proportionately to their availability. Kendeigh (1945) agreed with this conclusion. Although McAtee (1926) said that no detailed studies of warbler food habits had been made, and no general ones seem to have appeared since, two very suggestive sets of analyses covering the five species have been published. Kendeigh (1947) reported upon the stomach contents of a collection made near Lake Nipigon, and Mitchell (1952) analyzed the stomachs of many birds taken during a budworm infestation in Maine. These data show, first, that most species of warbler eat all major orders of local arboreal arthropods. Furthermore, although there are differences in proportion of types of foods eaten by various species, these differences are most easily explained in terms of feeding zone. Thus, black-throated green and blackburnian which are morphologically the most similar of the five species have quite different foods. Kendeigh's table shows that black-throated green eats 4% Coleoptera, 31% Araneida, and 20% Homoptera, which blackburnian eats 22% Coleoptera, 2% Araneida, and 3% Homoptera. Dr. W. R. Henson has pointed out (pers. comm.) that Coleoptera can reasonably be assumed to come from inner parts of the tree where blackburnian has been shown to feed, whereas the Homoptera and most of the Araneida would be caught in the current year's growth where the black-throated green feeds more often, thus explaining the observed difference. Black-throated green and bay-breasted, with the most vireo-like bills (high at the nares), seem to eat more Lepidoptera larvae which are typical vireo food, but Mitchell's table shows that the other species too can eat predominantly Lepidoptera larvae when these are abundant. Otherwise, the food of the bay-breasted is more like that of the blackburnian, the feeding habits of which are similar. There are not sufficient data to analyze Cape May in this fashion. The myrtle warbler's feeding behavior is so flexible that no correlation between insects caught and a specific feeding zone or behavior is expected. This is shown by its having the most even distribution of food of any of the species considered. Thus, these correlations show that the differences in warbler food can be readily explained by morphological and zonal characteristics of the species.

## Nest Location

The position of the nest is quite characteristic in warbler species. Nearly all species of the genus *Dendroica* nest off the ground. Figure 8 shows heights of the nests of the five species of warbler studied here. These data result from a combination of the records of Cruickshank (1956), the information in the egg collection of the American Museum of Natural History in New York, and that gathered in this study. Since the distributions are skewed and irregular, the median and confidence intervals for the median (Banerjee and Nair 1940) are appropriate measurements. As the figure shows, the Cape May, with 95% confidence interval for the median of 40-50 feet, and the blackburnian, whose interval is 30-50 feet, have quite similar nest heights, probably reflecting their tendency to feed at high elevations. The Cape May's nest is virtually always near the trunk in the uppermost dense cluster of branches in a spruce or occasionally a fir. The blackburnian may nest in a similar location or may nest farther out toward the branch tips. Myrtle and black-throated green have similar nesting heights, both species having 95% confidence interval for the median nest height of 15-20 feet. The black-throated green seems to prefer smaller trees for its nest, and is thus more likely to place its nest near the runk, but, in keeping with its other characteristics, the myrtle seems quite varied in this respect. Finally, the bay-breasted, which has the lowest feeding zone, has the lowest nest position, the median height being between 10 and 15 feet (95% confidence). Thus, the nest positions of the five species of warbler reflect their preferred feeding zones.

## Territoriality

Defining territory as any defended area, warbler territories in the breeding season are of what Hinde (1956) called type A ("Large breeding area within which nesting, courtship, and mating and most food-seeking usually occur"). He pointed out that, since the behavioral mechanisms involved in defending a territory against others of the same species are the same as those involved in defending it against other species, this distinction need not be specified in the definition. From the ecological point of view, the distinction is of very great importance, however, for, as G. E. Hutchinson pointed out in conversation, if each species has it density (even locally) limited by a territorial behavior which ignores the other species, then there need be no further differences between the species to permit them to persist together. A weaker form of the same process, in which territories were compressible but only under pressure of a large population, would still be effective, along with small niche differences, in making each species inhibit its own population growth more than the others'—th

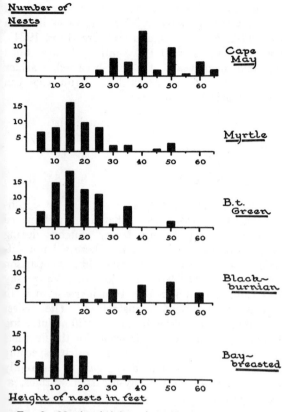

Fig. 8. Nesting heights of warblers.

necessary condition for the persistence of sympatric species.

Two further conditions make territory important for regulating populations. First, to have density dependent regulation, a species' regulating mechanism must have information of its own population density. Second, a predator ideally should keep its prey at that population level which permits the greatest rate of production. This means that the prey would not normally be particularly scarce. This, combined with the varied prey of the birds and the varied predators of the insects, would make food density a poorer criterion of a given bird species' density than size of territory. Thus, competition for food would be reduced from a "scramble" to a "contest" (Haldane 1955).

While the true nature of birds' territories has proved very elusive (Lack 1954, Hinde 1956), two separate lines of evidence suggest strongly that territories contribute to the regulation of local densities in warbler populations. Stewart and Aldrich (1951) and Hensley and Cope (1951) removed adult birds from their territories in 1949 and 1950 respectively, in a 40 acre plot in a budworm-infested area of Maine. The vacated territories were always filled by new pairs, the males

singing the vigorous song of a bird setting up a territory. It seems nearly inescapable that these were part of a large floating population of birds only prevented from breeding by the absence of unoccupied territories. Since this was in a budworm outbreak, there seems little doubt that there would have been adequate food for a larger breeding population.

In a study over a series of years on the birds in New Brunswick, Cheshire (1954) recorded the populations and territory sizes of the various species as a budworm outbreak began and progressed. He showed that while the bay-breasted warbler (the commonest bird during the outbreak) underwent a five- to seven-fold increase as the outbreak began, their mean territory sizes remained constant instead of decreasing correspondingly. That is, there had been unoccupied interstices between territories initially; these were filled in by the incoming birds but territory sizes were left unchanged.

The facts suggest that the territory size is more or less fixed in this region (although, of course, it may vary from region to region) and that if territorial compression occurs during high population densities, it only does so during higher population densities than those observed. Of course, if high population densities persisted, natural selection might be expected to reduce territory size, but this is a different situation.

As for interspecific territoriality, there is no exclusion of the kind found in intraspecific territoriality, as is clearly shown in Kendeigh's (1947) territory maps. It is very difficult to distinguish a mild repulsion of other species by territorialism from a preference for slightly different habitats. Adequate information does not exist to make the distinction at present. However, it seems quite certain that interspecific territoriality is weaker than intraspecific and, therefore, that the effect of a large density of one species is greater on that species than on the others. It is thus probable that, in the warblers, territoriality helps reduce competition and acts as a stabilizing factor (as well as performing the well-known functions of pair formation and maintenance).

### Natality and Mortality

In a population which has reached an equilibrium size, abundance is independent of birth and death rates. For species in equilibrium, then, a study of birth and death rates is not necessary to understand the control of the equilibrium abundance. However, as Darwin (1859) said, "A large number of eggs is of some importance to those species which depend upon a fluctuating amount of food, for it allows them rapidly to increase in numbers."

The five species of warbler studied here are very interesting in this respect. Table VI is a summary of the nesting data of the Museum of Comparative Zoology at Harvard, the American Museum of Natural History in New York, and the data of Harlow published by Street (1956).

TABLE VI. Mean clutch sizes for the 5 species

| Species | No. of Nests | CLUTCH SIZE | | | | | Mean | St. Dev. |
|---|---|---|---|---|---|---|---|---|
| | | 3 | 4 | 5 | 6 | 7 | | |
| Cape May........ | 48 | | 4 | 11 | 24 | 9 | 5.792 | .850 |
| Myrtle............ | 24 | 1 | 19 | 4 | | | 4.125 | .449 |
| Black-throated green......... | 45 | 2 | 39 | 4 | | | 4.044 | .366 |
| Blackburnian...... | 44 | 7 | 32 | 5 | | | 3.955 | .526 |
| Bay-breasted...... | 49 | | | 5 | 21 | 20 | 3 | 5.429 | .752 |

Cape May and bay-breasted warblers' nests were enough of a prize that it is quite certain that all found were kept and that the collections do not reflect any bias. There is a possibility of slight bias, collectors perhaps prizing larger clutches, in the other three species in the museum collections, but their clutch sizes are so constant that this seems improbable. The data of Harlow are not subject to his criticism, since he recorded all nests found.

While the sources of these collections vary in latitude from that of the Poconos of Pennsylvania to that of northern New Brunswick, there appears to be very little change in clutch size in this range of latitude. Thus the mean clutch size of 16 nests of the black-throated green in the Poconos is 4.06, while for the combined collections from Nova Scotia and New Brunswick (12 nests) the mean clutch is 4.17. The nests of the other species are from a narrow range of latitude and would not be expected to vary. Thus it was felt permissible to combine the data from different latitudes.

It is immediately apparent that Cape May and bay-breasted, the species which capitalize upon the periodic spruce budworm outbreaks, have considerably larger clutches than the other species, as Darwin would have predicted. It is of interest that the only other warbler regularly laying such large clutches is the Tennessee warbler (*Vermivora peregrina*) which is the other species regularly fluctuating with the budworms (Kendeigh 1947). Thus it seems that Darwin's statement provides an appropriate explanation for the larger clutches. It is also interesting that the standard deviation of the Cape May and bay-breasted warblers' clutch sizes is greater. This suggests a certain plasticity which can be verified, for the

bay-breasted at least, as follows. If the time of the budworm outbreak in New Brunswick is taken as 1911-1920 (Swaine and and Craighead 1924), and other years from 1903 until 1938 are called non-budworm years, the bay-breasted warbler clutches from northeastern New Brunswick can be summarized as follows:

| | Clutch Size | | | |
|---|---|---|---|---|
| | 4 | 5 | 6 | 7 |
| Budworm Years | 1 | 5 | 15 | 3 |
| Non-budworm Years | 4 | 8 | 5 | 0 |

The U test (Hoel 1954) shows this to be significant at the .0024 level; that is, bay-breasted warblers lay significantly larger clutches during years of budworm outbreaks. There are not sufficient data to make a corresponding comparison for Cape May warblers. It is known (Wangersky and Cunningham 1956) that an increase in birth rate is likely to lead to instability. The easiest way to increase the stability, while still maintaining the large clutch which is desirable for the fluctuating food supply, is to have the clutch especially large when food is abundant. This is apparently the solution which the bay-breasted warbler, at least, has taken.

Mortality during the breeding season is more difficult to analyze. Disease is not normally important as a mortality factor in passerines (Lack 1954) and this appeared to be the case for the warblers under observation. Predation may be important, however. Saw-whet owls (*Aegolius acadica*), Cooper's hawks (*Accipiter cooperii*), goshawks (*A. gentilis*), ravens (*Corvus corax*), crows (*C. brachyrhynchos*), and herring gull (*Larus argentatus*) all occasionally were noted in the Maine woods, but no evidence was obtained of their preying upon the warblers. In fact, none of the established pairs of birds were broken up by predation of this type. Red squirrels (*Tamiasciurus hudsonicus*) were continually present in all plots and were frequently observed searching for nests. They certainly destroyed the nest of a black-throated green and of a brown creeper (*Certhia familiaris*) and were quite probably responsible for plundering one myrtle warbler nest which was robbed soon after eggs were laid. The most common evidence of mortality, however, was the frequent observation of parents feeding only one or two newly fledged young. Thus two pair of myrtle warblers in 1956 and one in 1957 were observed the day the young left the nest feeding four young. One of the 1956 pairs succeeded in keeping all four young alive for at least three days, at which time they could no longer be fed lowed. The remaining two pairs were only feeding two young on the day following the departure of the young from the nest. Similarly, of two black-throated green pairs (one in 1956, one in 1957) where young could be followed, one kept all four young alive and the second only raised two of the fledged four. It was difficult to determine the number of young the parents were feeding. It was also difficult to be at the nest site when the young left the nest to determine the number of fledged young. Consequently, no more observations suitable to report were made. When the young leave the nest, they fly to nearby trees quite independently of one another and apparently never return to the nest. The result is that within a few hours the young are widely scattered. In this condition they are very susceptible to predators and exposure, and should one fly when its parents were not nearby, it would rapidly starve. Normally, the young only fly or chatter loudly when a parent with food is calling nearby, and the parents seem remarkably good at remembering where the young have gone. At best, however, this is a very dangerous period. It is of some interest to note that adult warblers will feed not only young of other birds of their own species but also of other species. Skutch (1954) reviewed several published cases of this. Hence, when a wood is densely settled with warblers, the members of a large clutch might have a better chance of surviving, the straying young being fed by neighbors. This high density is, of course, the situation which obtains during a budworm outbreak when bay-breasted and Cape May warblers are so successful.

### Time of Activities

So far, the nature and position of the species' activities during the breeding season have been compared. The time of these activities would also be a potential source of diversity. There could either be differences in the time of day in which feeding took place, or there could be differences in the dates during which eggs were laid and the young fed. The first type of difference (time of lay) seems inherently improbable since, at least while feeding the fledged young, the parents are kept busy throughout the daylight hours gathering food. Record was taken of the time at which the various warbler species began singing in the morning of 19 June 1956. The results (Eastern Daylight Time) are: 0352, first warbler (magnolia, *D. magnolia*); 0357, first myrtle; 0400, both myrtle and magnolia singing regularly; 0401, first black-throated green; 0402, first parula warbler (*Parula americana*); 0403, first bay-breasted;

0405, all warblers singing regularly. Thus, within 13 minutes after the first warbler sang all species were singing regularly. The sequence of rising corresponds to the degree of exposure of the usual feeding zones for that date (see Figures 2-6), and therefore probably depends only upon the time at which the light reaches a certain intensity.

As for the breeding season, there is good evidence of differences in time of completion of clutches. Since date of completion can be expected to change from place to place, comparisons must be made at one fixed locality. Of 15 nests of black-throated green warbler found by Harlow in the Poconos of Pennsylvania, the mean date of clutch completion was June 3, and of 21 blackburnian the mean date of clutch completion was June 1. Thus, for this region, and there is no reason to think that the relative dates are different in other regions, there is little difference in time of nesting between blackburnian and black-throated green warblers. From the extensive collections of P. B. Philipp near Tabusintac, N. B., now in the American Museum of Natural History, and from a smaller number collected in the same region by R. C. Harlow, now in the Museum of Comparative Zoology, bay-breasted and Cape May warbler nest dates can be compared (Figure 9). It is quite clear that the bay-breasted with the median date of nest discovery of 25 June (95% confidence interval for the median 23-27 June) nest substantially later than the Cape May whose median date is 17 June (95% confidence interval for the median of 16 June-20 June). As the figure shows, the small number of nests of black-throated green and myrtle from the same region show a fairly wide spread but strongly suggest median dates intermediate between Cape May and bay-breasted. (The dates recorded by Palmer (1949) for Maine give a roughly similar sequence; myrtle, 30 May-6 June; black-throated green, 26 May-20 June; bay-breasted, after 7 June.)

It might be expected that the insects caught by the species which feed in the T zones and near the tree tops would reach peak abundance sooner thus making it desirable for those species to nest earlier. The sequence of nesting dates just presented seems to be consistent with this hypothesis.

### Evidence from Winter Season

The five species of warbler migrate out of the coniferous forest through the deciduous forest and cultivated land in eastern North America and, mostly, into the West Indies and Central and South America. Therefore, any behavioral char-

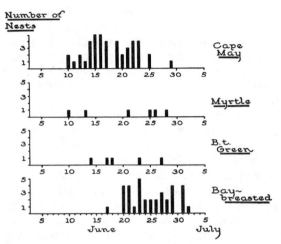

FIG. 9. Nesting dates of warblers in the Tabusintac, N. B., region.

acteristics that remain the same throughout the year must be nearly independent of the specific environment (at least within the range of environmental variation to which the bird is normally exposed). If any aspects of the breeding season behavior are retained throughout the year, these would be expected to be more fundamental than those aspects that varied with the local environment. This would be especially likely if the retained aspects of the behavior were controlled by morphological characteristics. The varying aspects would be interpreted as the result of interaction between the fundamental characteristics and the environment, as direct results of stimuli particular to that environment, or as seasonal aspects of birds' physiology. Thus it is of interest to compare behavior in different seasons.

### Winter Distribution

Although Salomonsen (1954) said that species which breed in the same place tend to winter in different geographic regions, there is no evidence for this in the five warblers. More precisely, Salomonsen's statement suggests that a certain amount of competition might be avoided by having allopatric wintering grounds. Probably the most satisfactory way to test this is to determine whether the five warblers' ranges show less winter overlap than a randomly chosen group of five eastern warblers (Western warblers tend to winter in a different region and hence should not be included). To make definitions precise, two species of warbler were said to have a significant overlap in winter ranges if at least half of one species' winter range is included in the other's. From the winter range data of Bent (1953) the twenty-three species of warbler breeding in Maine (Palmer, 1949) show 253 significant overlaps,

i.e., an average of 11 per species. Therefore, the probability that a randomly chosen pair of species of Maine warblers will show significant winter range overlap is 11/23 or .478. Considering the five species of warbler in the present study, Cape May overlaps with myrtle and possibly black-throated green; myrtle overlaps with Cape May, black-throated green, and blackburnian; black-throated green overlaps with Cape May (possibly), myrtle, and blackburnian; blackburnian overlaps with myrtle, black-throated green, and bay-breasted; and bay-breasted overlaps with blackburnian. There is thus a total of 10 certain overlaps among the 5 species, or 2 per species. There is thus a mean overlap per pair of species of 2/5 or .400 which is quite near the expected 0.478 suggesting that the five species overlap about randomly. It might be argued that the 23 species of Maine warblers themselves show a mutual repulsion in the winter ranges and hence are a poor standard of comparison. That this is not so can be seen as follows. The 23 species have a total of 315 significant summer overlaps in range, or 13.7 per species; i.e., 13.7/23 or 0.596 is the probability that a randomly chosen pair of species will overlap in summer. As discussed above, the probability is 0.478 that a randomly chosen pair will overlap in winter. Therefore, if winter range is chosen independently of summer, 0.478 x 0.596 = 0.285 would be the expected probability of significant overlap in both winter and summer. Significant summer and winter overlaps were recorded in 164 cases, giving 7.1 per species, or a probability of 7.1/23 = 0.309, which is even a very slightly higher figure than expected, showing a slight tendency for birds which summer together to winter together. Therefore, the Maine warblers do not repel one another in over-all winter range and they are therefore suitable for the comparison made earlier. It can be concluded that the five species show about the amount of overlapping of winter range that would be expected on a random basis.

This does not prove that the species occupy the same habitat in the winter, of course. Although there are no adequate data to investigate the problem, it is quite possible that because of habitat selection, wintering populations of the five species are isolated.

### Winter Feeding Behavior

The period of 22 December 1956 until 9 January 1957 was spent in Costa Rica observing winter behavior of warblers. Although myrtle, black-throated green, and blackburnian warblers include Costa Rica in their winter range (Skutch

Bent 1953, and pers. comm.), only black-
[thr]oated green of the five were found during the
[au]thor's study. However, many other species of
[wa]rbler were present, and detailed notes were
[ta]ken on them for comparison with summer be-
[ha]vior. Measurements of interval between flights
[we]re made for each species. These should be com-
[pa]rable with those made in other seasons. No
[str]ictly comparable measurement of feeding posi-
[tio]n could be made, however. In view of the great
[va]riety of tree heights in tropical forests, measure-
[me]nts of feeding height could not reasonably be
[ma]de in terms of distance from the top of the tree.
[In]stead, height above the ground was used, usual-
[ly] gauged by eye and occasionally checked by
[ca]mera viewfinder. Zones such as base, middle,
[an]d tip of branch were not reasonable, but gen-
[er]al reference to large limbs or leaves could be
[ma]de. The actual behavior while gathering food
[is] probably comparable with other seasons; it is
[fai]rly subjective, however, so that the comparison
[sh]ould be confirmed by the various other measure-
[me]nts. A general comparison of winter and
[su]mmer behavior of warblers wintering in Costa
[Ri]ca will be given first; this will be followed by
[a] more detailed analysis of two species.

Thirteen species of Parulidae were observed
[in] Costa Rica. Of these, nine, black and white
[(*M*]*niotilta varia*), Tennessee, golden-winged
[(*V*]*ermivora chrysoptera*), yellow, black-throated
[gr]een, sycamore (*Dendroica dominica albilora*)[2],
[ch]estnut-sided (*Dendroica pensylvanica*), Wil-
[so]n's (*Wilsonia pusilla*), and redstart (*Setophaga
[ru]ticilla*), breed in northeastern United States
[an]d/or adjacent Canada. Their summer be-
[ha]vior has been observed, somewhat casually, by
[or]nithologists for many years. These observa-
[tio]ns are summarized in a general way by Bent
[(1]953) and are part of the common knowledge of
[mo]st ornithologists. It is therefore of great in-
[te]rest that Skutch, who has made very careful
[ob]servations of Central American birds, has stated
[(p]ers. comm.) that he thinks all warblers winter-
[in]g in Costa Rica (except perhaps chestnut-sided
[wh]ich he feels spends more time in high trees in
[th]e winter) have the same general feeding be-
[ha]vior and feeding height in both seasons. Table
[V]II summarizes general results of this study
[an]d helps confirm Skutch's impression.

Tennessee and black-throated green were ob-
[se]rved in greater numbers than the others. Hence,
[a] detailed comparison of their winter behavior in
[re]lation to their summer behavior is possible.
[Te]nnessee warblers often hopped along branches,
[w]hile black-throated green more often hopped

[2] Rare in Costa Rica.

TABLE VII. Summary of observations in Costa Rica

| Species | COSTA RICA | | | BREEDING GROUNDS | |
|---|---|---|---|---|---|
| | Approx. Number Observed | Principal Feeding Height | Principal Feeding Activities | Principal Feeding Height | Principal Feeding Activities |
| Black and White.... | 5 | 0–35' | creeps on trunk and branches | same | same |
| Golden-winged...... | 1 | 5–25' | hops | same | same |
| Tennessee......... | 200 | 10–50'* | hops, esp. along branches* | 0–40' | same* |
| Yellow............ | 20 | 4–40' | hops | same | same |
| Black-th. green..... | 50 | 10–50'* | hops, esp. across branches* | same* | same* |
| Sycamore......... | 1 | 8–30' | creeps and hops | ? | same |
| Chestnut-sided...... | 15 | 0–50' | hops | 0–30' | same |
| Wilson's........... | 15 | 0–25' | hops | same | same |
| Amer. redstart...... | 10 | 5–50' | hawks for flying insects | same | same |

*See text for further information.

across branches. To measure this tendency, the
following procedure was adopted. A count was
made of the number of changes of feeding branch
which required hopping or flying over a gap.
The number of seconds of observation was also
recorded. If Tennessees moved along branches,
they should have had significantly fewer hops per
second than black-throated greens which moved
across branches. In the table below H stands
for the number of hops or flights across an air gap
in S seconds.

| *Black-throated green* | | *Tennessee* | |
|---|---|---|---|
| H | S | H | S |
| | | 4 | 30 |
| 8 | 90 | 3 | 48 |
| 5 | 38 | 6 | 105 |
| 7 | 43 | 4 | 54 |
| 1 | 14 | 6 | 100 |
| 12 | 85 | 11 | 74 |
| 12 | 60 | 8 | 83 |
| 14 | 70 | 8 | 82 |
| 59 | 400 | 50 | 576 |

Mean No. of Seconds per hop 6.78      11.52

Black-throated greens thus hopped 59 times in
400 seconds for a mean number of seconds per
hop of 6.78. Tennessees hopped 50 times in 576
seconds for a mean number of seconds per hop of
11.52. By an extended sign test (Dixon and
Massey 1951) this difference is well within the
5.5% level of significance. Hence, it is clear that
black-throated greens hop across branches more

often than Tennessees, partially confirming the subjective impression described above.

Strictly comparable measurements cannot be made in the breeding season since black-throated green feeds in coniferous and Tennessee in deciduous trees. However, the black-throated green has been shown to move principally in a tangential direction in the summer, while of eleven Tennessee warbler observations in the summer of 1957 all showed the hopping along branches which characterized the winter feeding behavior.

From these data, it is evident that the general aspects of warbler behavior are nearly the same in winter and summer. For warblers wintering in the West Indies the same situation obtains; namely, the winter habitats bear no obvious similarity to those chosen in the breeding season, but the feeding behavior and height are roughly the same (Eaton 1953). Cape May and myrtle warblers are particularly interesting and a little atypical in this respect. Both Bond (1957) and Eaton mention that Cape May frequents gardens and plantations, where it is often near the ground. This behavior parallels that observed by Brewster in the summer and reported earlier. In the winter it spends much of its time feeding upon flowers, a fact which will be used later. Bond (1957) and Skutch (in Bent 1953) both mention that myrtle warblers, in their West Indian and Central American wintering grounds, are found from beaches to forests, frequenting open ground especially. This variety of feeding location combined with its enormous winter range confirms the summer observation of great flexibility of behavior.

These observations on the flexibility of myrtle warblers can be extended by including observations made on their wintering grounds in the United States. It is well known (Pettingill 1951) that myrtles winter in the northeast wherever there are extensive patches of bayberry (*Myrica pensylvanica*). Montauk Point on Long Island, which is such a place, was visited on January 26, 1957. Here myrtles were the commonest bird in the habitat in which the bayberry is abundant. The myrtles were moving about in flocks, frequently, as in the summer, making long flights. They fed principally while hopping upon the fallen leaves under bayberries. (There was no snow.) This behavior was very similar to that observed in the summer while they were catching emerging crane flies. Some were feeding upon the "wax" coat of the berries which is readily digestible and contains nodules which are rich sources of proteins and carbohydrates (Hausman 1927).

## POPULATION CONTROL

Any factor that can control a local populati has a space distribution. Examples of such fa tors are food, nesting sites, and predators. Th all populations are limited by the amount of su able space. The meaning of "suitable" for a giv species is the interesting problem. Within a giv environment each necessary activity requires certain amount of space. That activity which quires the greatest amount of space is likely be limiting. Thus, animals such as barnac which wait for moving food to pass by and quire very little space to catch it are likely to limited by amount of surface on which to re Here "suitable space" means "space adequate f barnacle attachment." Similarly, for some inse the suitable space may be the space with sufficie food supply within easy dispersal distance; f some birds, suitable nest holes may be scarc than adequate food and suitable space will me proper nest hole. This section will be devoted the nature of suitable space for the five species warbler under consideration.

The five warblers do not seem to have spec nesting space or nesting material requiremer which would necessitate a larger amount of spa than food gathering. Territory defence is pro ably the only activity of the warblers that requir an area of comparable size to that needed for fo gathering. As discussed earlier, territoriality m exert a limiting effect upon populations und conditions of abundant food supply, thus acting a stabilizing factor. However, if territory r quirements limit populations under normal co ditions, it may be inquired why natural selecti has not reduced territory sizes thus permitti larger populations. Furthermore, variation warbler population density from plot to plot su gests that more than an incompressible territory responsible for population regulation. Therefor like nesting space and nesting material requir ments, territories probably require less space f warblers in normal years than does food gathe ing. Consequently, suitable space is probably t amount of space with an adequate food supply which the bird is adapted to feed. Direct measur ment of the food supply would require a ve elaborate sampling scheme. However, measur ment of the amount of foliage of the type in whic the species has been shown to feed is quite feasibl If the density of breeding pairs of a species proportional to the amount of foliage in a certa zone, then a census of a plot with twice the volum of this foliage should have twice the number birds of corresponding species. Since the fi species under consideration feed above 20 feet, only foliage above 20 feet was measured.

Five areas on Mt. Desert Island were censused and measured with this view in mind. All were in predominantly spruce forest, but except for this they were chosen to be as different as possible in order to exhibit as great a range of variation as possible. The volume of foliage above twenty feet was measured as follows. The volume of a cone is proportional to the product of its basal area with its height. The foliage of a spruce tree is roughly a hollow cone with walls of approximately constant thickness. The inner cone may be considered to begin ten feet below the outer. Finally, the basal area of the foliage is proportional to the trunk area. Consequently, the product of the height of foliage in the crown with the basal area of the trunks of the trees will give a figure proportional to the volume of the outer cone. A similar figure for the volume of the inner cone is calculated and the volume of foliage in the hollow shell is obtained by subtraction. The proportion of the volume lying above twenty feet of either the inner or the outer cone is the square of the proportion of the height lying above twenty feet, so that this adjustment is easily made. The number obtained is thus proportional to the desired volume. In practice, the height of foliage in the crown was measured with a rangefinder and the basal area was measured with a "Bitterlich releoscope" (Grosenbaugh 1952).

Plot A was a 3.8 acre section of an open sphagnum bog, the "Big Heath" on Mt. Desert Island. The only trees present were black spruce and tamarack (*Larix laricina*). Trees were very scattered and the highest were between 15 and 20 feet. While typical bog warblers were common, none of the five species considered here was present.

Plot B was a 4 acre strip along the edge of the bog. Red spruce largely replaced black in this plot, the trees occasionally reaching 50 feet in height. The strip was bordered on one side by a road and on the other by the open bog.

Plot C was a 9 acre area along the Hio Truck Trail near Seawall on Mt. Desert Island. The forest here was quite mature, trees reaching 70 feet, and was predominantly composed of red spruce, white spruce, and balsam fir, with a higher proportion of white birch than occurred in the other plots.

Plot D was a dense, 4 acre stand of red spruce of moderate age near Southwest Harbor, Maine. Trees reached a height of 60 feet in some places, and had been thinned in part of the plot.

Plot E was the 9 acre stand of white spruce at Bass Harbor Head on Mt. Desert Island in which the observations of 1956 were made. Here the trees reached a height of 70 feet quite frequently, although the mean was nearer 60. This plot apparently originated as an old field stand with numerous, large, low branches. These have died and become covered with a layer of lichens, especially *Usnea*.

For each plot the composition of the warbler population and the volume of the foliage above 20 feet are indicated in figure 10. Here "others" refers to other tree-nesting warblers which fed above 20 feet. It is quite clear that the total tree-nesting warbler population is very nearly proportional to the foliage volume. The abundance of the myrtle warbler is evidently quite constant, only increasing slowly as the volume of foliage increases. This is probably due to its flycatching and ground feeding habits which help to make it less dependent upon the foliage.

Black-throated green warblers were the dominant birds in all mature spruce forest habitats on Mt. Desert Island. As the figure indicates, their abundance was nearly proportional to the foliage volume above 20 feet. Their abundance did fall off slightly in the two plots, C and E, in which very tall trees were present. Black-throated greens seldom use these tall tree tops for feeding, so that the amount of foliage suitable for black-throated greens should be slightly reduced from the amount calculated for plots C and E.

Blackburnians, which require foliage near the tops of the trees, were present in small numbers in both plots which had trees of height greater than 60 feet. A true understanding of their population control on Mt. Desert Island probably cannot be acquired without considering competition with other species. It is reasonable that the blackburnian can only persist where the forest is sufficiently old that the feeding zone of the dominant black-throated green stops well before the tree tops in which the blackburnian prefers to feed.

On Mt. Desert Island, bay-breasted warblers are only common where there are dense growths of lichen-covered lower branches of spruce in the shade of the forest crown. It is in this zone that a large part of their activity takes place and here their sluggish, radially moving, feeding behavior is well suited. This habitat appears when the forest becomes dense and has large trees. Consequently, the bay-breasted warblers only remained permanently in plots D and E. (Two set up territories in plot C but had apparently left by June 8.) Again it appears that this habitat is occupied by the bay-breasted partly because it is not occupied by the black-throated green. In the budworm infested spruce and balsam stands near Ft. Kent, Maine, the bay-breasted warbler was the dominant bird; here they occupied the dense young stands of conifers and black-throated greens were forced to occupy the ridges covered with mixed growths of hemlock and hardwoods. The type of competition in heterogeneous regions mentioned in the first section provides an appropriate explanation for the change in dominance; the forest composition of the whole region is more important than the very local conditions.

Although Cape May warblers did not occupy any of the census plots, observations on their feeding behavior suggest that they would be quite similar to the myrtle warbler as far as dependence on tree foliage is concerned. This is partially confirmed by the fact that of the 18 stations studied in northern Maine, Cape Mays were present in all the lowland ones and dominant only in the fairly open stands with mature trees—a habitat which is unsuitable for the bay-breasted but is quite satisfactory for both myrtle and Cape May.

### Discussion and Conclusions

In this study competition has been viewed in the light of the statement that species can coexist only if each inhibits its own population more than the others'. This is probably equivalent to saying that species divide up the resources of a community in such a way that each species is limited by a different factor. If this is taken as a statement of the Volterra-Gause principle, there can be no exceptions to it. Ecological investigations of closely-related species then are looked upon as enumerations of the divers ways in which the resources of a community can be partitioned.

For the five species of warbler considered here, there are three quite distinct categories of "different factors" which could regulate populations. "Different factors" can mean different resources, the same resources at different places, or the same resources at different times. All three of these seem important for the warblers, especially if different places and times mean very different—different habitats and different years.

First, the observations show that there is every reason to believe that the birds behave in such a way as to be exposed to different kinds of food. They feed in different positions, indulge in hawking and hovering to different extents, move in different directions through the trees, vary from active to sluggish, and probably have the greatest need for food at different times corresponding to the different nesting dates. All of these differences are statistical, however; any two species show some overlapping in all of these activities.

The species of food organisms which were widespread in the forest and had high dispersal rates would be preyed upon by all the warblers. Thus, competition for food is possible. The actual food eaten does indicate that the species have certain foods in common. The slight difference in habitat preference resulting from the species' different feeding zones is probably more important. This could permit each species to have its own center of dispersal to regions occupied by all species. Coexistence in one habitat, then, may be the result of each species being limited by the availability of a resource in different habitats. Even although the insects fed upon may be basically of the same type in the different habitats, it is improbable that the same individual insects should fly back and forth between distant woods; consequently, there would be no chance for competition. The habitat differences and, equivalently, the feeding zone differences, between blackburnian, black-throated green, and bay-breasted are sufficiently large that this explanation of coexistence is quite reasonable.

The myrtle warbler is present in many habitats in the summer but is never abundant. It has a very large summer and winter range, feeds from the tree tops to the forest floor, and by rapid peering or by hawking. It makes frequent long flights and defends a large territory. Probably it can be considered a marginal species which, by being less specialized and thus more flexible in its requirements, manages to maintain a constant, low population (Figure 10).

The Cape May warbler is in a different category, at least in the region near the southern limit of its range. For here it apparently depends upon the occasional outbreaks of superabundant food (usually spruce budworms) for its continued existence. The bay-breasted warbler, to a lesser degree, does the same thing. During budworm outbreaks, probably because of their extra large clutches, they are able to increase more rapidly than the other species, obtaining a temporary advantage. During the years between outbreaks they suffer reductions in numbers and may even be eliminated locally. Lack's hypothesis, that the clutch is adjusted so as to produce the maximum number of surviving offspring, provides a suitable explanation of the decrease during normal years of these large-clutched species. It may be asked why, if Lack's hypothesis is correct, natural selection favored large clutches in Cape May and bay breasted. Cheshire's (1954) censuses suggest a tentative answer. During his years of censusing increases in the bay-breasted warbler population reached a figure of over 300% per year. This probably far exceeds the maximum possible in

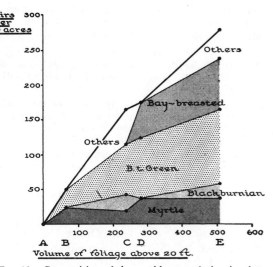

FIG. 10. Composition of the warbler population in plots , B, C, D, and E. "Others" refers to other warbler )ecies which feed at greater heights than 20 feet above ie ground. The units of volume measurement are only roportional to the volume, but each unit roughly equals 500 cubic feet per acre.

rease due to survival of nestlings raised in that lace; probably immigration is the explanation. ut if the species with large clutches search for reas in which food is superabundant and immirate into these regions, then, for the species as a hole, the large clutch may be adapted to the aximum survival of offspring. Cape May and ay-breasted warblers may therefore be considered ) be good examples of fugitive species (Hutchinon 1951).

Thus, of the five species, Cape May warblers nd to a lesser degree bay-breasted warblers are ependent upon periods of superabundant food, hile the remaining species maintain populations oughly proportional to the volume of foliage of ie type in which they normally feed. There are ifferences of feeding position, behavior, and nestig date which reduce competition. These, comined with slight differences in habitat preference nd perhaps a tendency for territoriality to have stronger regulating effect upon the same species ian upon others, permit the coexistence of the pecies.

## Acknowledgments

Prof. G. E. Hutchinson and Dr. S. D. Ripley ave played indispensable roles in the development f this work, providing advice, encouragement, and upport. The author had valuable discussion with )r. A. F. Skutch, James Bond, and Paul Slud conerning birds on their wintering grounds. Dr. .. R. Holdridge provided invaluable help in Costa ica, acting as naturalist and guide. Sincere thanks also go to the following persons. Miss Helen T. Mac Arthur prepared the illustrations. Drs. R. A. Paynter and Dean Amadon gave information about or provided access to the collections under their supervision. Drs. C. L. Remington, W. R. Henson, and P. B. Dowden provided entomological information. Dr. J. W. Mac Arthur helped with the observations. Finally, the author wishes to thank his wife who helped with observations, prepared the manuscript, and provided encouragement.

The work was supported by grants from the Peabody Museum of Natural History of Yale University and from the Chapman Memorial Fund of the American Museum of Natural History.

## References

Amadon, D. 1950. The Hawaiian honeycreepers (Aves, Drepaniidae). Bull. Amer. Mus. Nat. Hist. 95: 157-262.

Andrewartha, H. G. and L. C. Birch. 1954. The distribution and abundance of animals. Chicago: Univ. Chicago Press.

Banerjee, S. K. and K. R. Nair. 1940. Tables of confidence intervals for the median in samples from any continuous population. Sankya 4: 551-558.

Bent, A. C. 1953. Life histories of the North American wood warblers. U. S. Nat. Mus. Bull. 203.

Betts, M. 1955. The food of titmice in an oak woodland. Jour. Anim. Ecol. 24: 282-323.

Bond, J. 1937. The Cape May warbler in Maine. Auk 54: 306-308.

———. 1957. North American wood warblers in the West Indies. Audubon Mag. 59: 20-23.

Bourne, W. R. P. 1957. The breeding birds of Bermuda. Ibis 99: 94-105.

Breckenridge, W. J. 1956. Measurements of the habitat niche of the least flycatcher. Wilson Bull. 68: 47-51.

Cheshire, W. P. 1954. Bird populations and potential predation on the spruce budworm. Canada Dept. Agric. Sci. Serv., Annual Tech. Report, Green River Project 1953, Sect. 14.

Cruickshank, A. D. 1956. Aud. Field Notes 10: 431-432. (and earlier censuses of the same plot).

———. 1956a. Nesting heights of some woodland warblers in Maine. Wilson Bull. 68: 157.

Darwin, C. R. 1859. The origin of species by means of natural selection or the preservation of favoured races in the struggle for life. London: Murray.

Dixon, W. J. and F. J. Massey. 1951. Introduction to statistical analysis. New York: McGraw-Hill.

Eaton, S. W. 1953. Wood warblers wintering in Cuba. Wilson Bull. 65: 169-174.

Forbush, E. H. 1929. The birds of Massachusetts and other New England states. Vol. III. Boston: Mass. Dept. Agric.

Gardner, L. L. 1925. The adaptive modifications and the taxonomic value of the tongue in birds. Proc. U. S. Nat. Mus. 67, art. 19: 1-49.

Gause, G. F. 1934. The struggle for existence. Baltimore: Williams and Wilkins.

Greenbank, D. O. 1956. The role of climate and dispersal in the initiation of outbreaks of the spruce budworm in New Brunswick. Can. Jour. Zool. 34: 453-476.

Grinnell, J. 1914. Barriers to distribution as regards birds and mammals. Amer. Nat. 48: 249-254.

——. 1921. The principle of rapid peering in birds. Univ. Calif. Chron. 23: 392-396.

——. 1922. The trend of avian populations in California. Science 56: 671-676.

—— and T. Storer. 1924. Animal life in the Yosemite. Berkeley: Univ. Calif. Press.

Griscom, L. 1938. The birds of Lake Umbagog region of Maine. Compiled from the diaries and journals of William Brewster. Bull. Mus. Comp. Zool. 66: 525-620.

Grosenbaugh, L. R. 1952. Plotless timber estimates— new, fast, easy. Jour. Forestry 50: 33-37.

Haldane, J. B. S. 1955. Review of Lack (1954). Ibis 97: 375-377.

Hausman, L. A. 1927. On the winter food of the tree swallow (*Iridoprocne bicolor*) & the myrtle warbler (*Dendroica coronata*). Amer. Nat. 61: 379-382.

Hensley, M. M. and J. B. Cope. 1951. Further data on removal and repopulation of the breeding birds in a spruce-fir forest community. Auk 68: 483-493.

Hinde, R. A. 1956. The biological significance of territories of birds. Ibis 98: 340-369.

Hoel, P. G. 1954. Introduction to mathematical statistics. New York: Wiley.

Hutchinson, G. E. 1951. Copepodology for the ornithologist. Ecology 32: 571-577.

Huxley, J. 1942. Evolution, the modern synthesis. New York: Harper.

Kendeigh, S. C. 1945. Community selection birds on the Helderberg Plateau of New York. Auk 62: 418-436.

——. 1947. Bird population studies in the coniferous forest biome during a spruce budworm outbreak. Biol. Bull. 1, Ont. Dept. Lands and For.

Kluijver, H. N. and N. Tinbergen. 1953. Regulation of density in titmice. Arch. Ned. Zool. 10: 265-289.

Knight, O. W. 1908. The birds of Maine. Bangor.

Lack, D. 1947. Darwin's finches. Cambridge: Cambridge Univ. Press.

——. 1954. The natural regulation of animal numbers. Oxford: Oxford Univ. Press.

——. 1955. The mortality factors affecting adult numbers. In Cragg, J. B. and N. W. Pirie 1955. The numbers of man and animals. London: Oliver and Boyd.

MacKenzie, J. M. D. 1946. Some factors influencing woodland birds. Quart. Jour. For. 40: 82-88.

Mayr, E. 1950. Speciation in birds. Proc. Xth Int. Ornith. Cong. Uppsala.

McAtee, W. L. 1926. The relation of birds to woodlots in New York State. Roosevelt Wildlife Bull. 4: 7-157.

——. 1932. Effectiveness in nature of the so-called protective adaptations in the animal kingdom, chiefly as illustrated by the food habits of Nearctic birds. Smithsonian Misc. Coll. 85(7): 1-201.

Mitchell, R. T. 1952. Consumption of spruce budworms by birds in a Maine spruce-fir forest. Jour. For. 50: 387-389.

Palmer, R. S. 1949. Maine birds. Bull. Mus. Comp. Zool. 102: 1-656.

Pettingill, O. S. 1951. A guide to bird finding east of the Mississippi. New York: Oxford Univ. Press.

Salomonsen, F. 1954. Evolution and bird migration. Acta XI Cong. Int. Orn. Basil.

Skutch, A. F. 1954. Life histories of Central American birds. Pacific Coast Avifauna No. 31.

Smith, W. P. 1953. Aud. Field Notes 7: 337 (and earlier censuses of the same plot).

Stewart, R. E. and J. W. Aldrich. 1951. Removal and repopulation of breeding birds in a spruce-fir forest community. Auk 68: 471-482.

——. 1952. Ecological studies of breeding bird populations in northern Maine. Ecol. 33: 226-238.

Street, P. B. 1956. Birds of the Pocono Mountains, Pennsylvania. Delaware Valley Ornith. Club. Philadelphia.

Swaine, J. M. and F. C. Craighead. 1924. Studies of the spruce budworm (*Cacoecia fumiferana Clem.*) Part I. Dom. of Canada Dept. Agric. Bull. 37: 1-27

Swed, F. S. and C. Eisenhart. 1943. Tables for testing randomness of grouping in a sequence of alternatives. Ann. Math. Stat. 14: 66-87.

Volterra, V. 1926. Variazione e fluttuazione del numero d'individiu in specie animali conviventi. Mem. Accad. Lincei 2: 31-113. (Translated in Chapman, R. N. 1931. Animal ecology. New York: McGraw Hill.)

Wangersky, P. J. and W. J. Cunningham. 1956. On time lags in equations of growth. Proc. Nat. Acad. Sci. 42: 699-702.

Williams, A. B. 1950. Aud. Field Notes 4: 297-2 (and earlier censuses of the same plot).

Wilson, E. B. 1952. An introduction to scientific research. New York: McGraw-Hill.

# EXPERIMENTAL STUDIES ON PREDATION: DISPERSION FACTORS AND PREDATOR-PREY OSCILLATIONS[1,2]

## C. B. HUFFAKER[3]

## INTRODUCTION

THIS PAPER is the second covering a series of experiments designed to shed light upon the fundamental nature of predator-prey interaction, in particular, and the interrelations of this coaction with other important parameters of population changes, in general. In the first of this series (Huffaker and Kennett, 1956),[4] a study was made of the predatory mites, *Typhlodromus cucumeris* Oudemans[5] and *Typhlodromus reticulatus* Oudemans, and their prey species, *Tarsonemus pallidus* Banks, the cyclamen mite which attacks strawberries. In that paper the authors discussed in a broad way the need for detailed studies of this kind and the implications of such results for theories of population dynamics, particularly the role of predation—which role has been minimized by a number of researchers (e.g., Uvarov, 1931; Errington, 1937, 1946; Leopold, 1954).

A significant result of the experiments of Huffaker and Kennett (1956) was the demonstration of two types of fluctuations in density. Where predators were excluded there was a regularized pattern of fluctuations of **decreasing** amplitude, a result of reciprocal density-dependent interaction of the phytophagous mite and its host plant. The other, sharply contrasting type of regularized fluctuation occurred as a primary result of predation on the phytophagous mite by the predatory form. The interacting reciprocal dependence of the prey and predator populations resulted in greatly reduced densities and amplitude of fluctuations, comparing this with the status when predators were absent.

In the present effort a considerable body of quantitative data is presented. Also, the outlines of an experimental method and design sufficiently flexible for use in studying some of the principles of population dynamics are

---

[1] Received for publication August 16, 1957.

[2] These results were obtained during a period of sabbatical leave in 1955. The generous assistance of C. E. Kennett and F. E. Skinner in the preparation of the illustrations is gratefully acknowledged.

[3] Entomologist in Biological Control in the Experiment Station, Berkeley.

[4] See "References" on page 383.

[5] H. Womersley and C. E. Kennett now consider that this predator is really *Typhlodromus bellinus* Womersley.

delineated. The specific results are discussed with respect to the much-debated question of whether the predator-prey relation is inherently self-annihilative, and the bearing on this of the type of dispersion and hazards of searching. Certain trends are exhibited; if these are further verified by later experiments they may be theoretically significant, but such possibilities will be covered only after the accumulation of additional data from this continuing series of studies.

The immediate objective in the present effort has been the establishment of an ecosystem in which a predatory and a prey species could continue living together so that the phenomena associated with their interactions could be studied in detail. Once conditions are established giving a measure of assurance against overexploitation, various other features could be introduced to study their relations to the periods and amplitudes of such oscillations in density as are demonstrated. This could include such factors as differences in temperature, humidity, or physical terrain, for example. Also, the effects could be studied of using two or more predatory species competing for the one prey species, or the simultaneous employment of two species of prey acceptable to the one predator. Many variations along these lines could be expected to furnish valuable information, and the present data represent only a beginning.

Some of the many questions that could ultimately be answered include:

1. Are such oscillations inherently of **increasing** amplitude?

2. Even if so, are there commonly present forces which act to cancel this tendency, and if so, what are these forces?

3. Is the predator-prey relation adequately described by the Gause theory of overexploitation and auto-annihilation except under conditions involving immigration from other ecosystems?

4. Does the presence of other significant species in addition to the two primary or original coactors introduce a stabilizing or disturbing effect?

5. What may be the effect of changes in the physical conditions upon the degree of stability or permanence of the predator-prey relation?

6. Can evidence be obtained supporting or refuting the concept that the prey, as well as the predators, benefits from the relation?

7. What is the order of influence on stability of population density of such parameters as shelter (from physical adversity of environment), food, disease, and natural enemies of other kinds?

There are no published accounts wherein the predator-prey relation has been followed under controlled conditions beyond a single wave or "oscillation" in density. Authorities differ as to whether this relation is inherently disoperative, leading inevitably to annihilation of either the predatory species alone or both the predator and its prey in the given universe or microcosm employed. In this controversy there is confusion as to what constitutes a **suitable** experimental microcosm. Published examples of such studies have been contradictory or inconclusive.

In the classic experiments of Gause (1934) and Gause et al. (1936), the predator and prey species survived together only under quite arbitrary conditions—either when a portion of the prey population was protected by a "privileged sanctuary" or when reintroductions were made at intervals. Gause concluded that such systems are self-annihilative, that predators characteristically overexploit their prey, and that in nature immigrants must repopulate the local environments where this has occurred. He argued against the theory that repeated waves or oscillations conforming to mathematical formulae have an inherent meaning in the absence of immigrations.

Nicholson (1933, 1954) advocates the contrary view, and he and Winsor (1934) criticized Gause's experiments on the grounds that the universes or microcosms he employed were too small to even approximate a **qualitative,** to say nothing of a **quantitative,** conformity to theory.

DeBach and Smith (1941) conducted a stimulating experiment with a special type of predator (an entomophagous "parasite") in which they tested the biological parameter of searching capacity against Nicholson's formula. The results conformed to theory very neatly. Ecologists consider the results as based upon too arbitrary assignments or omission of other biological parameters—such as length of a generation, fecundity, undercrowding phenomena at very low densities, et cetera. However, their work remains a strikingly successful pioneer endeavor in this field, and their method of isolating the variables other than **searching** was productive,

In the present study an effort was made to learn if an adequately large and complex laboratory environment could be set up in which the predator-prey relation would not be self-exterminating, and in which all the biological parameters are left to the free play of the interacting forces inherent in the experiment, once established. Consequently, the procedure was to introduce the prey species and the predator species only at the initiation of an experiment and to follow population trends afterward without any further introductions or manipulations. No assignments of biological parameters were made. Furthermore, no areas restrictive to the predators were furnished. Food "conditioning" is the only complicating variable and this disturbance was minimized by the methods used. However, as experiments were terminated because of the annihilative force of predation in the initial, limited universes employed, the conditions set up for subsequent experiments were made progressively more complex in nature and the areas larger.

## EXPERIMENTAL DESIGN AND PROCEDURE

### General Aspects

The six-spotted mite, *Eotetranychus sexmaculatus* (Riley), was selected as the prey species and the predatory mite *Typhlodromus occidentalis* Nesbitt as the predator. These species were selected because successful methods of rearing them in the insectary were already known, and because earlier observations had revealed this *Typhlodromus* as a voracious enemy of the six-spotted mite. It was known to develop in great numbers on oranges infested with the prey species, to destroy essentially the entire infestation, and then to die *en masse*. At this author's suggestion, Waters (1955) had studied the detailed biology of both species and had followed population trends on individual

Fig. 1. Orange wrapped with paper and edges sealed, ready for use with sample areas delineated. (Photograph by F. E. Skinner.)

oranges as a problem in predator-prey dynamics.[6] This work was valuable in the conduct of the present research.

Uniformity in certain characteristics was maintained throughout the course of these experiments. Temperature was maintained constant at 83°F. Relative humidity varied some but was not allowed to fall below 55 per cent. There were no means of dehumidifying the room, but automatic humidity controls assured against the damaging action of low humidity. The room was kept dark.

Uniformity in total areas of the universes was achieved by utilizing various combinations of oranges and rubber balls equivalent to them in size (see figs. 1, 2, 3, and 4, for examples). This made it possible to change either or both the total primary food substrate (orange surface) and the degree of dispersion of that substrate without altering the total area of surfaces in the universes or the general distribution of units of surface in the systems. The object was to make it possible to vary the surface of orange utilized and its

---

[6] The design of Waters' experiments, however, was not such as to answer some of the questions posed by this study. His universes were restricted and simple, with no possibility for return to oranges by individuals leaving them by "dropping off." His results were similar to those of Gause, but he drew several conclusions which are more generally applicable than some of Gause' generalizations.

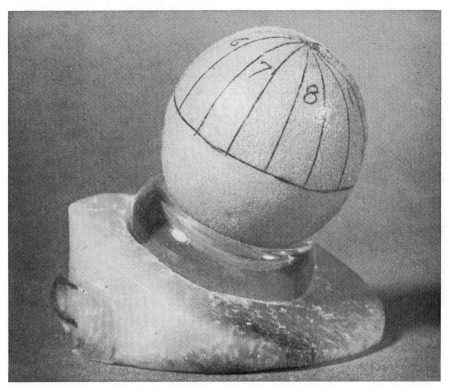

Fig. 2. Orange with lower half covered with paraffin and exposed upper half with sample areas delineated. Fuzzy surface is due to lint used. Paraffin base serves to bring all areas into focus under the microscope (see text). (Photograph by F. E. Skinner.)

Fig. 3. Four oranges, each with half-surfaces exposed (see fig. 2), grouped and joined with a wire loop, remainder of positions occupied by waxed, linted rubber balls, a 2-orange feeding area on a 4-orange dispersion, grouped. (Photograph by F. E. Skinner.)

distribution in order to complicate the search for food by both the prey and predator. Thus, a simple environment where all the food was concentrated to a maximum degree (fig. 3) could be compared with one in which the food was dispersed according to arbitrary degrees (fig. 4) throughout the system (the oranges being arranged or randomly dispersed among the rubber balls). Also, the quantity of food as well as the nature of the dispersion were varied by covering the oranges with paper to whatever degree desired, the paper being wrapped tightly, twisted and tied, and with circular holes then cut to expose the required areas of orange surface. The edges of the holes and the twisted ends were then sealed with paraffin to exclude the mites from gaining entrance to the covered surfaces. An example of an orange ready for use is shown in figure 1.

Fig. 4. Four oranges, each with half-surfaces exposed (see fig. 2), randomized among the 40 positions, remainder of positions occupied by waxed, linted rubber balls—a 2-orange feeding area on a 4-orange dispersion, widely dispersed. (Photograph by F. E. Skinner.)

Considerable difficulty was encountered in arriving at a proper means of limiting the feeding area on a given orange. The first method tried was to dip the naked oranges in hot paraffin, leaving the desired areas clean. Considerable time was lost during the operation of the first two series of experiments because the oranges which were almost completely coated with paraffin or, later, even those covered with polyethylene bags, rotted before results could be obtained. It was only subsequent to this difficulty that a good grade of typing paper was tried. The paper proved to be an excellent material but somewhat difficult to form to an adequately smooth, mite-excluding covering. This fault was corrected by very slightly dampening the paper before wrapping and by using paraffin as a sealing material.

A primary difficulty foreseen in this study was that of replenishing the food material as it is used or becomes conditioned. Under the conditions employed, oranges last from 60 to 90 days as suitable food for the prey species if not fed upon to the extent of conditioning. However, a heavy infestation can deplete an orange of suitable nourishment and thus condition it within three to five days. It is relatively impracticable to remove the food factor as a limiting feature. Also, localized food depletion by the prey species just as much as food depletion by the predator species is inherent to the natural scene. Yet, it was hoped that depletion of food could be evaluated and reduced to a minor position in limiting the populations. It was desirable to build into the design a schedule of removal of old oranges, whether or not conditioned, and their replacement by fresh ones. This would make possible a continuing system which would not automatically end if and when the original oranges became too old or conditioned. Also, by the use of careful notes on conditioning and by comparing universes where predators were introduced with universes which had none, conclusions could be drawn as to the relative importance of any interference occasioned by the conditioning of the oranges. The schedule consisted of removing ¼ of the oranges (the oldest or obviously most unsuitable ones) at intervals of 11 days. This gave a complete change of oranges every 44 days—a period amply in advance of general unsuitableness because of age alone. One restriction was imposed. No **significant last** of a population in a subsection was removed—any such orange otherwise "due" being held another 11 days.

Fig. 5. 120 oranges, each with 1/20 orange-area exposed (method of fig. 1), occupying all positions in a 3-tray universe with partial-barriers of vaseline and wooden posts supplied—a 6-orange feeding area on a 120-orange dispersion with a complex maze of impediments (see text). Trays are broadly joined by use of paper bridges. (Photograph by F. E. Skinner.)

An estimate was made from general observations and the results of Waters (1955) that an orange area equivalent to that of two oranges, each 2½ inches in diameter, would be adequate, as a beginning, to study the predator-prey relation. With this premise, the smallest working basis for this design would utilize four oranges with each orange half-covered. This is because it was not desired to change more than ¼ of the food surfaces at a given time; that is, one of the four oranges used. This made it impossible to go to the ultimate in simplicity of searching and greatest concentration of the orange surfaces by utilizing only two whole, uncovered oranges.

Each universe in the earlier experiments conformed to this pattern, but certain other changes were made later. Each universe consisted of a flat metal tray, 40 inches long and 16 inches wide, with a side wall 1 inch in height and with 40 Syracuse watch glasses on each of which rested either an orange or a rubber ball (see figs. 3, 4, and 5). The positions were arbitrarily arranged in rows to conform to the dimensions of the trays—10 oranges and/or balls along the long dimension and four along the short dimension. This gave a center to center distance of 4 inches. The upper rim of the bordering wall of each tray was kept coated with white petroleum jelly to prevent movement of mites into or out of the trays. The predators and prey were therefore free to move onto or leave oranges or rubber balls but were not permitted to leave or enter the universes.

Lint-covered oranges as used by Finney (1953) to culture the six-spotted mite were used in all the experiments. The lint gives an ideal physical environment for propagation of the species employed. It produces an orange surface similar to the covering of fine hairs and setae on the surfaces of many plant leaves. However, it also adds to the complexity of the searching problem for the predator and increases the maximal potentials in populations of both species. In addition, it was noted that populations on well-linted oranges were less subject to the adverse effects of low humidity.

Initially, experiments were arranged in duplicate; check units having the prey species alone were carried along with those having both the prey and predator species. However, as the experiments developed, certain universes automatically terminated, and new ones not synchronized chronologically or exactly comparable in other respects were substituted. With each new universe employed, some change designed to give a better chance for perpetuation of the predator and prey in the system was incorporated. These changes were based on deductive thought and trial and error processes. During this study, the author had the good fortune to have Dr. A. J. Nicholson of Australia, one of the world's leading theoreticians on population dynamics, examine the experiments, and he confirmed the view that these changes must largely be decided upon by trial and error processes. Concerning some points it was not known whether a given change would detract or add to the chances of perpetuation of the predator-prey relations—such is the reciprocal interdependence of some actions.

The exposed area of an orange was in the form of a circle which was stamped on the orange by use of a shell vial of the proper size and an inking pad. The space between the outer edge of this line was then covered with hot paraffin and joined with the edge of the paper surrounding the hole. Several layers of hot paraffin were laid down as a seal by use of a small camel's hair brush. The oranges were then placed in a refrigerator for about 1 hour to chill the surfaces. Upon removal to the laboratory, only two or three oranges at a time, condensation on the surfaces was sufficient for dampening the point of an indelible pencil as lines were drawn on the surfaces of the exposed circular areas. Diameter lines were drawn in this way, dividing the area into 16 or more sampling sections with each section numbered. This greatly facilitated the counting of the populations. The counting had to be done under a stereoscopic microscope.

When the populations reached very low levels, total populations were counted, but normally the populations were counted on only $\frac{1}{4}$ or $\frac{1}{8}$ of the total surfaces. The sample areas were taken in each case so as to be distributed evenly around the face of the "clock," but the first section to be counted was always taken at random.

Considering the universes employing oranges with all or one half their surfaces exposed, much difficulty was initially encountered in manipulating the oranges under the microscope so that the populations in the sample areas could be viewed fully, and without disturbance of the populations. However, the device shown in figure 2 solved this problem. It consists of a paraffin block cut so that one side at its highest point is $1\frac{1}{2}$ inches and is tapered to the other side which is only $\frac{1}{8}$ inch high. An orange placed on the Syracuse watch glass, which sits loosely in a depression in the block, can then be turned by rotating the watch glass so that any desired sample area can be brought into focus without touching or awkwardly manipulating the orange.

## Sampling Procedure

Sampling of partial areas and populations in the present study was necessary in order to reduce the time required in counting large populations. Hence, the populations in most cases were sampled. Statistical analyses of test examples furnished estimates of the loss in confidence occasioned by such sampling.

It was found that a population estimate based upon a subsample of a given size on an orange is more reproducible if composed of two or more non-contiguous areas evenly distributed among the position (see fig. 1). This method was used in all sampling.

TABLE 1

ANALYSIS OF VARIANCE FOR DATA OF APRIL 26 IN FIGURE 8.

| Orange no. | 1 | 2 | 3 | 4 | 5 | 6 | 7 | 8 | 9 | 10 | 11 | 12 | 13 | 14 | 15 | 16 | 17 | 18 | 19 | 20 |
|---|---|---|---|---|---|---|---|---|---|---|---|---|---|---|---|---|---|---|---|---|
| Subsample | | | | | | | | | | | | | | | | | | | | |
| 1 | 20 | 2 | 1 | 1 | 2 | 2 | 8 | 1 | 20 | 15 | 17 | 0 | 16 | 7 | 6 | 2 | 1 | 0 | 2 | 0 |
| 2 | 17 | 2 | 5 | 1 | 2 | 4 | 6 | 5 | 30 | 8 | 9 | 4 | 5 | 2 | 7 | 8 | 0 | 0 | 0 | 4 |
| 3 | 21 | 2 | 9 | 3 | 0 | 3 | 0 | 0 | 32 | 4 | 8 | 7 | 1 | 0 | 8 | 1 | 0 | 0 | 0 | 1 |
| 4 | 23 | 1 | 1 | 5 | 0 | 2 | 4 | 3 | 24 | 2 | 15 | 5 | 2 | 4 | 7 | 1 | 0 | 0 | 1 | 1 |
| Sums | 81 | 7 | 16 | 10 | 4 | 11 | 18 | 9 | 106 | 29 | 49 | 16 | 24 | 13 | 28 | 12 | 1 | 0 | 3 | 6 |

| Source V. | d.f. | S.S. | M.S. | |
|---|---|---|---|---|
| Total | 79 | 4,160 | | Standard error general mean, $S_{\bar{x}_g} = 0.81$, or 14.6% of $\bar{x}_g$. |
| Between oranges | 19 | 3,679 | 194* | Standard error between oranges, $S_{\bar{x}_o} = 6.9$, or 31.2% of $\bar{x}_o$. |
| Within oranges | 60 | 481 | 8 | |

Using this method of assignment of the positions of the subsamples on an orange, examples of data were analyzed to establish whether the within-orange variance which is associated with subsampling is significantly greater than the variance between the oranges. The data of Table 1 for April 26 illustrate the nature of the variance, and show that the within-orange variance, which is associated with the subsamples, is very small, and that if greater accuracy were required, it could best be achieved by counting populations on more oranges rather than by altering the technique of subsampling on a given orange.

It was therefore decided that the samples include every orange, but the subsamples on each orange would be varied with the approximate densities of the populations encountered, the usual proportion being ½ or ¼ the total exposed area on each orange.

Early in the study in deciding upon the technique of sampling, the **entire** population of the prey species was counted on a representative group of 44 orange units, with each unit exposing $\frac{1}{20}$ of an orange area. This population was thus finite and known. The data used were for July 5 from the experiment illustrated in figure 18. The mean, x, for the 44 items was 6.95 mites per exposed area, with a standard error of ± 1.09, which is 15.7 per cent of the mean. This standard error reflects the variance inherent to the particular type of conglomerate distribution exhibited by such populations.

In order to determine if the subsamples could be used to estimate the total populations, half-area counts were first used. Series of six half-area random lots of the component items were drawn from the aforementioned total population on the 44 representative oranges. The means, standard errors, and the coefficient of variation were then compared with the values based upon the total known population. These statistical parameters were little changed: the standard errors being ± 0.52, ± 0.68, ± 0.65, ± 0.63, ± 0.56, and ± 0.64, respectively, as compared with a half-value of ± 0.55 for the total population; the coefficient of variation varying from 16.2 per cent to 19.3 per cent compared with 15.7 per cent (the coefficient of variation of the whole population); and the means, as estimates of the mean of the total population, averaging only 4.7 per cent higher or lower than the corresponding half-value for the total population—the range being from 3.3 to 7.8.

A test was also made to determine if a further reduction in the counting (to ¼ the total area) would give adequate estimates of the population when large universes or high populations were encountered. Both the predator and prey populations on August 1 (see fig. 18) were analyzed for this purpose.

It should be noted that some basic change had occurred between July 5 and August 1 contributing to greater skewness of distribution. This is revealed by an increase in the coefficient of variation from 15.7 per cent for the whole population count of July 5 (analysis just discussed) to 22.3 per cent for the large sample count on August 1. The six subsamples of reduced size taken on August 1 closely approximated the large sample in coefficient of variation, these being 23.3 per cent, 23.9 per cent, 23.3 per cent, 22.8 per cent, 23.3 per cent, and 23.5 per cent, respectively.

There are two probable reasons for this change in the nature of the variation. In the former instance, the predators had not yet been introduced while they were significantly active on August 1. The predator-prey relation characteristically contributes to skewness, colonial, or conglomerate distribution. Also, the prey were introduced into the universe in equal numbers on all oranges at the initiation of the experiment, and some time is necessary for the typical conglomerate distribution to become manifested, even disregarding predation. Therefore, the larger, although uniform coefficient of variation of the samples on August 1 are not the result of inadequate sampling technique but express the nature of the distribution of the population.

Comparing the prey populations of the ¼-area samples with the composite "total" or ½-area sample on August 1, the standard errors were little changed: these being ± 2.43, ± 2.63, ± 2.70, ± 2.67, ± 2.60, and ± 2.48, respectively, for the six ¼-area samplings, as compared with a half-value of ± 2.39 for the ½-area sample; the coefficient of variation, previously listed, varied only from 22.8 per cent to 23.9 per cent, compared with 22.3 per cent for the sample of double size; and the means, as estimates of the mean of the population present on twice the area, averaging only 4.7 per cent higher or lower than the corresponding half-value for the larger sample—the range being from 1.6 to 9.2.

Predator populations were more variable than were the prey populations. The standard error for total counts of the large (½ area) sample was ± 0.254, with a half-value of ± 0.127, while the values for the counts made on six ¼-area samples were ± 0.117, ± 0.150, ± 0.155, ± 0.167, ± 0.153, and ± 0.151. The coefficient of variation also varied more than the corresponding values for the prey population, these being 24.6 per cent, 34.6 per cent, 32.6 per cent, 29.0 per cent, 32.8 per cent, and 27.2 per cent, compared with 26.7 per cent for the sample of double size. The same was true for the means, these values, as estimates of the mean of the population on the larger area, averaging 5.7 per cent higher or lower, but having a range from 0.0 to 12.1.

When such ranges of error relating to the various observed points in the illustrations are considered, comparing positions of high and low densities, it is obvious that there is adequate accuracy in the estimates to establish the validity of the major trends or patterns of population change exhibited with respect to the predators and their prey in the various experiments. Yet, obviously, some of the minor, inconsistent changes following no general trend in time may be the result of inadequacy of sampling, and hence have a random character independent of predation.

## RESULTS

A group of eight universes was started on February 4 and February 10. These were duplicates of an earlier group—which, as previously stated, had to be discarded because the oranges were rotting—except that the covering used on the oranges was part polyethelene material and part paraffin, rather than paraffin alone. This group also had to be discarded except for certain universes which utilized four oranges each, and these were half-covered with paraffin. Oranges only half-covered with paraffin proved satisfactory, and those units were retained.

A basic idea in this study has been the comparison of results when the plant food (oranges) is readily accessible (massed in one location in the universes) with other examples having the food widely dispersed, with the problems of dispersal and searching thus made more difficult for both the predators and the prey. The control universes which reveal the approximate levels of density of the prey species in the **absence** of predation, thus limited by the availability of food, were followed under several conditions of dispersion of the food material. These are considered representative of densities permitted by the respective levels of availability of food; and the degree to which the prey fail to reach these densities under the pressure of predation in the other universes is a measure of the effect of that predation.

The specific designs of experiments which differ from the general methods and procedures discussed previously will be covered, along with the results obtained, under each type of universe employed.

## I. Densities of Prey and Fluctuations
## in the Absence of Predation

The following three universes were used as a measure of the population dynamics of the prey species in the absence of predators.

**A. Predators Absent, Simplest Universe, Four Large Areas of Food, Grouped at Adjacent, Joined Positions.** In this universe a 2-orange feeding area on a 4-orange dispersion was employed, and the unit was started February 10 and ended July 1 (see figs. 3 and 6). The initial colony was established by placing 20 female six-spotted mites, *E. sexmaculatus* (the prey species), on one of the four oranges. Movement to the other oranges was delayed until the period between March 4 and March 8 at which time the orange originally colonized was beginning to become conditioned and migrants had started moving. Thus, on a feeding area as large as a half orange, overpopulation may be delayed for about three weeks. This is significant with respect to attempts to establish self-sustained existence of both the predator and its prey in a universe. If the prey do not move readily or at least are not moving from some arenas rather readily most of the time, the predators only have to locate a colony arena and stay with it until it is overexploited, resulting in its own extinction and possibly that of its prey as well. On a given orange, this predator commonly overexploits such a colony in much less than the three week period required for conditioning pressure under these conditions (see figs. 9, 10, and 11). This question will be discussed further in relation to the data of Subsections F, G, H, and I of Section II, and it led to the arrangements used in those universes.

Regarding densities, the approximate mean population reached in this universe (fig. 6) was 9,400 *E. sexmaculatus* (all stages), or 4,700 per orange-area. Two major peaks above that level, once population growth had progressed that far, and two subsequent, resultant depressions below it occurred. These indicate a trend of a somewhat "oscillatory" nature due to occurrence of waves of maximal or excessive utilization of the food, followed by inadequate food to support the high levels. This trend may be only a carry-over result of the arbitrary unnaturally high abundance of entirely "unconditioned" or unutilized food at the initiation of the experiment, in interaction with the pattern of orange replacement. This example was not continued long enough to learn if the degree of such fluctuations would continue undiminished in amplitude or whether an inherent oscillation associated with factors of dispersal and population density under related conditions is a real feature of well-established, long-term system—i.e., ones which have reached internal balance, or relative calm.

These results do establish that a relatively high mean population is characteristic of this experimental arrangement, contrasted to that which results when predators are present. Perhaps a sizeable part of the large fluctuations may be the result of variations in the nutritional qualities of the

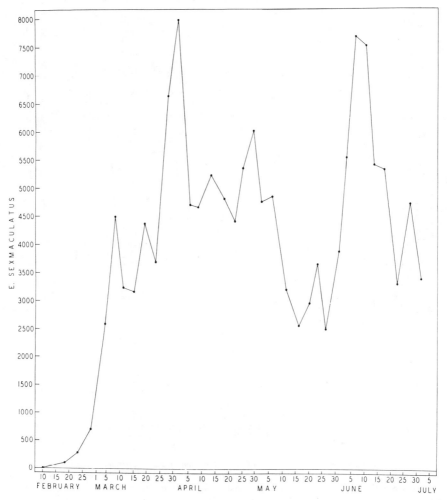

Fig. 6. Densities per orange-area of *Eotetranychus sexmaculatus* in the absence of predators in the simplest universe used, with four large areas of food (orange surface) grouped at adjacent, joined positions—a 2-orange feeding area on a 4-orange dispersion (see fig. 3 and text, Subsection A, Section I of "Results").

oranges supplied during the course of the experiment. It is known that oranges do vary in nutritional value for this mite. Beginning with March 30, at which time the population had first attained maximal utilization of the food, the oranges afterward removed in the replacement scheme were invariably fully utilized or conditioned. This full utilization is probably the most important reason why the mean level of this population was higher than that in the next two universes discussed. In fact, it was characteristic that the populations on these oranges reached conditioning levels well in advance of the dates for removal of the respective oranges, and such conditioning pressure, sometimes from two oranges at once, accomplished very prompt natural

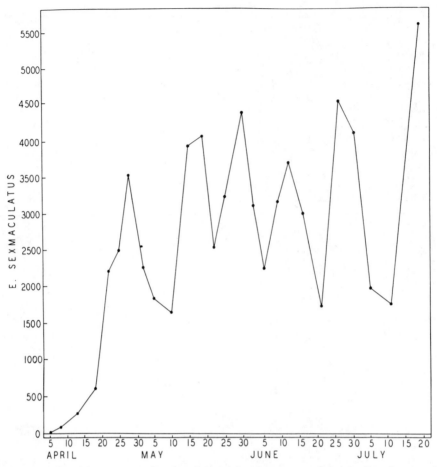

Fig. 7. Densities per orange-area of *Eotetranychus sexmaculatus* in the absence of predators, with four large areas of food (orange surface) widely dispersed among 36 foodless positions—a 2-orange feeding area on a 4-orange dispersion (see fig. 4 and text, Subsection B, Section I of "Results").

colonization of each new orange added, and thus little loss of time in utilization of the food was occasioned. Also, even after such prompt conditioning, the oranges continued to support for some time a much reduced but sizeable population of mites, and these factors support the position that in this universe the more complete utilization accounted for the higher mean level of density, comparing this universe with those of Subsections B, figure 7, and C, figure 8, of this section.

**B. Predators Absent, Four Large Areas of Food Widely Dispersed.** In this universe, as in the last, a 2-orange feeding area on a 4-orange dispersion was employed (in this case, not grouped), and the unit was started on April 5 and ended July 18 (see figs. 4 and 7).

The mean level of density of *E. sexmaculatus* subsequent to the initial period prior to May 20 was 7,000, or 3,500 per orange-area. It is seen, there-

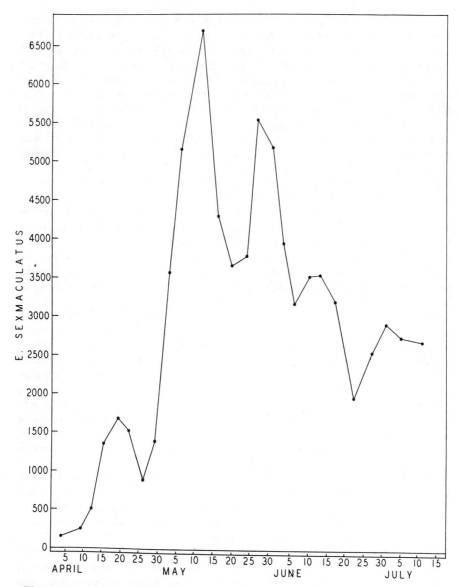

Fig. 8. Densities per orange-area of *Eotetranychus sexmaculatus* in the absence of predators with 20 small areas of food alternating with 20 foodless positions occupied by rubber balls—a 2-orange feeding area on a 20-orange dispersion (no photograph of this exact arrangement, but see text, Subsection C, Section I of "Results").

fore, that although the same quantity of food was supplied, the utilization was somewhat lower due to the difficulty the mites had in quickly locating the new orange units and the resulting loss in population in doing so, with reduced utilization during the time the oranges were in the universe.

There was also a different pattern of fluctuation in numbers, the changes being somewhat more regular in occurrence, and less marked maxima exhibited, than was so when the four oranges were placed adjacent and joined at one arena in the universe. The interaction between the difficulty of dispersal and the supply of food appears to have had a slightly stabilizing effect, compared with the condition when the supply of food alone was the primary feature and problems of dispersal minimal in effects. Unquestionably, the known variation in the quality of the oranges used is a source of error—but doubtfully sufficient to nullify this indication.

Tracing this population, 20 female mites were placed on a single orange and the population growth occurred almost entirely on the single originally stocked orange until just prior to April 28 at which time conditioning of that orange had forced migrants to search for food. By May 2 they had located the other three oranges, but not in sufficient numbers to forestall the decline in the general population resulting from conditioning of the orange originally stocked. The second ascent followed an expected course and was also short-circuited by conditioning on one of the first naturally colonized oranges on which the population first got well under way, at a time before the numbers which had located the other two oranges had increased enough to offset the decline. Subsequent events were similar; the distances between positions with food, and the difficulty the mites had in locating them were such that usually only one orange was highly productive at a time and occasionally an orange came due for removal prior to full utilization. However, none was removed which harbored a major portion of the total population. This would account for the mean density being somewhat lower than that which was experienced in the universe of Subsection A, figure 6, of this section, in which relatively full utilization was experienced.

Unusually high levels of density were the result of a partial chance occurrence of simultaneous productivity on two or more of the four oranges, but the resultant steep ascents such as those occurring during the last half of June and again between July 12 and July 18 are certain to be followed swiftly by corresponding declines in density.

**C. Predators Absent, 20 Small Areas of Food Alternating with 20 Positions with No Food.** In this universe, also, a 2-orange feeding area was employed, but this was segmented into 20 parts of $\frac{1}{10}$ orange-area each, with one part on each of 20 oranges. The 20 oranges were placed in alternate positions with 20 rubber balls. The universe was started on March 31 and ended on July 11, but the first count was made on April 4 (see fig. 8).

It should be noted that although the food material was segmented into 20 parts and dispersed over 20 oranges (equalizing to a much greater degree the variation in orange quality) and 20 positions in the universe, each orange was only one position distant from another and the positions having no food (the rubber balls) were much fewer in number. Consequently, although the food was widely dispersed it was readily accessible and sources of migrants were close at hand to any new orange added. In this respect the unit more nearly resembled those universes in which all the food was massed at one arena in the universe and on adjacent oranges.

The mean level of density of mites subsequent to the initiation period prior to May 20 was 6,600, or 3,300 per orange-area. This is slightly lower than the results of the previously discussed universe. It is likely that the differences in the actual levels of the means in these last two instances do not have real meaning, but the patterns of change in density are probably meaningful of an inherent relation to the types of dispersion employed. Yet, if the initial extreme high in density, occurring during the middle of May, is **included,** the mean level would be approximately 3,800 per orange-area— still somewhat below the mean level of the universe in which the oranges were grouped and joined (fig. 6), but slightly higher than that exhibited in the universe just discussed.

Tracing the history of this population, it was initiated by placing 10 female *E. sexmaculatus* on each of two of the 20 oranges. The first count on April 4 showed a mean population of 152 per orange-area, and these were still located only on the two colonized, or stocked, oranges. Not until April 19, at which time the population on these two oranges was first noted as causing conditioning and under competitive pressure, had migrants generally moved to other oranges; only one other orange had a few mites prior to that time. That date also marked the decline of the population, and this decline was due to the conditioning on the two oranges stocked originally, before the other 18 oranges had been located and population growth on them gotten under way. In this universe nearly all the oranges were found at this same initial period of migrants and the subsequent very steep population increase was the result of simultaneous utilization of the unused oranges in the entire universe. The second depression in the middle of May was due to rather general conditioning of many of those oranges, and the next increase was made possible by the replacement of utilized oranges by new ones according to the predetermined schedule.

There was in this case a strong indication that the period of initiation and establishment of a balance between density and the schedule of supplying food is prolonged much beyond a period of 45 days. The large amplitude of fluctuations in the early stages of the experiment, considered in relation to the successive **steady decrease** in this amplitude, and in view of the much reduced probable source of error associated with variations in orange quality, makes it likely that a position around 5,500, or 2,750 mites per orange-area, is nearer to a true equilibrium, and that the wide fluctuations and high densities which persisted during the early course of the experiment were adjustments prior to establishment of a semblance of such balance.

In contrast to this, the data illustrated in figure 7 probably represent a meaningful difference in patterns of population change. In that case the large fluctuations did **not** diminish with time. In the universe illustrated in figure 7, a position with food is found with great difficulty, but each such position has a supply five-fold in quantity. In the present example, figure 8, there are five times as many positions with food, but each has only ⅕ the quantity. The positions with food are more readily located but each is depleted more rapidly. Additional replicates would need to be run and continued over a longer period of time in order to answer the questions raised.

## II. Population Changes under Predator and
### Prey Interactions

**A. Predators Present, Simplest Universe, Four Large Areas of Food, Grouped at Adjacent Joined Positions.** In this universe a 2-orange feeding area on a 4-orange dispersion was employed. The unit was started February 4 by stocking with 20 female six-spotted mites. It ended April 5 (fig. 9). The

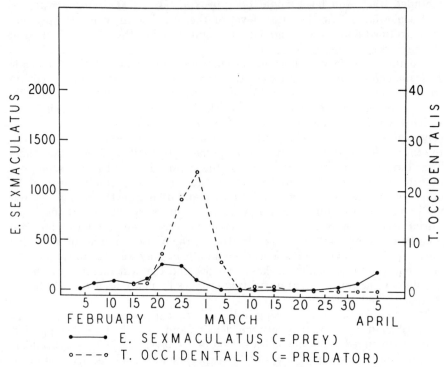

Fig. 9. Densities per orange-area of the prey, *Eotetranychus sexmaculatus*, and the predator, *Typhlodromus occidentalis*, with 4 large areas of food for the prey (orange surface) grouped at adjacent, joined positions—a 2-orange feeding area on a 4-orange dispersion (see fig. 3 and text, Subsection A, Section II of "Results").

arrangement was the same as the control universe of Subjection A of Section I (see also figs. 3 and 6) except that in this universe the predatory species was present. Two female predators were introduced 11 days after the introduction of the six-spotted mites. Both predators were placed on a single orange. This scheme was followed with all the universes except as otherwise stated.

The stocked orange spoiled between February 7 and February 11, and, consequently, the prey then declined in numbers and only increased after moving to the adjacent oranges. The prey then increased to a level of 500,

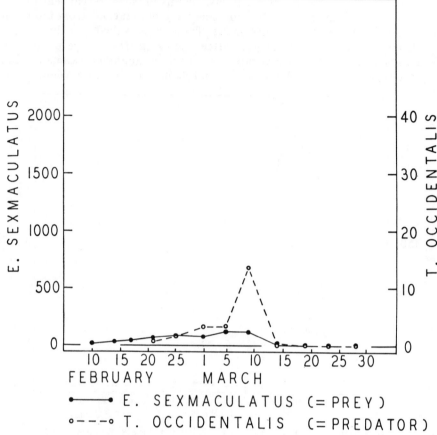

Fig. 10. Densities per orange-area of the prey, *Eotetranychus sexmaculatus*, and the predator, *Typhlodromus occidentalis*, with 8 large areas of food for the prey (orange surface) grouped at adjacent, joined positions—a 4-orange feeding area on an 8-orange dispersion (no photograph of this exact arrangement, but it was similar to that of figure 3 except that 8 oranges were used; see also text, Subsection B, Section II of "Results").

or 250 per orange-area, at which time it was preyed upon so severely that it was reduced to a nil density within 10 days and all the predators subsequently starved. The consequent characteristic, very gradual increase in the numbers of the prey was then prolonged for about 15 days before there was attained a state of vigorous population growth (see "Discussion").

**B. Predators Present, Eight Large Areas of Food, Grouped at Adjacent Joined Positions.** In this universe a 4-orange feeding area on an 8-orange dispersion was employed, and the unit was started February 10 and ended March 28 (fig. 10). The eight oranges were grouped in one end of the tray and joined with wire loops. In this case, because of the larger quantity of food supplied, 40 female six-spotted mites, or prey, were colonized initially, 20 on each of two of the eight oranges. Two female predators were added 11 days later.

The notes taken during the early days of this universe reveal that the female six-spotted mites used for colonizing were old and not from the usual stock colony of vigorous young females. These females died quickly without producing the usual quota of eggs after colonizing. Hence, the population could not increase at the usual rate until the first daughters became fecund. By the time that occurred and the normal population increase would other-

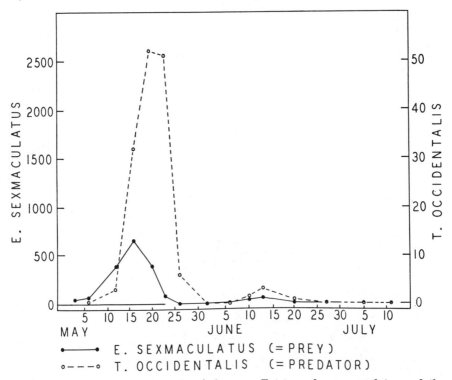

Fig. 11. Densities per orange-area of the prey, *Eotetranychus sexmaculatus*, and the predator, *Typhlodromus occidentalis*, with 6 large areas of food for the prey (orange surface) grouped at adjacent joined positions—a 6-orange feeding area on a 6-orange dispersion (no photograph of this exact arrangement, but it was similar to that of figure 3 except that 6 whole oranges were used; see text, Subsection C, Section II of "Results").

wise have ensued, the predators had become sufficiently abundant that the increase never occurred at all, even though migrants had moved to and populated at least six of the eight oranges. Hence, the population reached a maximal level of only 451 mites, or 113 per orange-area.

In this universe the predators overexploited the prey by March 14 to the extent that not only did they annihilate themselves but they also annihilated the prey species, even though the latter had dispersed successfully throughout the universe.

**C. Predators Present, Six Whole Oranges as Food, Grouped at Adjacent Joined Positions.** In this universe a 6-orange feeding area on a 6-orange dispersion was employed. The unit was started with 20 female six-spotted mites on April 26 and ended July 11 (fig. 11). The prey were introduced on two oranges, the two female predators on only one of them.

The prey temporarily thus escaped severe predator action on one of the oranges and a few migrants moved onto some of the other oranges, but this was not until about May 15, and before these were able to effect an appreci-

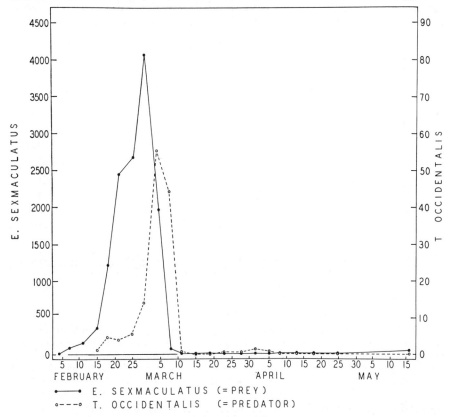

Fig. 12. Densities per orange-area of the prey, *Eotetranychus sexmaculatus,* and the predator, *Typhlodromus occidentalis,* with 4 large areas of food for the prey (orange surface) widely dispersed among 36 foodless positions—a 2-orange feeding area on a 4-orange dispersion (see fig. 4 and text, Subsection D, Section II of "Results").

able general population growth, the predators reached all the infested oranges. The peak population reached was 3,900 mites, or 650 per orange-area. After May 18 to 20, the prey suffered the characteristic crash effect. Contrary to what happened in most similar universes, there was limited temporary survival of the prey **and** the predator species. The prey increased very slightly from June 5 to June 13, and this was followed by a corresponding increase in the predators, after which time the predators quickly annihilated their prey and thus themselves.

**D. Predators Present, Four Large Areas of Food Widely Dispersed.** In this universe a 2-orange feeding area on a 4-orange dispersion was used (see figs. 4 and 12). The oranges were placed at randomized positions among rubber balls as shown in figure 4. Twenty female six-spotted mites were colonized on one orange on February 4, and two female predators were put on the same orange on February 11. The universe was ended May 17.

The wide dispersal of the food among the 40 positions presented an obstacle to movement of both the prey and the predators. In fact, neither species reached the unstocked oranges until March 28 when both did and, thus, densities on the other oranges were never substantial. The colonized orange was

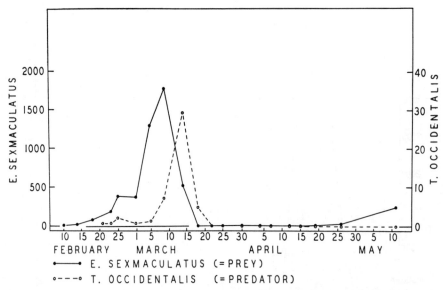

Fig. 13. Densities per orange-area of the prey, *Eotetranychus sexmaculatus*, and the predator, *Typhlodromus occidentalis*, with 8 large areas of food for the prey (orange surface) widely dispersed among 32 foodless positions—a 4-orange feeding area on an 8-orange dispersion (no photograph of this arrangement, but it was similar to that of figure 4 except that 8 oranges were used; see also text, Subsection E, Section II of "Results").

apparently phenomenal in nutritional quality for on it the prey reproduced at a very high rate, so much so that the predators did not quickly overtake it even though the latter were present on that orange from the eleventh day. The population of predators did not increase rapidly at first, although at the low density at that time it is probable that the numbers missed in the counting may have been enough to explain a part or most of this retarded increase in the midst of an abundance of prey.

At any rate, the prey population reached the high level of 8,113, or 4,056 per orange-area. This level could not be maintained on the single orange longer than a few days even in the absence of predation; thus, both conditioning of that orange and intense predation jointly accounted for the very abrupt crash which followed. Nearly all the predators then starved but a very few survived and prevented any resurgence of the prey until after April 8 at which time the last predator died and the prey began a very gradual increase in numbers (see "Discussion").

**E. Predators Present, Eight Large Areas of Food Widely Dispersed.** In

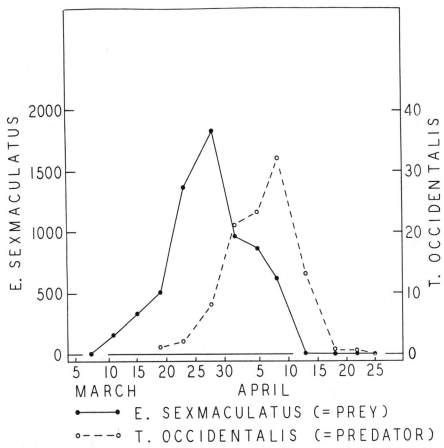

Fig. 14. Densities per orange-area of the prey, *Eotetranychus sexmaculatus*, and the predator, *Typhlodromus occidentalis*, with 20 small areas of food for the prey (orange surface) alternating with 20 foodless positions—a 2-orange feeding area on a 20-orange dispersion (no photograph of this exact arrangement, but see text, Subsection F, Section II of "Results").

this universe a 4-orange feeding area on an 8-orange dispersion was utilized, the remainder of the 40 positions being occupied by rubber balls. The unit was started February 10 and ended May 11 (fig. 13). Twenty female six-spotted mites were colonized on each of two of the eight oranges, whereas the two female predators were introduced 11 days later on one of the oranges colonized with the prey species.

There was a logical delay of about 14 days between the ascent in the prey population and the ascent in the predator population. Thus, the prey could increase unabated on the oranges which did not receive predators until such time as the latter moved onto them. The dispersed condition of the oranges made more likely such a lag in general predator action. In the examples of the universes otherwise comparable except that the food was grouped in one area and joined (figs. 9, 10, and 11), the ascents in predator densities fol-

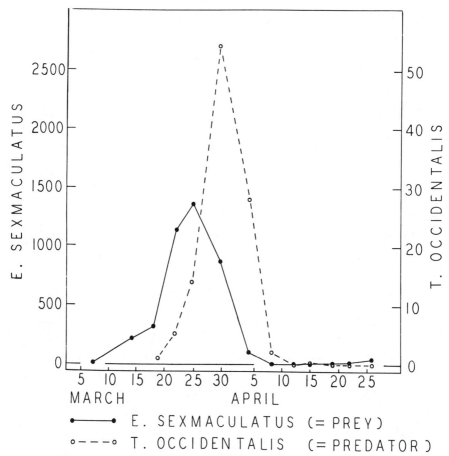

Fig. 15. Densities per orange-area of the prey, *Eotetranychus sexmaculatus*, and the predator, *Typhlodromus occidentalis*, with 20 small areas of food for the prey (orange surface) alternating with 20 foodless positions—a 2-orange feeding area on a 20-orange dispersion (no photograph of this exact arrangement, but see text, Subsection F, Section II of "Results").

lowed the respective ascents in prey densities within intervals of two or three days. Also, in those universes the prey never reached such high levels.

The lag period in this universe was sufficient for the general prey population to reach a level of 7,046, or 1,761 per orange-area before the predators moved through the universe and reduced the prey to a very low level, after which all the predators starved. The very gradual subsequent increase in the numbers of the prey up to May 25 is obvious in figure 13. After that date the undercrowding effects from the intense predator action had been overcome and a *substantial* increase followed.

**F. Predators Present, 20 Small Areas of Food Alternating with 20 Foodless Positions.** Two universes of this arrangement were used. In each, a 2-orange feeding area on a 20-orange dispersion was used and both were started on March 7. One was ended on April 25, the other on April 26 (figs.

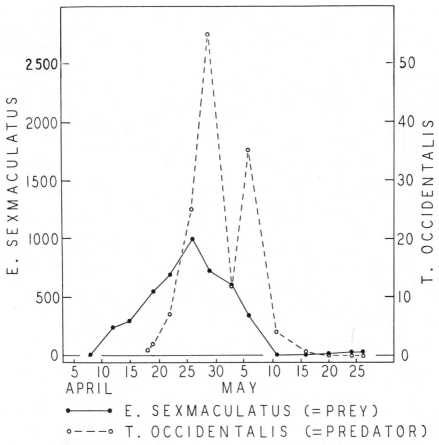

Fig. 16. Densities per orange-area of the prey, *Eotetranychus sexmaculatus*, and the predator, *Typhlodromus occidentalis*, with 40 small areas of food for the prey (orange surface) occupying all 40 positions—a 2-orange feeding area on a 40-orange dispersion, but with units of food thus adjacent (no photograph of this exact arrangement, but it was similar to ⅓ of the universe shown in figure 5 except that the wooden posts were not used and the maze of vaseline partial-barriers was much less complex; see also text, Subsection G, Section II of "Results").

14 and 15). In each universe, 10 female six-spotted mites were introduced onto each of two of the oranges, and in each, two female predators were introduced onto one of the two oranges 11 days later.

In these universes the feeding area employed on a given orange was reduced to a ¹⁄₁₀-orange area. Large areas support the prey species for long periods of time. Dispersal pressure, or overpopulation—which is now known to cause practically all movement from orange to orange—is delayed. It was felt that by decreasing the feeding surface at each orange position—thus having more positions—the prey would be kept on the move from more individual sources so that following a localized crash from predation, there would occur sooner a subsequent population pressure which would cause more rapid dispersal and resultant repopulation on a broader spatial basis in the universe. This seemed to offer a better possibility for achieving perpetuation of the predators and prey than would wider dispersion of the smaller number of larger areas of food.

With one of the examples, the period of lag in the increase in predators was just as long, and, with the other, it was three to four days shorter than it was for the units just previously discussed. However, the prey populations did not reach levels quite so high. The higher level, however, occurred in the universe where there was the longer period of lag in the predator response to prey increase (see fig. 14). In this universe the predators exterminated the prey by April 18 and then died themselves. In the other example (see fig. 15), the prey was almost, but not entirely, exterminated by April 8. The predators quickly starved after that date and subsequently the prey gradually increased in numbers. Thus, even when 20 positions of food were used, the prey was exterminated in one instance although it survived in the other (see "Discussion").

**G. Predators Present, 40 Small Areas of Food Occupying All Positions.** In this universe a 2-orange area was again utilized, but the feeding area on each orange was further reduced to $\frac{1}{20}$-orange area; thus, all 40 positions were occupied by oranges (a 40-orange dispersion)—i.e., no rubber balls were used. The unit was started April 8 and ended May 26 (fig. 16). Ten female six-spotted mites were colonized on each of two of the oranges and 10 days later two female predators were colonized on one of them.

The tray used was also divided into three areas, mostly, but not entirely, separated by vaseline barriers as an impediment but not an exclusion to movement. The barrier pattern was not as complicated as that used in the later experiments such those shown in figure 19. It was felt that the presence of the barriers would introduce greater difficulty for the predators in contacting all general positions of prey at a time, and the smaller areas of food would insure quicker movement of the prey and repopulation of depopulated areas by migrants from areas missed at the time of greatest predator abundance and pressure.

Subsequent to the expected initial increase, there was a sharp decline in the predators between April 29 and May 3 to a level below that which could be supported by the prey population in the total universe at the time. There was then a second sharp increase in the predators as they moved into one of the areas where they had not previously made contact with the prey. The second decline in predators and prey was general throughout the universe and the predators then starved since the prey reached a level which would not support a single predator. The prey population then began a gradual increase in numbers.

In this universe it became obvious that the history of events could not be properly illustrated by use of a simple line graph plotting densities, and this became increasingly true when still greater complexity was introduced. The counts made on the individual oranges revealed, unquestionably, that the sharp drop in predator abundance between April 29 and May 3, and the immediately subsequent sharp increase in numbers, were reliable reflections of the changes in the total populations in the universe. Only a pictorial record

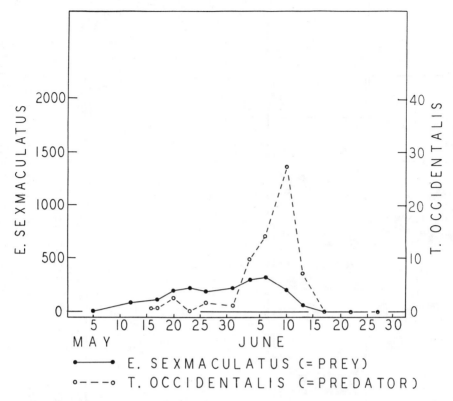

Fig. 17. Densities per orange-area of the prey, *Eotetranychus sexmaculatus,* and the predator, *Typhlodromus occidentalis,* with 120 small areas of food for the prey (orange surface) occupying all 120 positions in a 3-tray universe—a 6-orange feeding area on a 120-orange dispersion, with a simple maze of vaseline partial-barriers utilized (no wooden posts), but with the stocking done in a very restricted manner (see fig. 5 and text, Subsection H, Section II of "Results").

of the densities of the predators and the prey in the specific geographic areas in which the predators were active, and in which they were not active, could be expected accurately to portray the situation. Otherwise, the data reveal a sharp decline in predators, followed by a rapid increase, and then followed again by a rapid decline—all taking place synchronously with a rather steady general decline in density of the prey, if the data for the whole universe are plotted as a single unit as in figure 16.

Such events are contrary to the known fact of specific dependence of this predator upon this prey in these universes and, as well, contrary to the fact of the predator's rapid response to changes in the numbers of its prey by corresponding changes in its own numbers if it contacts its prey. Such a pictorial record was constructed for the data of the most important of these experiments (see fig. 18), but the time required to do this for each universe would be excessive. In any event, this does not appear to be necessary when simple universes are used (see "Discussion").

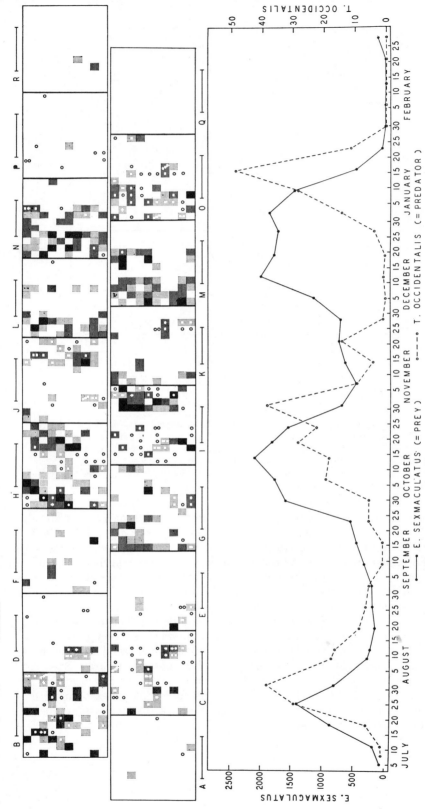

Prey: 0–5 nil density (white); 6–25 low density (light stipple); 26–75 medium density (horizontal lines); 76 or over, high density (solid black). Predator: 1–8 (one white circle).

Fig. 18. Three oscillations in density of a predator-prey relation in which the predatory mite, *Typhlodromus occidentalis*, preyed upon the orange feeding six-spotted mite, *Eotetranychus sexmaculatus*.

The graphic record below shows the sequence of densities per orange-area, while the pictorial record, charts A to R, above, shows both *densities and positions* within the universe. The horizontal line by each letter "A," "B," et cetera, shows the period on the time scale represented by each chart. A photograph of the arrangement of this universe is shown in figure 5 and a sketch of the complex maze of vaseline partial-barriers in figure 19—a 6-orange feeding area on a 120-orange dispersion (see text, Subsection II, Section II of "Results").

218

**H. Predators Present, 120 Small Areas of Food Occupying All 120 Positions, a 6-Orange Area.** In this universe the area of orange exposed at a position was the same as that used in the universe just discussed and the food occupied all positions (no rubber balls were used), but the need for an increase in the total potentials and complexity had become obvious. Hence, in this unit, the food potential and the total areas required to be covered in searching were trebled, i.e., a 6-orange area was used on a 120-orange dispersion. The universe consisted of three of the trays (previously used singly) joined together (see fig. 5). An arrangement of vaseline partial-barriers was again used (see fig. 19). The universe was started with 10 female six-spotted

| 1 | 2 | 3 | 4 | 5 | 6 | 7 | 8 | 9 | 10 |
| 11 | 12 | 13 | 14 | 15 | 16 | 17 | 18 | 19 | 20 |
| 21 | 22 | 23 | 24 | 25 | 26 | 27 | 28 | 29 | 30 |
| 31 | 32 | 33 | 34 | 35 | 36 | 37 | 38 | 39 | 40 |

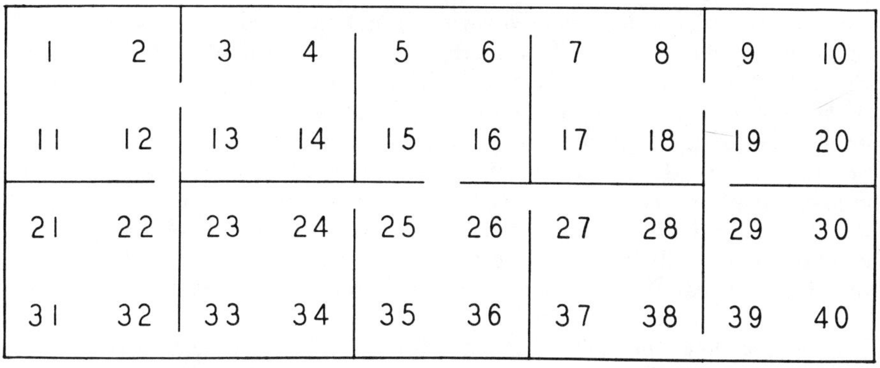

Fig. 19. Diagram of a tray used in the complex 3-tray universes (see figs. 17 and 18) with the positions of vaseline barriers shown by black lines.

mites, placed on each of two oranges in one of the trays on May 5. Two female predators were added on one of these oranges on May 16. The universe was ended June 27 (fig. 17).

In this universe the predator action was again delayed. However, movement of the prey from the one tray in which the initial colonies of both species were introduced never occurred, and it thus became obvious that with the use of such universes a wider arbitrary spread of the initial stock should be employed. Otherwise, the data of this universe added nothing new.

**I. Predator-Prey Oscillations, 120 Small Areas of Food Occupying all 120 Positions, a 6-orange Area.** This universe was basically like that of the last discussed but greater complexity and a different scheme of introducing the initial colonizing stock were employed. The universe was a three-tray arrangement, and a 6-orange feeding area on a 120-orange dispersion was again used. The partial barriers of vaseline were also used (see fig. 19). Contrary to previous procedure, 120 female six-spotted mites were introduced on June 30 (the graph of fig. 18 shows the first count date, July 5). That is, one mite was placed on each of the 120 oranges. In this universe also, the predators were added only five days later so as to permit them to become effective prior to general conditioning of the stocked oranges by the prey. Also contrary to the previous procedure, 27 female predators were introduced, and these were distributed, one on each of 27 oranges, these being representative of all major sections of the universe. This scheme assured that the populations would not become annihilated prior to dispersal to all parts of the universe—such as happened in the unit previously discussed. This experiment was ended March 27, although because of engraving difficulties, the data were plotted only to February 28 (see fig. 18).

In addition, small wooden posts were placed in upright positions in each of the major sections of the universe. This was to give the prey species a maximal opportunity to disperse over the vaseline barriers, thus utilizing its adaptive ability to drop by silken strands and be carried by air currents to new locations. An electric fan was used to create a mild air movement in the room. Although the predators have superior dispersal ability within a **limited** environment where movement by wind is not involved, they do not utilize this method of movement. On the other hand, by virtue of such adaptations the prey species has very superior abilities to disperse over greater distances to entirely new areas and environments. Therefore, a restricted environment or universe of the kind used in these experiments utilizes the superior dispersal power of the predator within local areas without giving chance for expression of the equally important superior dispersal power of the prey across greater distances and obstacles. The wooden posts were introduced in an effort to partially correct this condition in these experiments. They did not prove entirely satisfactory, and a more elaborate arrangement to accomplish this purpose should be employed.

Although they were joined into a single universe, the three trays may be looked upon as adjacent microenvironments, and so may the smaller subdivisions within the trays. By this scheme the changes in various areas or the geographic waves in distribution (see charts A to R of fig. 18), as well as the general density changes in the whole universe were followed. It should be noted that the horizontal dimensions of these charts were reduced (relative to the vertical dimensions) because of difficulties in reproduction on a single page. The horizontal dimension of each universe was 50 inches, the dimension shown vertically was 40 inches.

It is obvious in the charts of figure 18 that the divisions between trays, although not covered with a barrier, were an impediment to movement of somewhat greater effect than that caused by the vaseline barriers used **within** each tray.

The charts, A to R of figure 18 represent a compromise with the ideal of showing the exact locations in the universe and the densities of the entire population **on each** date of sampling. In order to have the charts on the same page and running synchronously with the linear graphs of density on the same time scale, the data for each pair of sampling dates were combined. The horizontal lines by each letter "A," "B," "C," et cetera indicate the corresponding time period of the two dates of counting. Note that the chart for the first period, "A," is below, the second, above, the third, below, the fourth, above, et cetera. The classes of density used for the predators and for the prey were limited in number.

In some instances a few prey were present but not enough to be shown. In some instances of predators being shown in areas where no prey are shown, that is a true condition; in others, it may mean only that although the prey were present, there were too few to justify shading. In either instance, such rarity of the prey means that the predators there would be doomed shortly to starvation, and the charts reveal this fact. Note also that the predators are shown in such "white" areas by white circles (ringed), whereas within the shaded areas indicating prey densities, they are shown by white circles also, but no bordering rings are used.

Considering the trays individually, or any sections of the trays individually, the predators either moved away or died in every case just as was true in Gause's experiments with protozoa and with cheese mites, or has been so in all the universes previously discussed herein. However, by utilizing the large and more complex environment so as to make less likely the predators' contact with the prey at all positions at once, or essentially so, it was possible to produce three waves or oscillations in density of predators and prey. That these waves represent a direct and reciprocal predator-prey dependence is obvious.

The maximal density of prey during the first oscillation was 8,550, or 1,425 per orange-area. The predator population responded quickly to the increase in abundance of the prey since the two species occupied the same arenas by virtue of the manual distribution in stocking of the oranges initially (see "Discussion").

The second peak density of prey occurred about October 15 and was somewhat higher than the first at 12,624, or 2,104 per orange-area. The higher level was an automatic effect of the greater lag in response by the predator population during the initial period of this oscillation—i.e., from September 10 to September 30 or somewhat beyond. This lag resulted from the predator's lack of contact with the main masses of the prey which were present in two of the three trays (left third and right third—see charts F and G, fig. 18), although they were in substantial contact with the prey of the center tray (lower center area of chart G) and slightly so with the much larger population in the left tray, or section. Thus the prey were able to sustain a marked increase in density in two of the three trays, as is shown by the progress seen from chart F to chart H and as seen in the graph for this period. More general contact with the prey was eventually achieved but the pattern of achievement reveals the reason for the rather erratic changes in density of the prey * during the process (from October 7 to October 31). On October 7 the predators had reached a moderate density in the universe of 19 per orange-area, but most of these were located in the lower section of the middle tray (chart G), the aftereffect of which is shown in chart H in the elimination of most of the prey in that area and the numbers of predators still present in that area but without food. This chart also shows that their general movement had been partly onto oranges where their prey was abundant and partly onto ones where they found little or no food. As shown in this chart, also, the predators had made substantial contact with the main mass of prey in the left tray but still had not done so in the right tray in which the prey were now rapidly increasing in numbers. It was not until later (chart I) that the right tray also was reached and general population decline of both predators

*The word "prey" should read "predator."

and prey ensued. Thus, localized discontinuity in contact accounts for the zig-zag pattern of increase in the density of the predators during the period involved. A smoothed curve of densities of the predators would correspond to the usual pattern of a predator-prey relation.

During the third major increase in the population of the prey, the maximal density reached was 11,956, or 1,993 per orange-area. In this instance, the prey had escaped substantial predation for a long period. Using chart K of figure 18 to represent the end of the second oscillatory wave, it is seen that the predators survived only in the lower right area of the universe where only a minor portion of the prey was present. With the near annihilation of this localized center of population by the predators, the latter then starved as is shown in the subsequent chart L, although one female predator had wandered off into an area where there was no food but from which position it later moved to the left and located the edge of the main mass of prey (chart M). During this time (charts K to M), the prey increased greatly in the absence of predators in the large area it inhabited. Considering the universes having predators, conditioning of the oranges for the first time became a dominant depressive feature for the prey population.

Shortage of food was the principal reason why the population leveled off at a high density of approximately 1,800 mites per orange-area between December 12 and January 2. Except for the fact that the main masses of the population encountered a shortage of food at that time because of the predators' loss of contact with it (charts L, M, and N of fig. 18), the numbers almost certainly would have increased to a position approximating at least 2,500 per orange-area. It is probable that such an increase would have contributed to a compensating, slightly earlier rise in the predator population and, consequently, a slightly earlier decline in the prey population. The resultant crash recorded just subsequent to January 2 was largely an effect of predation, although, as stated, the level from which it was initiated would have been higher (and the resultant aftereffect correspondingly more drastic) except for the ameliorating effect of the shortage of food for the prey just prior to that time. During this time and just subsequently, the approximate proportion of conditioned oranges among those which had reached the age for replacement was 38 per cent (see also "Discussion").

Also, during the peak period of the second oscillation there was a substantial but not principal contribution toward leveling off of the prey population at the approximate position of 1,700 mites per orange-area. In this instance, the proportion of conditioned oranges among those removed from the universe was 25 per cent, but the period of this influence was of shorter duration, and the predators earlier achieved more significant contact with the main masses of the prey, thus preventing a greater degree of food conditioning by the prey. In this instance, it is doubtful whether the prey would have increased to a significantly higher level even if the food had not become limiting to this degree. Thus, 75 per cent of the oranges remained unused to a damaging degree for the 56 days they were present in the universe, and predator action was the principal reason for this.

During the initial oscillatory wave, shortage of food did not enter as a contributive factor. Only six of the 120 oranges removed from the universe were conditioned, i.e., 5 per cent, 95 per cent remaining unconditioned for the 56 days (in this experiment only) each was present in the universe.

The data of this universe with relation to certain points will be covered further under the section on "Discussion."

## DISCUSSION
### The Experimental Data

Discussed in this section are certain topics pertaining to the data of the various universes (figs. 1 to 18), collectively, and, as well, the significance of these results as exemplifying the role of dispersion in the predator-prey relation.

Since the universe illustrated in figure 18 approaches in result one of the main objectives of this study, those data will be compared with the results in various of the other universes. The arbitrary imposition of wide distribution of both interacting species throughout all sections of the universe in the initial stocking of this universe had several effects which bear a relation to the subsequent events in this universe and to those occurring in other universes otherwise similar: 1) Both species found favorable quantities of food readily at hand for population growth, for during the initial period neither the predator nor the prey faced impediments. 2) The increase in density of the predator in response to increase in density of its prey was immediate. 3) There was very little conditioning of the oranges by the prey during this early phase, for the predators increased their action swiftly and precluded this. 4) The changes in general density of both species during this phase represent rather smooth curvilinear regressions, for the changes in density were relatively simultaneous throughout the universe, with few localized departures from the general pattern (the data thus support the contention that the actual error of sampling is small—see subsection on "Sampling Procedures"). Some of these interrelated points require clarification.

Since in this first oscillation it was not necessary that the predators overcome substantial impediments (with consequent lag effects and losses in numbers) in locating sources of prey, this oscillation is perhaps typical of one where dispersion of food and habitat and the hazards associated with finding them are minimal. In general, the simple universes previously used where the food was massed in one area gave similar results.

On the other hand, the lag effect of predator action exhibited in most of the complex universes discussed earlier, where the colonizing stock of predators was introduced at only a single or very restricted number of positions, is typical of the **second** and **third** oscillatory waves in density as shown for this universe (see fig. 18). Furthermore, the gradual, progressive change in the nature of the distributions (from one oscillation to another) in this universe was such that introductions of the predators into more than a limited number of arenas or introductions of the prey into all sections or arenas of universes would appear to create a condition of distribution not at all natural to such interactions of predators and prey. In this still-too-restricted universe, the predators survived the two critical, post-crash periods only at a single arena and in extremely small numbers, perhaps only a single female in each instance, certainly so in the second. During the third critical, post-crash phase, all the predators perished. Thus, the time required for the interacting populations to adjust to patterns of spatial and quantitative distribution more characteristic of a predator-prey relation which has come closer to **internal** balance may be the principal reason why the lag effect was accumulative from oscillation to oscillation.

Regarding the results of the universes illustrated in figures 14 and 15, the significant fact is that the exact course which may be taken locally at such very low levels of density is a product of chance events, the course of which could be best expressed as a probability of occurrence under various stipulated conditions. In the one instance, the prey were annihilated by the predators, whereas in the other identical universe the predators starved before all the prey were dead, and the prey population then gradually recovered.

Thus, generally, as to whether the participants survive the critical phase and thus make possible the second oscillation is locally a matter of chance, but as the universe considered is increased in complexity and total potentials, the probability that the participants **will** survive is increased.

In this connection it is obvious that the prey must survive the exploitation by the predator as a prerequisite to any possibility of the predator's survival. Thus, the first object is to devise an ecosystem in which there is a near certainty that the prey will survive. In the first universes employed, this condition was not even approached, but the larger, more complex universe employed (see fig. 18) comes closer to this requirement (but, considering the position of the predator, is still far from adequate).

Obviously, for given conditions, the probability that three or four successive oscillations will occur is progressively more remote and is the **product** of the separate probabilities of survival of both participants through **each** component critical phase. This would be true even disregarding the view of Nicholson (1933, 1954) that the amplitude of such oscillations will increase with time. If his view is correct and its tenets **not** modified by damping features, the probability of such a relation continuing for a successively longer number of oscillations would be correspondingly even more reduced. Yet, this cannot be interpreted as contrary to the principle that as density of the prey decreases, the pressure of predator action on it will also decrease.

In this connection, Huffaker and Kennett (1956), as previously stated, demonstrated that biotic interaction between a phytophagous form and its plant host, (with examples which feed in a way as to cause **reaction** by the plant in a manner as to alter the food potential produced subsequently) may be such that the oscillations in the absence of predation may be of **decreasing** amplitude, due to progressive weakening of the plants. Franz (in press) also showed that such interaction may predetermine in a rather subtle way the potentials of subsequent populations of plant feeding forms and, correspondingly, the natural enemies which attack them. Such mechanisms tend to reduce the amplitude of predator-prey oscillations as interactions occur between predator actions and nutritional limitations in time and place.

Shortage of food was also discussed in Subsection I of Section II in relation to damping of the amplitude in a predator-prey universe. It should be noted also that in the universe illustrated in figure 12, there was substantial shortage of food for the prey in local arenas, such was the interaction of problems of dispersal (in this universe where the oranges were widely dispersed) and predator action (see also Subsection D of Section II). While ¼ of the orange supply was fully utilized at its replacement, the predators prevented the utilization of the other ¾ of the food.

Thus, it is obvious that even though action of a predator may be **locally** insignificant at a given time and compensatory in nature (only a substitute for food conditioning which would surely limit the density **there** anyway), the predation may be **far more significant** throughout the larger sphere which would be reached by migrants from the nutritionally overpopulated area. That is, such migrants could proceed to overpopulate the new areas as well but for the predators which preclude the possibility in an example such as this.

This type of control by predation, associated or not with shortage of food for the prey in local arenas, is generally illustrated by the data of this study. The degree of lag in appearance or introduction of the predators into the ecosystem or local arenas is the critical feature of how much of the plant food may be depleted prior to effective curtailment of the plant feeding form. Significantly, in the presence of an effective predator, overpopulation by the plant feeding form in one arena is to a marked degree an assurance against such overpopulation in other arenas. Thus, the common contention by biological control specialists that the farmer should be willing to accept some crop injury is theoretically sound and has been practically demonstrated many times.

In the universes of Subsections A, B, and C of Section II (illustrations of figures 9, 10, and 11), the food of the prey was readily accessible, joined and grouped (a minimum of dispersion). In those universes the predators readily found their prey, responded more quickly to changes in density of the prey and were able quickly to destroy them. This condition appears to offer greater likelihood that **both** the predators and the prey will be annihilated, although in one of the three examples the prey escaped that end.

The occurrence of an almost imperceptible second wave or increase in the universe in which six whole oranges were used (see fig. 11) does not justify the conclusion that simple increase in the area or quantity of food used necessarily greatly increases the chances of creating a self-perpetuating predator-prey system. It is logical to assume that increased complexity is a more important element of the prerequisites than increased area or quantity of food for the prey. Such complexity creates greater relative refuge or protection against the prey's being overexploited, and also reduces its effective reproduction, but it is significant that refuges **restrictive** to the predators such as envisaged by Gause (1934) and Gause, *et al.* (1936) are not implied as essential.

Comparatively, increase of a prey population recovering from the effects of extreme predation is much less rapid than that which results when an original colony is started with an equally low number of colonizing individuals. This has been a characteristic feature in these experiments. Examples of this may be seen in figures 9, 12, 15, 16, and 18 by comparing the steepness of the curves, at the initiation of the universes, with the obviously very gradual increases which resulted from the small numbers which escaped the predators at the end of the crashes in the populations and subsequent to starvation of all the predators.

The reason seems to lie with certain undercrowding phenomena and with the fact that very few females escape the predators, and these are often unmated. Unless copulation occurs later they produce only male offspring. If the female survives long enough and remains in the area, promoting likelihood of contact, she may then copulate with one of her own sons or perhaps another male, and female progeny would result. Two or more generations may be required for the population to attain a favorable proportion of fertilized females and, thus, vigorous population growth, even when predators are no longer present.

Another partial explanation is the observed fact that the females which survive are more commonly found on partially or heavily conditioned oranges. On these oranges the presence of a much greater quantity of webbing, cast skins, and bodies of dead mites affords a relative sheltering effect and thus reduces the probability of the predators' destroying the last survivors. These heavily conditioned oranges are very poor sources of food for population increase; hence, a slow recovery results from the survivors.

## CONCLUSIONS

The aforestated considerations suggest that the most satisfactory universe employed (see fig. 18) is still far too restricted, and that, for a perpetuating system, sufficient potentialities must be incorporated to assure several or many such arenas of "last survivors" of predators. This system would leave little probability that all such "last survivors" will simultaneously starve and none find new arenas inhabited by the prey. Thus, there is envisaged in such a system many intergrading, larger, nearly self-sustaining subuniverses or ecosystems, each one as adequate or more adequate than the one illustrated in figure 18.

A major difficulty in demonstrating the existence of reciprocal predator-prey oscillations in nature is associated with the patchy or wavelike occurrence of the predation in time and place, particularly true with examples which are wingless such as the mites and which may have limited extensive dispersal power over distances or from tree to tree, for example. In such studies an inherent oscillatory relation would be confused if the sample area taken to reveal the dynamics of a population unit is too large and, obviously, if it is too small.

Nearly any field entomologist who has studied the action of natural enemies of insect pests has noted that the pattern of action is often patchy in occurrence, proceeding in irregular waves from one or more centers. It is obvious that in one local arena the predator-prey relation may be in one phase of an oscillation while in an adjacent arena it may be in a diametrically opposed phase. Therefore, any combining of two such populations into one would not give a reliable picture of the inherent oscillatory nature of the relation.

Thus, in selecting an environmental area it must be large enough to permit the continued existence of both the predator and its prey, yet not so large that the populations in its several sections may proceed asynchronously, due to too limited interchange of the biotic participants.

It is thus more philosophical than factual to discuss whether or not the predator-prey relation is "inherently" disoperative or self-exterminative in arbitrarily restricted environments. To use an extreme example, the end result would be certain if a small universe or enclosure were employed in which only one pair of mountain lions was confined with only one pair of mule deer. Although in the case of this predatory mite and its prey, an orange is a far more nearly adequate base for a suitable ecosystem, yet, on a single orange the predator has invariably overexploited its prey and become exterminated as a local population. With many examples, the prey has been exterminated also, but with others the prey has been able to recover after the starvation of all the predators. Obviously, if the area is sufficiently small and arbitrarily simple, the biological parameters which have been present during the long evolutionary origins of the relations involving the participants are absent, and capture is so simple that the coaction is disoperative. It is necessary that a system be adequate to assure a high probability that some prey will be missed and that somewhere reasonably accessible, but not too readily so, there are local populations of prey which are thriving and sending emigrants to repopulate the depopulated areas. Also, this predator cannot survive on very low populations (although it requires many fewer prey than does the beetle, *Stethorus* spp., which feeds on the same prey— see also Kuenen, 1945), but must contact a fair density of prey at least at small micro-arenas in order to reproduce and survive.

That self-sustaining predator-prey coactions cannot be maintained without "migration" is self-evident. In this type of study the distinction between migration and any movement at all becomes rather ephemeral. The author disagrees that these migrations must be from beyond the limits of a reasonably adequate system. They may be a result of normal movements within the system—if the system is adequate to give expression to the inherent balance in the biological relations of the predator, its prey, and their coinhabited environment. In an unpublished study, the author and C. E. Kennett have demonstrated that a single strawberry plant is an adequate universe during its life span to sustain a predator-prey coaction. No smaller universe utilizing strawberries is conceivable since a single leaf or flower is not a self-perpetuating living unit.

The speed of local-arena extermination by a predator does not define the period of an oscillation. In fact, it appears to bear little relation to that period. Local extermination of the prey on an orange exposing only $\frac{1}{20}$ orange area has often occurred within three days of the entry of a female predator in that area. Even if the density of the prey population is high, with several hundreds on such an area, they are often exterminated within a period of five or six days. If the environment considered is increased to a single half-orange unit, the time required for self-extermination has been, on the average, longer. In most of the more complicated environments, and involving at least a 2-orange area, the time required to produce the drastic decline in population sufficiently general to jeopardize the predator's existence or cause its extermination has been greatly extended—20 to 40 days for a complicated arrangement involving a single-tray universe and a 2-orange feeding area widely dispersed. The same interval was increased to 30 to 60 days for the most complicated system employing a 6-orange feeding area dispersed over 120 oranges and including a maze-effect of vaseline partial-barriers.

It seems, therefore, that the complexity of the dispersal and searching relationships, combined with the period of time required for the prey species to recover in local arenas from the effects of severe predation and accomplish general repopulation, is more important in determining the period of oscillation than is the intensity of predation once contact is made with local arenas of prey. The rapid recovery of the prey is essential to maintain the predator unless there are arenas of high population which are missed.

It is thought that the existence of barriers increases the chances that the prey species will survive at a level conducive to its rapid recovery. However, it is recognized that the barriers may act as a double-edge sword and defeat the purpose of their use. They do increase the incompleteness of contact and cause marked delay in predator increase. This delay also subsequently causes a greater predator population, which then tends to offset the purpose of the barriers during the crash period. Only further experimentation would really prove whether the barrier feature of this experiment has been a deterrent or an aid to continuance of the coaction. Theoretically, the greater violence of oscillation caused by the barriers would be disoperative in nature, but, on the other hand, they do create the partial asynchrony in geographic position and promote earlier population recovery of the prey species. These features are essential to survival of the predator. They may be more than enough to offset the disoperative pressure created by the higher populations achieved at the crests of population densities. Perhaps, also, the partial ameliorating effect from conditioning of the food in local arenas tends to cancel the greater amplitude otherwise occasioned by the use of the barriers.

The complexity of the environment being searched by both predators and prey lends to the relations a marked inconstancy of hazards from micro-area to micro-area. The idea of a constant area of discovery for the predator or of a constancy in dispersal effectiveness for the prey is difficult to visualize in this environment or in nature. There is not only inconstancy, but nothing resembling a progressive gradation in the hazards. The area of discovery, or that area effectively covered and in which all prey are destroyed by a predator of this species, would vary with its hunger, the density of the prey population independently of hunger of the predator (due to the greater webbing, the added cast skins, debris, et cetera present), the complexity of the general environment with respect to the variability of physical barriers or restrictions of all kinds, and the degree of synchrony in responses, preferences, and tolerances between predator and the prey to such conditions as gravity, light, temperature, moisture, the physical surfaces, air movements, et cetera. The idea of a constant area of discovery has theoretical meaning, particularly where simple, uniform areas are involved to which both predators and prey are rigidly restricted and no chance afforded them to express the broad or narrow ranges of asynchrony in behavior and ecology.

The author feels that the balance or stability observed in nature is characteristic of the total environments in which the evolution of a relation occurred, and forms related to one another in a manner notable for the lack of stability in the community would tend to be replaced by others whose relations are more stable and, thus, the assets of the environment more efficiently utilized. The same effect would be achieved if they were forced by better adjusted competitors to occupy progressively less significant niches within which adequate stability does prevail. It cannot be overstressed that what happens with one predator-prey relation, in one ecosystem, or under a given environmental complex, as to seasons or period of years, for instance, does not necessarily apply to others.

While these data indicate that, other things being equal, simplified monocultures of crops are likely to have greater problems with insect pests than are diversified plantings, it is, nevertheless, known that a single species of introduced natural enemy has in many cases throughout the world permanently solved the most severe problems relating to such pests of monocultures. In this connection, it is interesting to note that Taylor (1955) expressed the opinion that because of the variety and mosaic of small plantings in Britain, the complex of forces for solid natural control are more favorable than in regions where extensive acreages of monocultures are the rule—the reasons for which he considered are yet unknown.

## SUMMARY

An experimental study of the role of dispersion in the predator-prey relation was made, using the predatory mite, *Typhlodromus occidentalis,* and the phytophagous mite, *Eotetranychus sexmaculatus,* as the prey. Earlier experimental work by G. F. Gause and associates had led to some acceptance among ecologists of the view that the predator-prey relation is inherently self-annihilative and that continuation of this relation or coaction is dependent upon either: 1) immigrations into the depopulated areas from without, or 2) the existence of definite refuges restrictive to the predators.

In this study, a wide variety of different arrangements in dispersion of plant food (and microhabitat) was tested experimentally. In all the simple universes employed the conclusions of Gause with respect to the predator, but not to the prey, seemed to apply. The unacceptability of that view was demonstrated by the use of a larger, much more complex universe utilizing wide dispersion and incorporating also partial barriers, thus increasing still further the relative dispersion while still not incorporating restrictive refuges. By this method, predator-prey coaction was maintained for three successive oscillations. It is thus quite probable that a controlled, experimental ecosystem can be established in which the predator-prey coaction would not be inherently self-annihilative. It is believed also that various damping mechanisms would come into play which would serve to ameliorate the theoretically sound concept that oscillations arising from this coaction are inherently of increasing severity in amplitude.

The whole controversy becomes rather more philosophical than factual, considering that the earlier view incorporated the purely relative concept of immigration of new stock from without, and any distinction between immigration or emigration and any movement at all on the part of the participants can hardly be upheld. The suggestion seems more appropriate that artificial universes are inadequate if they do not give possibility of expression of the major parameters intrinsic to the specific predator-prey coaction in the natural habitat, and that conclusions drawn from such data as to principles have limited value. The success we have in sustaining such a coaction under experimental conditions is probably a measure of the degree to which we have duplicated the inherent essentials.

In this study, arbitrary selection of different degrees of dispersion and segmentation of the units of food for the prey was accomplished without altering the total surfaces to be searched, and, when desired, without altering the total amounts of food used. This was done by covering oranges to various degrees, leaving known exposed portions, and dispersing them as desired among waxed rubber balls of the same size. The technique offers possibilities of elaborate and varied studies along these lines. For example, further modifications could make it possible to study the predator-prey relation with greater assurance against overexploitation, and, thus, various other features, such as the introduction of a competing predatory species or a competing prey species, could be introduced in order to study their relations to the periods and amplitudes of the oscillations. By elaboration along these lines it should be possible to establish empirically whether employment of quite diversified agricultures may offer prospects of relief from insect pests—in comparison with extensive cultivations of single crops.

# REFERENCES

DeBach, P., and H. S. Smith
> 1941. Are population oscillations inherent in the host-parasite relations? Ecology 22: 363–69.

Errington, P.
> 1937. What is the meaning of predation? Smithsn. Inst. Ann. Rpt. 1936:243–52.
> 1946. Predation and vertebrate populations. Quart. Rev. Biol. 21:144–77.

Finney, G. L.
> 1953. A technique for mass-culture of the six-spotted mite. Jour. Econ. Ent. 46:712–13.

Franz, J.
> In Press. The effectiveness of predators and food as factors limiting gradations of *Adelges* (*Dreyfusia*) *piceae* (Ratz.) in Europe. Tenth Inter. Cong. Ent., 1956.

Gause, G. F.
> 1934. The struggle for existence. (163 pp.) Williams & Wilkins, Baltimore. Md.

Gause, G. F., N. P. Smaragdova, and A. A. Witt
> 1936. Further studies of interaction between predators and prey. Jour. Anim. Ecol. 5:1–18.

Huffaker, C. B., and C. E. Kennett
> 1956. Experimental studies on predation: Predation and cyclamen-mite populations on strawberries in California. Hilgardia 26(4):191–222.

Kuenen, D. J.
> 1945. On the ecological significance of *Metatetranychus ulmi* C. L. Koch (Acari, Tetranychidae). Tijdschr. v. Ent. 88:303–12.

Leopold, A. S.
> 1954. The predator in wildlife management. Sierra Club Bul. 39:34–38.

Nicholson, A. J.
> 1933. The balance of animal populations. Jour. Anim. Ecol. 2, Supp.:132–78.
> 1954. An outline of the dynamics of animal populations. Austral. Jour. Zool. 2:9–65.

Taylor, T. H. C.
> 1955. Biological control of insect pests. Ann. Appl. Biol. 42:190–96.

Uvarov, B. P.
> 1931. Insects and climate. Ent. Soc. London, Trans. 78:1–247.

Waters, N. D.
> 1955. Biological and ecological studies of *Typhlodromus* mites as predators of the six-spotted mite. (Unpublished Ph.D. dissertation, University of California, Berkeley.)

Winsor, C. P.
> 1934. Mathematical analysis of growth of mixed populations. Cold Spring Harbor Symposia on Quant. Biol. 2:181–89.

# The Components of Predation as Revealed by a Study of Small-Mammal Predation of the European Pine Sawfly[1]

By C. S. HOLLING

Forest Insect Laboratory, Sault Ste. Marie, Ont.

## INTRODUCTION

The fluctuation of an animal's numbers between restricted limits is determined by a balance between that animal's capacity to increase and the environmental checks to this increase. Many authors have indulged in the whimsy of calculating the progressive increase of a population when no checks were operating. Thus Huxley calculated that the progeny of a single *Aphis* in the course of 10 generations, supposing all survived, would "contain more ponderable substance than five hundred millions of stout men; that is, more than the whole population of China", (in Thompson, 1929). Checks, however, do occur and it has been the subject of much controversy to determine how these checks operate. Certain general principles—the density-dependence concept of Smith (1955), the competition theory of Nicholson (1933)—have been proposed both verbally and mathematically, but because they have been based in part upon untested and restrictive assumptions they have been severely criticized (e.g. Andrewartha and Birch 1954). These problems could be considerably clarified if we knew the mode of operation of each process that affects numbers, if we knew its basic and subsidiary components. Predation, one such process, forms the subject of the present paper.

Many of the published studies of predation concentrate on discrete parts rather than the whole process. Thus some entomologists are particularly interested in the effect of selection of different kinds of prey by predators upon the evolution of colour patterns and mimicry; wildlife biologists are similarly interested in selection but emphasize the role predators play in improving the condition of the prey populations by removing weakened animals. While such specific problems should find a place in any scheme of predation, the main aim of the present study is to elucidate the components of predation in such a way that more meaning can be applied to considerations of population dynamics. This requires a broad study of the whole process and in particular its function in affecting the numbers of animals.

Such broad studies have generally been concerned with end results measured by the changes in the numbers of predator and prey. These studies are particularly useful when predators are experimentally excluded from the environment of their prey, in the manner adopted by DeBach and his colleagues in their investigations of the pests of orchard trees in California. This work, summarized recently (DeBach, 1958) in response to criticism by Milne (1957), clearly shows that in certain cases the sudden removal of predators results in a rapid increase of prey numbers from persistently low densities to the limits of the food supply. Inasmuch as these studies have shown that other factors have little regulatory function, the predators appear to be the principal ones responsible for regulation. Until the components of predation are revealed by an analysis of the processes leading to these end results, however, we will never know whether the conclusions from such studies apply to situations other than the specific predator—prey relationship investigated.

Errington's investigations of vertebrate predator—prey situations (1934, 1943, 1945 and 1956) suggest, in part, how some types of predation operate. He has

[1]Contribution from the Dept. of Zoology, University of British Columbia and No. 547, Forest Biology Division, Research Branch, Department of Agriculture, Ottawa, Canada. Delivered in part at the Tenth International Congress of Entomology, Montreal, 1956.

postulated that each habitat can support only a given number of animals and that predation becomes important only when the numbers of prey exceed this "carrying capacity". Hence predators merely remove surplus animals, ones that would succumb even in the absence of natural enemies. Errington exempts certain predator-prey relations from this scheme, however, and quotes the predation of wolves on deer as an example where predation probably is not related to the carrying capacity of the habitat. However logical these postulates are, they are only indirectly supported by the facts, and they do not explain the processes responsible.

In order to clarify these problems a comprehensive theory of predation is required that on the one hand is not so restrictive that it can only apply in certain cases and on the other not so broad that it becomes meaningless. Such a comprehensive answer requires a comprehensive approach, not necessarily in terms of the number of situations examined but certainly in terms of the variables involved, for it is the different reactions of predators to these variables that produce the many diverse predator-prey relations. Such a comprehensive approach is faced with a number of practical difficulties. It is apparent from the published studies of predation of vertebrate prey by vertebrate predators that not only is it difficult to obtain estimates of the density of predator, prey, and destroyed prey, but also that the presence of many interacting variables confuses interpretation.

The present study of predation of the European pine sawfly, *Neodiprion sertifer* (Geoff.) by small mammals was particularly suited for a general comprehensive analysis of predation. The practical difficulties concerning population measurement and interpretation of results were relatively unimportant, principally because of the unique properties of the environment and of the prey. The field work was conducted in the sand-plain area of southwestern Ontario where Scots and jack pine have been planted in blocks of up to 200 acres. The flat topography and the practice of planting trees of the same age and species at standard six-foot spacings has produced a remarkably uniform environment. In addition, since the work was concentrated in plantations 15 to 20 years of age, the closure of the crowns reduced ground vegetation to a trace, leaving only an even layer of pine needles covering the soil. The extreme simplicity and uniformity of this environment greatly facilitated the population sampling and eliminated complications resulting from changes in the quantity and kind of alternate foods of the predators.

The investigations were further simplified by the characteristics of the prey. Like most insects, the European pine sawfly offers a number of distinct life-history stages that might be susceptible to predation. The eggs, laid in pine needles the previous fall, hatch in early spring and the larvae emerge and feed upon the foliage. During the first two weeks of June the larvae drop from the trees and spin cocoons within the duff on the forest floor. These cocooned sawflies remain in the ground until the latter part of September, when most emerge as adults. A certain proportion, however, overwinter in cocoons, to emerge the following autumn. Observations in the field and laboratory showed that only one of these life-history stages, the cocoon, was attacked by the small-mammal predators, and that the remaining stages were inaccessible and/or unpalatable and hence completely escaped attack. These data will form part of a later paper dealing specifically with the impact of small mammal predation upon the European pine sawfly.

Cocooned sawflies, as prey, have some very useful attributes for an investigation of this kind. Their concentration in the two-dimensional environment of the duff-soil interface and their lack of movement and reaction to predators considerably simplify sampling and interpretation. Moreover, the small mammals' habit of making a characteristically marked opening in the cocoon to permit removal of the insect leaves a relatively permanent record in the ground of the number of cocooned sawflies destroyed. Thus, the density of the destroyed prey can be measured at the same time as the density of the prey.

Attention was concentrated upon the three most numerous predators—the masked shrew, *Sorex cinereus cinereus* Kerr, the short-tail shrew, *Blarina brevicauda talpoides* Gapper, and deer mouse, *Peromyscus maniculatus bairdii* Hoy and Kennicott. It soon became apparent that these species were the only significant predators of the sawfly, for the remaining nine species trapped or observed in the plantations were either extremely rare or were completely herbivorous.

Here, then, was a simple predator-prey situation where three species of small mammals were preying on a simple prey—sawfly cocoons. The complicating variables present in most other situations were either constant or absent because of the simple characteristics of the environment and of the prey. The absence or constancy of these complicating variables facilitated analysis but at the expense of a complete and generally applicable scheme of predation. Fortunately, however, the small-mammal predators and the cocoons could easily be manipulated in laboratory experiments so that the effect of those variables absent in the field situation could be assessed. At the same time the laboratory experiments supported the field results. This blend of field and laboratory data provides a comprehensive scheme of predation which will be shown to modify present theories of population dynamics and to considerably clarify the role predators play in population regulation.

I wish to acknowledge the considerable assistance rendered by a number of people, through discussion and criticism of the manuscript: Dr. I. McT. Cowan, Dr. K. Graham and Dr. P. A. Larkin at the University of British Columbia and Dr. R. M. Belyea, Mr. A. W. Ghent and Dr. P. J. Pointing, at the Forest Biology Laboratory, Sault Ste. Marie, Ontario.

## FIELD TECHNIQUES

A study of the interaction of predator and prey should be based upon accurate population measurements, and in order to avoid superficial interpretations, populations should be expressed as numbers per unit area. Three populations must be measured—those of the predators, prey, and destroyed prey. Thus the aim of the field methods was to measure accurately each of the three populations in terms of their numbers per acre.

### Small-Mammal Populations

Since a complete description and evaluation of the methods used to estimate the density of the small-mammal predators forms the basis of another paper in preparation, a summary of the techniques will suffice for the present study.

Estimates of the number of small mammals per acre were obtained using standard live-trapping techniques adapted from Burt (1940) and Blair (1941). The data obtained by marking, releasing and subsequently recapturing animals were analysed using either the Lincoln index (Lincoln, 1930) or Hayne's method for estimating populations in removal trapping procedures (Hayne, 1949). The resulting estimates of the number of animals exposed to traps were converted to per acre figures by calculating, on the basis of measurements of the home range of the animals (Stickel, 1954), the actual area sampled by traps.

The accuracy of these estimates was evaluated by examining the assumptions underlying the proper use of the Lincoln index and Hayne's technique and by comparing the efficiency of different traps and trap arrangements. This analysis showed that an accurate estimate of the numbers of *Sorex* and *Blarina* could be obtained using Hayne's method of treating the data obtained from trapping with bucket traps. These estimates, however, were accurate only when the populations had not been disturbed by previous trapping. For *Peromyscus*, Lincoln-index estimates obtained from the results of trapping with Sherman traps provided an ideal way of estimating numbers that was both accurate and unaffected by previous trapping.

### N. sertifer Populations

Since small-mammal predation of *N. sertifer* was restricted to the cocoon stage, prey populations could be measured adequately by estimating the number of cocoons containing living insects present immediately after larval drop in June. This estimate was obtained using a method outlined and tested by Prebble (1943) for cocoon populations of the European spruce sawfly, *Gilpinia hercyniae* (Htg.), an insect with habits similar to those of *N. sertifer*. Accurate estimates were obtained when cocoons were collected from sub-samples of litter and duff distributed within the restricted universe beneath the crowns of host trees. This method was specially designed to provide an index of population rather than an estimate of numbers per acre. But it is obvious from this work that any cocoon-sampling technique designed to yield a *direct* estimate of the number of cocoons per acre would require an unpractically large number of sample units. It proved feasible in the present study, however, to convert such estimates from a square-foot to an acre basis, by stratifying the forest floor into three strata, one comprising circles with two-foot radii around tree trunks, one comprising intermediate rings with inner radii two feet and outer radii three feet, and one comprising the remaining area (three to five feet from the tree trunks).

At least 75 trees were selected and marked throughout each plantation, and one or usually two numbered wooden stakes were placed directly beneath the crown of each tree, on opposite sides of the trunk. Stakes were never placed under overlapping tree crowns. The four sides of each stake were lettered from A to D and the stake was placed so that the numbered sides bore no relation to the position of the trunk. Samples were taken each year, by collecting cocoons from the area delimited by one-square-foot frames placed at one corner of each stake. In the first year's sample the frames were placed at the AB corner, in the second year's at the BC corner, etc. Different-sized screens were used to separate the cocoons from the litter and duff.

Cocoons were collected in early September before adult sawflies emerged and those from each quadrat were placed in separate containers for later analysis. These cocoons were analysed by first segregating them into "new" and "old" categories. Cocoons of the former category were a bright golden colour and were assumed to have been spun in the year of sampling, while those of the latter were dull brown in colour and supposedly had been spun before the sampling year. These assumptions proved partly incorrect, however, for some of the cocoons retained their new colour for over one year. Hence the "new" category contained enough cocoons that had been spun before the sampling year to prevent its use, without correction, as an estimate of the number of cocoons spun in the year of sampling. A correction was devised, however, which reduced the error to negligible proportions.

This method provided the best available estimate of the number of healthy cocoons per acre present in any one year. The population figures obtained ranged from 39,000 (Plot 1, 1954) to 1,080,000 (Plot 2, 1952) cocoons per acre.

### Predation

Small-mammal predation has a direct and indirect effect on *N. sertifer* populations. The direct effect of predation is studied in detail in this paper. The indirect effect, resulting from the mutual interaction of various control factors (parasites, disease, and predators) has been discussed in previous papers (Holling, 1955, 1958b).

The direct effect of predation was measured in a variety of ways. General information was obtained from studies of the consumption of insects by caged animals and from the analysis of stomach contents obtained from animals trapped in sawfly-infested plantations. More particular information was obtained from the analysis of cocoons collected in the regular quadrat samples and from laboratory experiments which studied the effect of cocoon density upon predation.

The actual numbers of *N. sertifer* cocoons destroyed were estimated from cocoons collected in the regular quadrat samples described previously. As shown in an earlier paper (Holling, 1955), cocoons opened by small mammals were easily recognized and moreover could be classified as to species of predator. These estimates of the number of new and old cocoons per square foot opened by each species of predator were corrected, as before, to provide an estimate of the number opened from the time larvae dropped to the time when cocoon samples were taken in early September.

It has proved difficult to obtain a predation and cocoon-population estimate of the desired precision and accuracy. The corrections and calculations that had to be applied to the raw sampling data cast some doubt upon the results and conclusions based upon them. It subsequently developed, however, that a considerable margin of error could be tolerated without changing the results and the conclusions that could be derived from them. In any case, all conclusions based upon cocoon-population estimates were supported and substantiated by results from controlled laboratory experiments.

## LABORATORY TECHNIQUES

Several experiments were conducted with caged animals in order to support and expand results obtained in the field. The most important of these measured the number of cocoons consumed by *Peromyscus* at different cocoon densities. These experiments were conducted at room temperature (ca. 20°C) in a screen-topped cage, 10' x 4' x 6". At the beginning of an experiment, cocoons were first buried in sand where the lines of a removable grid intersected, the grid was then removed, the sand was pressed flat, and a metal-edged levelling jig was finally scraped across the sand so that an even 12 mm. covered the cocoons. A single deer mouse was then placed in the cage together with nesting material, water, and an alternate food—dog biscuits. In each experiment the amount of this alternate food was kept approximately the same (i.e. 13 to 17 gms. dry weight). After the animal had been left undisturbed for 24 hours, the removable grid was replaced, and the number of holes dug over cocoons, the number of cocoons opened and the dry weight of dog biscuits eaten were recorded. Consumption by every animal was measured at either four or five different densities ranging from 2.25 to 36.00 cocoons per sq. ft. The specific densities were provided at random until all were used, the consumption at each density being measured for three to six consecutive days. Ideally the size of the cage should remain constant at all densities but since this would have required over 1,400 cocoons at the highest density, practical considerations necessitated a compromise whereby the cage was shortened at the higher densities. In these experiments the total number of cocoons provided ranged from 88 at the lowest density to 504 at the highest. At all densities, however, these numbers represented a surplus and no more than 40 per cent were ever consumed in a single experiment. Hence consumption was not limited by shortage of cocoons, even though the size of the cage changed.

The sources and characteristics of the cocoons and *Peromyscus* used in these experiments require some comment. Supplies of the prey were obtained by collecting cocoons in sawfly-infested plantations or by collecting late-instar larvae and allowing them to spin cocoons in boxes provided with foliage and litter. Sound cocoons from either source were then segregated into those containing healthy, parasitized, and diseased prepupae using a method of X-ray analysis (Holling, 1958a). The small male cocoons were separated from the larger female cocoons by size, since this criterion had previously proved adequate (Holling, 1958b). To simplify the experiments, only male and female cocoons containing healthy, living prepupae were used and in each experiment equal numbers of cocoons of each sex were provided, alternately, in the grid pattern already described.

Three mature non-breeding male deer mice were used in the experiments. Each animal had been born and raised in small rearing cages 12 x 8 x 6 in. and had been isolated from cocoons since birth. They therefore required a period to become familiar with the experimental cage and with cocoons. This experience was acquired during a preliminary three-week period. For the first two weeks the animal was placed in the experimental cage together with nesting material, water, dog biscuits and sand, and each day was disturbed just as it would be if an experiment were in progress. For the final week cocoons were buried in the sand at the first density chosen so that the animal could learn to find and consume the cocoon contents. It has been shown (Holling, 1955, 1958b) that a seven-day period is more than ample to permit complete learning.

## THE COMPONENTS OF PREDATION

A large number of variables could conceivably affect the mortality of a given species of prey as a result of predation by a given species of predator. These can conveniently be classified, as was done by Leopold (1933), into five groups:

(1) density of the prey population.
(2) density of the predator population.
(3) characteristics of the prey, e.g., reactions to predators, stimulus detected by predator, and other characteristics.
(4) density and quality of alternate foods available for the predator.
(5) characteristics of the predator, e.g., food preferences, efficiency of attack, and other characteristics.

Each of these variables may exert a considerable influence and the effect of any one may depend upon changes in another. For example, Errington (1946) has shown that the characteristics of many vertebrate prey species change when their density exceeds the number that the available cover can support. This change causes a sudden increase in predation. When such complex interactions are involved, it is difficult to understand clearly the principles involved in predation; to do so we must find a simplified situation where some of the variables are constant or are not operating. The problem studied here presents such a situation. First, the characteristics of cocoons do not change as the other factors vary and there are no reactions by the cocooned sawflies to the predators. We therefore can ignore, temporarily, the effect of the third factor, prey characteristics. Secondly, since the work was conducted in plantations noted for their uniformity as to species, age, and distribution of trees, there was a constant and small variety of possible alternate foods. In such a simple and somewhat sterile environment, the fourth factor, the density and quality of alternate foods, can therefore be initially ignored, as can the fifth factor, characteristics of the predator, which is really only another way of expressing factors three and four. There are thus only two basic variables affecting predation in this instance, i.e., prey density and predator density. Furthermore, these are the only essential ones, for the remainder, while possibly important in affecting the amount of predation, are not essential to describe its fundamental characteristics.

## The Basic Components

It is from the two essential variables that the basic components of predation will be derived. The first of these variables, prey density, might affect a number of processes and consumption of prey by individual predators might well be one of them.

The data which demonstrate the effect of changes of prey density upon consumption of cocooned sawflies by *Peromyscus* were obtained from the yearly cocoon quadrat samples in Plots 1 and 2. In 1951, Dr. F. T. Bird, Laboratory of Insect Pathology, Sault Ste. Marie, Ont., had sprayed each of these plots with a low concentration of a virus disease that attacked *N. sertifer* larvae, (Bird 1953). As a result, populations declined from 248,000 and 1,080,000 cocoons per acre, respectively, in 1952, to 39,000 and 256,000 in 1954. Thus predation values at six different cocoon densities were obtained. An additional sample in a neighbouring plantation in 1953 provided another value.

Predation values for *Sorex* and *Blarina* were obtained from one plantation, Plot 3, in one year, 1952. In the spring of that year, virus, sprayed from an aircraft flying along parallel lines 300 feet apart, was applied in three concentrations, with the lowest at one end of the plantation and the highest at the other. An area at one end, not sprayed, served as a control. When cocoon populations were sampled in the autumn, a line of 302 trees was selected at right angles to the lines of spray and the duff under each was sampled with one one-square-foot quadrat. The line, approximately 27 chains long, ran the complete length of the plantation. When the number of new cocoons per square foot was plotted against distance, discrete areas could be selected which had fairly constant populations that ranged from 44,000 to 571,000 cocoons per acre. The areas of low population corresponded to the areas sprayed with the highest concentration of virus. In effect, the plantation could be divided into rectangular strips, each with a particular density of cocoons. The width of these strips varied from 126 to 300 feet with an average of 193 feet. In addition to the 302 quadrats examined, the cocoons from another 100 quadrats were collected from the areas of lowest cocoon densities. Thus, in this one plantation in 1952, there was a sufficient number of different cocoon densities to show the response of consumption by *Sorex* and *Blarina* to changes of prey density.

The methods used to estimate predator densities in each study plot require some further comment. In Plots 1 and 2 this was done with grids of Sherman traps run throughout the summer. In Plot 3 both a grid of Sherman traps and a line of snap traps were used. This grid, measuring 18 chains by 4 chains, was placed so that approximately the same area sampled for cocoons was sampled for small mammals. The populations determined from these trapping procedures were plotted against time, and the number of "mammal-days" per acre, from the start of larval drop (June 14) to the time cocoon samples were made (Aug. 20-30), was determined for each plot each year. This could be done with *Peromyscus* and *Blarina* since the trapping technique was shown to provide an accurate estimate of their populations. But this was not true for *Sorex*. Instead, the number of *Sorex*-days per acre was approximated by dividing the number of cocoons opened at the highest density by the known number consumed by caged *Sorex* per day, i.e. 101. Since the number of cocoons opened at the highest cocoon density was

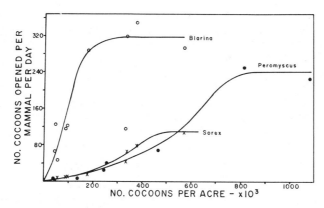

Fig. 1. Functional responses of *Blarina, Sorex* and *Peromyscus* in plots 1, 2, and 3.

151,000 per acre, then the number of *Sorex*-days per acre should be 151,000/101 = 1,490. This is approximately 10 times the estimate that was obtained from trapping with Sherman traps. When the various trapping methods were compared, estimates from Sherman trapping were shown to underestimate the numbers of *Sorex* by about the same amount, i.e. one-tenth.

With estimates of the numbers of predators, prey and destroyed prey available, the daily number of prey consumed per predator at different cocoon densities can be calculated. As seen in Fig. 1, the number of cocoons opened by each species increased with increasing cocoon density until a maximum daily consumption was reached that corresponded approximately to the maximum number that could be consumed in any one day by caged animals. For *Sorex* this of course follows from the method of calculation. The rates at which these curves rise differ for the different species, being greatest for *Blarina* and least for *Peromyscus*. Even if the plateaus are equated by multiplying points on each curve by a constant, the rates still decrease in the same order, reflecting a real difference in species behaviour.

The existence of such a response to cocoon density may also be demonstrated by data from the analysis of stomach contents. The per cent occurrence and per cent volume of the various food items in stomachs of *Peromyscus* captured immediately after larval drop and two months later is shown in Table I. When cocoon densities were high, immediately after larval drop, the per cent occurrence and per cent volume of *N. sertifer* material was high. Two months later when various cocoon mortality factors had taken their toll, cocoon densities were lower and

TABLE I

Stomach contents of *Peromyscus* trapped immediately before larval drop and two months later

| Time trapped | Approx. no. cocoons per acre | No. of stomachs | Analysis | Plant | *N. sertifer* | Other insects | All insects |
|---|---|---|---|---|---|---|---|
| June 16–21 | 600,000 | 19 | % occurrence | 37% | 95% | 53% | 100% |
| Aug. 17–19 | 300,000 | 14 | | 79% | 50% | 64% | 86% |
| June 16–21 | 600,000 | 19 | % volume | 5% | 71% | 24% | 95% |
| Aug. 17–19 | 300,000 | 14 | | 47% | 19% | 34% | 53% |

TABLE II

Occurrence of food items in stomachs of *Microtus* trapped before and after larval drop

| Time trapped | Plant | | *N. sertifer* | | All insects | |
|---|---|---|---|---|---|---|
| | No. of stomachs | % occurrence | No. of stomachs | % occurrence | No. of stomachs | % occurrence |
| before larval drop | 25 | 100% | 2 | 8% | 2 | 8% |
| after larval drop | 29 | 100% | 8 | 28% | 11 | 38% |

*N. sertifer* was a less important food item. The decrease in consumption of *N. sertifer* was accompanied by a considerable increase in the consumption of plant material and a slight increase in the consumption of other insect material. Plants and other insects acted as buffer or alternate foods. *Microtus*, even though they ate few non-plant foods in nature, also showed an increase in the per cent occurrence of *N. sertifer* material in stomachs as cocoon density increased (Table II). Before larval drop, when cocoon densities were low, the incidence of *N. sertifer* in *Microtus* stomachs was low. After larval drop, when cocoon densities were higher, the incidence increased by 3.5 times. Even at the higher cocoon densities, however, *N. sertifer* comprised less than one per cent of the volume of stomach contents so that this response to changes in prey density by *Microtus* is extremely low.

The graphs presented in Fig. I and the results of the analyses of stomach contents leave little doubt that the consumption of cocooned sawflies by animals in the field increases with increase in cocoon density. Similar responses have been demonstrated in laboratory experiments with three *Peromyscus*. As shown in Fig. 2, the number of cocoons consumed daily by each animal increased with increase in cocoon density, again reaching a plateau as did the previous curves. Whenever the number of prepupae consumed did not meet the caloric requirements, these were met by consumption of the dog biscuits, the alternate food provided. Only one of the animals (A) at the highest density fulfilled its caloric requirements by consuming prepupae; the remaining animals (B and C) consumed

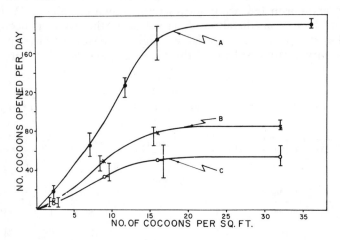

Fig. 2. Functional responses of three caged *Peromyscus* (means and ranges shown).

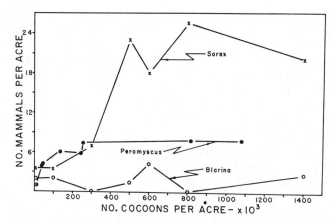

Fig. 3. Numerical responses of *Blarina, Sorex* and *Peromyscus*.

less than one-half the number of sawflies they would consume if no alternate foods were present. The cocoons used in experiments involving animals B and C, however, had been spun 12 months earlier than those involving animal A. When the characteristics of the functional response are examined in another paper, it will be shown that the strength of stimulus from older cocoons is less than that from younger cocoons, and that these differences are sufficient to explain the low consumption by animals B and C. The shape of the curves and the density at which they level is very similar for all animals, so similar that multiplying points along any one curve by the proper constant will equate all three. These curves are very similar to the ones based upon field data. All show the same form, the essential feature of which is an S-shaped rise to a plateau.

The effect of changes of prey density need not be restricted exclusively to consumption of prey by individual predators. The density of predators may also be affected and this can be shown by relating the number of predators per acre to the number of cocoons per acre. Conclusions can be derived from these relations but they are tentative. The data were collected over a relatively short period of time (four summers) and thus any relationship between predator numbers and prey density may have been fortuitous. Only those data obtained in plantations over 12 years old are included since small mammal populations were most stable in these areas. The data for the three most important species of predators are shown in the curves of Fig. 3, where each point represents the highest summer population observed either in different plantations or in the same plantation in different years.

The densities of *Blarina* were lowest while those of *Sorex* were highest. In this situation, *Blarina* populations apparently did not respond to prey density, for its numbers did not noticeably increase with increase in cocoon density. Some agent or agents other than food must limit their numbers. Populations of *Peromyscus* and *Sorex*, on the other hand, apparently did initially increase with increase in cocoon density, ultimately ceasing to increase as some agents other than food became limiting. The response of *Sorex* was most marked.

Thus two responses to changes of prey density have been demonstrated. The first is a change in the number of prey consumed per predator and the second is a change in the density of predators. Although few authors appear to recognize the existence and importance of *both* these responses to changes of prey density, they have been postulated and, in the case of the change of predator density, demonstrated. Thus Solomon (1949) acknowledged the two-fold nature of the response to changes of prey density, and applied the term *functional response* to the change in the number of prey consumed by individual predators, and the term *numerical response* to the change in the density of predators. These are apt terms and, although they have been largely ignored in the literature, they will be adopted in this paper. The data available to Solomon for review did not permit him to anticipate the form the functional response of predators might take, so that he could not assess its importance in population regulation. It will be shown, however, that the functional response is as important as the numerical.

It remains now to consider the effect of predator density, the variable that, together with prey density, is essential for an adequate description of predation. Predator density might well affect the number of prey consumed per predator. Laboratory experiments were designed to measure the number of cocoons opened by one, two, four, and eight animals in a large cage provided with cocoons at a density of 15 per square foot and a surplus of dog biscuits and water. The average number of cocoons opened per mouse in eight replicates was 159, 137, 141 and 159 respectively. In this experiment, therefore, predator density apparently did not greatly affect the consumption of prey by individual animals. This conclusion is again suggested when field and laboratory data are compared, for the functional response of *Peromyscus* obtained in the field, where its density varied, was very similar to the response of single animals obtained in the laboratory.

In such a simple situation, where predator density does not greatly affect the consumption by individuals, the total predation can be expressed by a simple, additive combination of the two responses. For example, if at a particular prey density the functional response is such that 100 cocoons are opened by a single predator in one day, and the numerical response is such that the predator density is 10, then the total daily consumption will be simply 100 x 10. In other situations, however, an increase in the density of predators might result in so much competition that the consumption of prey by individual predators might drop significantly. This effect can still be incorporated in the present scheme by adopting a more complex method of combining the functional and numerical responses.

This section was introduced with a list of the possible variables that could affect predation. Of these, only the two operating in the present study — prey and predator density — are essential variables, so that the basic features of predation can be ascribed to the effects of these two. It has been shown that there are two responses to prey density. The increase in the number of prey consumed per predator, as prey density rises, is termed the functional response, while the change in the density of predators is termed the numerical response. The total amount of predation occurring at any one density results from a combination of the two responses, and the method of combination will be determined by the way predator density affects consumption. This scheme, therefore, describes the effects of the basic variables, uncomplicated by the effects of subsidiary ones. Hence the two responses, the functional and numerical, can be considered the basic components of predation.

The total amount of predation caused by small mammals is shown in Fig. 4, where the functional and numerical responses are combined by multiplying the number of cocoons opened per predator at each density by the number of effective mammal-days observed. These figures were then expressed as percentages opened. This demonstrates the relation between per cent predation and prey density during the 100-day period between cocoon formation and adult emergence. Since the data obtained for the numerical responses are tentative, some reservations must be applied to the more particular conclusions derived

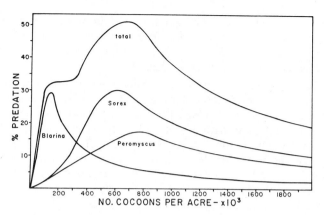

Fig. 4. Functional and numerical responses combined to show the relation between per cent predation and cocoon density.

from this figure. The general conclusion, that per cent predation by each species shows an initial rise and subsequent decline as cocoon density increases holds, however. For this conclusion to be invalid, the numerical responses would have to decrease in order to mask the initial rise in per cent predation caused by the S-shaped form of the functional responses. Thus from zero to some finite cocoon density, predation by small mammals shows a direct density-dependent action and thereafter shows an inverse density-dependent action. The initial rise in the proportion of prey destroyed can be attributed to both the functional and numerical responses. The functional response has a roughly sigmoid shape and hence the proportion of prey destroyed by an individual predator will increase with increase in cocoon density up to and beyond the point of inflection. Unfortunately the data for any one functional response curve are not complete enough to establish a sigmoid relation, but the six curves presented thus far and the several curves to be presented in the following section all suggest a point of inflection. The positive numerical responses shown by *Sorex* and *Peromyscus* also promote a direct density-dependent action up to the point at which predator densities remain constant. Thereafter, with individual consumption also constant, the per cent predation will decline as cocoon density increases. The late Dr. L. Tinbergen apparently postulated the same type of dome-shaped curves for the proportion of insects destroyed by birds. His data were only partly published (1949, 1955) before his death, but Klomp (1956) and Voûte (1958) have commented upon the existence of these "optimal curves". This term, however, is unsatisfactory and anthropocentric. From the viewpoint of the forest entomologist, the highest proportion of noxious insects destroyed may certainly be the optimum, but the term is meaningless for an animal that consumes individuals and not percentages. Progress can best be made by considering predation first as a behaviour before translating this behaviour in terms of the proportion of prey destroyed. The term "peaked curve" is perhaps more accurate.

Returning to Fig. 4, we see that the form of the peaked curve for *Blarina* is determined solely by the functional response since this species exhibited no numerical response. The abrupt peak occurs because the maximum consumption of prepupae was reached at a very low prey density before the predation was "diluted" by large numbers of cocoons. With *Sorex* both the numerical and functional responses are important. Predation by *Sorex* is greatest principally because of the marked numerical response. The two responses again determine the form of the peaked curve for *Peromyscus*, but the numerical response, unlike that of *Sorex*, was not marked, and the maximum consumption of cocoons was reached only at a relatively high density; the result is a low per cent predation with a peak occurring at a high cocoon density.

Predation by all species destroyed a considerable number of cocooned saw-flies over a wide range of cocoon densities. The presence of more than one species of predator not only increased predation but also extended the range of prey densities over which predation was high. This latter effect is particularly important, for if the predation by several species of predators peaked at the same prey density the range of densities over which predation was high would be slight and if the prey had a sufficiently high reproductive capacity its density might jump this vulnerable range and hence escape a large measure of the potential control that could be exerted by predators. Before we can proceed further in the discussion of the effect of predation upon prey numbers, the additional components that make up the behaviour of predation must be considered.

### The Subsidiary Components

Additional factors such as prey characteristics, the density and quality of alternate foods, and predator characteristics have a considerable effect upon predation. It is necessary now to demonstrate the effect of these factors and how they operate.

There are four classes of prey characteristics: those that influence the caloric value of the prey; those that change the length of time prey are exposed; those that affect the "attractiveness" of the prey to the predator (e.g. palatability, defence mechanisms); and those that affect the strength of stimulus used by predators in locating prey (e.g. size, habits, and colours). Only those characteristics that affect the strength of stimulus were studied experimentally. Since small mammals detect cocoons by the odour emanating from them (Holling, 1958b), the strength of this odour perceived by a mammal can be easily changed in laboratory experiments by varying the depth of sand covering the cocoons.

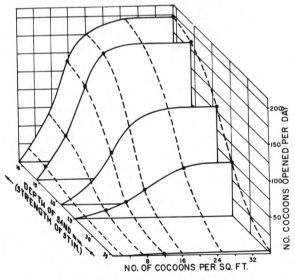

Fig. 5. Effect of strength of stimulus from cocoons upon the functional response of one caged *Peromyscus*. Each point represents the average of three to six replicates.

One *Peromyscus* was used in these experiments and its daily consumption of cocoons was measured at different cocoon densities and different depths of sand. These data are plotted in Fig. 5. Since the relation between depth of sand and strength of stimulus must be an inverse one, the depths of sand are reversed on the axis so that values of the strength of stimulus increase away from the origin. Each point represents the mean of three to six separate measurements. Decreasing the strength of the perceived stimulus by increasing the depth of sand causes a marked decrease in the functional response. A 27 mm. increase in depth (from nine to 36 mm.), for example, causes the peak consumption to drop from 196 to four cocoons per day. The daily number of calories consumed in all these experiments remained relatively constant since dog biscuits were always present as alternate food. The density at which each functional-response curve levels appear to increase somewhat as the strength of stimulus perceived by the animal decreases. We might expect that the increase in consumption is directly related to the increase in the proportion of cocoons in the amount of food available, at least up to the point where the caloric requirements are met solely by sawflies. The ascending portions of the curves, however, are S-shaped and the level portions are below the maximum consumption, approximately 220 cocoons for this animal. Therefore, the functional response cannot be explained by random searching for cocoons. For the moment, however, the important conclusion is that changes in prey characteristics can have a marked effect on predation but this effect is exerted through the functional response.

In the plantations studied, cocoons were not covered by sand but by a loose litter and duff formed from pine needles. Variations in the depth of this material apparently did not affect the strength of the perceived odour, for as many cocoons were opened in quadrats with shallow litter as with deep. This material must be so loose as to scarcely impede the passage of odour from cocoons.

The remaining subsidiary factors, the density and quality of alternate foods and predator characteristics, can also affect predation. The effect of alternate foods could not be studied in the undisturbed plantations because the amount of these "buffers" was constant and very low. The effect of quality of alternate foods on the functional response, however, was demonstrated experimentally using one *Peromyscus*. The experiments were identical to those already described except that at one series of densities an alternate food of low palatability (dog biscuits) was provided, and at the second series one of high palatability (sunflower seeds) was provided. When both foods are available, deer mice select sunflower seeds over dog biscuits. In every experiment a constant amount of alternate food was available: 13 to 17 gms. dry weight of dog biscuits, or 200 sunflower seeds.

Fig. 6 shows the changes in the number of cocoons opened per day and in the amount of alternate foods consumed. The functional response decreased with an increase in the palatability of the alternate food (Fig. 6A). Again the functional response curves showed an initial, roughly sigmoid rise to a constant level.

As cocoon consumption rose, the consumption of alternate foods decreased (Fig. 6B) at a rate related to the palatability of the alternate food. Each line indicating the change in the consumption of alternate food was drawn as a mirror image of the respective functional response and these lines closely follow the mean of the observed points. The variability in the consumption of sunflower seeds at any one cocoon density was considerable, probably as a result of the extreme variability in the size of seeds.

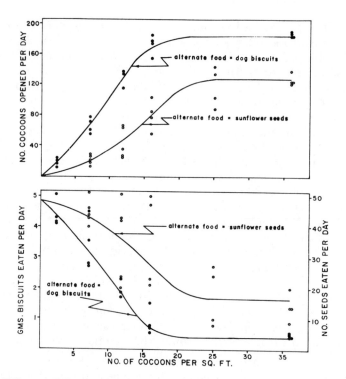

Fig. 6. Effect of different alternate foods upon the functional response of one *Peromyscus*. *A* (upper) shows the functional responses when either a low (dog biscuits) or a high (sunflower seeds) palatability alternate food was present in excess. *B* (lower) shows the amount of these alternate foods consumed.

Again we see that there is not a simple relation between the number of cocoons consumed and the proportion of cocoons in the total amount of food available. This is most obvious when the functional response curves level, for further increase in density is not followed by an increase in the consumption of sawflies. The plateaus persist because the animal continued consuming a certain fixed quantity of alternate foods. L. Tinbergen (1949) observed a similar phenomenon in a study of predation of pine-eating larvae by tits in Holland. He presented data for the consumption of larvae of the pine beauty moth, *Panolis griseovariegata*, and of the web-spinning sawfly *Acantholyda pinivora*, each at two different densities. In each case more larvae were eaten per nestling tit per day at the higher prey density. This, then, was part of a functional response, but it was that part above the point of inflection, since the proportion of prey eaten dropped at the higher density. It is not sufficient to explain these results as well as the ones presented in this paper by claiming, with Tinbergen, that the predators "have the tendency to make their menu as varied as possible and therefore guard against one particular species being strongly dominant in it". This is less an explanation than an anthropocentric description. The occurrence of this phenomenon depends upon the strength of stimulus from the prey, and the amount and quality of the alternate foods. Its proper explanation must await the collection of further data.

We now know that the palatability of alternate foods affects the functional response. Since the number of different kinds of alternate food could also have

TABLE III

The effect of alternate foods upon the number of cocoons consumed per day by one *Peromyscus*

| Alternate food | No. of exp'ts | No. of cocoons opened | |
|---|---|---|---|
| | | $\overline{X}$ | S.E.$\overline{x}$ |
| none..................................... | 7 | 165.9 | 11.4 |
| dog biscuits........................... | 5 | 143.0 | 8.3 |
| sunflower seeds....................... | 8 | 60.0 | 6.2 |
| sunflower seeds and dog biscuits......... | 8 | 21.5 | 4.2 |

an important effect, the consumption of cocoons by a caged *Peromyscus* was measured when no alternate foods, or one or two alternate foods, were present. Only female cocoons were used and these were provided at a density of 75 per sq. ft. to ensure that the level portion of the functional response would be measured. As in the previous experiments, the animal was familiarized with the experimental conditions and with cocoons for a preliminary two-week period. The average numbers of cocoons consumed each day with different numbers and kinds of alternate foods present are shown in Table III. This table again shows that fewer cocoons were consumed when sunflower seeds (high palatability) were present than when dog biscuits (low palatability) were present. In both cases, however, the consumption was lower than when no alternate foods were available. When two alternate foods were available, i.e., both sunflower seeds and dog biscuits, the consumption dropped even further. Thus, increase in both the palatability and in the number of different kinds of alternate foods decreases the functional response.

## DISCUSSION

### General

It has been argued that three of the variables affecting predation—characteristics of the prey, density and quality of alternate foods and characteristics of the predators — are subsidiary components of predation. The laboratory experiments showed that the functional response was lowered when the strength of stimulus, one prey characteristic, detected from cocoons was decreased or when the number of kinds and palatability of alternate foods was increased. Hence the effect of these subsidiary components is exerted through the functional response. Now the numerical response is closely related to the functional, since such an increase in predator density depends upon the amount of food consumed. It follows, therefore, that the subsidiary components will also affect the numerical response. Thus when the functional response is lowered by a decrease in the strength of stimulus detected from prey, the numerical response similarly must be decreased and predation will be less as a result of decrease of the two basic responses.

The density and quality of alternate foods could also affect the numerical response. Returning to the numerical responses shown in Fig. 3, if increase in the density or quality of alternate foods involved solely increase in food "per se", then the number of mammals would reach a maximum at a lower cocoon density, but the maximum itself would not change. If increase in alternate foods also involved changes in the agents limiting the numerical responses (e.g. increased cover and depth of humus), then the maximum density the small mammals could attain would increase. Thus increase in the amount of alternate foods could increase the density of predators.

Increase in alternate foods *decreases* predation by dilution of the functional response, but *increases* predation by promoting a favourable numerical response. The relative importance of each of these effects will depend upon the particular problem. Voûte (1946) has remarked that insect populations in cultivated woods show violent fluctuations, whereas in virgin forests or mixed woods, where the number of alternate foods is great, the populations are more stable. This stability might result from alternate foods promoting such a favourable numerical response that the decrease in the functional response is not great enough to lower predation.

The importance of alternate foods will be affected by that part of the third subsidiary component — characteristics of the predators — that concerns food preferences. Thus an increase in plants or animals other than the prey will most likely affect the responses of those predators, like the omnivore *Peromyscus*, that are not extreme food specialists. Predation by the more stenophagous shrews, would only be affected by some alternate, animal food.

Food preferences, however, are only one of the characteristics of predators. Others involve their ability to detect, capture, and kill prey. But again the effect of these predator characteristics will be exerted through the two basic responses, the functional and numerical. The differences observed between the functional responses of the three species shown earlier in Fig. 1 undoubtedly reflect differences in their abilities to detect, capture, and kill. The amount of predation will similarly be affected by the kind of sensory receptor, whether visual, olfactory, auditory, or tactile, that the predator uses in locating prey. An efficient nose, for example, is probably a less precise organ than an efficient eye. The source of an undisturbed olfactory stimulus can only be located by investigating a gradient in space, whereas a visual stimulus can be localized by an efficient eye from a single point in space — the telotaxis of Fraenkel and Gunn (1940). As N. Tinbergen (1951) remarked, localization of direction is developed to the highest degree in the eye. Thus the functional response of a predator which locates prey by sight will probably reach a maximum at a much lower prey density than the response of one that locates its prey by odour. In the data presented by Tothill (1922) and L. Tinbergen (1949), the per cent predation of insects by birds was highest at very low prey densities, suggesting that the functional responses of these "visual predators" did indeed reach a maximum at a low density.

### The Effect of Predation on Prey Populations

One of the most important characteristics of mortality factors is their ability to regulate the numbers of an animal — to promote a "steady density" (Nicholson, 1933; Nicholson and Bailey, 1935) such that a continued increase or decrease of numbers from this steady state becames progressively unlikely the greater the departure from it. Regulation in this sense therefore requires that the mortality factor change with change in the density of the animal attacked, i.e. it requires a direct density-dependent mortality (Smith, 1935, 1939). Density-independent factors can affect the numbers of an animal but alone they cannot *regulate* the numbers. There is abundant evidence that changes in climate, some aspects of which are presumed to have a density-independent action, can lower or raise the numbers of an animal. But this need not be regulation. Regulation will only result from an interaction with a density-dependent factor, an interaction

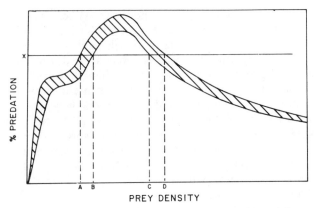

Fig. 7. Theoretical model showing regulation of prey by predators. (see text for explanation).

that might be the simplest, i.e. merely additive. Recently, the density-dependent concept has been severely criticized by Andrewartha and Birch (1954). They call it a dogma, but such a comment is only a criticism of an author's use of the concept. Its misuse as a dogma does not militate against its value as a hypothesis.

We have seen from this study that predation by small mammals does change with changes in prey density. As a result of the functional and numerical responses the proportion of prey destroyed increases from zero to some finite prey density and thereafter decreases. Thus predation over some ranges of prey density shows a direct density-dependent action. This is all that is required for a factor to regulate.

The way in which predation of the type shown in this study can regulate the numbers of a prey species can best be shown by a hypothetical example. To simplify this example we will assume that the prey has a constant rate of reproduction over all ranges of its density, and that only predators are affecting its numbers. Such a situation is, of course, unrealistic. The rate of reproduction of real animals probably is low at low densities when there is slight possibility for contact between individuals (e.g. between male and female). It would rise as contacts became more frequent and would decline again at higher densities when the environment became contaminated, when intraspecific stress symptoms appeared, or when cannibalism became common. Such changes in the rate of reproduction have been shown for experimental populations of *Tribolium confusum* (MacLagan, 1932) and *Drosophila* (Robertson and Sang, 1944). Introducing more complex assumptions, however, confuses interpretations without greatly changing the conclusions.

This hypothetical model is shown in Fig. 7. The curve that describes the changes in predation with changes in prey density is taken from the actual data shown earlier in Fig. 4. It is assumed that the birth-rate of the prey at any density can be balanced by a fixed per cent predation, and that the variation in the environment causes a variation in the predation at any one density. The per cent predation necessary to balance the birth-rate is represented by the horizontal line, x%, in the diagram and variation in predation is represented by the thickness of the mortality curve. The death-rate will equal the birth-rate at two density ranges, between A and B and between C and D. When the densities of the prey are below A, the mortality will be lower than that necessary to balance reproduction and the population will increase. When the densities of the animal are between B and C, death-rate will exceed birth-rate and the populations will decrease. Thus, the density of the prey will tend to fluctuate between densities A and B. If the density happens to exceed D, death-rate will be lower than birth-rate and the prey will increase in numbers, having "escaped" the control exerted by predators. This would occur when the prey had such a high rate of reproduction that its density could jump, in one generation, from a density lower than A to a density higher than D. If densities A and D were far apart, there would be less chance of this occurring. This spread is in part determined by the number of different species of predators that are present. Predation by each species peaks at a different density (see Fig. 4), so that increase in the number of species of predator will increase the spread of the total predation. This will produce a more stable situation where the prey will have less chance to escape control by predators.

Predation of the type shown will regulate the numbers of an animal whenever the predation rises high enough to equal the effective birth-rate. When the prey is an insect and predators are small mammals, as in this case, the reproductive rate of the prey will be too high for predation *alone* to regulate. But if other mortality occurs, density-independent or density-dependent, the total mortality could rise to the point where small mammals were contributing, completely or partially, to the regulation of the insect.

Predation of the type shown will produce stability if there are large numbers of different species of predators operating. Large numbers of such species would most likely occur in a varied environment, such as mixed woods. Perhaps this explains, in part, Voûte's (1946) observation that insect populations in mixed woods are less liable to show violent fluctuations.

I cannot agree with Voûte (1956 and 1958) that factors causing a peaked mortality curve are not sufficient for regulation. He states (1956) that "this is due to the fact that mortality only at low densities increases with the increase of the population. At higher densities, mortality decreases again. The growth of the population is at the utmost slowed down, never stopped". All that is necessary for regulation, however, is a rise in per cent predation over some range of prey densities and an *effective* birth-rate that can be matched at some density by mortality from predators.

Neither can I agree with Thompson (1930) when he ascribes a minor role to vertebrate predators of insects and states that "the number of individuals of any given species (i.e. of vertebrate predators) is . . . relatively small in comparison with those of insects and there is no reason to suppose that it varies primarily in function of the supply of insect food, which fluctuates so rapidly that it is impossible for vertebrates to profit by a temporary abundance of it excepting to a very limited extent". We know that they do respond by an increase in numbers and even if this is not great in comparison with the numerical response of parasitic flies, the number of prey killed per predator is so great and the increase in number killed with increase in prey density is so marked as to result in a heavy proportion of prey destroyed; a proportion that, furthermore, increases initially with increase of prey density. Thompson depreciates the importance of the numerical response of predators and ignores the functional response.

In entomological literature there are two contrasting mathematical theories of regulation. Each theory is based on different assumptions and the predicted results are quite different. Both theories were developed to predict the interaction between parasitic flies and their insect hosts but they can be applied equally well to predator-prey relations. Thompson (1939) assumes that a predator has a limited appetite and that it has no difficulty in finding its prey. Nicholson (1933) assumes that predators have insatiable appetites and that they have a specific capacity to find their prey. This searching capacity is assumed to remain constant at all prey densities and it is also assumed that the searching is random.

The validity of these mathematical models depends upon how closely their assumptions fit natural conditions. We have seen that the appetites of small mammal predators in this study are not insatiable. This fits one of Thompson's assumptions but not Nicholson's. When the functional response was described, it was obvious that predators did have difficulty in finding their prey and that their searching ability did not remain constant at all prey densities. Searching by small mammals was not random. Hence in the present study of predator-prey relations, the remaining assumptions of both Thompson and Nicholson do not hold.

Klomp (1956) considers the damping of oscillations of animal numbers to be as important as regulation. If the oscillations of the numbers of an animal affected by a delayed density-dependent factor (Varley, 1947) like a parasite, do increase in amplitude, as Nicholson's theory predicts (Nicholson and Bailey, 1935), then damping is certainly important. It is not at all certain, however, that this prediction is true. We have already seen that the assumptions underlying Nicholson's theory do not hold in at least some cases. In particular he ignores the important possibility of an S-shaped functional response of the type shown by small mammal predators. If the parasites did show an S-shaped functional response, there would be an *immediate* increase in per cent predation when host density increased, an increase that would modify the effects of the delayed numerical response of parasites emphasized by Nicholson and Varley. Under these conditions the amplitude of the oscillations would not increase as rapidly, and might well not increase at all. An S-shaped functional response therefore acts as an intrinsic damping mechanism in population fluctuations.

Oscillations undoubtedly do occur, however, and whether they increase in amplitude or not, any extrinsic damping is important. The factor that damps oscillations most effectively will be a concurrent density-dependent factor that reacts immediately to changes in the numbers of an animal. Predation by small mammals fulfils these requirements when the density of prey is low. The consumption of prey by individual predators responds immediately to increase in prey density (functional response). Similarly, the numerical response is not greatly delayed, probably because of the high reproductive capacity of small mammals. Thus if the density of a prey is low, chance increases in its numbers will immediately increase the per cent mortality caused by small mammal predation. When the numbers of the prey decrease, the effect of predation will be immediately relaxed. Thus, incipient oscillations can be damped by small-mammal predation.

We have seen that small mammals theoretically can regulate the numbers of prey and can damp their oscillations under certain conditions. Insufficient information was obtained to assess precisely the role of small mammals as predators of N. sertifer in the pine plantations of southwestern Ontario, however. Before the general introduction of a virus disease in 1952 (Bird, 1952, 1953), the sawfly was exhausting its food supplies and 70 to 100% defoliation of Scots, jack and red pines was observed in this area. Predators were obviously not regulating the numbers of the sawfly. After the virus was introduced, however, sawfly populations declined rapidly. In Plot 1, for example, their numbers declined from 248,000 cocoons per acre in 1952 to 39,000 per acre in 1954. The area was revisited in 1955 and larval and cocoon population had obviously increased in this plot, before the virus disease could cause much mortality. It happened, however, that *Peromyscus* was the only species of small mammal residing in Plot 1 and it is interesting that similar increases were not observed in other plantations where sawfly numbers had either not decreased so greatly, or where shrews, the most efficient predators, were present. These observations suggest that predation by shrews was effectively damping the oscillations resulting from the interaction of the virus disease with its host.

### Types of Predation

Many types of predation have been reported in the literature. Ricker (1954) believed that there were three major types of predator-prey relations, Leopold (1933) four, and Errington (1946, 1956) two. Many of these types are merely minor deviations, but the two types of predation Errington discusses are quite different from each other. He distinguishes between "compensatory" and "noncompensatory" predation. In the former type, predators take a heavy toll of individuals of the prey species when the density of prey exceeds a certain threshold. This "threshold of security" is determined largely by the number of secure habitable niches in the environment. When prey densities become too high some individuals are forced into exposed areas where they are readily captured by predators. In this type of predation, predators merely remove surplus animals, ones that would succumb even in the absence of enemies. Errington feels, however, that some predator-prey relations depart from this scheme, so that predation occurs not only *above* a specific threshold density of prey. These departures are ascribed largely to behaviour characteristics of the predators. For example, he does not believe that predation of ungulates by canids is compensatory and feels that this results from intelligent, selective searching by the predators.

If the scheme of predation presented here is to fulfill its purpose it must be able to explain these different types of predation. Non-compensatory predation is easily described by the normal functional and numerical responses, for predation of *N. sertifer* by small mammals is of this type. Compensatory predation can also be described using the basic responses and subsidiary factors previously demonstrated. The main characteristic of this predation is the "threshold of security". Prey are more vulnerable above and less vulnerable below this threshold. That is, the strength of stimulus perceived from prey increases markedly when the prey density exceeds the threshold. We have seen from the present study that an increase in the strength of stimulus from prey increases both the functional and numerical responses. Therefore, below the "threshold of security" the functional responses of predators will be very low and as a result there will probably be no numerical response. Above the threshold, the functional response will become marked and a positive numerical response could easily occur. The net effect will result from a combination of these functional and numerical responses so that per cent predation will remain low so long as there is sufficient cover and food available for the prey. As soon as these supply factors are approaching exhaustion the per cent predation will suddenly increase.

Compensatory predation will occur (1) when the prey has a specific density level near which it normally operates, and (2) when the strength of stimulus perceived by predators is so low below this level and so high above it that there is a marked change in the functional response. Most insect populations tolerate considerable crowding and the only threshold would be set by food limitations. In addition, their strength of stimulus is often high at all densities. For *N. sertifer* at least, the strength of stimulus from cocoons is great and the threshold occurs at such high densities that the functional responses of small mammals are at their maximum. Compensatory predation upon insects is probably uncommon.

Entomologists studying the biological control of insects have largely concentrated their attention on a special type of predator — parasitic insects. Although certain features of a true predator do differ from those of a parasite, both predation and parasitism are similar in that one animal is seeking out another. If insect parasitism can in fact be treated as a type of predation, the two basic responses to prey (or host) density and the subsidiary factors affecting these responses should describe parasitism. The functional response of a true predator is measured by the number of prey it destroys; of a parasite by the number of hosts in which eggs are laid. The differences observed between the functional responses of predators and parasites will depend upon the differences between the behaviour of eating and the behaviour of egg laying. The securing of food by an individual predator serves to maintain that individual's existence. The laying of eggs by a parasite serves to maintain its progenies' existence. It seems likely that the more a behaviour concerns the maintenance of an individual, the more demanding it is. Thus the restraints on egg laying could exert a greater and more prolonged effect than the restraints on eating. This must produce differences between the functional responses of predators and parasites. But the functional responses of both are similar in that there is an upper limit marked by the point at which the predator becomes satiated and the parasite has laid all its eggs. This maximum is reached at some finite prey or host density above zero. The form of the rising phase of the functional response would depend upon the characteristics of the individual parasite and we might expect some of the same forms that will be postulated for predators at the end of this section. To summarize, I do not wish to imply that the characteristics of the functional response of a parasite are identical with those of a predator. I merely wish to indicate that a parasite has a response to prey density — the laying of eggs — that can be identified as a functional response, the precise characteristics of which are unspecified.

The effects of host density upon the number of hosts parasitized have been studied experimentally by a number of workers (e.g., Ullyett, 1949a and b; Burnett, 1951 and 1954; De Bach and Smith, 1941). In each case the number of hosts attacked per parasite increased rapidly with initial increase in host density but tended to level with further increase. Hence these functional response curves showed a continually decreasing slope as host density increased and gave no indication of the S-shaped response shown by small mammals. Further information is necessary, however, before these differences can be ascribed solely to the difference between parasitism and predation. It might well reflect, for example, a difference between an instinctive response of an insect and a learned response of a mammal or between the absence of an alternate host and the presence of an alternate food.

The numerical response of both predators and parasites is measured by the way in which the number of adults increases with increase in prey or host density. At first thought, the numerical response of a parasite would seem to be so intimately connected with its functional response that they could not be separated. But the two responses of a predator are just as intimately connected.

The predator must consume food in order to produce progeny just as the parasite must lay eggs in order to produce progeny.

The agents limiting the numerical response of parasites will be similar to those limiting the response of predators. There is, however, some difference. During at least one stage of the parasites' life, the requirements for both food and niche are met by the same object. Thus increase in the amount of food means increase in the number of niches as well, so that niches are never limited unless food is. This should increase the chances for parasites to show pronounced numerical responses. The characteristics of the numerical responses of both predators and parasites, however, will be similar and will range from those in which there is no increase with increase in the density of hosts, to those in which there is a marked and prolonged increase.

A similar scheme has been mentioned by Ullyett (1949b) to describe parasitism. He believed that "the problem of parasite efficiency would appear to be divided into two main phases, viz.: (a) the efficiency of the parasite as a mortality factor in the host population, (b) its efficiency as related to the maintenance of its own population level within the given area". His first phase resembles the functional response and the second the numerical response. Both phases or responses will be affected, of course, by subsidiary components similar to those proposed for predation—characteristics of the hosts, density and quality of alternate hosts, and characteristics of the parasite. The combination of the two responses will determine the changes in per cent parasitism as the result of changes in host density. Since both the functional and numerical responses presumably level at some point, per cent parasitism curves might easily be peaked, as were the predation curves. If these responses levelled at a host density that would never occur in nature, however, the decline of per cent parasitism might never be observed.

The scheme of predation revealed in this study may well explain all types of predation as well as insect parasitism. The knowledge of the basic components and subsidiary factors underlying the behaviour permits us to imagine innumerable possible variations. In a hypothetical situation, for example, we could introduce and remove alternate food at a specific time in relation to the appearance of a prey, and predict the type of predation. But such variations are only minor deviations of a basic pattern. The major types of predation will result from major differences in the form of the functional and numerical responses.

If the functional responses of some predators are partly determined by their behaviour, we could expect a variety of responses differing in form, rate of rise, and final level reached. All functional responses, however, will ultimately level, for it is difficult to imagine an individual predator whose consumption rises indefinitely. Subsistence requirements will fix the ultimate level for most predators, but even those whose consumption is less rigidly determined by subsistence requirements (e.g., fish, Ricker 1941) must have an upper limit, even if it is only determined by the time required to kill.

The functional responses could conceivably have three basic forms. The mathematically simplest would be shown by a predator whose pattern of searching was random and whose rate of searching remained constant at all prey densities. The number of prey killed per predator would be directly proportional to prey density, so that the rising phase would be a straight line. Ricker (1941) postulated this type of response for certain fish preying on sockeye salmon, and De Bach and Smith (1941) observed that the parasitic fly, *Muscidifurax raptor*, parasitized puparia of *Musca domestica*, provided at different densities, in a similar fashion. So few prey were provided in the latter experiment, however, that the initial linear rise in the number of prey attacked with increase in prey density may have been an artifact of the method.

A more complex form of functional response has been demonstrated in laboratory experiments by De Bach and Smith (1941), Ullyett (1949a) and Burnett (1951, 1956) for a number of insect parasites. In each case the number of prey attacked per predator increased very rapidly with initial increase in prey density, and thereafter increased more slowly approaching a certain fixed level. The rates of searching therefore became progressively less as prey density increased.

The third and final form of functional response has been demonstrated for small mammals in this study. These functional responses are S-shaped so that the rates of searching at first increase with increase of prey density, and then decrease.

Numerical responses will also differ, depending upon the species of predator and the area in which it lives. Two types have been demonstrated in this study. *Peromyscus* and *Sorex* populations, for example, increased with increase of prey density to the point where some agent or agents other than food limited their numbers. These can be termed direct numerical responses. There are some cases, however, where predator numbers are not affected by changes of prey density and in the plantations studied *Blarina* presents such an example of no numerical response. A final response, in addition to ones shown here, might also occur. Morris *et al.* (1958) have pointed out that certain predators might decrease in numbers as prey density increases through competition with other predators. As an example of such inverse numerical responses, he shows that during a recent outbreak of spruce budworm in New Brunswick the magnolia, myrtle, and black-throated green warblers decreased in numbers. Thus we have three possible numerical responses — a direct response, no response, and an inverse response.

The different characteristics of these types of functional and numerical responses produce different types of predation. There are four major types conceivable; these are shown diagramatically in Fig. 8. Each type includes the three possible numerical responses — a direct response (a), no response (b), and an inverse response (c), and the types differ because of basic differences in the functional response. In type 1 the number of prey consumed per predator is assumed to be directly proportional to prey density, so that the rising phase of the functional response is a straight line. In type 2, the functional response is presumed to rise at a continually decreasing rate. In type 3, the form of the functional response is the same as that observed in this study. These three types of predation may be considered as the basic ones, for changes in the subsidiary components are not involved. Subsidiary components can, however, vary in response to changes of prey density and in such cases the basic types of predation are modified. The commonest modification seems to be Errington's compensatory predation which is presented as Type 4 in Fig. 8. In this figure the vertical dotted line represents the "threshold of security" below which the strength of stimulus from prey is low and above which it is high. The functional response curves at these two strengths of stimulus are given the form of the functional responses observed in this study. The forms of the responses shown in Types 1 and 2 could also be used, of course.

The combination of the two responses gives the total response shown in the

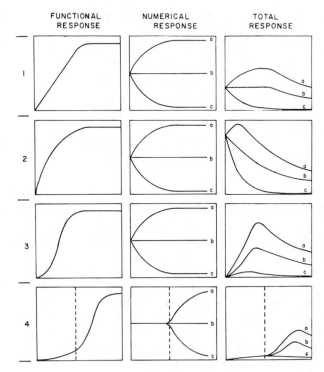

Fig. 8.  Major types of predation.

final column of graphs of Fig. 8.  Both peaked (curves 1a; 2a; 3a, b, c; 4a, b, c) and declining (1b, c; 2b, c) types of predation can occur, but in the absence of any other density-dependent factor, regulation is possible only in the former type.

This method of presenting the major types of predation is an over-simplification since predator density is portrayed as being directly related to prey density.  Animal populations, however, cannot respond *immediately* to changes in prey density, so that there must be a delay of the numerical response.  Varley (1953) pointed this out when he contrasted "delayed density dependence" and "density dependence".  The degree of delay, however, will vary widely depending upon the rate of reproduction, immigration, and mortality.  Small mammals, with their high reproductive rate, responded so quickly to increased food that the delay was not apparent.  In such cases the numerical response graphs of Fig. 8 are sufficiently accurate, for the density of predators in any year is directly related to the density of prey in the same year.  The numerical response of other natural enemies can be considerably delayed, however.  Thus the density of those insect parasites that have one generation a year and a low rate of immigration results from the density of hosts in the preceding generation.

In these extreme cases of delay the total response obtained while prey or hosts are steadily increasing will be different than when they are steadily de-creasing.  The amount of difference will depend upon the magnitude and amount of delay of the numerical response, for the functional response has no element of delay.

## SUMMARY AND CONCLUSIONS

The simplest and most basic type of predation is affected by only two vari-ables — prey and predator density.  Predation of cocooned *N. sertifer* by small mammals is such a type, for prey characteristics, the number and variety of alternate foods, and predilections of the predators do not vary in the plantations where *N. sertifer* occurs. In this simple example of predation, the basic components of predation are responses to changes in prey density. The increase in the number of prey consumed per predator, as prey density rises, is termed the functional response. The change in the density of predators, as a result of increase in prey density, is termed the numerical response.

The three important species of small mammal predators (*Blarina*, *Sorex*, and *Peromyscus*) each showed a functional response, and each curve, whether it was derived from field or laboratory data, showed an initial S-shaped rise up to a constant, maximum consumption. The rate of increase of consumption decreased from *Blarina* to *Sorex* to *Peromyscus*, while the upper, constant level of consumption decreased from *Blarina* to *Peromyscus* to *Sorex*. The characteristics of these functional responses could not be explained by a simple relation between consumption and the proportion of prey in the total food available. The form of the functional response curves is such that the proportion of prey consumed per predator increases to a peak and then decreases.

This peaked curve was further emphasized by the direct numerical response of *Sorex* and *Peromyscus*, since their populations rose initially with increase in prey density up to a maximum that was maintained with further increase in cocoon density. *Blarina* did not show a numerical response. The increase in density of predators resulted from increased breeding, and because the reproductive rate of small mammals is so high, there was an almost immediate increase in density with increase in food.

The two basic components of predation — the functional and numerical responses — can be affected by a number of subsidiary components: prey characteristics, the density and quality of alternate foods, and characteristics of the predators. It was shown experimentally that these components affected the amount of predation by lowering or raising the functional and numerical responses. Decrease of the strength of stimulus from prey, one prey characteristic, lowered both the functional and numerical responses. On the other hand, the quality of alternate foods affected the two responses differently. Increase in the palatability or in the number of kinds of alternate foods lowered the functional response but promoted a more pronounced numerical response.

The peaked type of predation shown by small mammals can theoretically regulate the numbers of its prey if predation is high enough to match the effective reproduction by prey at some prey density. Even if this condition does not hold, however, oscillations of prey numbers are damped. Since the functional and numerical responses undoubtedly differ for different species of predator, predation by each is likely to peak at a different prey density. Hence, when a large number of different species of predators are present the declining phase of predation is displaced to a higher prey density, so that the prey have less chance to "escape" the regulation exerted by predators.

The scheme of predation presented here is sufficient to explain all types of predation as well as insect parasitism. It permits us to postulate four major types of predation differing in the characteristics of their basic and subsidiary components.

## REFERENCES

Andrewartha, H. G. and L. C. Birch. 1954. The distribution and abundance of animals. *The Univ. of Chicago Press*, Chicago.

Bird, F. T. 1952. On the artificial dissemination of the virus disease of the European saw-fly, *Neodiprion sertifer* (Geoff.). *Can. Dept. Agric., For. Biol. Div., Bi-Mon. Progr. Rept.* 8(3): 1-2

Bird, F. T. 1953. The use of a virus disease in the biological control of the European pine sawfly, *Neodiprion sertifer* (Geoff.). *Can. Ent.* 85: 437-446.

Blair, W. F. 1941. Techniques for the study of mammal populations. *J. Mamm.* 22: 148-157.

Buckner, C. H. 1957. Population studies on small mammals of southeastern Manitoba. *J. Mamm.* 38: 87-97.

Burnett, T. 1951. Effects of temperature and host density on the rate of increase of an insect parasite. *Amer. Nat.* 85: 337-352.

Burnett, T. 1954. Influences of natural temperatures and controlled host densities on oviposition of an insect parasite. *Physiol. Ecol.* 27: 239-248.

Burt, W. H. 1940. Territorial behaviour and populations of some small mammals in southern Michigan. *Misc. Publ. Univ. Mich. Mus. Zool.* no. 45: 1-52.

De Bach, P. 1958. The role of weather and entomophagous species in the natural control of insect populations. *J. Econ. Ent.* 51: 474-484.

De Bach, P., and H. S. Smith. 1941. The effect of host density on the rate of reproduction of entomophagous parasites. *J. Econ. Ent.* 34: 741-745.

De Bach, P., and H. S. Smith. 1947. Effects of parasite population density on rate of change of host and parasite populations. *Ecology* 28: 290-298.

Errington, P. L. 1934. Vulnerability of bob-white populations to predation. *Ecology* 15: 110-127.

Errington, P. L. 1943. An analysis of mink predation upon muskrats in North-Central United States. *Agric. Exp. Sta. Iowa State Coll. Res. Bull.* 320: 797-924.

Errington, P. L. 1945. Some contributions of a fifteen-year local study of the northern bob-white to a knowledge of population phenomena. *Ecol. Monog.* 15: 1-34.

Errington, P. L. 1946. Predation and vertebrate populations. *Quart. Rev. Biol.* 21: 144-177, 221-245.

Fraenkel, G., and D. L. Gunn. 1940. The orientation of animals. Oxford.

Hayne, D. W. 1949. Two methods for estimating population from trapping records. *J. Mamm.* 30: 339-411.

Holling, C. S. 1955. The selection by certain small mammals of dead, parasitized, and healthy prepupae of the European pine sawfly, *Neodiprion sertifer* (Goeff.). *Can. J. Zool.* 33: 404-419.

Holling, C. S. 1958a. A radiographic technique to identify healthy, parasitized, and diseased sawfly prepupae within cocoons. *Can. Ent.* 90: 59-61.

Holling, C. S. 1958b. Sensory stimuli involved in the location and selection of sawfly cocoons by small mammals. *Can. J. Zool.* 36: 633-653.

Klomp, H. 1956. On the theories on host-parasite interaction. *Int. Union of For. Res. Organizations, 12th Congress, Oxford, 1956.*

Leopold, A. 1933. Game management. Charles Scribner's Sons.

Lincoln, F. C. 1930. Calculating waterfowl abundance on the basis of banding returns. *U.S. Dept. Agric.* Circular 118.

MacLagan, D. S. 1932. The effect of population density upon rate of reproduction, with special reference to insects. *Proc. Roy. Soc. Lond.* 111: 437-454.

Milne, A. 1957. The natural control of insect populations. *Can. Ent.* 89: 193-213.

Morris, R. F., W. F. Chesire, C. A. Miller, and D. G. Mott. 1958. Numerical response of avian and mammalian predators during a gradation of the spruce budworm. *Ecology* 39(3): 487-494.

Nicholson, A. J. 1933. The balance of animal populations. *J. Anim. Ecol.* 2: 132-178.

Nicholson, A. J., and V. A. Bailey. 1935. The balance of animal populations. Part 1, *Proc. Zool. Soc. Lond.* 1935, p. 551-598.

Prebble, M. L. 1943. Sampling methods in population studies of the European spruce saw-fly, *Gilpinia hercyniae* (Hartig.) in eastern Canada. *Trans. Roy. Soc. Can.,* Third Series, Sect. V. 37: 93-126.

Ricker, W. E. 1941. The consumption of young sockeye salmon by predaceous fish. *J. Fish. Res. Bd. Can.* 5: 293-313.

Ricker, W. E. 1954. Stock and recruitment. *J. Fish. Res. Bd. Can.* 11: 559-623.

Robertson, F. W., and J. H. Sang. 1944. The ecological determinants of population growth in a *Drosophila* culture. I. Fecundity of adult flies. *Proc. Roy. Soc. Lond.,* B., 132: 258-277.

Solomon, M. E. 1949. The natural control of animal populations. *J. Anim. Ecology* 18: 1-35.

Stickel, L. F. 1954. A comparison of certain methods of measuring ranges of small mammals. *J. Mamm.* 35: 1-15.

Thompson, W. R. 1929. On natural control. *Parasitology* 21: 269-281.

Thompson, W. R. 1930. The principles of biological control. *Ann. Appl. Biol.* 17: 306-338.

Thompson, W. R. 1939. Biological control and the theories of the interactions of populations. *Parasitology* 31: 299-388.

Tinbergen, L. 1949. Bosvogels en insecten. *Nederl. Boschbouue. Tijdschr.* 21: 91-105.

Tinbergen, L. 1955. The effect of predators on the numbers of their hosts. *Vakblad voor Biologen* 28: 217-228.

Tinbergen, N. 1951. The study of instinct. Oxford.

Tothill, J. D. 1922. The natural control of the fall webworm (*Hyphantria cunea* Drury) in Canada. *Can. Dept. Agr. Bull.* 3, new series (Ent. Bull. 19): 1-107.

Ullyett, G. C. 1949a. Distribution of progeny by *Cryptus inornatus* Pratt. (Hym. Ichneumonidae). *Can. Ent.* 81: 285-299, 82: 1-11.

Ullyett, G. C. 1949b. Distribution of progeny by *Chelonus texanus* Cress. (Hym. Braconidae). *Can. Ent.* 81: 25-44.

Varley, G. C. 1947. The natural control of population balance in the knapweed gall-fly (*Urophora jaceana*). *J. Anim. Ecol.* 16: 139-187.

Varley, G. C. 1953. Ecological aspects of population regulation. *Trans. IXth Int. Congr. Ent.* 2: 210-214.

Voûte, A. D. 1946. Regulation of the density of the insect populations in virgin forests and cultivated woods. *Archives Neerlandaises de Zoologie* 7: 435-470.

Voûte, A. D. 1956. Forest entomology and population dynamics. *Int. Union For. Res. Organizations*, Twelfth Congress, Oxford.

Voûte, A. D. 1958. On the regulation of insect populations. *Proc. Tenth Int. Congr. of Ent.* Montreal, 1956.

# PART IV

# COMMUNITY
# METABOLISM:
# ENERGETICS
# AND PRODUCTIVITY

# THE TROPHIC-DYNAMIC ASPECT OF ECOLOGY

Raymond L. Lindeman

*Osborn Zoological Laboratory, Yale University*

Recent progress in the study of aquatic food-cycle relationships invites a re-appraisal of certain ecological tenets. Quantitative productivity data provide a basis for enunciating certain trophic principles, which, when applied to a series of successional stages, shed new light on the dynamics of ecological succession.

## "Community" Concepts

A chronological review of the major viewpoints guiding synecological thought indicates the following stages: (1) the static species-distributional viewpoint; (2) the dynamic species-distributional viewpoint, with emphasis on successional phenomena; and (3) the trophic-dynamic viewpoint. From either species-distributional viewpoint, a lake, for example, might be considered by a botanist as containing several distinct plant aggregations, such as marginal emergent, floating-leafed, submerged, benthic, or phytoplankton communities, some of which might even be considered as "climax" (cf. Tutin, '41). The associated animals would be "biotic factors" of the plant environment, tending to limit or modify the development of the aquatic plant communities. To a strict zoologist, on the other hand, a lake would seem to contain animal communities roughly coincident with the plant communities, although the "associated vegetation" would be considered merely as a part of the environment[1] of the animal community. A more "bio-ecological" species-distributional approach would recognize both the plants and animals as co-constituents of restricted "biotic" communities, such as "plankton communities," "benthic communities," etc., in which members of the living community "co-act" with each other and "re-act" with the non-living environment (Clements and Shelford, '39; Carpenter, '39, '40; T. Park, '41). Coactions and reactions are considered by bio-ecologists to be the dynamic effectors of succession.

The trophic-dynamic viewpoint, as adopted in this paper, emphasizes the relationship of trophic or "energy-availing" relationships within the community-unit to the process of succession. From this viewpoint, which is closely allied to Vernadsky's "biogeochemical" approach (cf. Hutchinson and Wollack, '40) and to the "oekologische Sicht" of Friederichs ('30), a lake is considered as a primary ecological unit in its own right, since all the lesser "communities" mentioned above are dependent upon other components of the lacustrine food cycle (cf. figure 1) for their very existence. Upon further consideration of the trophic cycle, the discrimination between living organisms as parts of the "biotic community" and dead organisms and inorganic nutritives as parts of the "environment" seems arbitrary and unnatural. The difficulty of drawing clear-cut lines between the living *community* and the non-living *environment* is illustrated by the difficulty of determining the status of a slowly dying pondweed covered with periphytes, some of which are also continually dying. As indicated in figure 1, much of the non-living nascent ooze is rapidly reincorporated through "dis-

---

[1] The term *habitat* is used by certain ecologists (Clements and Shelford, '39; Haskell, '40; T. Park, '41) as a synonym for *environment* in the usual sense and as here used, although Park points out that most biologists understand "habitat" to mean "simply the place or niche that an animal or plant occupies in nature" in a species-distributional sense. On the other hand, Haskell, and apparently also Park, use "environment" as synonymous with the *cosmos*. It is to

be hoped that ecologists will shortly be able to reach some sort of agreement on the meanings of these basic terms.

solved nutrients" back into the living "biotic community." This constant organic-inorganic cycle of nutritive substance is so completely integrated that to consider even such a unit as a lake primarily as a biotic community appears to force a "biological" emphasis upon a more basic functional organization.

This concept was perhaps first expressed by Thienemann ('18), as a result of his extensive limnological studies on the lakes of North Germany. Allee ('34) expressed a similar view, stating: "The picture than finally emerges . . . is of a sort of superorganismic unity not alone between the plants and animals to form biotic communities, but also between the biota and the environment." Such a concept is inherent in the term *ecosystem*, proposed by Tansley ('35) for the fundamental ecological unit.[2] Rejecting the terms "complex organism" and "biotic community," Tansley writes, "But the more fundamental conception is, as it seems to me, the whole *system* (in the sense of physics), including not only the organism-complex, but also the whole complex of physical factors forming what we call the environment of the biome. . . . It is the systems so formed which, from the point of view of the ecologist, are the basic units of nature on the face of the earth. . . . These *ecosystems*, as we may call them, are of the most various kinds and sizes. They form one category of the multitudinous physical systems of the universe, which range from the universe as a whole down to the atom." Tansley goes on to discuss the ecosystem as a category of rank equal to the "biome" (Clements, '16), but points out that the term can also be used in a general sense, as is the word "community." The *ecosystem* may be formally defined as the system composed of physical-chemical-biological processes active within a space-time unit of any

magnitude, i.e., the biotic community *plus* its abiotic environment. The concept of the ecosystem is believed by the writer to be of fundamental importance in interpreting the data of dynamic ecology.

## TROPHIC DYNAMICS

### *Qualitative food-cycle relationships*

Although certain aspects of food relations have been known for centuries, many processes within ecosystems are still very incompletely understood. The basic process in trophic dynamics is the transfer of energy from one part of the ecosystem to another. All function, and indeed all life, within an ecosystem depends upon the utilization of an external source of energy, solar radiation. A portion of this incident energy is transformed by the process of photosynthesis into the structure of living organisms. In the language of community economics introduced by Thienemann ('26), autotrophic plants are *producer* organisms, employing the energy obtained by photosynthesis to synthesize complex organic substances from simple inorganic substances. Although plants again release a portion of this potential energy in catabolic processes, a great surplus of organic substance is accumulated. Animals and heterotrophic plants, as *consumer* organisms, feed upon this surplus of potential energy, oxidizing a considerable portion of the consumed substance to release kinetic energy for metabolism, but transforming the remainder into the complex chemical substances of their own bodies. Following death, every organism is a potential source of energy for saprophagous organisms (feeding directly on dead tissues), which again may act as energy sources for successive categories of consumers. Heterotrophic bacteria and fungi, representing the most important saprophagous consumption of energy, may be conveniently differentiated from animal consumers as special-

[2] The ecological system composed of the "biocoenosis + biotop" has been termed the *holocoen* by Friederichs ('30) and the *biosystem* by Thienemann ('39).

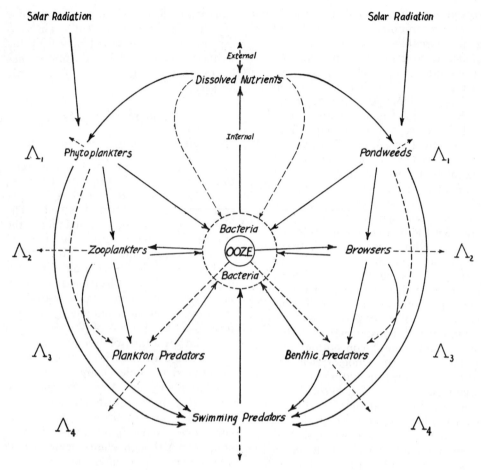

Fig. 1. Generalized lacustrine food-cycle relationships (after Lindeman, '41b).

ized *decomposers*[3] of organic substance. Waksman ('41) has suggested that certain of these bacteria be further differentiated as *transformers* of organic and inorganic compounds. The combined action of animal consumers and bacterial decomposers tends to dissipate the potential energy of organic substances, again transforming them to the inorganic state. From this inorganic state the autotrophic plants may utilize the dis-

solved nutrients once more in resynthesizing complex organic substance, thus completing the food cycle.

The careful study of food cycles reveals an intricate pattern of trophic predilections and substitutions underlain by certain basic dependencies; food-cycle diagrams, such as figure 1, attempt to portray these underlying relationships. In general, predators are less specialized in food habits than are their prey. The ecological importance of this statement seems to have been first recognized by Elton ('27), who discussed its effect on the survival of prey species when predators are numerous and its effect in enabling predators to survive when their

[3] Thienemann ('26) proposed the term *reducers* for the heterotrophic bacteria and fungi, but this term suggests that decomposition is produced solely by chemical reduction rather than oxidation, which is certainly not the case. The term *decomposers* is suggested as being more appropriate.

usual prey are only periodically abundant. This ability on the part of predators, which tends to make the higher trophic levels of a food cycle less discrete than the lower, increases the difficulties of analyzing the energy relationships in this portion of the food cycle, and may also tend to "shorten the food-chain."

Fundamental food-cycle variations in different ecosystems may be observed by comparing lacustrine and terrestrial cycles. Although dissolved nutrients in the lake water and in the ooze correspond directly with those in the soil, the autotrophic producers differ considerably in form. Lacustrine producers include macrophytic pondweeds, in which massive supporting tissues are at a minimum, and microphytic phytoplankters, which in larger lakes definitely dominate the production of organic substance. Terrestrial producers are predominantly multicellular plants containing much cellulose and lignin in various types of supporting tissues. Terrestrial herbivores, belonging to a great number of specialized food groups, act as *primary consumers* (sensu Jacot, '40) of organic substance; these groups correspond to the "browsers" of aquatic ecosystems. Terrestrial predators may be classified as more remote (secondary, tertiary, quaternary, etc.) consumers, according to whether they prey upon herbivores or upon other predators; these correspond roughly to the benthic predators and swimming predators, respectively, of a lake. Bacterial and fungal decomposers in terrestrial systems are concentrated in the humus layer of the soil; in lakes, where the "soil" is overlain by water, decomposition takes place both in the water, as organic particles slowly settle, and in the benthic "soil." Nutrient salts are thus freed to be reutilized by the autotrophic plants of both ecosystems.

The striking absence of terrestrial "life-forms" analogous to plankters[4] (cf.

figure 1) indicates that the terrestrial food cycle is essentially "mono-cyclic" with macrophytic producers, while the lacustrine cycle, with two "life-forms" of producers, may be considered as "bi-cyclic." The marine cycle, in which plankters are the only producers of any consequence, may be considered as "mono-cyclic" with microphytic producers. The relative absence of massive supporting tissues in plankters and the very rapid completion of their life cycle exert a great influence on the differential productivities of terrestrial and aquatic systems. The general convexity of terrestrial systems as contrasted with the concavity of aquatic substrata results in striking trophic and successional differences, which will be discussed in a later section.

### Productivity

*Definitions.*—The quantitative aspects of trophic ecology have been commonly expressed in terms of the productivity of the food groups concerned. Productivity has been rather broadly defined as the general rate of production (Riley, '40, and others), a term which may be applied to any or every food group in a given ecosystem. The problem of productivity as related to biotic dynamics has been critically analyzed by G. E. Hutchinson ('42) in his recent book on limnological principles. The two following paragraphs are quoted from Hutchinson's chapter on "The Dynamics of Lake Biota":

The dynamics of lake biota is here treated as primarily a problem of energy transfer . . . the biotic utilization of solar energy entering the lake surface. Some of this energy is transformed by photosynthesis into the structure of phytoplankton organisms, representing an energy content which may be expressed as $\Lambda_1$ (first level). Some of the phytoplankters will be eaten by

plankton. This concept appears to have a number of adherents in this country. The author feels that this analogy is misleading, as the edaphon, which has almost no producers, represents only a dependent side-chain of the terrestrial cycle, and is much more comparable to the lacustrine microbenthos than to the plankton.

---

[4] Francé ('13) developed the concept of the *edaphon*, in which the soil microbiota was represented as the terrestrial equivalent of aquatic

zooplankters (energy content $\Lambda_2$), which again will be eaten by plankton predators (energy content $\Lambda_3$). The various successive levels (i.e., stages[5]) of the food cycle are thus seen to have successively different energy contents ($\Lambda_1$, $\Lambda_2$, $\Lambda_3$, etc.).

Considering any food-cycle level $\Lambda_n$, energy is entering the level and is leaving it. The rate of change of the energy content $\Lambda_n$ therefore may be divided into a positive and a negative part:

$$\frac{d\Lambda_n}{dt} = \lambda_n + \lambda_n',$$

where $\lambda_n$ is by definition positive and represents the rate of contribution of energy from $\Lambda_{n-1}$ (the previous level) to $\Lambda_n$, while $\lambda_n'$ is negative and represents the sum of the rate of energy dissipated from $\Lambda_n$ and the rate of energy content handed on to the following level $\Lambda_{n+1}$. The more interesting quantity is $\lambda_n$ which is defined as the true *productivity* of level $\Lambda_n$. In practice, it is necessary to use mean rates over finite periods of time as approximations to the mean rates $\lambda_0$, $\lambda_1$, $\lambda_2$. . . .

In the following pages we shall consider the quantitative relationships of the following productivities: $\lambda_0$ (rate of incident solar radiation), $\lambda_1$ (rate of photosynthetic production), $\lambda_2$ (rate of primary or herbivorous consumption), $\lambda_3$ (rate of secondary consumption or primary predation), and $\lambda_4$ (rate of tertiary consumption). The total amount of organic structure formed per year for any level $\Lambda_n$, which is commonly expressed as the annual "yield," actually represents a value uncorrected for dissipation of energy by (1) respiration, (2) predation, and (3) post-mortem decomposition. Let us now consider the quantitative aspects of these losses.

*Respiratory corrections.*—The amount of energy lost from food levels by catabolic processes (respiration) varies considerably for the different stages in the life histories of individuals, for different levels in the food cycle and for different seasonal temperatures. In terms of annual production, however, individual deviates cancel out and respiratory differences between food groups may be observed.

[5] The term *stage*, in some respects preferable to the term *level*, cannot be used in this trophic sense because of its long-established usage as a successional term (cf. p. 23).

Numerous estimates of average respiration for photosynthetic producers may be obtained from the literature. For terrestrial plants, estimates range from 15 per cent (Pütter, re Spoehr, '26) to 43 per cent (Lundegårdh, '24) under various types of natural conditions. For aquatic producers, Hicks ('34) reported a coefficient of about 15 per cent for Lemna under certain conditions. Wimpenny ('41) has indicated that the respiratory coefficient of marine producers in polar regions (diatoms) is probably much less than that of the more "animal-like" producers (peridinians and coccolithophorids) of warmer seas, and that temperature may be an important factor in determining respiratory coefficients in general. Juday ('40), after conducting numerous experiments with Manning and others on the respiration of phytoplankters in Trout Lake, Wisconsin, concluded that under average conditions these producers respire about $\frac{1}{3}$ of the organic matter which they synthesize. This latter value, 33 per cent, is probably the best available respiratory coefficient for lacustrine producers.

Information on the respiration of aquatic primary consumers is obtained from an illuminating study by Ivlev ('39a) on the energy relationships of *Tubifex*. By means of ingenious techniques, he determined calorific values for assimilation and growth in eleven series of experiments. Using the averages of his calorific values, we can make the following simple calculations: *assimilation* (16.77 cal.) − *growth* (10.33 cal.) = *respiration* (6.44 cal.), so that respiration in terms of growth = $\frac{6.44}{10.33}$ = 62.30 per cent. As a check on the growth stage of these worms, we find that $\frac{growth}{assimilation}$ = 61.7 per cent, a value in good agreement with the classical conclusions of Needham ('31, III, p. 1655) with respect to embryos: the efficiency of all developing embryos is numerically similar, between 60 and 70 per cent, and independent of temperature within the range of biological tolerance. We may therefore conclude that the worms were growing at nearly maximal efficiency, so that the above respiratory coefficient is nearly minimal. In the absence of further data, we shall tentatively accept 62 per cent as the best available respiratory coefficient for aquatic herbivores.

The respiratory coefficient for aquatic predators can be approximated from data of another important study by Ivlev ('39b), on the energy transformations in predatory yearling carp. Treating his calorific values as in the preceding paragraph, we find that *ingestion* (1829 cal.) − *defecation* (454 cal.) = *assimilation* (1375 cal.), and *assimilation* − *growth* (573 cal.) = *respiration* (802 cal.), so that respiration in terms of growth $= \dfrac{802}{573} = 140$ per cent, a much higher coefficient than that found for the primary consumer, *Tubifex*. A rough check on this coefficient was obtained by calorific analysis of data on the growth of yearling green sunfishes (*Lepomis cyanellus*) published by W. G. Moore ('41), which indicate a respiratory coefficient of 120 per cent with respect to growth, suggesting that these fishes were growing more efficiently than those studied by Ivlev. Since Moore's fishes were fed on a highly concentrated food (liver), this greater growth efficiency is not surprising. If the maximum growth efficiency would occur when $\dfrac{\text{growth}}{\text{assimilation}}$ = 60–70 per cent (AEE of Needham, '31), the AEE of Moore's data (about 50 per cent) indicates that the minimum respiratory coefficient with respect to growth might be as low as 100 per cent for certain fishes. Food-conversion data from Thompson ('41) indicate a minimum respiratory coefficient of less than 150 per cent for young black bass (*Huro salmoides*) at 70° F., the exact percentage depending upon how much of the ingested food (minnows) was assimilated. Krogh ('41) showed that predatory fishes

have a higher rate of respiration than the more sluggish herbivorous species; the respiratory rate of *Esox* under resting conditions at 20° C. was $3\frac{1}{2}$ times that of *Cyprinus*. The form of piscian growth curves (cf. Hile, '41) suggests that the respiratory coefficient is much higher for fishes towards the end of their normal life-span. Since the value obtained from Ivlev (above) is based on more extensive data than those of Moore, we shall tentatively accept 140 per cent as an average respiratory coefficient for aquatic predators.

Considering that predators are usually more active than their herbivorous prey, which are in turn more active than the plants upon which they feed, it is not surprising to find that respiration with respect to growth in producers (33 per cent), in primary consumers (62 per cent) and in secondary consumers (>100 per cent) increases progressively. These differences probably reflect a trophic principle of wide application: the percentage loss of energy due to respiration is progressively greater for higher levels in the food cycle.

*Predation corrections.*—In considering the predation losses from each level, it is most convenient to begin with the highest level, $\Lambda_n$. In a mechanically perfect food cycle composed of organically discrete levels, this loss by predation obviously would be zero. Since no natural food cycle is so mechanically constituted, some "cannibalism" within such an arbitrary level can be expected, so that the actual value for predation loss from $\Lambda_n$ probably will be somewhat above zero. The predation loss from level $\Lambda_{n-1}$ will represent the total amount of assimilable energy passed on into the higher level (i.e., the true productivity, $\lambda_n$), plus a quantity representing the average content of substance killed but not assimilated by the predator, as will be discussed in the following section. The predation loss from level $\Lambda_{n-2}$ will likewise represent the total amount of assimilable energy passed on to the next level (i.e., $\lambda_{n-1}$), plus a similar factor for unassimilated material, as illustrated by the data of tables II and III. The various categories of parasites are somewhat comparable to those of predators, but the details of their energy relationships have not yet been clarified, and cannot be included in this preliminary account.

*Decomposition corrections.* — In conformity with the principle of Le Chatelier, the energy of no food level can be completely extracted by the organisms which feed upon it. In addition to the energy represented by organisms which survive to be included in the "annual yield," much energy is contained in "killed" tissues which the predators are unable to digest and assimilate. Average coefficients of indigestible tissues, based largely of the calorific equivalents of the "crude fiber" fractions in the chemical analyses of Birge and Juday ('22), are as follows:

Nannoplankters....................... ca. 5%
Algal mesoplankters................. 5–35%
Mature pondweeds.................. ca. 20%
Primary consumers................. ca. 10%
Secondary consumers............... ca. 8%
Predatory fishes.................... ca. 5%

Corrections for terrestrial producers would certainly be much higher. Although the data are insufficient to warrant a generalization, these values suggest increasing digestibility of the higher food levels, particularly for the benthic components of aquatic cycles.

The loss of energy due to premature death from non-predatory causes usually must be neglected, since such losses are exceedingly difficult to evaluate and under normal conditions probably represent relatively small components of the annual production. However, considering that these losses may assume considerable proportions at any time, the above "decomposition coefficients" must be regarded as correspondingly minimal.

Following non-predated death, every organism is a potential source of energy for myriads of bacterial and fungal saprophages, whose metabolic products provide simple inorganic and organic solutes reavailable to photosynthetic producers. These saprophages may also serve as energy sources for successive levels of consumers, often considerably supplementing the normal diet of herbivores (ZoBell and Feltham, '38). Jacot ('40) considered saprophage-feeding or coprophagous animals as "low" primary consumers, but the writer believes that in the present state of our knowledge a quantitative subdivision of primary consumers is unwarranted.

*Application.* — The value of these theoretical energy relationships can be illustrated by analyzing data of the three ecosystems for which relatively comprehensive productivity values have been published (table I). The summary ac-

TABLE I. *Productivities of food-groups in three aquatic ecosystems, as g-cal/cm²/year, uncorrected for losses due to respiration, predation and decomposition. Data from Brujewicz ('39), Juday ('40) and Lindeman ('41b).*

|  | Caspian Sea | Lake Mendota | Cedar Bog Lake |
|---|---|---|---|
| Phytoplankters: $\Lambda_1$............ | 59.5 | 299 | 25.8 |
| Phytobenthos: $\Lambda_1$........... | 0.3 | 22 | 44.6 |
| Zooplankters: $\Lambda_2$.............. | 20.0 | 22 | 6.1 |
| Benthic browsers: $\Lambda_2$.......... |  | 1.8* | 0.8 |
| Benthic predators: $\Lambda_3$.......... | 20.6 |  | 0.2 |
| Plankton predators: $\Lambda_3$........ |  | 0.9* | 0.8 |
| "Forage" fishes: $\Lambda_3(+\Lambda_2?)$...... | 0.6 | ? | 0.3 |
| Carp: $\Lambda_3(+\Lambda_2?)$.............. | 0.0 | 0.2 | 0.0 |
| "Game" fishes: $\Lambda_4(+\Lambda_3?)$....... | 0.6 | 0.1 | 0.0 |
| Seals: $\Lambda_5$..................... | 0.01 | 0.0 | 0.0 |

* Roughly assuming that $\frac{2}{3}$ of the bottom fauna is herbivorous (cf. Juday, '22).

count of Brujewicz ('39) on "the dynamics of living matter in the Caspian Sea" leaves much to be desired, as bottom animals are not differentiated into their relative food levels, and the basis for determining the annual production of phytoplankters (which on theoretical grounds appears to be much too low) is not clearly explained. Furthermore, his values are stated in terms of thousands of tons of dry weight for the Caspian Sea as a whole, and must be roughly transformed to calories per square centimeter of surface area. The data for Lake Mendota, Wisconsin, are taken directly from a general summary (Juday, '40) of the many productivity studies made on that eutrophic lake. The data for Cedar Bog Lake, Minnesota, are taken from the author's four-year analysis (Lindeman, '41b) of its food-cycle dynamics. The calorific values in table I, representing annual production of organic matter, are uncorrected for energy losses.

TABLE II. *Productivity values for the Cedar Bog Lake food cycle, in g-cal/cm²/year, as corrected by using the coefficients derived in the preceding sections.*

| Trophic level | Uncorrected productivity | Respiration | Predation | Decomposition | Corrected productivity |
|---|---|---|---|---|---|
| Producers: $\Lambda_1$ | $70.4 \pm 10.14$ | 23.4 | 14.8 | 2.8 | 111.3 |
| Primary consumers: $\Lambda_2$ | $7.0 \pm 1.07$ | 4.4 | 3.1 | 0.3 | 14.8 |
| Secondary consumers: $\Lambda_3$ | $1.3 \pm 0.43^*$ | 1.8 | 0.0 | 0.0 | 3.1 |

* This value includes the productivity of the small cyprinoid fishes found in the lake.

Correcting for the energy losses due to respiration, predation and decomposition, as discussed in the preceding sections, casts a very different light on the relative productivities of food levels. The calculation of corrections for the Cedar Bog Lake values for producers, primary consumers and secondary consumers are given in table II. The application of similar corrections to the energy values for the food levels of the Lake Mendota food cycle given by Juday ('40), as shown in table III, indicates that Lake Mendota is much more productive of producers and primary consumers than is Cedar Bog Lake, while the production of secondary consumers is of the same order of magnitude in the two lakes.

In calculating total productivity for Lake Mendota, Juday ('40) used a blanket correction of 500 per cent of the annual production of all consumer levels for "metabolism," which presumably includes both respiration and predation. Thompson ('41) found that the "carry-

TABLE III. *Productivity values for the Lake Mendota food cycle, in g-cal/cm²/year, as corrected by using coefficients derived in the preceding sections, and as given by Juday ('40).*

| Trophic Level | Uncorrected productivity | Respiration | Predation | Decomposition | Corrected productivity | Juday's corrected productivity |
|---|---|---|---|---|---|---|
| Producers: $\Lambda_1$ | 321* | 107 | 42 | 10 | 480 | 428 |
| Primary consumers: $\Lambda_2$ | 24 | 15 | 2.3 | 0.3 | 41.6 | 144 |
| Secondary consumers: $\Lambda_3$ | 1† | 1 | 0.3 | 0.0 | 2.3 | 6 |
| Tertiary consumers: $\Lambda_4$ | 0.12 | 0.2 | 0.0 | 0.0 | 0.3 | 0.7 |

* Hutchinson ('42) gives evidence that this value is probably too high and may actually be as low as 250.

† Apparently such organisms as small "forage" fishes are not included in any part of Juday's balance sheet. The inclusion of these forms might be expected to increase considerably the productivity of secondary consumption.

ing-capacity" of lakes containing mostly carp and other "coarse" fishes (primarily $\Lambda_3$), was about 500 per cent that of lakes containing mostly "game" fishes (primarily $\Lambda_4$), and concluded that "this difference must be about one complete link in the food chain, since it usually requires about five pounds of food to produce one pound of fish." While such high "metabolic losses" may hold for tertiary and quaternary predators under certain field conditions, the physiological experiments previously cited indicate much lower respiratory coefficients. Even when predation and decomposition corrections are included, the resultant productivity values are less than half those obtained by using Juday's coefficient. Since we have shown that the necessary corrections vary progressively with the different food levels, it seems probable that Juday's "coefficient of metabolism" is much too high for primary and secondary consumers.

### Biological efficiency

The quantitative relationships of any food-cycle level may be expressed in terms of its efficiency with respect to lower levels. Quoting Hutchinson's ('42) definition, "the efficiency of the productivity of any level $(\Lambda_n)$ relative to the productivity of any previous level $(\Lambda_m)$ is defined as $\frac{\lambda_n}{\lambda_m} 100$. If the rate of solar energy entering the ecosystem is denoted as $\lambda_0$, the efficiencies of all levels may be referred back to this quantity $\lambda_0$." In general, however, the most interesting efficiencies are those referred to the previous level's productivity $(\lambda_{n-1})$, or those expressed as $\frac{\lambda_n}{\lambda_{n-1}} 100$. These latter may be termed the *progressive efficiencies* of the various food-cycle levels, indicating for each level the degree of utilization of its potential food supply or energy source. All efficiencies discussed in the following pages are progressive efficiencies, expressed in terms of relative productivities $\left(\frac{\lambda_n}{\lambda_{n-1}} 100\right)$. It is important to remember that efficiency and productivity are not synonymous. Productivity is a rate (i.e., in the units here used, cal/cm²/year), while efficiency, being a ratio, is a dimensionless number. The points of reference for any efficiency value should always be clearly stated.

The progressive efficiencies $\left(\frac{\lambda_n}{\lambda_{n-1}} 100\right)$ for the trophic levels of Cedar Bog Lake and Lake Mendota, as obtained from the productivities derived in tables II and III, are presented in table IV. In view of the uncertainties concerning some of the Lake Mendota productivities, no definite conclusions can be drawn from their relative efficiencies. The Cedar Bog Lake ratios, however, indicate that the progressive efficiencies increase from about 0.10 per cent for production, to 13.3 per cent for primary consumption, and to 22.3 per cent for secondary consumption. An uncorrected efficiency of tertiary consumption of 37.5 per cent ± 3.0 per cent (for the weight ratios of "carnivorous" to "forage" fishes in Alabama ponds) is indicated in data published by Swingle and Smith ('40). These progressively increasing efficiencies may well represent a fundamental trophic principle, namely, that the consumers at progressively higher levels in the food cycle are progressively more efficient in the use of their food supply.

At first sight, this generalization of increasing efficiency in higher consumer groups would appear to contradict the previous generalization that the loss of energy due to respiration is progressively greater for higher levels in the food cycle. These can be reconciled by remembering that increased activity of predators considerably increases the chances of encountering suitable prey. The ultimate effect of such antagonistic principles would present a picture of a predator completely wearing itself out in the process of completely exterminating its prey, a very improbable situation. However, Elton ('27) pointed out that food-cycles rarely have more than five trophic levels. Among the several factors involved, increasing respiration of successive levels of predators contrasted with their successively increasing efficiency of predation appears to be important in restricting the number of trophic levels in a food cycle.

The effect of increasing temperature is alleged by Wimpenny ('41) to cause a decreasing consumer/producer ratio, presumably because he believes that the "acceleration of vital velocities" of consumers at increasing temperatures is more rapid than that of producers. He

TABLE IV. *Productivities and progressive efficiencies in the Cedar Bog Lake and Lake Mendota food cycles, as g-cal/cm²/year*

| | Cedar Bog Lake | | Lake Mendota | |
|---|---|---|---|---|
| | Productivity | Efficiency | Productivity | Efficiency |
| Radiation......... | ≦118,872 | | 118,872 | |
| Producers: $\Lambda_1$...... | 111.3 | 0.10% | 480* | 0.40% |
| Primary consumers: $\Lambda_2$............. | 14.8 | 13.3% | 41.6 | 8.7% |
| Secondary consumers: $\Lambda_3$.... | 3.1 | 22.3% | 2.3† | 5.5% |
| Tertiary consumers: $\Lambda_4$.... | — | — | 0.3 | 13.0% |

* Probably too high; see footnote of table III.
† Probably too low; see footnote of table III.

cites as evidence Lohmann's ('12) data for relative *numbers* (not biomass) of Protophyta, Protozoa and Metazoa in the centrifuge plankton of "cool" seas (741:73:1) as contrasted with tropical areas (458:24:1). Since Wimpenny himself emphasizes that many metazoan plankters are larger in size toward the poles, these data do not furnish convincing proof of the allegation. The data given in table IV, since Cedar Bog Lake has a much higher mean annual water temperature than Lake Mendota, appear to contradict Wimpenny's generalization that consumer/producer ratios fall as the temperature increases.

### The Eltonian pyramid

The general relationships of higher food-cycle levels to one another and to community structure were greatly clarified following recognition (Elton, '27) of the importance of size and of numbers in the animals of an ecosystem. Beginning with primary consumers of various sizes, there are as a rule a number of food-chains radiating outwards in which the probability is that predators will become successively larger, while parasites and hyper-parasites will be progressively smaller than their hosts. Since small primary consumers can increase faster than larger secondary consumers and are so able to support the latter, the animals at the base of a food-chain are relatively abundant while those toward the end are progressively fewer in number. The resulting arrangement of sizes and numbers of animals, termed the pyramid of Numbers by Elton, is now commonly known as the Eltonian Pyramid. Williams ('41), reporting on the "floor fauna" of the Panama rain forest, has recently published an interesting example of such a pyramid, which is reproduced in figure 2.

The Eltonian Pyramid may also be expressed in terms of biomass. The weight of all predators must always be much lower than that of all food animals, and the total weight of the latter much lower than the plant production (Bodenheimer, '38). To the human ecologist, it is noteworthy that the population density of the essentially vegetarian Chinese, for example, is much greater than that of the more carnivorous English.

The principle of the Eltonian Pyramid has been redefined in terms of productivity by Hutchinson (unpublished) in the following formalized terms: the rate of production cannot be less and will almost certainly be greater than the rate of primary consumption, which in turn cannot be less and will almost certainly be greater than the rate of secondary consumption, which in turn . . . , etc. The energy-relationships of this principle may be epitomized by means

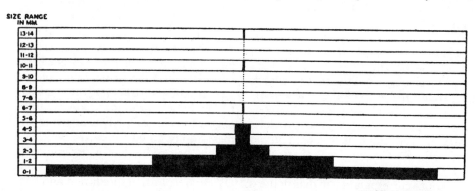

FIG. 2. Eltonian pyramid of numbers, for floor-fauna invertebrates of the Panama rain forest (from Williams, '41).

of the productivity symbol $\lambda$, as follows:

$$\lambda_0 > \lambda_1 > \lambda_2 \ldots > \lambda_n.$$

This rather obvious generalization is confirmed by the data of all ecosystems analyzed to date.

### Trophic-Dynamics in Succession

Dynamic processes within an ecosystem, over a period of time, tend to produce certain obvious changes in its species-composition, soil characteristics and productivity. Change, according to Cooper ('26), is the essential criterion of succession. From the trophic-dynamic viewpoint, succession is the process of development in an ecosystem, brought about primarily by the effects of the organisms on the environment and upon each other, towards a relatively stable condition of equilibrium.

It is well known that in the initial phases of hydrarch succession (oligotrophy → eutrophy) productivity increases rapidly; it is equally apparent that the colonization of a bare terrestrial area represents a similar acceleration in productivity. In the later phases of succession, productivity increases much more slowly. As Hutchinson and Wollack ('40) pointed out, these generalized changes in the rate of production may be expressed as a sigmoid curve showing a rough resemblance to the growth curve of an organism or of a homogeneous population.

Such smooth logistic growth, of course, is seldom found in natural succession, except possibly in such cases as bare areas developing directly to the climax vegetation type in the wake of a retreating glacier. Most successional seres consist of a number of *stages* ("recognizable, clearly-marked subdivisions of a given sere"—W. S. Cooper), so that their productivity growth-curves will contain undulations corresponding in distinctness to the distinctness of the stages. The presence of stages in a successional sere apparently represents the persistent influence of some combination of limiting factors, which, until they are overcome by species-substitution, etc., tend to decrease the acceleration of productivity and maintain it at a more constant rate. This tendency towards *stage-equilibrium* of productivity will be discussed in the following pages.

### Productivity in hydrarch succession

The descriptive dynamics of hydrarch succession is well known. Due to the essentially concave nature of the substratum, lake succession is internally complicated by a rather considerable influx of nutritive substances from the drainage basin surrounding the lake. The basins of lakes are gradually filled with sediments, largely organogenic, upon which a series of vascular plant stages successively replace one another until a more or less stable (climax) stage is attained. We are concerned here, however, primarily with the productivity aspects of the successional process.

*Eutrophication.* — Thienemann ('26) presented a comprehensive theoretical discussion of the relation between lake succession and productivity, as follows: In oligotrophy, the pioneer phase, productivity is rather low, limited by the amount of dissolved nutrients in the lake water. Oxygen is abundant at all times, almost all of the synthesized organic matter is available for animal food; bacteria release dissolved nutrients from the remainder. Oligotrophy thus has a very "thrifty" food cycle, with a relatively high "efficiency" of the consumer populations. With increasing influx of nutritives from the surrounding drainage basin and increasing primary productivity ($\lambda_1$), oligotrophy is gradually changed through mesotrophy to eutrophy, in which condition the production of organic matter ($\lambda_1$) exceeds that which can be oxidized ($\lambda_1'$) by respiration, predation and bacterial decomposition. The oxygen supply of the hypolimnion becomes depleted, with disastrous effects on the oligotrophconditioned bottom fauna. Organisms especially adapted to endure temporary anaerobiosis replace the oligotrophic species, accompanied by anaerobic bacteria which during the stagnation period cause reduction rather than oxidation of the organic detritus. As a result of this process, semi-reduced organic ooze, or *gyttja*, accumulates on the bottom. As oxygen supply thus becomes a limiting factor of productivity, relative efficiency of the consumer groups in utilizing the synthesized organic substance becomes correspondingly lower.

The validity of Thienemann's interpretation, particularly regarding the trophic mechanisms, has recently been challenged by Hutchinson ('41, '42), who states that three distinct factors are involved: (1) the edaphic factor, representing the potential nutrient supply (primarily phosphorus) in the surrounding drainage basin; (2) the age of the lake at any stage, indicating the degree of utilization of the nutrient supply; and (3) the morphometric character at any stage, dependent on both the original morphometry of the lake basin and the age of the lake, and presumably influencing the oxygen concentration in the hypolimnion. He holds that true eutrophication takes place only in regions well supplied with nutrients, lakes in other regions developing into "ideotrophic types." The influx of phosphorus is probably very great in the earliest phases, much greater than the supply of nitrogen, as indicated by very low N/P ratios in the earliest sediments (Hutchinson and Wollack, '40). A large portion of this phosphorus is believed to be insoluble, as a component of such mineral particles as apatite, etc., although certainly some of it is soluble. The supply of available nitrogen increases somewhat more slowly, being largely dependent upon the fixation of nitrogen by microorganisms either in the lake or in the surrounding soils. The photosynthetic productivity ($\lambda_1$) of lakes thus increases rather rapidly in the early phases, its

quantitative value for lakes with comparable edaphic nutrient supplies being dependent on the morphometry (mean depth). Since deep lakes have a greater depth range for plankton photosynthesis, abundant oxygen and more chance for decomposition of the plankton detritus before reaching the bottom, such deep lakes may be potentially as productive as shallower lakes, in terms of unit surface area. Factors tending to lessen the comparative productivity of deep lakes are (1) lower temperature for the lake as a whole, and (2) greater dilution of nutrients in terms of volume of the illuminated "trophogenic zone" of the lake. During eutrophication in a deep lake, the phosphorus content of the sediment falls and nitrogen rises, until a N/P ratio of about 40/1 is established. "The decomposition of organic matter presumably is always liberating some of this phosphorus and nitrogen. Within limits, the more organic matter present the easier will be such regeneration. It is probable that benthic animals and anion exchange play a part in such processes" (Hutchinson, '42). The progressive filling of the lake basin with sediments makes the lake shallower, so that the oxygen supply of the hypolimnion is increasingly, and finally completely, exhausted during summer stagnation. Oxidation of the sediments is less complete, but sufficient phosphorus is believed to be regenerated from the ooze surface so that productivity in terms of surface area remains relatively constant. The nascent ooze acts as a trophic buffer, in the chemical sense, tending to maintain the productivity of a lake in stage-equilibrium (*typological equilibrium* of Hutchinson) during the eutrophic stage of its succession.

The concept of eutrophic stage-equilibrium seems to be partially confused (cf. Thienemann, '26; Hutchinson and Wollack, '40) with the theoretically ideal condition of complete *trophic equilibrium*, which may be roughly defined as the dynamic state of continuous, complete utilization and regeneration of chemical nutrients in an ecosystem, without loss or gain from the outside, under a periodically constant energy source—such as might be found in a perfectly balanced aquarium or terrarium. Natural ecosystems may tend to approach a state of trophic equilibrium under certain conditions, but it is doubtful if any are sufficiently autochthonous to attain, or maintain, true trophic equilibrium for any length of time. The biosphere as a whole, however, as Vernadsky ('29, '39) so vigorously asserts, may exhibit a high degree of true trophic equilibrium.

The existence of prolonged eutrophic stage-equilibrium was first suggested as a result of a study on the sediments of Grosser Plöner See in Germany (Groschopf, '36). Its significance was recognized by Hutchinson and Wollack ('40), who based their critical discussion on chemical analyses (ibid.) and pollen analyses (Deevey, '39) of the sediments of Linsley Pond, Connecticut. They reported a gradual transition from oligotrophy to eutrophy (first attained in the oak-hemlock pollen period), in which stage the lake has remained for a very long time, perhaps more than 4000 years. They report indications of a comparable eutrophic stage-equilibrium in the sediments of nearby Upper Linsley Pond (Hutchinson and Wollack, unpublished). Similar attainment of stage-equilibrium is indicated in a preliminary report on the sediments of Lake Windermere in England (Jenkin, Mortimer and Pennington, '41). Every stage of a sere is believed to possess a similar stage-equilibrium of variable duration, although terrestrial stages have not yet been defined in terms of productivity.

The trophic aspects of eutrophication cannot be determined easily from the sediments. In general, however, the ratio of organic matter to the silt washed into the lake from the margins affords an approximation of the photosynthetic productivity. This undecomposed organic matter, representing the amount of energy which is lost from the food cycle, is derived largely from level $\Lambda_1$, as plant structures in general are decomposed less easily than animal structures. The quantity of energy passed on into consumer levels can only be surmised from undecomposed fragments of organisms which are believed to occupy those levels. Several types of animal "microfossils" occur rather consistently in lake sediments, such as the carapaces and post-abdomens of certain cladocerans, chironomid head-capsules, fragments of the phantom-midge larva *Chaoborus*, snail shells, polyzoan statoblasts, sponge spicules and rhizopod shells. Deevey ('42), after making comprehensive microfossil and chemical analyses of the sediments of Linsley Pond, suggested that the abundant half-carapaces of the planktonic browser *Bosmina* afford "a reasonable estimate of the quantity of zooplankton produced" and that "the total organic matter of the sediment is a reasonable estimate of the organic matter produced by phytoplankton and littoral vegetation." He found a striking similarity in the shape of the curves representing *Bosmina* content and total organic matter plotted against depth, which, when plotted logarithmically against each other, showed a linear relationship expressed by an empirical power equation. Citing Hutchinson and Wollack ('40) to the effect that the developmental curve for organic matter was analogous to that for the development of an organism, he pressed the analogy further by suggesting that the increase of zooplankton (*Bosmina*) with reference to the increase of organic matter ($\lambda_1$) fitted the formula $y = bx^k$ for allometric growth (Huxley, '32), "where $y = Bosmina$, $x =$ total organic matter, $b =$ a constant giving the value of $y$ when $x = 1$, and $k =$ the 'allometry constant,' or the slope of the line when a double log plot is made." If we represent the organic matter produced as $\lambda_1$ and further assume that *Bosmina* represents the primary consumers ($\lambda_2$), neglecting benthic browsers, the formula becomes $\lambda_2 = b\lambda_1{}^k$. Whether this formula would express the relationship found in other levels of the food cycle, the development of other stages, or other ecosystems, remains to be demonstrated.[6] Stratigraphic analyses in Cedar Bog Lake (Lindeman and Lindeman, unpublished) suggest a roughly similar increase of both organic matter and *Bosmina* carapaces in the earliest sediments. In the modern senescent lake, however, double logarithmic plottings of the calorific values for $\lambda_1$ against $\lambda_2$, and $\lambda_2$ against $\lambda_3$, for the four years studied, show no semblance of linear relationship, i.e., do not fit any power equation. If Deevey is correct in his interpretation of the Linsley Pond microfossils, allometric growth would appear to characterize the phases of pre-equilibrium succession as the term "growth" indeed implies.

The relative duration of eutrophic stage-equilibrium is not yet completely understood. As exemplified by Linsley Pond, the relation of stage-equilibrium to succession is intimately concerned with the trophic processes of (1) external influx and efflux (partly controlled by climate), (2) photosynthetic productivity, (3) sedimentation (partly by physiographic silting) and (4) regeneration of nutritives from the sediments. These processes apparently maintain a relatively constant ratio to each other during the extended equilibrium period. Yet the food cycle is not in true trophic equilibrium, and continues to fill the lake with organic sediments. *Succession* is continuing, at a rate corresponding to the rate of sediment accumulation. In the words of Hutchinson and Wollack ('40), "this means that during the equilibrium period the lake, through the internal activities of its biocoenosis, is continually approaching a condition when it ceases to be a lake."

*Senescence.*—As a result of long-continued sedimentation, eutrophic lakes attain senescence, first manifested in bays and wind-protected areas. Senescence is usually characterized by such pond-like conditions as (1) tremendous increase in shallow littoral area populated with pondweeds and (2) increased marginal invasion of terrestrial stages. Cedar Bog Lake, which the author has studied for several years, is in late senescence, rapidly changing to the terrestrial stages of its succession. On casual inspection, the massed verdure of pondweeds and epiphytes, together with sporadic algal blooms, appears to indicate great photosynthetic productivity. As pointed out by Wesenberg-Lund ('12), littoral areas of lakes are virtual hothouses, absorbing more radiant energy per unit volume than deeper areas. At the present time the entire aquatic area of Cedar Bog Lake is essentially littoral in nature, and its productivity per cubic meter of water is probably greater than at any time in its history. However, since radiant energy ($\lambda_0$) enters a lake only from the surface, productivity must be defined in terms of surface area. In these terms, the present photosynthetic productivity pales into insignificance when compared with less advanced lakes in similar edaphic regions; for instance, $\lambda_1$ is less than $\frac{1}{3}$ that of Lake Mendota, Wisconsin (cf. table IV). These facts attest the essential accuracy of Welch's ('35) generalization that productivity declines greatly during senescence. An interesting principle demonstrated in Cedar Bog Lake (Lindeman, '41b) is that during late lake senescence general productivity ($\lambda_n$) is increasingly influenced by climatic factors, acting through

[6] It should be mentioned in this connection that Meschkat ('37) found that the relationship of population density of tubificids to organic matter in the bottom of a polluted "Buhnenfeld" could be expressed by the formula $y = a^x$, where $y$ represents the population density, $x$ is the "determining environmental factor," and $a$ is a constant. He pointed out that for such an expression to hold the population density must be maximal. Hentschel ('36), on less secure grounds, suggested applying a similar expression to the relationship between populations of marine plankton and the "controlling factor" of their environment.

water level changes, drainage, duration of winter ice, snow cover, etc., to affect the presence and abundance of practically all food groups in the lake.

*Terrestrial stages.*—As an aquatic ecosystem passes into terrestrial phases, fluctuations in atmospheric factors increasingly affect its productivity. ⋅ As succession proceeds, both the species-composition and the productivity of an ecosystem increasingly reflect the effects of the regional climate. Qualitatively, these climatic effects are known for soil morphology (Joffe, '36), autotrophic vegetation (Clements, '16), fauna (Clements and Shelford, '39) and soil microbiota (Braun-Blanquet, '32), in fact for every important component of the food cycle. Quantitatively, these effects have been so little studied that generalizations are most hazardous. It seems probable, however, that productivity tends to increase until the system approaches maturity. Clements and Shelford ('39, p. 116) assert that both plant and animal productivity is generally greatest in the subclimax, except possibly in the case of grasslands. Terrestrial ecosystems are primarily convex topographically and

thus subject to a certain nutrient loss by erosion, which may or may not be made up by increased availability of such nutrients as can be extracted from the "C" soil horizon.

*Successional productivity curves.*—In recapitulating the probable photosynthetic productivity relationships in hydrarch succession, we shall venture to diagram (figure 3) a hypothetical hydrosere, developing from a moderately deep lake in a fertile cold temperate region under relatively constant climatic conditions. The initial period of oligotrophy is believed to be relatively short (Hutchinson and Wollack, '40; Lindeman '41a), with productivity rapidly increasing until eutrophic stage-equilibrium is attained. The duration of high eutrophic productivity depends upon the mean depth of the basin and upon the rate of sedimentation, and productivity fluctuates about a high eutrophic mean until the lake becomes too shallow for maximum growth of phytoplankton or regeneration of nutrients from the ooze. As the lake becomes shallower and more senescent, productivity is increasingly influenced by climatic fluctuations and

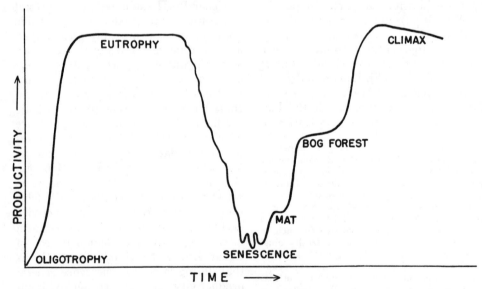

FIG. 3. Hypothetical productivity growth-curve of a hydrosere, developing from a deep lake to climax in a fertile, cold-temperate region.

gradually declines to a minimum as the lake is completely filled with sediments.

The terrestrial aspects of hydrarch succession in cold temperate regions usually follow sharply defined, distinctive stages. In lake basins which are poorly drained, the first stage consists of a mat, often partly floating, made up primarily of sedges and grasses or (in more coastal regions) such heaths as *Chamaedaphne* and *Kalmia* with certain species of sphagnum moss (cf. Rigg, '40). The mat stage is usually followed by a bog forest stage, in which the dominant species is *Larix laricina*, *Picea mariana* or *Thuja occidentalis*. The bog forest stage may be relatively permanent ("edaphic" climax) or succeeded to a greater or lesser degree by the regional climax vegetation. The stage-productivities indicated in figure 3 represent only crude relative estimates, as practically no quantitative data are available.

### Efficiency relationships in succession

The successional changes of photosynthetic efficiency in natural areas (with respect to solar radiation, i.e., $\dfrac{\lambda_1}{\lambda_0} 100$) have not been intensively studied. In lake succession, photosynthetic efficiency would be expected to follow the same course deduced for productivity, rising to a more or less constant value during eutrophic stage-equilibrium, and declining during senescence, as suggested by a photosynthetic efficiency of at least 0.27 per cent for eutrophic Lake Mendota (Juday, '40) and of 0.10 per cent for senescent Cedar Bog Lake. For the terrestrial hydrosere, efficiency would likewise follow a curve similar to that postulated for productivity.

Rough estimates of photosynthetic efficiency for various climatic regions of the earth have been summarized from the literature by Hutchinson (unpublished). These estimates, corrected for respiration, do not appear to be very reliable because of imperfections in the original observations, but are probably of the correct order of magnitude. The mean photosynthetic efficiency for the sea is given as 0.31 per cent (after Riley, '41). The mean photosynthetic efficiency for terrestrial areas of the earth is given as 0.09 per cent ± 0.02 per cent (after Noddack, '37), for forests as 0.16 per cent, for cultivated lands as 0.13 per cent, for steppes as 0.05 per cent, and for deserts as 0.004 per cent. The mean photosynthetic efficiency for the earth as a whole is given as 0.25 per cent. Hutchinson has suggested (cf. Hutchinson and Lindeman, '41) that numerical efficiency values may provide "the most fundamental possible classification of biological formations and of their developmental stages."

Almost nothing is known concerning the efficiencies of consumer groups in succession. The general chronological increase in numbers of *Bosmina* carapaces with respect to organic matter and of *Chaoborus* fragments with respect to *Bosmina* carapaces in the sediments of Linsley Pond (Deevey, '42) suggests progressively increasing efficiencies of zooplankters and plankton predators. On the other hand, Hutchinson ('42) concludes from a comparison of the P : Z (phytoplankton : zooplankton) biomass ratios of several oligotrophic alpine lakes, ca 1 : 2 (Ruttner, '37), as compared with the ratios for Linsley Pond, 1 : 0.22 (Riley, '40) and three eutrophic Bavarian lakes, 1 : 0.25 (Heinrich, '34), that "as the phytoplankton crop is increased the zooplankton by no means keeps pace with the increase." Data compiled by Deevey ('41) for lakes in both mesotrophic (Connecticut) and eutrophic regions (southern Wisconsin), indicate that the deeper or morphometrically "younger" lakes have a lower ratio of bottom fauna to the standing crop of plankton (10–15 per cent) than the shallower lakes which have attained eutrophic equilibrium (22–27 per cent). The ratios for senescent Cedar Bog Lake, while not directly comparable because of its essentially littoral nature, are even higher. These meager data suggest that the efficiencies of consumer groups may increase throughout the aquatic phases of succession.

For terrestrial stages, no consumer efficiency data are available. A suggestive series of species-frequencies in mesarch succession was published by Vera Smith-Davidson ('32), which indicated greatly increasing numbers of arthropods in successive stages approaching the regional climax. Since the photosynthetic productivity of the stages probably also increased, it is impossible to determine progressive efficiency relationships. The problems of biological efficiencies present a practically virgin field, which appears to offer abundant rewards for studies guided by a trophic-dynamic viewpoint.

In conclusion, it should be emphasized that the trophic-dynamic principles indicated in the following summary cannot be expected to hold for every single case, in accord with the known facts of biological variability. à priori, however, these principles appear to be valid for the vast majority of cases, and may be expected to possess a statistically significant probability of validity for any case selected at random. Since the available data summarized in this paper are far too meager to establish such generalizations on a statistical basis, it is highly important that further studies be initiated to test the validity of these and other trophic-dynamic principles.

## Summary

1. Analyses of food-cycle relationships indicate that a biotic community cannot be clearly differentiated from its abiotic environment; the *ecosystem* is hence regarded as the more fundamental ecological unit.

2. The organisms within an ecosystem may be grouped into a series of more or less discrete trophic levels ($\Lambda_1$, $\Lambda_2$, $\Lambda_3$, . . . $\Lambda_n$) as producers, primary consumers, secondary consumers, etc., each successively dependent upon the preceding level as a source of energy, with the producers ($\Lambda_1$) directly dependent upon the rate of incident solar radiation (productivity $\lambda_0$) as a source of energy.

3. The more remote an organism is from the initial source of energy (solar radiation), the less probable that it will be dependent solely upon the preceding trophic level as a source of energy.

4. The progressive energy relationships of the food levels of an "Eltonian Pyramid" may be epitomized in terms of the productivity symbol $\lambda$, as follows:

$$\lambda_0 > \lambda_1 > \lambda_2 \ldots > \lambda_n.$$

5. The percentage loss of energy due to respiration is progressively greater for higher levels in the food cycle. Respiration with respect to growth is about 33 per cent for producers, 62 per cent for primary consumers, and more than 100 per cent for secondary consumers.

6. The consumers at progressively higher levels in the food cycle appear to be progressively more efficient in the use of their food supply. This generalization can be reconciled with the preceding one by remembering that increased activity of predators considerably increases the chances of encountering suitable prey.

7. Productivity and efficiency increase during the early phases of successional development. In lake succession, productivity and photosynthetic efficiency increase from oligotrophy to a prolonged eutrophic stage-equilibrium and decline with lake senescence, rising again in the terrestrial stages of hydrarch succession.

8. The progressive efficiencies of consumer levels, on the basis of very meager data, apparently tend to increase throughout the aquatic phases of succession.

### Acknowledgments

The author is deeply indebted to Professor G. E. Hutchinson of Yale University, who has stimulated many of the trophic concepts developed here, generously placed at the author's disposal several unpublished manuscripts, given valuable counsel, and aided the final development of this paper in every way possible. Many· of the concepts embodied in the successional sections of this paper were developed independently by Professor Hutchinson at Yale and by the author as a graduate student at the University of Minnesota. Subsequent to an exchange of notes, a joint preliminary abstract was published (Hutchinson and Lindeman, '41). The author wishes to express gratitude to the mentors and friends at the University of Minnesota who encouraged and helpfully criticized the initial development of these concepts, particularly Drs. W. S. Cooper, Samuel Eddy, A. C. Hodson, D. B. Lawrence and J. B. Moyle, as well as other members of the local Ecological Discussion Group. The author is also indebted to Drs. J. R. Carpenter, E. S. Deevey, H. J. Lutz, A. E. Parr, G. A. Riley and V. E. Shelford, as well as the persons mentioned above, for critical reading of preliminary manuscripts. Grateful acknowledgment is made to the Graduate School, Yale University, for the award of a Sterling Fellowship in Biology during 1941–1942.

## Literature Cited

Allee, W. C. 1934. Concerning the organization of marine coastal communities. Ecol. Monogr., **4**: 541–554.

Birge, E. A., and C. Juday. 1922. The inland lakes of Wisconsin. The plankton. Part I. Its quantity and chemical composition. Bull. Wisconsin Geol. Nat. Hist. Surv., **64**: 1–222.

Bodenheimer, F. S. 1938. Problems of Animal Ecology. London. Oxford University Press.

Braun-Blanquet, J. 1932. Plant Sociology. N. Y. McGraw-Hill Co.

Brujewicz, S. W. 1939. Distribution and dynamics of living matter in the Caspian Sea. Compt. Rend. Acad. Sci. URSS, **25**: 138–141.

Carpenter, J. R. 1939. The biome. Amer. Midl. Nat., **21**: 75–91.

——. 1940. The grassland biome. Ecol. Monogr., **10**: 617–687.

Clements, F. E. 1916. Plant Succession. Carnegie Inst. Washington Publ., No. 242.

—— and V. E. Shelford. 1939. Bio-Ecology. N. Y. John Wiley & Co.

Cooper, W. S. 1926. The fundamentals of vegetational change. Ecology, **7**: 391–413.

Cowles, H. C. 1899. The ecological relations of the vegetation of the sand dunes of Lake Michigan. Bot. Gaz., **27**: 95–391.

Davidson, V. S. 1932. The effect of seasonal variability upon animal species in a deciduous forest succession. Ecol. Monogr., **2**: 305–334.

Deevey, E. S. 1939. Studies on Connecticut lake sediments: I. A postglacial climatic chronology for southern New England. Amer. Jour. Sci., **237**: 691–724.

——. 1941. Limnological studies in Connecticut: VI. The quantity and composition of the bottom fauna. Ecol. Monogr., **11**: 413–455.

——. 1942. Studies on Connecticut lake sediments: III. The biostratonomy of Linsley Pond. Amer. Jour. Sci., **240**: 233–264, 313–338.

Elton, C. 1927. Animal Ecology. N. Y. Macmillan Co.

Francé, R. H. 1913. Das Edaphon, Untersuchungen zur Oekologie der bodenbewohnenden Mikroorganismen. Deutsch. Mikrolog. Gesellsch., Arbeit. aus d. Biol. Inst., No. 2. Munich.

Friederichs, K. 1930. Die Grundfragen und Gesetzmässigkeiten der land- und forstwirtschaftlichen Zoologie. 2 vols. Berlin. Verschlag. Paul Parey.

Groschopf, P. 1936. Die postglaziale Entwicklung des Grosser Plöner Sees in Ostholstein auf Grund pollenanalytischer Sedimentuntersuchungen. Arch. Hydrobiol., **30**: 1–84.

Heinrich, K. 1934. Atmung und Assimilation im freien Wasser. Internat. Rev. ges. Hydrobiol. u. Hydrogr., **30**: 387–410.

Hentschel, E. 1933–1936. Allgemeine Biologie des Südatlantischen Ozeans. Wiss. Ergebn. Deutsch. Atlant. Exped. a. d. Forschungs- u. Vermessungsschiff "Meteor" 1925–1927. Bd. **XI**.

Hicks, P. A. 1934. Interaction of factors in the growth of *Lemna:* V. Some preliminary observations upon the interaction of temperature and light on the growth of *Lemna.* Ann. Bot., **48**: 515–523.

Hile, R. 1941. Age and growth of the rock bass *Ambloplites rupestris* (Rafinesque) in Nebish Lake, Wisconsin. Trans. Wisconsin Acad. Sci., Arts, Lett., **33**: 189–337.

Hutchinson, G. E. 1941. Limnological studies in Connecticut: IV. Mechanism of intermediary metabolism in stratified lakes. Ecol. Monogr., **11**: 21–60.

——. 1942. Recent Advances in Limnology (*in manuscript*).

—— and R. L. Lindeman. 1941. Biological efficiency in succession (Abstract). Bull. Ecol. Soc. Amer., **22**: 44.

—— and Anne Wollack. 1940. Studies on Connecticut lake sediments: II. Chemical analyses of a core from Linsley Pond, North Branford. Amer. Jour. Sci., **238**: 493–517.

Huxley, J. S. 1932. Problems of Relative Growth. N. Y. Dial Press.

Ivlev, V. S. 1939a. Transformation of energy by aquatic animals. Internat. Rev. ges. Hydrobiol. u. Hydrogr., **38**: 449–458.

——. 1939b. Balance of energy in carps. Zool. Zhurn. Moscow, **18**: 303–316.

Jacot, A. P. 1940. The fauna of the soil. Quart. Rev. Biol., **15**: 28–58.

Jenkin, B. M., C. H. Mortimer, and W. Pennington. 1941. The study of lake deposits. Nature, 147: 496–500.

Joffe, J. S. 1936. Pedology. New Brunswick, New Jersey. Rutgers Univ. Press.

Juday, C. 1922. Quantitative studies of the bottom fauna in the deeper waters of Lake Mendota. Trans. Wisconsin Acad. Sci., Arts, Lett., 20: 461–493.

——. 1940. The annual energy budget of an inland lake. Ecology, 21: 438–450.

Krogh, A. 1941. The Comparative Physiology of Respiratory Mechanisms. Philadelphia. Univ. Pennsylvania Press.

Lindeman, R. L. 1941a. The developmental history of Cedar Creek Bog, Minnesota. Amer. Midl. Nat., 25: 101–112.

——. 1941b. Seasonal food-cycle dynamics in a senescent lake. Amer. Midl. Nat., 26: 636–673.

Lohmann, H. 1912. Untersuchungen über das Pflanzen- und Tierleben der Hochsee, zugleich ein Bericht über die biologischen Arbeiten auf der Fahrt der "Deutschland" von Bremerhaven nach Buenos Aires. Veröffentl. d. Inst. f. Meereskunde, N.F., A. Geogr.-naturwissen. Reihe, Heft 1, 92 pp.

Lundegårdh, H. 1924. Kreislauf der Kohlensäure in der Natur. Jena. G. Fischer.

Meschkat, A. 1937. Abwasserbiologische Untersuchungen in einem Buhnenfeld unterhalb Hamburgs. Arch. Hydrobiol., 31: 399–432.

Moore, W. G. 1941. Studies on the feeding habits of fishes. Ecology, 22: 91–95.

Needham, J. 1931. Chemical Embryology. 3 vols. N. Y. Cambridge University Press.

Noddack, W. 1937. Der Kohlenstoff im Haushalt der Natur. Zeitschr. angew. Chemie, 50: 505–510.

Park, Thomas. 1941. The laboratory population as a test of a comprehensive ecological system. Quart. Rev. Biol., 16: 274–293, 440–461.

Rigg, G. B. 1940. Comparisons of the development of some Sphagnum bogs of the Atlantic coast, the interior, and the Pacific coast. Amer. Jour. Bot., 27: 1–14.

Riley, G. A. 1940. Limnological studies in Connecticut. III. The plankton of Linsley Pond. Ecol. Monogr., 10: 279–306.

——. 1941. Plankton studies. III. Long Island Sound. Bull. Bingham Oceanogr. Coll. 7 (3): 1–93.

Ruttner, F. 1937. Limnologische Studien an einigen Seen der Ostalpen. Arch. Hydrobiol., 32: 167–319.

Smith-Davidson, Vera. 1932. The effect of seasonal variability upon animal species in a deciduous forest succession. Ecol. Monogr., 2: 305–334.

Spoehr, H. A. 1926. Photosynthesis. N. Y. Chemical Catalogue Co.

Swingle, H. S., and E. V. Smith. 1940. Experiments on the stocking of fish ponds. Trans. North Amer. Wildlife Conf., 5: 267–276.

Tansley, A. G. 1935. The use and abuse of vegetational concepts and terms. Ecology, 16: 284–307.

Thienemann, A. 1918. Lebensgemeinschaft und Lebensraum. Naturw. Wochenschrift, N.F., 17: 282–290, 297–303.

——. 1926. Der Nahrungskreislauf im Wasser. Verh. deutsch. Zool. Ges., 31: 29–79. (or) Zool. Anz. Suppl., 2: 29–79.

——. 1939. Grundzüge einen allgemeinen Oekologie. Arch. Hydrobiol., 35: 267–285.

Thompson, D. H. 1941. The fish production of inland lakes and streams. Symposium on Hydrobiology, pp. 206–217. Madison. Univ. Wisconsin Press.

Tutin, T. G. 1941. The hydrosere and current concepts of the climax. Jour. Ecol. 29: 268–279.

Vernadsky, V. I. 1929. La biosphere. Paris. Librairie Felix Alcan.

——. 1939. On some fundamental problems of biogeochemistry. Trav. Lab. Biogeochem. Acad. Sci. URSS, 5: 5–17.

Waksman, S. A. 1941. Aquatic bacteria in relation to the cycle of organic matter in lakes. Symposium on Hydrobiology, pp. 86–105. Madison. Univ. Wisconsin Press.

Welch, P. S. 1935. Limnology. N. Y. McGraw-Hill Co.

Wesenberg-Lund, C. 1912. Über einige eigentümliche Temperaturverhaltnisse in der Litoralregion. . . . Internat. Rev. ges. Hydrobiol. u. Hydrogr., 5: 287–316.

Williams, E. C. 1941. An ecological study of the floor fauna of the Panama rain forest. Bull. Chicago Acad. Sci., 6: 63–124.

Wimpenny, R. S. 1941. Organic polarity: some ecological and physiological aspects. Quart. Rev. Biol., 16: 389–425.

ZoBell, C. E., and C. B. Feltham. 1938. Bacteria as food for certain marine invertebrates. Jour. Marine Research, 1: 312–327.

### Addendum

While this, his sixth completed paper, was in the press, Raymond Lindeman died after a long illness on 29 June, 1942, in his twenty-seventh year. While his loss is grievous to all who knew him, it is more fitting here to dwell on the achievements of his brief working life. The present paper represents a synthesis of Lindeman's work on the modern ecology and past history of a small senescent lake in Minnesota. In studying this locality he came to realize, as others before him had done, that the most profitable method of analysis lay in reduction of all the interrelated biological events to energetic terms. The attempt to do this led him far beyond the immediate problem in hand, and in stating his conclusions he felt that he was providing a program for further studies. Knowing that one man's life at best is too short for intensive studies of more than a few localities, and before the manuscript was completed, that he might never return again to the field, he wanted others to think in the same terms as he had found so stimulating, and for them to collect material that would confirm, extend, or correct his theoretical conclusions. The present contribution does far more than this, as here for the first time, we have the interrelated dynamics of a biocoenosis presented in a form that is amenable to a productive abstract analysis. The question, for instance, arises, "What determines the length of a food chain?"; the answer given is admittedly imperfect, but it is far more important to have seen that there is a real problem of this kind to be solved. That the final statement of the structure of a biocoenosis consists of pairs of numbers, one an integer determining the level, one a fraction determining the efficiency, may even give some hint of an undiscovered type of mathematical treatment of biological communities. Though Lindeman's work on the ecology and history of Cedar Bog Lake is of more than local interest, and will, it is hoped, appear of even greater significance when the notes made in the last few months of his life can be coordinated and published, it is to the present paper that we must turn as the major contribution of one of the most creative and generous minds yet to devote itself to ecological science.

G. EVELYN HUTCHINSON.

YALE UNIVERSITY.

# ECOLOGICAL ENERGY RELATIONSHIPS AT THE
# POPULATION LEVEL*

## L. B. SLOBODKIN

Department of Zoology, University of Michigan, Ann Arbor, Michigan

I will be concerned with the ecologically significant energy relationships of single species populations. The theoretical analysis and data deal primarily with laboratory populations of *Daphnia pulex*, but I believe that the conclusions have significance for nature as will be indicated in the discussion.

The number and kind of organisms found in nature is variable from year to year and even from day to day. Despite this variability, it can be said that a sufficiently detailed and temporally extensive examination of any one species, or even of an isolated population of a species, will show that the number of organisms and volume of protoplasm represented by that species or population remain approximately constant. Some populations may vary in size in a cyclic way, either annually or possibly with some other period; others may vary in a random way, but in any case there is some definite mean population size, if data over a period of the order of ten times the mean generation time is considered.

Mean population size does not represent an equilibrium value in the sense that the position of a pendulum bob at rest represents an equilibrium, but rather represents a steady state. The steady state can be characterized by the fact that it requires energy for its maintenance. Just as the steady state temperature gradients in a metal bar heated at one end would disappear in the absence of an energy source, so the steady state properties of the ecological world would vanish in the absence of the radiant energy of sunlight.

It is possible to conceive of a series of metal bars in contact at their ends, with the terminal bar converting radiant energy into heat and this heat then being transmitted by conduction through the whole series of bars. Again a steady state temperature gradient would characterize each bar. Similarly in nature radiant energy is converted into potential energy by the green plants and this potential energy is transmitted through a chain of organisms. There will be various steady state values characterizing this chain of organisms. We will be concerned with some of the values that are more or less immediately recognizable as functions of energy, in particular the potential energy, contained in the various single species populations, that is, the standing crops, and with the ratios between the various steady state rates of energy transfer in the system, that is, the efficiencies (Lindeman, 1942).

*Presented at "Interactions in Nature: A Symposium on Modern Ecology" at the meeting of the American Society of Naturalists, cosponsored by the Ecological Society of America and the American Society of Limnology and Oceanography, Chicago, Illinois, December 27–28, 1959.

I have confined myself to steady state values since a short period of very high ecological efficiency or standing crop maintenance has very little applicability to long term values that are likely to occur in nature. Non-steady state efficiencies or standing crops must eventually receive intensive study, but I feel that more immediate progress will be made by considering them as minor perturbations of the steady state values for the moment.

Examining the analogy between metal bars, electric wires, flowing water and other inanimate models on one hand and an ecological community on the other, it is seen that the analogy breaks down almost immediately. In a heat transmission system or in an electric wiring diagram the continued physical existence of the energy transmitting elements is not contingent on the maintenance of energy flow. In a biological system, if energy flow ceases there is almost immediate dissolution of the system's components.

The process of energy flow in ecological systems does not lend itself to discussion in terms of gradients or flow diagrams, except on the most rudimentary level. Flow diagrams are primarily suitable to discussion of heat or radiant energy transport in which physical contact or simply suitable geometric distribution of the physical elements will permit energy flow to occur. In ecological interactions the energy involved is in the form of potential energy, which in general can not be transmitted between parts of a system without displacement or distortion of the physical elements. That is, energy flows from a plant population to an animal population only when a concrete plant or piece of plant is physically removed into the body of some particular animal. It only remains for the ecologist, if he is to concern himself with energy at all, to develop his theories and concepts on a biological basis rather than by assuming the direct applicability of the laws developed for the simple systems of physics and electronics.

Even such elementary concepts as efficiency and energy, and such universal generalizations as the second law of thermodynamics have very peculiar properties on the level of the ecological community.

I will therefore discuss the concepts of efficiency, energy and entropy as they apply to ecology. Ecological efficiency will then be shown to have at least three distinct, operationally defined meanings. These three different concepts of efficiency will be evaluated from the data on *Daphnia pulex*. I will then suggest that certain kinds of efficiency are actually constant for most populations in nature. I will finish with some speculations on the relation between energetics and the future development of a complete theory of community ecology.

### AN ELEMENTARY CLARIFICATION OF EFFICIENCY, ENTROPY AND ENERGY IN ECOLOGICAL SYSTEMS

The superficial simplicity of the concept of ecological efficiency requires careful analysis.

The efficiency of an energy machine is easy to define. A machine, in general, is designed and constructed to do a particular kind of work or to produce a particular form of energy. The ratio of the output to the input (both in energy units) is the efficiency of the machine. The output of a moving locomotive is in energy used to overcome the forces that tend to stop the train; the input is in the potential energy of coal or oil burned in the process. The output of a light bulb is in visible radiation; the input in electrical energy and the ratio of the two is the efficiency. But notice that it is possible to read by the light of a coal locomotive's fire box or to warm oneself at a cloth-draped light bulb. These do not seem particularly clever ways to read or to keep warm, but they are conceivable. From the standpoint of a moronic bookworm the efficiency of a locomotive might be measured as the ratio of visible radiant energy from the fire box to potential energy consumption. For most locomotives this efficiency is lower than our initial calculations of the efficiency of the locomotive. Our chilled illiterate in front of the draped light bulb might measure efficiency as total radiant energy output over total electrical energy input and this ratio would be higher than our original estimate of the efficiency of the bulb. I conclude from this that the magnitude of an efficiency need have nothing to do with the importance of the process to which the efficiency ratio refers, even in the case of a machine.

An organism must do many things that require energy. Movement of its internal parts, movement of itself in its environment, producing new protoplasm to compensate for attrition of its own body, adding new protoplasm to its own body and producing offspring are all energy utilizing processes involving single organisms. On the level of the individual we will be concerned with the efficiency of the last two of these only.

This limitation of our concern is due to a peculiar property of ecological interactions. In order to maintain an ecological community of several kinds of animals and plants at a steady state, the new protoplasm made by any population of organisms of any one species, above and beyond replacement requirements, must be consumed during the process of maintaining the steady state of one or more of the other species present. The new protoplasm produced by any population is in one sense a sum of the new growth occurring in all the individuals of that population. I will therefore consider only new protoplasm to be an ecologically useful kind of potential energy and will largely ignore other possible uses of energy on the individual level.

It is impossible to refer to *the efficiency* of a population. The term must, at all times, be qualified. We can speak only of the efficiency of producing energy in some form which we arbitrarily consider useful (the output) from some other form which we arbitrarily define as useless (the input).

The concept of energy is used rather loosely in ecological literature, and recently the concepts of entropy, negative entropy and information have been used equally loosely. We have statements in print that organisms live on order or that communities consume negative entropy, eat information, etc. It therefore seems appropriate to present a statement of the role of energy in ecology.

Radiant energy is absorbed by green plants and part of this is converted to potential energy by the process of photosynthesis. The slow conversion of this potential energy to kinetic energy permits ecological communities to survive.

Particular compounds in the plant will be converted into other compounds in the herbivore. To the extent that individual reversible chemical reactions are being considered the various terms in the equation

$$\Delta H = \Delta F + T \Delta S \tag{1}$$

may be evaluated and the change in entropy per mole computed. An appropriate summation of the entropy contributions of all the reactions that occur in the process of incorporating plant material into the herbivore might be considered the entropy production of the herbivore, were it not that:

1. All of the reactions tend to interact with each other.
2. Phase differences and structural restrictions of complicated kinds occur in both plants and animals and the reactions producing these phase differences are, in general, not reversible in any practical sense, at least in the aggregate.

In other words, it is very difficult by simply supplying energy to get an organism to undigest a meal and thereby measure the $\Delta F$ associated with the digestion process. The entropy associated with the process of food assimilation is therefore not conveniently measurable.

It is possible to consider the state of all materials entering an organism and the state of the material leaving the organism, duplicate the degradation process in a reversible way and make the appropriate entropy calculation. To my knowledge this has never been explicitly done for all of the ingested and waste products of any particular organism. It is clear, in principle, that it could be done and if it were done we would find an increase in entropy associated with this passage through the organism as illustrated:

$$\Delta H \rightarrow \boxed{\text{organism}} \rightarrow \Delta F + T \Delta S + Q'$$

$$\Delta H = \Delta F + Q' + T \Delta S \tag{2}$$

This requires explication. $\Delta H$ can be defined as calories ingested per unit time and $\Delta F$ in this context is the calories egested which are still of use to organisms as a supply of energy. $T \Delta S + Q'$ are the caloric equivalent of the heat produced in the utilization of the energy $\Delta H$.

$T \Delta S$ is the heat that would be produced in the various transformations occurring in the organism on the assumption that all reactions were reversible, independent, and of infinitely slow occurrence. None of these conditions is met.

$Q'$ is the heat produced from friction within the organism and from work done by the organism on its environment. In principle, $Q'$ can be evaluated experimentally, but the problem is technically difficult; and except for very simple systems is not likely to be done. It is possible, in an ecological steady state, to write the equation:

Caloric equivalent of the potential energy ingested = caloric equivalent of the potential energy removed from the population by egestion, predation, mortality, etc., plus the heat produced by the population.

It may be legitimate to equate this heat to entropy, but it is not clear what proportion of the potential energy ingested actually shows up as entropy. Estimates of anywhere from two to 50 per cent might be offered.

The notion of entropy content of a living organism is extremely complex. Normal thermodynamic theories apply to an equilibrium state, which is equivalent in one sense to death. The theory of thermodynamics of steady states (Denbigh, 1951) is not yet capable of handling elaborate multiphasic systems. The Onsager equations which permit some development of steady state thermodynamics depend on the rigorous definition of fluxes and on their associated forces.

Any energy gradient of an appropriate sort can be considered a generalized force. This·is particularly evident in the relation between a temperature gradient and heat flow. The interesting ecological energy flow is in the form of potential energy. Potential energy can have a gradient, as in the glucose gradient in a single cell. Ecologically, however, the gradient is a rather coarse histogram, of standing crop vs. trophic level. The precise procedure for the interpretation of this histogram as a generalized force seems unclear.

The fluxes can, therefore, be stated but the forces can only be dealt with on an almost metaphorical level in ecology. While metaphor leads to certain sorts of insight it does not have predictive power.

A further complication in the application of thermodynamics to steady state systems has been considered by Foster, Rappoport and Trucco (1957) who find that Prigogine's theorem, which states that steady state systems tend to a condition of minimum entropy production, is not applicable to certain types of feedback systems. It is now generally conceded that individual organisms, populations of organisms, and natural communities must be treated as complex feedback systems and it is quite likely that Prigogine's theorem does not apply to ecological systems, or at least its validity can not simply be assumed.

Potential energy ($\Delta H$) can be approximately measured by direct combustion of dried tissue. A certain amount of entropy ought to be subtracted from the combustion calories but this is not practical for reasons indicated above. Some free energy is lost prior to combustion in the drying process but this has not yet been evaluated.

When I speak of the energy content of an organism I will be referring to the calories released by burning that organism under normal atmospheric conditions and measured as heat. This is equal to the difference in potential energy per gram between dried protoplasm and the various oxidation products of that protoplasm and includes both the free energy and the entropy.

When I refer to a flow of energy through a population I will be considering only the steady state in which the rate of energy accumulation is zero.

### THEORY OF ECOLOGICAL EFFICIENCIES AND THEIR INTERACTIONS

A population of organisms is characterized by new animals being born, by animals dying or being consumed (by other animals or by man). I will be concerned with the potential energy content of the animals removed from the population by predators or man as a useful energy output and will consider the food consumed by the population as the energy input. That is, when I speak of ecological efficiency, I am assuming the viewpoint of a predator.

In one sense, the removal of an animal by a predator can be considered a divergence of energy from the other possible roles it might play in the population. In particular, the greater the rate at which yield is removed from the population the smaller the standing crop that the population is capable of maintaining. The yield to the predator divided by the difference between the energy used in maintaining a population in the absence of predation and that used in maintaining the same population under predation will be called the population efficiency.

The ratio of the potential energy in an individual organism to the potential energy utilized in its birth and growth will be called growth efficiency, or individual growth efficiency.

The interrelation between these three concepts of efficiency is discussed below.

The gross inflow will be in units of calories per time per volume and will be designated $I_F$. This will be the amount of food made available to the population from some outside source. In nature food is available to an animal population as a result of the activities of some other population or populations of plants, animals or both. In the laboratory $I_F$ is the potential energy in the food made available to the population by the experimenter. The population does not necessarily consume all of this food. In nature part of it may pass through the ecological space of a particular population without being altered at all. In the laboratory the experimenter may periodically remove excess food.

We must therefore distinguish between $I_F$, the food available, and I, the energy input or ingested food. $I_F \geq I$ is always trivially valid.

I is the potential energy ingested per day per population and therefore is slightly different in concept from $I_F$, unless the volume considered only contains one population. In experimental situations discussed here this difference is not significant.

Population size is effectively constant at a steady state in the absence of cropping, fishing and predation. In a typical experimental study of efficiency the population is cropped and censused at regular intervals so that a plot of population size as a function of time would be saw-toothed. For our present discussion we will consider the population size as the size at the base of the saw teeth. This is equivalent to assuming that no energy must be expended in maintaining those animals which are destined to be cropped at the next census. This assumption is not dangerous so long as the ratio $\left(\dfrac{\text{yield/census interval}}{\text{population size}}\right)$ is small. (See Armstrong, 1960.)

Let P′ be the caloric content of the standing crop of a population subjected to some arbitrary predation process and let P be the caloric content of the appropriate control population in the absence of predation. P and P′

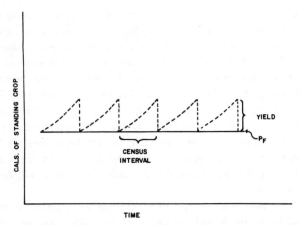

FIGURE 1. The term standing crop ($P_F$) is used as indicated in this diagram, ignoring the maintenance cost of the animals destined to constitute yield. A more precise but less convenient measure of standing crop would be the dotted line.

have the dimensions of calories and represent the potential energy maintained in the living protoplasm of the population. Occasionally we will use the letters P and P′ as names for populations.

In order to maintain living protoplasm, energy must be expended. The greater this energy expenditure per calorie of standing crop per time the smaller will be the value of P that can be maintained by a given energy income per day (I).

In general, increase of I will imply increase of P. The precise relation between P and I is not obvious *a priori* since the maintenance cost per calorie of standing crop may be a complicated function of the interactions between individual organisms in the population.

In the most general case, since there is a unique age distribution and total number of organisms corresponding to any steady state caloric content we can write

(3) $$I = Pc + P^2c' + P^3c'' \ldots$$

where c is the proportion of the total cost in (calories/calorie day) of maintaining one calorie of standing crop which is assignable to first order interactions in the population, c′ the proportion assignable to second order interactions, etc.

It has been experimentally demonstrated in Daphnia that only first order interactions are significant over a wide range of population densities (Slobodkin, 1954) so that for the present discussion (3) reduces to

(3′) $$I = Pc.$$

When a population is subjected to predation it either becomes extinct or it comes to a new steady state caloric content P′. If the population can survive steady predation potential energy now leaves the population at some steady state rate as yield to the predator. The ratio of yield (Y) in calories per day to I is the ecological efficiency.

The age and size of the individuals that make up the yield is determined by the interaction between the predator's method and intensity of capturing the yield animals and the population dynamics of the prey and predator.

Assuming that I is not altered by predation, we can take account of the change in maintenance cost associated with predation by writing

$$(4) \qquad I = P'(c + \Delta c) + (P')^2(c' + \Delta c') + \dots$$

and in the case of Daphnia populations

$$(4') \qquad I = P'c + P'\Delta c .$$

Assume the prey to consist only of animals of age i, taken by the predator at the rate $Y_i$ calories/day. Then

$$(5) \qquad P'\Delta c = \frac{Y_i}{E_{pi}}$$

where $E_{pi}$ is the efficiency, in one sense, of this predation process. An efficiency of this type will be referred to as a population efficiency. Since

$$(5') \qquad E_{pi} = \frac{Y_i}{P'\Delta c}$$

population efficiency can be interpreted as the ratio of yield of a particular kind to the increase of maintenance cost associated with the production of that yield. It will vary with the kind of organism taken as yield. It is independent of the intensity of predation so long as the linearity implicit in equation (4') holds.

The precise value of $E_{pi}$ depends on growth and survival and their interaction with age in an intimate way which will be indicated below.

In order to clarify the meaning of $E_{pi}$ we must examine an individual organism more closely. At the time an individual organism begins to take nourishment, say age j, it already represents the end product of a series of metabolic processes, all of which have involved the degradation of potential energy. As it grows to some arbitrary age, say i, it will consume more potential energy and may have increased its caloric content. In any case the total potential energy that must be used to replace an animal of age $i > j$ will be greater than that required to replace an animal of age j.

If we designate the total energetic cost of replacing an animal age i as $\frac{S_i}{E_i}$, in which $S_i$ is the caloric content of the animal age i, then $E_i$ is the growth efficiency of this animal. The caloric content ($S_i$) is usually proportional to the size of the animal. $E_i$ can be evaluated as the inverse of the total calories consumed in the production of one calorie of protoplasm at age i and is the "individual growth efficiency" of an animal aged i. It varies with the age and feeding rate of the animal concerned and with the energy expended by the parents of that individual in producing it.

The concept of growth efficiency has suffered in the past from failure to specify precisely the time interval over which the growth of the animal is to be considered. Here we have taken this as the entire life span over which an energetic cost can be meaningfully associated with the individual, following the suggestion of Armstrong (1960).

The relation between $E_i$ and $E_{pi}$ can be clarified as follows.

Let $N_o$ and $N'_o$ be the number of newborn animals produced per day in populations P and P' respectively, and let $l_x$ and $l'_x$ be the per cent survival to age x in the two populations respectively. Define $q_x$ as

$$q_x = \frac{l_x - l_{x+1}}{l_x}$$

and correspondingly define $q'_x$.

Also let

(6) $\qquad\qquad d_x = q_x l_x$ and similarly for $d'_x$

and

(7) $\qquad\qquad D_x = d_x N_o$ and similarly for $D'_x$.

The deaths per day in population P is $\sum_o^\infty D_x$ and in population P', $\sum_o^\infty D'_x$. The primary characteristic of a steady state population is that births and deaths are equal and there is no change in mean total biomass with time.

The caloric cost per day of replacing the dying individuals and maintaining biomass constancy is $\sum \frac{D_x S_x}{E_x}$ in population P and assuming that caloric content as a function of age and growth efficiency are both dependent on predation $\sum \frac{D'_x S'_x}{E'_x}$ in population P'.

In other words

(8) $\qquad\qquad I = \sum_o^\infty \frac{D_x S_x}{E_x} = Pc$

$$= \sum_o^\infty \frac{D'_x S'_x}{E'_x} = P'(c + \Delta c)$$

whence

(9) $\qquad\qquad c = \frac{1}{P} \sum_o^\infty \frac{D_x S_x}{E_x}$

and

(10) $\qquad\qquad \Delta c = \frac{1}{P'}\left(\sum_o^\infty \frac{D'_x S'_x}{E'_x}\right) - \frac{1}{P}\left(\sum_o^\infty \frac{D_x S_x}{E_x}\right)$

and substituting (10) in (5') we define the population efficiency of animals age i as

(11)
$$E_{pi} = \frac{Y_i}{\left(\sum_{0}^{\infty} \frac{D'_x S'_x}{E'_x}\right) - \frac{P'}{P}\left(\sum_{0}^{\infty} \frac{D_x S_x}{E_x}\right)}$$

or if food ingestion is constant under predation simply:

(11′)
$$E_{pi} = \frac{Y_i}{I\left(1 - \frac{P'}{P}\right)}$$

From equation (11) it can be seen that population efficiency varies inversely with the depletion of standing crop population size associated with the removal of the yield. Decrease in life expectancy with predation also lowers population efficiency. A predator would be acting with maximum prudence if he removed yield from his prey in such a way as to maximize population efficiency.

We will return to this concept after we have considered ecological efficiency. The commonest usage of the term efficiency in ecological literature is the ratio of the energy per unit time taken from some population (the prey) as yield by some other population (the predator) to the energy per unit time ingested by the prey population. I am deliberately ignoring the often made distinction between ingestion and assimilation, since the meaning of ingestion seems fairly clear while it is an almost arbitrary matter to decide when, or what portion of, a particular mouthful of food is assimilated.

Food chain efficiency (a term borrowed from LaMont Cole) is similar to ecological efficiency except that the denominator is the food available ($I_F$) rather than the food ingested ($I$).

Ecological efficiency ($E$) is therefore defined by $\frac{Y}{I}$. Since population efficiency is defined for any constant predation method, if $I$ is not changed by predation

(12)
$$E = E_p\left(1 - \frac{P'}{P}\right),$$

from which it is clear that for any predation method

(13)
$$E \le E_p .$$

The relation $E = E_p$ will hold only for a scavenger or for a predator which replaces some other source of mortality. If there is any selective advantage in maintaining a large standing crop, a predator population will tend to maximize yield from its prey. This is equivalent to maximizing food chain efficiency $\left(\frac{Y}{I_F}\right)$. As predation becomes more intense, the food consuming capacity and standing crop of the prey population will decrease. The decrease of prey standing crop associated with a given yield can be minimized by the predator if he chooses his yield in such a way as to maximize population efficiency. This can generally be accomplished by taking yield animals which are about to die in any case, so that their replacement cost would have to be paid even in the absence of the predator.

### APPLICATION OF THE THEORY

First order evaluations of the various concepts of efficiency have been made in laboratory populations of *Daphnia pulex* by Richman (1958), Armstrong (1960) and Slobodkin (1959). All three workers have depended on the caloric determinations of *D. pulex* and *Chlamydomonas reinhardi* made by Richman.

Richman (1958) analyzed the growth and feeding of *Daphnia pulex*.

Slobodkin provided an initial theoretical analysis of laboratory predation experiments (1959) and that analysis has been considerably amplified and modified in the present paper.

Armstrong has reconsidered certain of the theoretical assumptions of both Richman and Slobodkin and has amplified their calculations, in addition to providing new data on growth and predation.

All three workers dealt with a system consisting of *Daphnia pulex* and *Chlamydomonas reinhardi* in which the Daphnia were maintained in conditioned tap water and the algae were grown on sterile agar. Algae was fed to the Daphnia by washing it off the agar, measuring its optical density with a photometer and adding an aliquot of suspension to the Daphnia. Any of the three above cited papers will provide more detailed information on culture techniques.

Richman collected 50 mg. dry samples of Chlamydomonas. These were combined with 250 mg. of benzoic acid and burned in a semi-micro calorimeter bomb. Twelve determinations gave a mean of 5289 cal./gm. on a dry weight basis or 5506 on an ash-free dry weight basis. These figures are very close to those for other Chlorophyceae. The mean of 17 analysis of five species reported by Ketchum and Redfield (1949) is 5340 cal./gm. dry weight and 6154 cal./gm. ash-free dry weight. The caloric content of one Chlamydomonas cell is given by Richman as $1.308 \times 10^{-6}$ cal.

He sorted *Daphnia pulex* into three size categories. Dried samples of 10–25 mg. were combined with c. 275 mg. of benzoic acid and burned. Mean caloric contents per gram were $4059 \pm 203$, $4124 \pm 229$ and $5075 \pm 235$ respectively for animals of mean length 0.7, 1.3 and 1.8 mm.

Trama found from 5295 to 5975 cal./gm. in the may fly *Stenonema pulchellum* (Trama, 1957). Golley (undated mimeographed sheets) reports cal./gm. determinations for a variety of animals. The extremes are 1780 for the mud crab *Panopius herbsti* and 6273 for *Mus musculus*. Presumably the cal./gm. ash-free dry weight would be somewhat higher since all his reported values for whole Malacostraca seem low, indicating possible inclusion of the mineralized exoskeletons in the samples.

There is sufficiently close agreement between Richman's analyses and the various values reported by Golley and Ketchum and Redfield, to indicate that neither *Daphnia pulex* nor Chlamydomonas are at all extraordinary

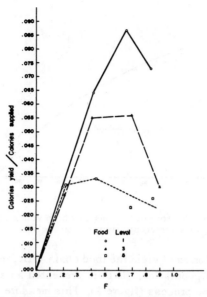

FIGURE 2a. Food chain efficiency on the ordinate vs. F on the abscissa for populations in which adult animals were preferentially removed as yield.

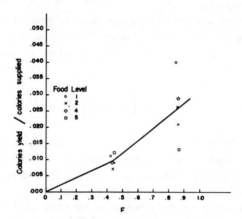

FIGURE 2b. Identical with 2a except that young animals were preferentially removed as yield.

in caloric content. This point is of some importance since I will later make the claim that ecological efficiencies are quite likely as similar as caloric contents.

Using Richman's caloric content data Slobodkin (1959) assumed three conversion constants which were used to translate numerical census and yield data, derived from 22 laboratory populations, into terms of calories. In addition, the number of Chlamydomonas cells provided for these populations was estimated and translated into calories by using Richman's value for calories per algal cell. This provides a direct estimate of $I_F$.

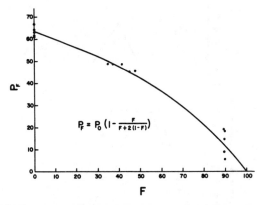

FIGURE 3. $P_F$, for populations in which young animals were preferentially removed, vs. F.

From $I_F$ and the calories of yield the food chain efficiency could be evaluated directly for each population. This is presented as a function of the intensity of the predation process (figure 2). This measure of fishing intensity is defined elsewhere (Slobodkin, 1957, 1959) and for present purposes we need simply indicate that it is a fishing rate set as a per cent of the births occurring in the population.

Daphnia population standing crops are linearly proportional to their food consumption in the absence of predation (Slobodkin, 1954). There is a simple relation between F and standing crop when all food is consumed, namely

$$(14) \qquad \frac{P_F}{P_O} = \left(1 - \frac{F}{2 - F}\right)$$

(Slobodkin, 1957) figure 3. These two relations were assumed generally valid for Daphnia populations and were used to estimate the proportion of the food provided ($I_F$) that was actually eaten. From this, values of I, the food ingested, could be computed for each population.

Armstrong (1960) computed food ingestion for some of the populations discussed by Slobodkin (1959) on the basis of filtration rate estimates. Comparative values are shown in table 1 and are seen to be of the same order of

TABLE 1

| Population | Armstrong (1960) | Slobodkin (1959) | |
| --- | --- | --- | --- |
| | | I | I′ |
| 1.25 A | 8.1 | 8.3 | 8.6 |
| 1.50 A | 8.1 | 7.1 | 7.9 |
| 1.75 A | 8.1 | 8.1 | 7.7 |
| 1.90 A | 7.7 | 6.2 | 4.9 |
| 1.50 Y | 8.1 | 8.1 | 9.0 |
| 1.90 Y | 8.0 | 7.3 | 9.5 |

magnitude, but in general somewhat lower estimates of I are derived by the method of Slobodkin than by the more direct method of Armstrong.

Having estimates of I/four days, standing crop calories and also yield/four days of small animals, large animals and eggs, for 22 experimental populations, an equation of the form

$$(15) \qquad I = P'c + \sum \frac{Y_i}{E_{pi}}$$

was set up for each population. The subscript i can take the values A for large animals, S for small animals and E for eggs.

This system of 22 equations was then reduced to a set of four equations:

$$(16) \qquad \begin{aligned}
\sum_{1}^{22} P'I &= (c) \sum (P')^2 + \frac{\sum P'Y_A}{E_{pA}} + \frac{\sum P'Y_Y}{E_{pY}} + \frac{\sum P'Y_E}{E_{pE}} \\
\sum Y_A I &= (c) \sum Y_A P' + \frac{\sum Y_A{}^2}{E_{pA}} + \frac{\sum Y_A Y_Y}{E_{pY}} + \frac{\sum Y_A Y_E}{E_{pE}} \\
\sum Y_Y I &= (c) \sum Y_Y P' + \frac{\sum Y_Y Y_A}{E_{pA}} + \frac{\sum Y_Y{}^2}{E_{pA}} + \frac{\sum Y_Y Y_E}{E_{pE}} \\
\sum Y_E I &= (c) \sum Y_E P' + \frac{\sum Y_E Y_A}{E_{pA}} + \frac{\sum Y_E Y_Y}{E_{pY}} + \frac{\sum Y_E{}^2}{E_{pE}}
\end{aligned}$$

This set of equations was then solved for c, and the three $E_{pi}$.

$$c = 1.68 \text{ cal./cal. day}, \quad E_{pA} = .48, \quad E_{pY} = .036, \quad E_{pE} = .062.$$

We have implicitly assumed that the increments in standing crop maintenance cost associated with the various kinds of yield are additive. This assumption probably does not hold at high rates of yield production but precise analysis of the interaction has not yet been made. The $E_{pi}$ are dimensionless, while c has the dimensions $\frac{\text{cal.}}{\text{cal.} \times \text{days}}$

The values $E_{pi}$ found from equation (16) are the population efficiencies that would presumably be associated with predation that took only one category of organism as yield. The calculated value of c successfully predicted the mean standing crop of five control populations which did not enter directly into the analysis of equation (15). (Observed 4.8, calculated 4.7). The control populations were used in computing I for each population by means of the relation shown in figure 3.

There also exists a population efficiency for any distribution of the age and size of yield organisms at a steady state in a particular population.

From our previous assumptions and equations (11) and (14) this can be determined for each population, as

$$(17) \qquad E_p = \frac{\frac{2Y}{F} - Y}{I} \, .$$

The only explicit free variables in this equation are Y and F, since I has already been adjusted in value by the use of (14). In addition, the age and

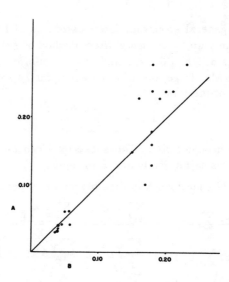

FIGURE 4. The ordinate (A) is given by $E_p = \dfrac{\dfrac{2Y}{F} - Y}{I}$ . The abscissa (B)

is $E_p = \sum \dfrac{Y_i/\sum Y_i}{E_{pi}}$ . The line assumes A = B.

size distribution of the yield are free to vary from population to population, thereby permitting the estimation of $E_p$ from the composition of the yield and the $E_{pi}$ as

$$(18) \qquad \frac{1}{E_p} = \sum \frac{Y_i/\sum Y_i}{E_{pi}}$$

The relation between population efficiency estimated from (17) and from the relative composition of the yield (18) is shown in figure 4.

The I′ values listed in table 1 are the result of substituting c and the $E_{pi}$ from the solution of equation (16) back into equation (15) for each population and solving for the input. The fact that the individual values I′ tend to diverge from Armstrong's estimates more than do the values of I must be attributed to non-linear effects. Ecological efficiency, expressed as $\dfrac{Y}{I'}$ is presented in figure 5 as a maximum estimate of ecological efficiency. The maximum estimate obtained is 12.5 per cent and it seems clear that ecological efficiency would not exceed 14 per cent under any conceivable experimental circumstances.

Values for ecological efficiency of animals in the field, summarized by Patten (1959) include a value of 75 per cent from Teal (1957) which seems almost impossible, a rather high value of 21 per cent (Lindeman, 1942) and eight other non-zero values ranging from 5.5 per cent to 13.3 per cent. There is no significant relation between trophic level and efficiency in these eight values. Top trophic levels have zero ecological efficiency by definition.

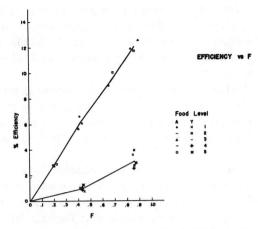

FIGURE 5. A maximum estimate of ecological efficiency in the Daphnia populations. Ordinate: $Y/I'$; abscissa: F.

The Daphnia experimental maximum is therefore in good accord with other data. It seems likely on general grounds that any population in nature will be producing yield at close to its maximum steady state efficiency.

Combining life table data with growth data Armstrong could compute a table of $E_i$ for the age categories "eggs," "young," "small," "large" and "adult." The process of solution was remarkably ingenious but would involve excessive digression to present here. These efficiencies are presented diagrammatically in figure 6, with the omission of the data for eggs.

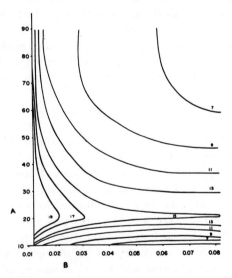

FIGURE 6. Individual growth efficiency × 100 of *Daphnia pulex* as a function of Chlamydomonas concentration in thousands of cells per ml. (ordinate) and the caloric content of the animals (abscissa). (Using data from Armstrong, 1960).

In excessively low concentrations of algae, growth efficiency is low, since the effort involved in feeding is not compensated adequately by the food acquired. As algal concentrations increase, individual efficiencies increase and then decrease as the rate of ingestion of food exceeds the capacity of the gut to digest the food.

Individual growth efficiencies in Daphnia are somewhat higher in maximum value than ecological efficiencies. They are dependent on the food consumption and growth of individual animals as a function of time and on the energetic cost of producing an egg. (See Armstrong, 1960; Slobodkin, 1959, Appendix B.)

The rather startling difference in age dependence between population efficiency and growth efficiency is explicable in terms of the distribution of life expectancy and food consumption as a function of age. Frank, Boll and Kelly (1957) and Pratt (1943) have shown that Daphnia life expectancy decreases as a function of age, after the first week of life. Various workers (Richman, 1958; Ryther, 1954) have shown the rate of filtration to be considerably greater for an adult Daphnia than for a small Daphnia. • Removal of an adult Daphnia will therefore be expected to make relatively little difference in the mean life expectancy of the animals in the population, not only because the adult animals' probability of survival in the absence of predation is not particularly high but also because its removal results in a food increase for the survivors which tends to lengthen their life expectancy. This, in effect, decreases the denominator of equation (11). At the same time the large size of an adult tends to increase the numerator. The older and bigger an animal gets, the greater this effect. To remove animals that are growing slowly, have lived most of their time and have a low reproductive value (see Fisher, 1958) is the epitome of prudent predation and therefore has a high population efficiency. The consumption of old sows will do little to deplete a pig population, while consuming suckling pig in equal quantity will be disastrous, despite the high growth efficiency of the piglet and the low growth efficiency of the sow. This may be verified at any meat market.

## CONCLUSIONS

Three types of efficiency have been defined. These are:

1. Ecological efficiency, the steady state ratio of yield to food ingested. This is of primary interest in analysis of natural community interactions. There is some reason to believe that ecological efficiency, at least in aquatic environments, will always have values of from five to 15 per cent.

2. Population efficiency, the steady state ratio of yield to the alteration in population maintenance produced by the removal process. The precise value of population efficiency will depend on the age distribution of the animals removed and the population and growth dynamics of the population in question. It may have values greater than one, under some circumstances. In Daphnia it varies from four per cent for the removal of young animals to

48 per cent for old animals. It is of primary interest in establishing criteria for the removal of yield, by relating efficiency to standing crop size.

3. Growth efficiency, the ratio of the calories in an individual organism to the calories expended in the course of its development. This is dependent on a variety of physiological responses of the organism to its immediate environment and has no direct relation to community dynamics. In Daphnia the extreme values found by Armstrong (1960) are 37 per cent for eggs at 20,000 algal cells per ml. and six per cent for adults at algal concentrations of 70,000 cells per ml.

The Daphnia values for all three types of efficiency may be considered typical, at least until more data are available for other species, since the ecological efficiencies determined from Daphnia seem of the same order as those determined from various natural situations.

SPECULATION

A single laboratory population requires approximately two to five hours of work per week for a year, not counting data reduction time or effort. A significant number of populations must be run in any one experiment.

Field studies are even more time consuming and expensive. The laboratory suffers from a lack of reality and the field from a lack of repeatability. At those points where concepts are comparable, the Daphnia laboratory studies agree with various field studies, enhancing my faith in the applicability of the laboratory and the reliability of the field.

As the phenomena that cry for explanation by the physiologist and biochemist are the simple observational facts of animal life, so the phenomena that must be predictable from any ecological theory are the facts of natural history and species abundance distributions. So far we are a long way from explaining these facts. The hope is raised by the present study that just as the metabolism of all organisms turned out to be essentially the same, so the economy of all populations may turn out to be roughly the same. The only way to tell is to repeat these rather painful studies on as many organisms as possible in the laboratory, if possible with considerable increase in precision. I expect to find that ecological efficiency will have approximately the same maximum throughout the animal kingdom, that growth efficiency will vary as a function of age to the same degree as growth rate and that population efficiency as a function of age will vary somewhat more widely, just as population growth curves are more variable than individual growth curves.

In further field studies, it is more difficult to make clear predictions of the pattern that future data will show. I can, however, make a guess. Sampling errors and errors in the conversion of animals to energy units and errors due to failure to have steady state data will all diminish.

In my own laboratory, Richman and I are getting equipment in operating order which will permit us to measure the calories released on combustion of tissue samples weighing as little as four mg. Golley, in Georgia, is now collecting data on larger animals. In a few years it should be possible to convert biomass data from field studies directly into energetic units, not only for large animal studies but for studies of terrestrial and aquatic micro-fauna. I expect that the use of direct conversion constants for each species will considerably increase the precision of field studies of energetics.

Concurrently, the laboratory predation studies are now being repeated on two species of Hydra and on Chlorohydra. I hope that this will test the applicability of the efficiency values determined for Daphnia to carnivorous animals.

The apparent differences between the estimates of food chain efficiency of corresponding trophic levels in different communities will also tend to vanish. I would guess that herbivores in general will have an efficiency of from ten to 13 per cent. Higher trophic levels may quite likely have slightly lower efficiencies. The presently accepted order of magnitude for food chain efficiencies of from c. six to c. 15 per cent is almost certainly correct.

In the absence of yield removal, the corpses in a laboratory Daphnia population represent five per cent of the energy input. Even on high trophic levels, in which predation in the normal sense is not occurring, an efficiency of conversion to decomposer of the same order as the other efficiencies in the system might be expected.

Assuming that we do find constancy of the food chain efficiencies in a steady state community, what type of theoretical structure can be built with this information? By itself, it tells us relatively little that would not have been predictable from elementary thermodynamics or elementary biochemistry. In combination with other ecological information it may provide a set of restrictions that will severely limit the range of possible ecological speculation.

The basic theoretical problem of community ecology is to construct a model or metamodel (Slobodkin, 1958) based on a simple set of assumptions that will generate not only the steady state conditions of the biosphere at a particular instant but the responses of these steady states to various climatic and geologic perturbations. These responses will constitute a theoretical reconstruction of evolution and almost incidentally will be a guide to exploitation of the natural world by man.

It seems possible that the following ecological generalizations are valid.

1. Food chain efficiencies can only have a narrow range of values.

2. Species abundance distribution patterns can only take the form of distributions generated from the theory of interspecific competition (Hairston, 1959; MacArthur, 1957).

3. Pairs of competing species must have a certain minimum of ecological difference if they are to coexist in a steady state (Hutchinson, 1959).

If we now demand that all models of the ecological world that make any pretense to reality must meet all of these conditions simultaneously we will be saved from unbridled speculations and misleading metaphors.

To the degree that these and other generalizations hold we may eventually be able to turn to the mathematician or even to his idiot cousin, the IBM machine, and ask him, or it, to build us all the theoretical models which will meet our restrictions and still maintain steady states and evolve properly under perturbation. At that time, community and population ecology will enter the company of the exact sciences.

In the interim we must increase the precision of those measurements which we know must be made and test the range of applicability of those generalizations which now seem valid.

### SUMMARY

The energetic relation between different trophic levels and populations in a community involves primarily potential energy transfer in complex feedback systems, making the applicability of existing steady state thermodynamic theory questionable, since the requirements for direct evaluation of entropy are not met by ecological systems. The only form of energy considered here was potential energy.

The efficiency of a population does not have a unique meaning. Three different concepts of efficiency were defined and evaluated for *Daphnia pulex*. Two of these, the ecological efficiency and population efficiency, refer to the population level. The growth efficiency refers to individual organisms.

Ecological efficiency is a function of the rate of removal of yield and of the kind of yield animals removed. Population efficiency is a function of the kind of animals removed as yield and the interaction between these animals and the population. Growth efficiency does not depend on the removal of yield at all. It is a function of individual food consumption, growth rate and the energetic cost of reproduction.

These three are interrelated. In general, for a particular system of predation ecological efficiency is proportional to population efficiency. Population efficiency is related to the individual growth efficiency through the effect of the removal of animals on the maintenance cost per calorie of standing crop, which in turn is a function of growth efficiency.

The maximum ecological efficiencies found in the Daphnia experiments are of the same order as ecological efficiencies found in nature, implying that ecological efficiency is effectively constant. Presumably the observed value of c. ten per cent has selective significance.

In speculating on the future development of community ecology, I suggested that certain generalizations now available, including the approximate constancy of ecological efficiency, restrict the development of possible theories. When a sufficient number of these generalizations have been stated and tested a comprehensive predictive general theory of community ecology will appear, if only by the elimination of all conceivable theories whose predictions do not conform to the generalizations.

### ACKNOWLEDGMENTS

The studies reported here were initially supported by The Rockefeller Foundation and The Phoenix Memorial Project of the University of Michigan.

For the past three years they have been supported by the National Science Foundation.

I am grateful to the staff and graduate students that have participated in the community ecology seminar at the University of Michigan for their discussion of this work. Drs. Armstrong and Richman have been particularly helpful. Dr. Peter Ovenburg has criticized the mathematical presentation. Profs. G. E. Hutchinson, Anatol Rappoport and Karl Guthe have been liberal with their knowledge and encouragement.

LITERATURE CITED

Armstrong, J. T., 1960, Ph.D. dissertation, Department of Zoology. University, of Michigan, Ann Arbor, Mich.

Cole, L. C., 1959, Personal communication.

Denbigh, K. G., 1951, The thermodynamics of the steady state. 103 pp. Methuen & Co., London, England.

Fisher, R. A., 1958, The genetical theory of natural selection. pp. 27-30. Dover Publications, Inc., New York, N. Y.

Foster, C., A. Rappoport and E. Trucco, 1957, Some unsolved problems in the theory of non-isolated systems. General Systems 3: 9-29.

Frank, P. W., C. D. Boll and R. W. Kelly, 1957, Vital statistics of laboratory cultures of *Daphnia pulex* DeGeer as related to density. Physiol. Zool. 30: 287-305.

Golley, F. B., 1959, Table of caloric equivalents. Mimeographed, 7 pp. Available from the author. Department of Zoology, University of Georgia, Athens, Ga.

Hairston, N. G., 1959, Species abundance and community organization. Ecology 40: 404-416.

Hutchinson, G. E., 1959, Homage to Santa Rosalia or why there are so many kinds of animals. Amer. Nat. 93: 145-159.

Ketchum, B. H., and A. C. Redfield, 1949, Some physical and chemical characteristics of algae grown in mass culture. J. Cell. and Comp. Physiol. 33: 281-300.

Lindeman, R. L., 1942, The trophic-dynamic aspect of ecology. Ecology 23: 399-418.

MacArthur, R. H., 1957, On the relative abundance of bird species. Proc. Nat. Acad. Sci. U.S. 43: 293-295.

Patten, B. C., 1959, An introduction to the cybernetics of the ecosystem: the trophic-dynamic aspect. Ecology 40: 221-231.

Pratt, D. M., 1943, Analysis of population development in Daphnia at different temperatures. Biol. Bull. 85: 116-140.

Richman, S., 1958, The transformation of energy by *Daphnia pulex*. Ecol. Monogr. 28: 273-291.

Ryther, J. H., 1954, Inhibitory effects of phytoplankton upon the feeding of *Daphnia magna* with reference to growth, reproduction, and survival. Ecology 35: 522-533.

Slobodkin, L. B., 1954, Population dynamics in *Daphnia obtusa* Kurz. Ecol. Monogr. 24: 69-88.

1957, A laboratory study of the effect of removal of newborn animals from a population. Proc. Nat. Acad. Sci. U. S. 43: 780-782.

1958, Meta-models in theoretical ecology. Ecology 39: 550–551.

1959, Energetics in *Daphnia pulex* populations. Ecology 40: 232–243.

Teal, J. M., 1957, Community metabolism in a temperate cold spring. Ecol. Monogr. 27: 283–302.

Trama, F. B., 1957, The transformation of energy by an aquatic herbivore, *Stenonema pulchellum* (Ephemeroptera). Ph.D. dissertation, Department of Zoology, University of Michigan, Ann Arbor, Mich.

## GLOSSARY OF SYMBOLS

| Symbol | Units | Meaning |
|---|---|---|
| $c$ | calories/(calories × days) | Maintenance cost of one calorie of standing crop for one unit of time |
| $\Delta c$ | calories/(calories × days) | Increment in maintenance cost per calorie of standing crop attributable to the removal of yield. |
| $d_x$ | animals/animals | The fraction of animals born at time 0 that die during the age interval x. |
| $D_x$ | animals/days | The number of animals that die during the age interval x. |
| $E$ | $\dfrac{\text{calories/time}}{\text{calories/time}}$ | Yield calories divided by input calories. Ecological efficiency. |
| $E_i$ | $\dfrac{\text{calories}}{\text{calories}}$ | Potential energy in an individual of age i, divided by the potential energy needed to replace that individual. Growth efficiency. |
| $E_p$ | $\dfrac{\text{calories/time}}{\text{calories/time}}$ | Yield calories divided by the difference in maintenance cost between the population producing the yield and a corresponding control population. Population efficiency. |
| $E_{pi}$ | $\dfrac{\text{calories/time}}{\text{calories/time}}$ | Population efficiency for the situation in which the yield consists exclusively of animals age i. |
| i and j | days | Age categories. |
| $l_x$ | animals/animals | The fraction of animals born at time 0 that survive to time x. |
| $N_0$ | animals/days | Number of newborn animals produced in a population during one time interval. |
| $P$ | calories | Steady state standing crop caloric content of a population. |
| $q_x$ | animals/animals | The proportion of animals that survive up to an age interval that die during that interval. |

## GLOSSARY OF SYMBOLS (*continued*)

| Symbol | Units | Meaning |
|--------|-------|---------|
| $S_x$ | calories | The calories of potential energy contained in an animal of age x. |
| $\sum$ | | Summation sign. |
| x | days | An age category. (Occasionally used as a size category.) |
| Y | calories/time | Total steady state yield removed from a population per unit time. |
| $Y_i$ | calories/time | Steady state yield of animals age i removed from a population per unit time. |

Note: Except for $c'$ and $\Delta c'$, in equations (3) and (4), a symbol with a prime (that is, $P'$ or $S'_x$) refers to a property of a population subject to predation, but is otherwise understood to have the same meaning as the corresponding symbol without the prime (that is, P or $S_x$).

In the discussion of entropy the symbols all have their conventional meanings.

| Symbol | Meaning |
|--------|---------|
| $\Delta F$ | Change in free energy |
| $\Delta H$ | Change in enthalpy |
| $Q'$ | Non-entropic heat. |
| $\Delta S$ | Change in entropy. |
| T | Absolute temperature |

# Potential Productivity
# of the Sea

Organic production by marine plankton algae
is comparable to agricultural yields on land.

John H. Ryther

Under ideal conditions for photosynthesis and growth, what is the maximum potential rate of production of organic matter in the sea? Is this potential ever realized, or even approached? How does the sea compare with the land in this respect? These questions may be approached empirically with some measure of success but, aside from the time and effort required by this method, one can never be certain how close to the optimum a given environment may be and, hence, to what extent the biotic potential is realized.

However, we do know with some degree of certainty the maximum photosynthetic efficiency of plants under carefully controlled laboratory conditions; and there is a considerable literature concerning the effects of various environmental conditions on photosynthesis, respiration, and growth, particularly with respect to the unicellular algae. From such information it should be possible to estimate photosynthetic efficiencies and, for given amounts of solar radiation, organic production under natural conditions. This indirect and theoretical approach cannot be expected to

provide exact values, but it does furnish a supplement to the empirically derived data which may help substantiate our concepts both of the environmental physiology of the plankton algae and the level of organic production in the sea.

An attempt has been made to use this joint approach for the marine environment in the following discussion. The only variable considered is light, and the assumption is made that virtually all of the light which enters the water (and remains) is absorbed by plants. Such situations are closely approximated in plankton blooms, dense stands of benthic algae, eelgrass, and other plants. For the rest, it is assumed that temperature, nutrients, and other factors are optimal, or at least as favorable as occur under ideal culture conditions. Given these conditions, I have attempted to calculate the organic yields which might be expected within the range of solar radiation incident to most of the earth. These data are then compared with maximal and mean observed values in the marine environment and elsewhere, and an attempt is made to explain discrepancies.

The calculations which appear below are based, for the most part, upon experimentally derived relationships between unicellular algae and the envi-

The author is on the staff of the Woods Hole Oceanographic Institution, Woods Hole, Mass. This article is based on a paper presented by the author at the AAAS meeting in Washington, D.C., December 1958.

ronment, and are therefore applicable only to this group. This must be kept in mind when, later in the discussion, comparisons are drawn between the theoretical yields and observed values of production by larger aquatic and terrestrial plants.

The values for the efficiency of photosynthesis under natural conditions are based on the utilization of the visible portion of the solar spectrum only (400 to 700 mμ), or roughly half of the total incident radiation. In converting these efficiencies to organic yields, it is assumed that the heat of combustion of the dry plant material is 5.5 kcal per gram, which closely approximates values for unicellular algae reported by Krogh and Berg (1), Ketchum and Redfield (2), Kok (3), Aach (4), Wassink et al. (5), and others.

## Reflection and Backscattering

Of the sunlight which strikes the surface of the ocean, a certain fraction is reflected from its surface and never enters the water. The remainder penetrates to depths which depend upon the concentration of absorbing and scattering particles or dissolved colored substances. While scattering may be as important as absorption in the vertical attenuation of the light, it makes little difference as far as the biological utilization of the radiation is concerned, since the scattered light is eventually absorbed, with the exception of a small fraction which is backscattered up out of the water. The combined reflected and backscattered light is lost to the aquatic system; the rest remains in the water, where, under the ideal conditions postulated, it is absorbed entirely by plants.

The fraction of the incident radiation which is reflected and backscattered has been studied by Powell and Clarke (6), Utterback and Jorgenson (7), and Hulburt (8). The two factors have been treated separately, but they may be considered together here. Their combined effect is rather small, ranging from about 3 to 6 percent, depending somewhat upon who made the measurements and the conditions under which the measurements were made. The highest values were observed when the sky was overcast. Sea states, ranging from flat calm to whitecap conditions, made surprisingly little difference. Reflection and backscattering were also found by Hulburt to be independent of the sun's angle, despite the fact that reflection increases greatly with the angle (from the zenith) of the incident light, particularly at angles above 60°. The explanation for this apparent contradiction lies in the fact that as the sun approaches the horizon, indirect sky light becomes increasingly important, and it eventually exceeds the intensities of the sun itself.

Hulburt's data also indicate that backscattering is not greatly influenced by the amount of particulate matter in the water, since his values in the clear Gulf Stream did not differ appreciably from those made in the turbid waters of Chesapeake Bay.

For the calculations which are made here, it is considered that an average of 5 percent of the incident radiation is lost through the combined effects of reflection and backscattering.

## Photosynthesis and the Visible Spectrum

We first consider the efficiency of photosynthesis in sunlight at levels below the saturation intensity. Within this range, photosynthesis is directly proportional to the light intensity (or very nearly so), and the efficiency is therefore constant.

Despite the vast numbers of studies of quantum yield (that is, photosynthetic efficiency) in the literature, few data are available for the entire visible spectrum. Figure 1A shows two such series of measurements, one with the green alga *Chlorella* (Emerson and Lewis, 9), the other with the diatom *Navicula minima* (Tanada, 10). The ordinate is expressed as quantum requirement (the number of quanta required to reduce 1 mole of $CO_2$) rather than a reciprocal, quantum yield (moles of $CO_2$ reduced per quantum) as shown originally by the authors. Although the two organisms have strikingly different pigment complements, the curves are surprisingly similar, with minimal requirements in the red and yellow parts of the spectrum, maximal in the blue-green. *Navicula* appears to be somewhat more efficient than *Chlorella,* but the differences may not be significant.

Figure 1*B* illustrates the fact that the energy per quantum between 400 and 700 mµ decreases from a maximum of 71 kcal per mole quanta of blue light to 41 cal per mole quanta of red light. The heat of combustion of one reduced mole of $CO_2$ (reduced to $CH_2O$) is 112 kcal. A quantum requirement of 10 therefore represents an efficiency of $112/(41 \times 10)$ = 27.3 percent in red light and $112/(71 \times 10) = 15.7$ percent in blue light. Figure 1*C* shows the efficiencies of *Chlorella* and *Navicula* throughout the visible solar spectrum.

The spectral distribution of daylight varies with solar altitude and with the water vapor, carbon dioxide, and dust content of the atmosphere. Figure 2 shows the spectral distribution of daylight under average atmospheric conditions and with an air mass of 2 (solar angle = 30° from zenith) as given by Moon (*11*).

If the curves in Fig. 1*C* are averaged and the mean efficiency for the entire visible spectrum is calculated, weighing the mean for the average spectral distribution of sunlight as given in Fig. 2, this value turns out to be 18.4 percent. Taking into consideration a 5-percent reflection and backscattering loss, the efficiency of photosynthetic utilization of visible sunlight *below saturation intensity* incident to the water surface is 17.5 percent.

In extremely turbid waters and in those containing organic stains (the "yellow substance" described by Kalle, *12*), blue and green light may be selectively absorbed, resulting in somewhat higher efficiencies in the utilization of the light penetrating to greater depths. On the other hand, in normal, clear oceanic water the red light is selectively absorbed by the water and blue-green light penetrates to the greatest depths, where it is used still less effectively than the average incident daylight considered above. These modifications are not considered in this article, since we are dealing with an idealized situation in which all of the light entering the water is absorbed by plants.

## Intensity Effect

Above the saturation point, photosynthesis does not increase in proportion to light intensity, but remains constant or, at high intensities, is actually depressed, owing to photooxidation or other inhibitory processes.

Figure 3*A* shows a curve of photosynthesis by marine plankton algae as a function of light intensity, from Ryther (*13*). This is a mean curve of experiments with cultures of 14 species of organisms, preconditioned to a variety of different light regimes. Photosynthesis was measured by $C^{14}$ uptake under solar radiation during the 4-hour period (10 A.M. to 2 P.M.) when the intensity is nearly constant and maximum. Graded intensities were obtained with neutral density filters. Almost identical curves were obtained by Steemann Nielsen and Jensen (*14*) for natural plankton populations.

Photosynthetic efficiencies remain constant, or nearly so, up to the saturation point, but then decline sharply at higher intensities. This decrease is illustrated by the difference between the actual photosynthesis curve in Fig. 3*A* and the dotted line, which is an extrapolation of the linear portion of the solid curve and represents photosynthesis if the efficiency remained constant. Figure 3*B* shows relative efficiencies as a function of light intensity, obtained from the ratio between the solid and dotted lines in Fig. 3*A*.

Using the data in Fig. 3*A,* Ryther (*13*) has calculated relative photosynthesis throughout the day and at various depths within the euphotic (illuminated) zone of the ocean for days with different values for total incident radiation. Several curves were thereby produced showing values for total daily photosynthesis at several depths within

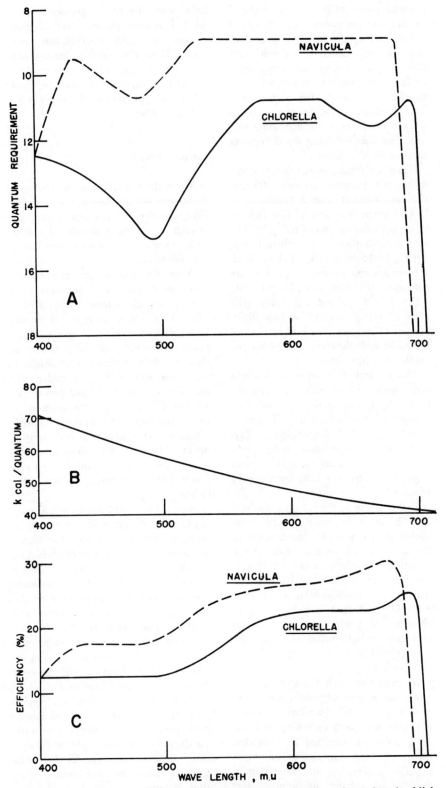

Fig. 1. (*A*) Quantum requirement of photosynthesis as a function of wavelength of light for *Chlorella* [after Emerson and Lewis, *9*] and for *Navicula* [after Tanada, *10*]. (*B*) Energy per mole quantum of light as a function of wavelength. (*C*) Efficiency of photosynthesis as a function of wavelength, calculated from (*A*) and (*B*).

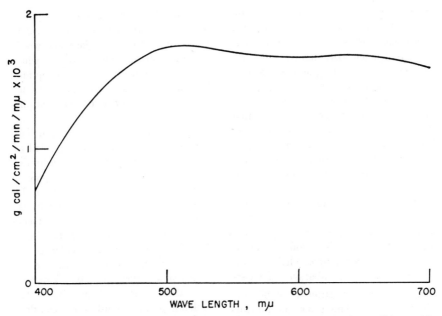

Fig. 2. The spectral distribution of daylight under average atmospheric conditions with air mass equal to 2. [After Moon, *11*]

the euphotic zone relative to the hourly rate of photosynthesis at light saturation.

On extremely dull days, when the intensity never reaches the saturation region, photosynthesis is directly proportional to light intensity at all depths, and the curve of photosynthesis with depth shows an exponential decrease from the surface, as does that of light. On bright, sunny days, intensities at the surface exceed saturation and normally produce inhibition (which occurs at $\frac{1}{3}$ or less the intensity of full sunlight). On such days, photosynthesis at the surface is less than that at intermediate depths. In all cases, photosynthesis at depths where the surface light is reduced to 10 percent or less is directly proportional to intensity, and in this region it decreases exponentially, following the light curve.

By extrapolating the lower, exponential portion of the photosynthesis curve to the surface, one may create a hypothetical curve of photosynthesis if the latter maintained the same efficiency at all depths. The ratio of the actual photosynthesis curve to this hypothetical exponential curve will then show the reduction in efficiency caused by light intensities above saturation in the up-

per waters. This has been done in Fig. 4 for a series of photosynthesis curves on days of varying incident radiation. Since photosynthesis at the various depths is a function of light intensity and not of depth per se, the units on the ordinate of Fig. 4 are natural logarithms of $I_0/I$ and thus represent the depths to which given fractions of the incident radiation penetrate. The curve for the day with lowest radiation (20 gcal/cm² day) is exponential all the way to the surface, indicating that on such a day there is no reduction in photosynthetic efficiency from the effects of light intensity. On days of progressively higher light intensity, the photosynthesis curve departs more and more from the exponential curve illustrating the increasing reduction in efficiency.

If it is assumed that the maximum efficiency (with no intensity effect) is 17.5 percent, as calculated in the previous section, Fig. 5 shows the cumulative intensity effect with efficiencies plotted as a function of total daily incident radiation. The points were obtained from Fig. 4 from the ratio of the actual photosynthesis curves for each value of radiation to the exponential curve of maximum (17.5 percent efficiency. It may be seen that efficiencies decrease from 17.5 percent at low intensities to 6.5 percent on a day when 600 g cal/cm² reaches the earth's surface. It is noteworthy that the efficiency curve does not decrease in a regular way with increasing intensities, but that the rate of decrease becomes less at higher intensities. This is due to the fact that higher values of daily radiation are caused not only by higher intensities of sunlight but to an even greater extent by longer days including more hours of low intensity light.

We are now ready to calculate photosynthesis for different values of incident radiation from the efficiency curve shown in Fig. 5. This is done by multiplying the efficiency by one-half the appropriate values of radiation (that portion of the solar spectrum available for photosynthesis). This gives the amount of energy fixed in photosynthesis. Dividing this by 5.5 (the heat of combustion of a gram of average plant material, as discussed in the first section) we obtain a value which represents grams of organic matter produced per day beneath a square meter of water surface, provided that all the light entering this 1-meter-square column of water is effectively absorbed by plants. These values, shown as the upper broken line in Fig. 5, are equivalent to "real photosynthesis" or "gross production." They are hypothetical in the sense that they cannot be observed as a yield, since the plants must draw upon this organic matter to satisfy their own metabolic requirements. We must therefore subtract an amount of organic matter equivalent to the plants' respiration in order to calculate the amount of material available for harvest, the so-called "net production."

### Respiratory Loss

Under conditions of active growth, photosynthesis at light saturation is some 10 to 20 times as great as dark respiration (see Ryther, 15). Higher values have been reported, but it seems doubtful that they could represent steady-state conditions in natural populations. If we take a ratio of 15:1 as average for $P:R$

(photosynthesis:respiration) at optimal light, it is obvious that over a 24-hour period, half of which is dark, and within an entire plant community, of which many of the plants are in suboptimal light at all times, respiration must account for a much greater fraction of photosynthesis.

In calculating the ratio $P:R$ in natural communities, the oversimplified assumption will be made that respiration remains constant and independent of light and photosynthesis. While the literature pertaining to this subject is contradictory and in a state of great confusion (see, for example, Rabinowitch, 16), there is mounting evidence that respiration and photosynthesis are not wholly independent processes. However, since there is no good quantitative formulation of a relationship between them which may be incorporated into our calculations, it must be neglected here.

As mentioned above, the data from Fig. 3A together with light intensity values for a group of days with varying total incident radiation have been used to calculate photosynthesis as a function of radiation. (See Ryther, 13, for a full description of these calculations). The values given by this treatment represent photosynthesis per day beneath a square meter of surface relative to the value for photosynthesis per cubic meter per hour at light saturation. For example, a value of 100 would mean that daily photosynthesis beneath a 1-meter-square water column is 100 times as great as photosynthesis within a 1-cubic-meter aliquot of that water column for 1 hour at optimal light intensity (assuming that the plant population is evenly distributed within this water column).

Since respiration is 1/15 photosynthesis at light saturation and is also stipulated to be constant with respect to light, depth, and time of day, we may calculate total daily respiration in the same relative units as photosynthesis. The curves of photosynthesis and respiration as functions of radiation are shown in Fig. 6. They cross at 100 g cal/cm² × day, which may be considered the daily compensation level for an entire plant community. The value $(R/P)$ × 100 is the percentage of respiratory

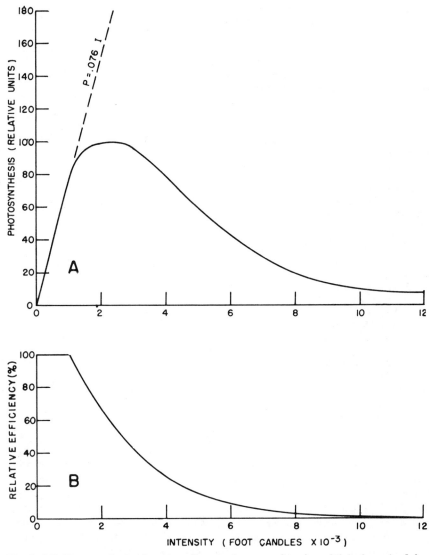

Fig. 3. (*A*) Photosynthesis of marine phytoplankton as a function of light intensity [after Ryther, *13*]. Broken line is the extrapolation of the linear portion of the solid line representing hypothetical sustained maximum photosynthetic efficiency. (*B*) Efficiency of photosynthesis as a function of light intensity, calculated from *A*.

loss and is shown as the lower broken line in Fig. 6. It ranges from 100 percent at radiation values of 100 g cal/cm² day or less to 28 percent on extremely bright, long days.

### Net Production

Returning to Fig. 5, gross production may be reduced by the respiratory loss (Fig. 6), giving the curve of net production, which begins at 100 g cal/cm²

day and reaches a value of 25 g/m² day under radiation of 600 g cal/m² day (the lower broken line in Fig. 5).

Although the annual range of daily incident radiation is extremely wide, even for a given latitude, this short-term variability is probably not very significant in affecting the general level of organic production of a given area. If one examines the tables compiled by Kimball (*17*) showing mean monthly radiation for different latitudes, it appears that over 80 percent of the data

Table 1. Gross and net organic production of various natural and cultivated systems in grams dry weight produced per square meter per day.

| System | Gross | Net |
|---|---|---|
| *A. Theoretical potential* | | |
| Average radiation (200 to 400 g cal/cm² day) | 23–32 | 8–19 |
| Maximum radiation (750 g cal/cm² day) | 38 | 27 |
| *B. Mass outdoor* Chlorella *culture (26)* | | |
| Mean | | 12.4 |
| Maximum | | 28.0 |
| *C. Land (maximum for entire growing seasons) (18)* | | |
| Sugar cane | | 18.4 |
| Rice | | 9.1 |
| Wheat | | 4.6 |
| *Spartina* marsh | | 9.0 |
| Pine forest (best growing years) | | 6.0 |
| Tall prairie | | 3.0 |
| Short prairie | | 0.5 |
| Desert | | 0.2 |
| *D. Marine (maxima for single days)* | | |
| Coral reef (27) | 24 | (9.6) |
| Turtle grass flat (28) | 20.5 | (11.3) |
| Polluted estuary (29) | 11.0 | (8.0) |
| Grand Banks (Apr.) (30) | 10.8 | (6.5) |
| Walvis Bay (23) | 7.6 | |
| Continental Shelf (May) (19) | 6.1 | (3.7) |
| Sargasso Sea (Apr.) (31) | 4.0 | (2.8) |
| *E. Marine (annual average)* | | |
| Long Island Sound (32) | 2.1 | 0.9 |
| Continental Shelf (19) | 0.74 | (0.40) |
| Sargasso Sea (31) | 0.88 | 0.40 |

(including all latitudes and seasons) fall within a range of 200 to 400 g cal/cm² day. Thus, over most of the earth for most of the year a potential production of organic matter of some 10 to 20 g/m² day may be expected, while for shorter periods of fine summer weather, a net production of 25 g/m² day or slightly more may occur.

## Comparison of Theoretical and Observed Production Rates

We may now compare the production rates which were calculated in the preceding sections with some values which have been observed empirically. Since the former are based on hypothetical situations in which all light entering the water is absorbed by plants, the observational data, to be comparable, must be restricted to natural environments in which these conditions are at least closely approximated (for example, in dense plankton blooms, thick stands of benthic algae and rooted plants). In addition to these maximal values, the theoretical potential may be contrasted with average oceanic productivity rates.

We may also extend this comparison to the terrestrial environment, including some of the better agricultural yields, bearing in mind, however, that the physiology and hence, perhaps, the biotic potential of land plants may differ significantly from those of algae.

Finally, we may include the yields of *Chlorella* grown in outdoor mass culture, drawing here upon the excellent, continuing studies of H. Tamiya and his collaborators. These are of particular interest, since the conditions of these experiments were as optimal as possible and since the physiology of *Chlorella* is identical or closely similar to that of the organisms upon which our calculations are based. Thus the *Chlorella* yields will serve as a check for the theoretical production rates.

It is important, in making these comparisons, to keep in mind the distinction

## RELATIVE PHOTOSYNTHESIS

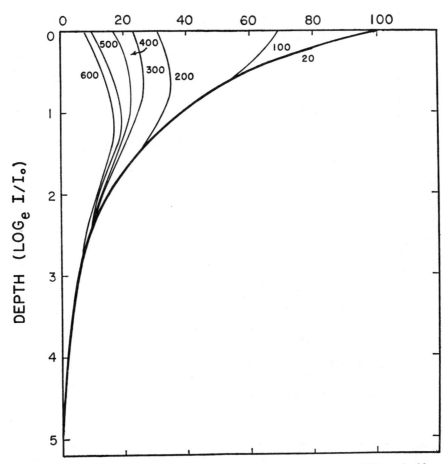

Fig. 4. Relative photosynthesis as a function of water depth for days of different incident radiation. Numbers beside curves show gram calories per square centimeter per day.

between gross and net production as defined above. Some of the data refer to true photosynthesis measurements (gross production) while others, sucn as the *Chlorella* experiments and the agricultural yields, are based on the actual harvest of organic matter (net production). In those cases in which only gross production values are available and where radiation data are given, net production has been obtained from Figure 5 and is shown in parentheses.

The theoretical production potential for average and maximal radiation, and the observational data for both marine and terrestrial environments, are given in Table 1. In each case the original source is given, except for the land values, where reference is made to the recent compilation by Odum (*18*). The

various methods by which the values were obtained will not be discussed here except in the case of the unpublished data, in which gross production was calculated from chlorophyll and light, according to the method of Ryther and Yentsch (*19*) and net production was measured by the $C^{14}$ method, uncorrected for respiration as this method is interpreted by Ryther (*20*). Where gross production (photosynthesis) was originally reported as oxygen evolution, this has been converted to carbon assimilation, using an assimilatory quotient

$$\left( \Delta \frac{+O_2}{-CO_2} \right)$$

of 1.25 (see Ryther, *20*). Carbon uptake, in turn, has been converted to total

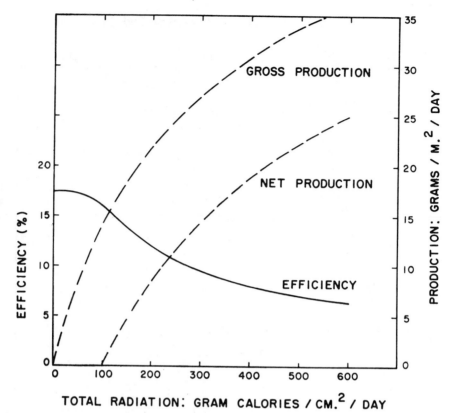

Fig. 5. Photosynthetic efficiency and theoretical maximum potential gross and net production as a function of incident radiation.

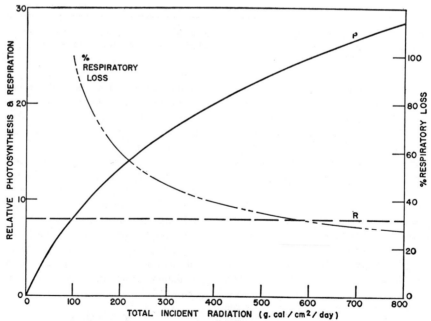

Fig. 6. Relative photosynthesis, respiration, and percentage of respiratory loss as a function of incident radiation.

organic production by assuming that the latter is 50 percent carbon by weight.

The maximal values for the marine environment represent the seven highest such values known to me. In addition to these, data are given for three regions (one inshore, one coastal, and one offshore) which have been studied over long enough periods of time to justify the calculation of annual means.

## Discussion

The mean yield of *Chlorella* obtained by the Japanese workers is almost identical to the mean theoretical production for days of average radiation (12.4 versus 13.5 g/m² day). These yields of *Chlorella* were produced only during the warmer part of the year, presumably owing to the poor growth of *Chlorella* at low temperatures. The highest yields of *Chlorella* (up to 28 g/m² day) were, according to Tamiya, "obtained on fair days in the warmer months." This maximum is approximately the same as the theoretical net production for days of maximum radiation. Thus, the *Chlorella* yields agree very well with the theoretical productive potential of the sea.

The land values for net production quoted from Odum's tables range from 18.4 g/m² day for the highest yields of sugar cane to 0.2 g/m² day for deserts. The best agricultural yields are generally of the same order of magnitude as the theoretical net production of the sea, as are the values for the salt marsh and the pine forest (during its years of best growth). Uncultivated grasslands range from 3.0 for tall prairie to 0.2 for desert conditions. Because of the extreme contrasts among terrestrial environments, mean values for the land as a whole are difficult to determine and would have little meaning. It is interesting, however, that Schroeder's estimate (*21*) of the annual production of all the land is equivalent to a mean daily production of 0.55 g/m², roughly the same as the value given in Table 1 for short prairie grass.

With regard to the marine data, it is perhaps surprising that net production rates differ by less than a factor of 2 in such diverse environments as a coral reef, a turtle grass flat, a polluted creek, and the Grand Banks. This alone would indicate that production in each case is limited by the same basic factor, the photosynthetic potential of the plants, and indeed these and the other high values in *D* in Table 1 all closely approach the theoretical potential.

Seasonal studies have been made of three marine areas, Long Island Sound, the continental shelf off New York, and the Sargasso Sea off Bermuda. In each case temporary rates of production were observed during the spring flowering which approached the theoretical maximum, but the annual means were more than an order of magnitude lower (*E* in Table 1). True, these regions do not, throughout the year, satisfy the postulated conditions necessary to obtain this maximum, namely, that all light entering the water be absorbed by plants. For example, in his Long Island Sound studies, Riley (*22*) found that no more than one-third of the incident radiation was utilized by plants, the remainder presumably being absorbed by nonliving particulate and dissolved materials. Using Riley's techniques, I estimated that only 25 to 40 percent of the light penetrating the continental shelf waters was absorbed by the phytoplankton. This alone, however, is insufficient to account for the discrepancy between observed and potential production rates. In the clear waters of the Sargasso Sea only 10 to 20 percent of the light is absorbed by the phytoplankton during most of the year. But there is little if any other particulate matter present; the remainder of the light is absorbed by the water itself. This is not a cause but an effect of low production. The underlying reason for low production rates here and in most parts of the ocean is the limitation of essential nutrients in the upper, euphotic layers and the inadequacy of vertical mixing processes in bringing deep, nutrient-rich water to the surface.

With the exception of the three planktonic communities which have been discussed, the seasonal cycles of marine production are largely unknown and can only be surmised. Probably high levels may be maintained throughout the year in benthic populations such as the coral reef, the turtle grass flats (see *D* in Table

1) and in thick beds of seaweeds, provided that seasonal temperature extremes do not impair growth. While the concentrations of nutrients in the surrounding waters may be very low, the fact that they are continually being replenished as the water moves over the plants probably prevents their ever being limiting. Plankton organisms, on the other hand, suspended as they are in their milieu, can probably never maintain high production rates in a given parcel of water, for their growth rapidly exhausts the nutrients from their surrounding environment and any mixing process which enriches the water must, at the same time, dilute the organisms. However, high plankton production may be sustained in a given geographic area (a polluted estuary, a region of permanent upwelling of deep water, and so forth), which is continually replenished with enriched water. In these situations, the productive capacity of the sea may be sustained for long periods, perhaps permanently.

For most of the ocean, as stated above, no such mechanism for nutrient replenishment is available. The combined meteorological and hydrographic conditions which produce the typical spring flowering of the phytoplankton over much of the oceans have been adequately described elsewhere and need not be discussed here. Suffice it to say that, in the oceans as a whole, as seasonal studies have demonstrated, high production approaching the theoretical maximum under optimal conditions is restricted to periods of a few days or, at most, weeks, per year.

Steemann Nielsen (23) has recently estimated the net production of the entire hydrosphere as 1.2 to $1.5 \times 10^{10}$ tons of carbon per year, roughly one-tenth the earlier estimates made by Riley (24) and others, and about comparable to Schroeder's figure (21) for the land. Our production estimates are somewhat higher than those of Steemann Nielsen, the annual mean net production of organic matter for the Sargasso Sea (0.40 g/m² day) being about 6 times as great as his value for the same area, and twice his average for the oceans as a whole. This discrepancy appears to be largely due to the fact that Steemann Nielsen's values are based on single observations which probably seldom included seasonal maxima. His observations in the Sargasso Sea, for example, were made in June and did not differ greatly from our June values, which were the seasonal minima. If the Sargasso Sea is one of the less fertile parts of the ocean, as is generally believed, then our data would indicate that the seas are more than twice as productive as the land (25).

### References and Notes

1. A. Krogh and K. Berg, *Intern. Rev. ges. Hydrobiol. Hydrog.* 25, 205 (1931).
2. B. H. Ketchum and A. C. Redfield, *J. Cellular Comp. Physiol.* 33, 281 (1949).
3. B. Kok, *Acta Botan. Neerl.* 1, 445 (1952).
4. H. G. Aach, *Arch. Mikrobiol.* 17, 213 (1952).
5. E. C. Wassink, B. Kok, J. L. P. van Oorschot, "The efficiency of light-energy conversion in *Chlorella* cultures as compared with higher plants," in "Algal Culture from Laboratory to Pilot Plant," *Carnegie Inst. Wash. Publ. No. 600* (1953), pp. 55–62.
6. W. M. Powell and G. L. Clarke, *J. Opt. Soc. Am.* 26, 111 (1936).
7. C. L. Utterback and W. Jorgensen, *ibid.* 26, 257 (1936).
8. E. O. Hulburt, *ibid.* 35, 698 (1945).
9. R. Emerson and C. M. Lewis, *Am. J. Botany* 30, 165 (1943).
10. T. Tanada, *ibid.* 39, 276 (1951).
11. P. Moon, *J. Franklin Inst.* 230, 583 (1940).
12. K. Kalle, *Ann. Hydrog. mar. Meteor.* 66, 1 (1938).
13. J. H. Ryther et al., *Biol. Bull.* 115, 257 (1958).
14. E. Steemann Nielsen and E. A. Jensen, *Galathea Repts.* 1, 49 (1957).
15. J. H. Ryther, *Deep-Sea Research* 2, 134 (1954).
16. E. I. Rabinowitch, *Photosynthesis and Related Processes* (Interscience, New York, 1956), vol. 2, part 2, pp. 1925–1939.
17. H. H. Kimball, *Monthly Weather Rev.* 56, 393 (1928).
18. E. P. Odum, *Fundamentals of Ecology* (Saunders, Philadelphia, ed. 2, 1959).
19. J. H. Ryther and C. S. Yentsch, *Limnol. Oceanog.* 2, 281 (1957).
20. ———, *ibid.* 1, 72 (1956).
21. H. Schroeder, *Naturwissenschaften* 7, 8 (1919).
22. G. A. Riley, *Bull. Bingham Oceanog. Coll.* 15, 15 (1956).
23. E. Steemann Nielsen, *J. conseil, Conseil permanent intern. exploration mer* 19, 309 (1954).
24. G. A. Riley, *Bull. Bingham Oceanog. Coll.* 7, 1 (1941).
25. This paper is contribution No. 1016 of the Woods Hole Oceanographic Institution. The work was supported in part by research grant G-3234 from the National Science Foundation and under contract AT (30-1)-1918 with the Atomic Energy Commission.
26. H. Tamiya, *Ann. Rev. Plant Physiol.* 8, 309 (1957).
27. H. T. Odum and E. P. Odum, *Ecol. Monographs* 25, 291 (1955).
28. H. T. Odum, *Limnol. Oceanog.* 2, 85 (1957).
29. J. H. Ryther et al., *Biol. Bull.* 115, 257 (1958).
30. J. H. Ryther and C. S. Yentsch, unpublished data.
31. J. H. Ryther and D. W. Menzel, unpublished data.
32. G. A. Riley, *Bull. Bingham Oceanog. Coll.* 15, 324 (1956).

# ENERGY DYNAMICS OF A FOOD CHAIN OF AN OLD-FIELD COMMUNITY

Frank B. Golley

*Department of Zoology, Michigan State University, East Lansing, Michigan**

## INTRODUCTION

In recent years there has been a growing interest in the study of the transfer of energy through natural systems (ecosystems, Tansley 1935). Park (1946) stated that "probably the most important ultimate objective of ecology is an understanding of community structure and function from the viewpoint of its metabolism and energy relationships." Aquatic biologists have taken the initiative in the study of community energetics, and most of the information available today concerns fresh water or marine communities. A great need exists for similar studies on terrestrial communities.

In this study a food chain of the old field community, from perennial grasses and herbs to the meadow mouse, *Microtus pennsylvanicus pennsylvanicus* Ord, and to the least weasel, *Mustela rixosa allegheniensis* Rhoads, was chosen for investigation. This food chain included the dominant vertebrate of the community (*Microtus*) and one of its main predators (*Mustela*) but excluded the otherwise important insects, other invertebrates, bacteria, and fungi. The primary objectives of the study were to determine (1) the rate of synthesis of organic matter by the primary producers—the vegetation, (2) the path of this energy from the vegetation through the mouse to the weasel, and (3) the losses of energy at each step in the food chain.

The writer wishes to acknowledge with gratitude the suggestions and guidance of Dr. Don W. Hayne, Institute of Fisheries Research, Michigan Department of Conservation, especially concerning that portion of the study dealing with the population dynamics and productivity of the *Microtus* population. The writer also thanks Dr. John E. Cantlon, Department of

* Present Address: Department of Zoology, University of Georgia, Athens, Georgia.

Botany, and Dr. Robert C. Ball, Department of Fisheries and Wildlife, Michigan State University, for aid given throughout the project. The investigation was supported by the Michigan Agricultural Experiment Station through a project administered by Dr. Hayne.

## DESCRIPTION OF THE AREA

The study area was located in a large field on the Michigan State University State Farm approximately one mile south-east of Okemos, Ingham County, Michigan (sec. 27, T. 4N, R. 1W). As far as is known, this farm was last tilled in 1918 when it was given to the State of Michigan by Mr. John Fink. It was acquired by Michigan State University in 1940 and was pastured from 1940 to 1942. The study area has been undisturbed since 1942, with the exception of some tree planting by the Department of Forestry, Michigan State University, and probably occasional burning. The tree plantings appeared to be only slightly successful. The vegetation on the area was unburned from January 1952 to March 1957.

The field in which the study area was located was situated on the north terrace of the Red Cedar River, approximately 20 ft above the level of the river. The topography was gently undulating, with a relief of 15 ft or less. A shallow depression ran through the center of one of the trapping areas and served as a drain during the heavy rains in the winter and spring. On February 9, 1957, the snow melt-water was approximately 7 in. deep in this drainage area. As the snow melted in February and March much of the study area was inundated, with grass hummocks and hillocks on the border of the trap area providing the only dry sites.

The soils on the study area were predominantly Conover and Miami loam (determined from the soil map by Veatch *et al.* 1941).

On the east the field was separated from similar habitat by a paved county road. The north boundary was predominantly pasture land and orchard. The west boundary was an experimental alfalfa field left uncut in 1957. To the south the field was bounded by an unused gravel road, which ran along the ridge top above the river terrace and separated the field from other old field vegetation containing more woody cover and indicating a later stage of old field development. The field itself contained approximately 10 ha of relatively homogeneous habitat.

The climate in this area of Michigan is characterized by cold winters and mild summers (Baten & Eichmeier 1951). Yearly precipitation at East Lansing (1911-1949) averages 31 in.; growing season (last day in spring to the first day in fall when the temperature reaches 32°F) precipitation averages 17 in. The mean annual temperature is approximately 47°F, with extremes ranging from −20° to +102°F. The growing season averages 147 days. Solar radiation at East Lansing (3 mi west of the study area) is peculiar in that a plateau in the insolation curve may be expected about April 25 to May 20. When solar energy received at East Lansing is compared with that at most of the 92 weather stations in North America measuring solar insolation, it is evident that East Lansing receives annually less solar heat than any other station, with the exception of Fairbanks, Alaska (Crabb 1950b).

No attempt was made to make a complete survey of the flora and fauna of the community. The vegetation of the study area was transitional between the perennial grass stage (perennial grasses predominant) and the perennial herb stage (perennial herbs co-dominant with the grasses) of old field succession (Beckwith 1954). The vegetation is considered similar to the bluegrass-upland association of Blair (1948) and the upland community of Evans & Cain (1952).

Canada blue grass, *Poa compressa*[1], was dominant over the entire area, with three herb species, *Daucus carota*, *Cirsium arvense*, and *Linaria vulgaris*, sharing dominance in portions of the area. The study area was divided into four facies on the basis of co-dominance of the above herbs with *Poa compressa*. Mosses, undeveloped small herbs, and grass shoots formed a subordinate layer beneath the grass and perennial herb layer. A woody overstory occurred sporadically over the area, consisting primarily of *Crataegus* spp., *Pyrus communis*, *Prunus pennsylvanica*. The woody plants were a relatively unimportant component of the vegetation, the percentage cover for all woody plants averaging approximately 0.5.

The vertebrate dominants of the community, excluding birds, were *Microtus pennsylvanicus* and *Blarina brevicauda*, when total number observed was used as the criterion of dominance.

[1] Authorities for vascular plant binomials are those given in Fernald (1950).

## METHODS

As energy flows through a terrestrial food chain there is a successive transfer and loss of energy at each step in the chain (Fig. 1). As a result of the continual loss of energy through respiration and through nonutilization of food, each successive population is faced with a smaller energy source. In this report the writer's approach has been to study the energy flow through each separate population, rather than to emphasize the energy exchange through the food chain as a whole. In the traditional style of presenting research methods and results separately, this concern for each species population becomes especially evident and necessarily obscures the picture of energy flow through the entire food chain. The writer believes that this method of presentation is most satisfactory for an exploratory study of this nature. However, by referring to Fig. 1, the reader will be able to follow the flow of energy through the food chain without difficulty.

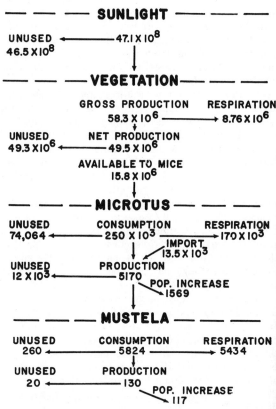

Fig. 1. The energy flow through the food chain from May, 1956 to May, 1957, on one hectare. All figures are Calories per hectare. Solar input represents that for the 1956 growing season.

### Measurement of Solar Insolation

Records of solar insolation (the rate at which solar energy is received on a horizontal surface at the surface of the earth) were obtained from the Michigan Hydrologic Research Station (the Agricultural Research Service, USDA, and the Michigan Agricultural

Experiment Station cooperating). The station operates an Eppley ten-junction thermopile, thermoelectric pyrheliometer, mounted on a small instrument house on an isolated section of the Michigan State University Farm, East Lansing. There is little smoke contamination at this location (Crabb 1950a) and it is assumed that the records obtained at the pyrheliometer were applicable to the study area approximately 3 mi to the east.

### STUDIES OF VEGETATION

The vegetation was studied from August 1956 to September 1957. Midway through the investigation (March 1957) a fire destroyed the vegetation on one-half of the study area, and it was necessary to move the entire operation to another portion of the same field. Fortunately there was no discernible difference in vegetation or topography at these two locations.

Square clip-plots (0.5 × 0.5 m) were used to estimate the standing crop of vegetation. All plant stems within the quadrats were clipped at the ground level. The cut vegetation was transferred to plastic bags and transported to the laboratory, where live grasses, live herbs, and dead vegetative materials were separated according to species. These materials were then dried at 100°C for 24 hrs and weighed. Monthly data were averaged and the standing crop of vegetation was expressed in grams of dry weight per 0.25 m². Ten to twenty random clip-plots were chosen for investigation each collection period, with the exception of late March. The adverse weather conditions in the latter part of March allowed an estimate to be made of green vegetation on only two plots.

Samples of several months' collections of dried grasses and herbs were randomly chosen for calorific analyses. These materials were ground in a Wiley Mill. Three subsamples from each species sample were analyzed in a Parr adiabatic bomb calorimeter.

The standing crop of roots and above-ground portions of the plants which escaped clipping were also determined at three periods during the 1957 growing season. At each collection, five of the plots which had been clipped were chosen at random and a 225-cm² piece of sod was cut from each plot. The sod was later washed in running water, oven dried at 100°C and weighed to determine average weight of roots per square meter. The samples were taken to a depth of 15 cm and did not represent the complete root biomass. Although Shively & Weaver 1939) show that the roots of many prairie plants extend at least several feet into the soil, for this study it was assumed that the main mass of roots in the old field community were concentrated within 15 cm of the surface.

The standing crop of vegetation measured here was less than the total amount of organic matter synthesized over the growing season. This is because the standing crop includes neither the amount of vegetation which grew and died between the periods of measurement, nor the amount of vegetation consumed by animals. In this study, some dead vegetation of the current growing season was unavoidably included with the green vegetation since no effort was made to separate the dead and living portions of one leaf or small plant. The material that grew and died back to the ground during the current growing season could not be separated from the dead vegetation and is therefore a source of error in determination of net production. The magnitude of this error was not estimated.

The amount of vegetation consumed by *Microtus* was estimated from feeding experiments and stomach sample analyses. The food consumption of herbivorous insects and other invertebrates, which in the pasture community may be of considerable magnitude (Wolcott 1937), was undetermined.

Another source of error in estimating the net production of the vegetation is pointed out by Pearsall & Gorham (1956). They suggest that in perennial vegetation the peak standing crop is formed from (1) the accumulation of the organic matter during the present season and from (2) the organic matter stored in the roots the previous season. The techniques used in this study allowed no estimate of the contribution of the previous season's production to the current peak standing crop.

To obtain a complete estimate of the energy utilization of vegetation (gross production, Odum 1956), the energy used in respiration of the vegetation must be added to the net production. A field respirometer was devised to make a rough measure of the respiration of the vegetation and the soil organisms. Two 5-qt oil cans were forced 5 cm into the ground at randomly chosen sites on the study area. Gases were withdrawn from the cans into Bailey gas analysis bottles. Carbon dioxide and oxygen content of the air in the cans was determined in an Orsat-Henderson gas analysis apparatus. The cans were placed in the ground and the first samples were withdrawn approximately 1 hr after dark. The second sample was taken in the early morning when the air temperature at the ground surface was approximately equal to the air temperature observed when the first samples were withdrawn the previous night. The consumption of oxygen and production of carbon dioxide over the night (12 hrs) was determined as the differences in the percentage composition of oxygen and carbon dioxide in the air in the cans at the first and second sampling. No measurement was made of the diffusion of gases between the soil and the air under the cans. The RQ ($CO_2/O_2$) was calculated and the thermal equivalent (in Calories) of the oxygen used and the carbon dioxide produced was extrapolated from the tables in Brody (1945). Respiration was then expressed as Calories used per gram of plant tissue per hour respiration during the night.

### STUDIES OF THE *Microtus* POPULATION

The energy dynamics of the *Microtus* population were studied both in the field and by laboratory experiments. In the field a live-trapping program was

TABLE 1. Dynamics of the *Microtus* population on one hectare

| Date | Average Number Captured Per Line | Fraction[1] Per cent | Population Density Per Hectare Numbers | Size of Trap Area Hectares | Average Individual Weight Grams | Standing Crop per Hectare Calories[2] | MORTALITY BETWEEN SUCCESSIVE TRAPPING PERIODS | |
|------|------|------|------|------|------|------|------|------|
| | | | | | | | Rate[3] | Calories |
| May 22-28......... | 4 | 29.4 | 5.2 | 2.6 | 29 | 205 | 75 | 393 |
| July 24-30......... | 12 | 41.7 | 9.6 | 3.0 | 29 | 382 | 37 | 232 |
| Sept. 4-10......... | 20 | 41.0 | 16.5 | 3.0 | 29 | 654 | 52 | 539 |
| Oct. 9-15.......... | 19 | 32.4 | 21.2 | 2.7 | 31 | 898 | 42 | 710 |
| Nov. 17-23........ | 28 | 22.2 | 42.4 | 2.4 | 29 | 1685 | 39 | 1162 |
| Jan. 6-23.......... | 22 | (13.3)[4] | 77.3 | 2.1 | 27 | 2847 | 27 | 1245 |
| Feb. 21-27......... | 39 | 13.0 | 139.1 | 2.1 | 29 | 5525 | (55)[4] | 3284 |
| March 19-26....... | 22 | 13.6 | 75.3 | 2.2 | 25 | 2578 | 35 | 937 |
| April 25-1......... | 43 | 30.4 | 53.2 | 2.6 | 32 | 2330 | 57 | 1931 |

[1] The percentage of total captures taken in common to both lines.
[2] Caloric value of *Microtus* was 1.37 Calories per gram.
[3] Percentage disappearing from one trap period to the next.
[4] Estimated values.

initiated in May 1956 and continued to September 1957. This paper includes only the data for one annual cycle, May 1956 to May 1957. The program was designed to yield information on population density, mortality, growth rate, and production of young. The trapping design was developed by D. W. Hayne and consisted of two crossed trap lines, 100 m long, with the live traps spaced 2 m apart. One trap line was operated for 24 hrs, it was then unset and the line crossing it was set for 24 hrs. The total trapping period extended for 6 days, with 3 days for each line. Since by the sixth day of trapping unmarked animals were generally caught only in the end traps in a line, it was assumed that six days of trapping was adequate to capture most of the animals living in the trap area. It was desirable to use as short a trapping period as possible because trap mortality tended to increase progressively during the trapping period.

Captured animals were toe clipped, sexed, aged, weighed, and examined for breeding condition before being released. Traps were baited with oatmeal, and during the colder months corn was also placed in the traps to serve as a high energy supplement. It was thought that the use of corn materially reduced trap mortality during the winter. Covers, made of asphalt shingles covered with aluminum foil, shielded the traps from sunlight, rain, and snow and were thought to reduce trap mortality especially in the summer.

A ratio method was used to estimate population density. The following formula was suggested by D. W. Hayne:

$$P = \frac{bc}{ad} \qquad (1)$$

where $a$ is the number of animals captured in common to both lines, $b$ the average number of animals captured in each of the two lines (both $a$ and $b$ exclude those animals dying in the traps during the trapping period), $c$ average for the two lines of all captures including deaths due to trapping, $d$ the effective area trapped, and $P$ the population density per unit area.

The trap area, bisected by each trap line, was a square of 10,000 $m^2$. Since the home ranges of the mice extended an unknown distance beyond these lines the square was increased on both sides and ends. On each side the area added was set arbitrarily as the fraction $\frac{a}{b}$ (in Formula 1) times one-half the trap line length, 50 m, times the length of one side, 100 m. At each end of the trapping square, the area was increased by a semicircle with a radius of one-half the length of the trap line plus the fractional increase computed above. Information on numbers captured and population estimates are shown in Table 1.

In calculating the production of (or total weight grown by) the *Microtus* population, it was necessary to use one method for the animals which were susceptible to capture (the adults and an unknown proportion of the juveniles) but to use an entirely different method for the nestling young which do not enter traps. For the trapped animals, production was calculated from the rates of growth and mortality observed among the trapped individuals, while for the nestling young, production was inferred from the observed rate of pregnancy, the known rate of growth of young, and the calculated rate at which the young entered the trap-susceptible population.

In calculations of production, the use of instantaneous rates has been advantageous (Clarke 1946, Clarke Edmondson & Ricker 1946, Ricker 1946). Assuming constant rates, the products of the instantaneous rates and the mean population for a period will yield, respectively, the production of animal tissue by the population and the quantity of tissue lost from the population. This approach is especially useful here since it allows estimation of the biomass or number of animals which were produced, grew, and were lost between measurements of the standing crop.

The recapture of resident animals in two consecutive trapping periods allowed an estimate to be made of the rate of weight gain or loss of the individual

This rate was estimated separately for the animals in a number of 10-gm weight classes, since the rate of growth changes with body weight (Table 2). For each weight class, the daily instantaneous rate of growth was multiplied by the mean biomass for the period to calculate the daily production by growth or the daily weight loss in that particular weight class. A proportionate weight change of less than one indicated that the animals in that class lost weight (Table 2).

To determine the production of the nestling young, it was necessary to establish (1) the potential production of young by the population (potential natality), (2) the number of young which entered the trap-susceptible population, and (3) the growth rate of the young. The estimate of the potential production of young was based on the rate of pregnancy determined in the field and on the gestation period and litter size as reported in the literature. Pregnancy rates were established by abdominal palpation of all females. Davis (1956) suggests that pregnancy is "visible" for 18 days in small rodents—this would mean that 86% of the pregnancies could be determined by abdominal palpation. Although Davis's findings could probably be extended to *Microtus*, the percentage of adult females found to be pregnant in this study (Table 3) was so large during most of the breeding season that Davis's correction could not be made. The average number of days required for a female in the population to produce one litter can be found by dividing the gestation period (21 days, Hamilton 1941) by the proportion of females pregnant, here termed $f$. With the additional assumptions that there is an even sex ratio and an average of five young per litter (Hamilton 1941, Hatt 1930, Blair 1940), we can infer that in each time interval of $21/f$ days, one female increases to 3.5 females—2.5 young females plus the mother. With the use of the following formula it is then possible to calculate the production of young:

$$\frac{\text{nat log } 3.5}{\dfrac{21}{f}} \times t \times p' \qquad (2)$$

where $f$ is the percentage pregnancy among females, $t$ is the time between trapping periods, and $p'$ is the mean population.

The number of young entering the trap-susceptible population was assumed to equal the number of adults and juveniles lost to mortality plus the number needed to fulfill the population increase.

The growth rate of the nestling young was based on the weight increase from an assumed birth weight to the weight of the lightest juvenile captured in the live traps between trapping periods. Whitmoyer (1956) showed that the mean birth weight of laboratory *Microtus pennsylvanicus* was approximately 3 gm. The lightest weights of live-trapped juveniles ranged from 10 to 16 gm. The products of the instantaneous rate of growth of the nestling young and the mean biomass of young yielded the increase

TABLE 2. Tissue production of juveniles and adults per hectare.

| Interval | Proportionate Weight Change Weight Classes in Grams | | | | Daily Instantaneous Rate of Growth[1] | | Growth Calories | Weight Loss Calories |
| | 11-20 | 21-50 | 31-40 | 41-50 | + | − | | |
|---|---|---|---|---|---|---|---|---|
| May...... | data not available | | | | | | | |
| July...... | data not available | | | | | | | |
| Sept...... | 2.06 | 1.00 | 1.10 | — | 3.08 | — | 74 | — |
| Oct...... | **1.86**[2] | 1.20 | 1.00 | .96 | 3.03 | .19 | 81 | 5 |
| Nov...... | **1.70** | 1.04 | .82 | .69 | 1.32 | 2.28 | 56 | 95 |
| Jan...... | — | .99 | .86 | — | — | 5.15 | — | 123 |
| Feb...... | — | — | .94 | — | — | 8.20 | — | 152 |
| March.... | 1.71 | 1.27 | .99 | .91 | 20.92 | .68 | 516 | 17 |
| April..... | **1.87** | 1.21 | 1.03 | .91 | 9.92 | 1.72 | 190 | 33 |

[1] Positive and negative daily instantaneous rates of growth derived from proportionate weight gains and losses of all weight classes within the month.
[2] Boldface growth rates were calculated by the increment method.

TABLE 3. Potential production of new *Microtus* per hectare.

| Date | Time Interval Between Trapping Days | Pregnancy Rate Per Cent | Mean Adult Population Numbers | Potential Production | |
| | | | | Numbers | Calories |
|---|---|---|---|---|---|
| May.......... | 64 | 90 | 7.2 | 24.8 | 102 |
| July.......... | 42 | 90 | 12.6 | 28.5 | 117 |
| Sept.......... | 35 | 90 | 18.5 | 34.8 | 143 |
| Oct.......... | 39 | 90 | 30.7 | 64.5 | 265 |
| Nov.......... | 61 | 65 | 58.2 | 137.9 | 567 |
| Jan.......... | 35 | 00 | 104.7 | — | — |
| Feb.......... | 27 | 00 | 103.7 | — | — |
| March...... | 36 | 11 | 63.5 | 15.2 | 63 |
| April........ | 28 | 92 | 51.5 | 79.3 | 326 |
| Totals...... | | | | 385.0 | 1583 |

in mouse tissue due to the nestlings between the two trapping periods. The contribution of nestling young is shown in Table 4.

TABLE 4. Growth of nestling young per hectare.

| Date | Mean Biomass Grams | Growth Rate | Total Growth | |
| | | | Grams | Calories |
|---|---|---|---|---|
| May........ | 144 | 5.33 | 242 | 331 |
| July........ | 135 | 5.33 | 226 | 309 |
| September... | 180 | 5.33 | 302 | 414 |
| October..... | 333 | 4.67 | 516 | 706 |
| November... | 893 | 7.67 | 1231 | 1686 |
| March...... | 100 | 4.67 | 154 | 211 |
| April....... | 361 | 3.30 | 435 | 596 |
| Totals.... | | | 3106 | 4253 |

When the amount of energy leaving the *Microtus* population through respiratory processes is added to the production of tissue, the result is a measure of the assimilation of the population. Assimilation is defined here as the energy which enters the population and is actually used in productive or maintenance processes. An estimate of the respiratory energy loss was made by studying the metabolic rate of *Microtus* by the McLagan-Sheahan (1950) closed circuit method. This technique utilized a series of desiccator jars connected to a pure $O_2$ source, a vacuum pump, and mercury manometers. Soda lime, in the bottom of jars, absorbed $CO_2$. The system was of known volume (approximately 2600 ml) and was kept at a constant temperature of 26°C. Wild *Microtus* were trapped the day before the experiment and fasted over night (12 hrs). Three or four mice of the same sex and weight were placed in each jar and, after air was evacuated from the jars to a negative pressure of 200 mm Hg, pure $O_2$ was introduced until pressure returned to equilibrium. As the $O_2$ was consumed in the jars, the pressure changes were measured on mercury manometers. The mice were allowed about 30 min to become accustomed to the apparatus before readings were made on the manometers. After this initial period, the mice were maintained in the jars for 1 hr. A respiratory quotient (RQ) of .85 was assumed in the computations of metabolic rate.

Metabolic rate determined by this method can not be considered a basal rate (BMR) because the animals were slightly active in the jars during the experiments. Rather than basal rate, this study determined the fasting metabolic rate (FMR) of *Microtus*. The FMR (Table 5) was calculated in terms of cc of $O_2$ consumed per gm mouse tissue per hour and in Cal per 24 hrs per individual mouse. The respiration of the adult biomass was estimated by multiplying the metabolic rate in Cal per 24 hrs per mouse by the population density at a trap period and by the number of days between succeeding trap periods. The product of the metabolic rate of the young (assumed to be 1.7 Cal per 24 hrs), the mean population of young, and the time interval between trapping periods yielded the respiration of the nestling young.

TABLE 5. Respiration of experimental animals.

| Date | Ave. Weight Individuals Grams | Oxygen Consumption cc/gm/hr | Calories Per 24 Hours Per Mouse |
|---|---|---|---|
| Oct. | 25.5 | 2.86 | 8.2 |
| Feb. | 34.9 | 2.55 | 10.6 |
| April | 31.0 | 2.83 | 10.2 |
| Average | 29.9 | 2.75 | 9.7 |

The FMR when applied to animals in the field should be considered a minimal figure of metabolism. Brody (1945: 477) considers that the maintenance energy expense is twice the basal metabolic rate. The energy cost of maintenance is the net dietary energy needed to carry on life processes, excluding the production of flesh, milk, or young.

To determine the caloric value of *Microtus* carcasses, four wild mice were sacrificed, minced, and dehydrated in a lyophilizing apparatus. This dried material was then burned in the bomb calorimeter to determine average caloric value per gm of dry mouse tissue. The wild mice were of average weight, ranging from 10 to 39 gm, and did not exhibit large fat deposits around the internal organs.

Food consumption by mice was studied both in the field and in the laboratory. For the field studies, wild *Microtus* were snap-trapped every three months in other areas which were characterized by a bluegrass-perennial herb vegetation similar to that found on the study area. At least 24 mice were captured during each trapping period (Table 6). These mice were brought into the laboratory and their stomachs were removed and weighed. A portion of the stomach contents was placed on a glass slide with several drops of Turtox CMC-10 mounting media. A smear was made of this mixture and, after a cover glass was placed on the slide, the slide was examined under the low power objective of a microscope.

TABLE 6. Percentage importance of food materials from stomach samples.

| Food Material | Fall | Winter | Spring | Summer |
|---|---|---|---|---|
| Number of stomachs | 35 | 27 | 31 | 24 |
| Grass | 54 | 75 | 74 | 54 |
| Herbs | 28 | 18 | 23 | 44 |
| Insects | T | T | 1.8 | T |
| Fruits | 17 | 3 | .1 | 1 |
| Wood | 1 | 4 | .3 | — |
| Seeds | T | — | .6 | T |
| Moss | T | — | .1 | T |
| Fungi | T | — | T | 1 |
| Grasses and herbs alone | | | | |
| Grass | 66 | 81 | 76 | 55 |
| Herbs | 34 | 19 | 24 | 45 |

A stomach content key was devised by feeding in the laboratory 5 *Microtus* on diets of natural foods, each mouse receiving only one food substance. These animals were sacrificed and slides of their stomach contents served as a reference key when examining the stomachs of wild mice. Under the microscope it was possible to distinguish the following food types: grasses, herbs, woody materials, roots, seeds, fruits, mosses, fungi, and insect remains. These identifications were made on the basis of cell shape, cell wall structure, arrangement of stomata, presence of parenchyma cells, sclereids, tracheids, and other elements. An estimate was made of the percentage that each food type contributed to the bulk of the plant material on each slide. The percentage importance of the food types was determined for the collection period by averaging the data for each individual stomach.

The quantity of food consumed was measured for caged mice in two laboratory experiments. In the first experiment, 15 mice in 5 cages were fed a "standard" laboratory diet of lettuce, carrots, and oatmeal (Whitmoyer 1956) for 30 days. In the second experiment, 5 mice were maintained on fresh-cut alfalfa for 30 days. Water was available in both experiments. Animals gained weight, bred, and gave birth to normal litters on both diets. Food material

ere weighed in and out of the cages daily; the
eight loss of fresh food between weighings was de-
rmined by using a control cage. The information
a food consumption is summarized in Table 7. The
loric value of the standard diet was determined
om Wooster & Blanck (1950) and that of the alfalfa
y combustion in the bomb calorimeter.

TABLE 7. Daily food consumption of individual mice
a experimental diets.

| | STANDARD DIET | | | | Alfalfa Diet Alfalfa |
|---|---|---|---|---|---|
| | Lettuce | Carrot | Oatmeal | Total | |
| nsumption gms wet wgt... | 24.8 | 10.2 | 4.4 | 39.4 | 28.1 |
| nsumption gms dry wgt... | 1.3 | 1.2 | 4.0 | 6.5 | 12.0 |
| loric value of food per gm wet wgt... | .18 | .45 | 3.96 | — | — |
| loric value of food per gm dry wgt... | — | — | — | — | 4.1 |
| lories consumed... | 4.5 | 4.6 | 17.4 | 26.5 | 49.3 |
| e wgt mice (gms)... | | | | 46.0 | 46.0 |
| ns food consumed per gm mouse tissue... | | | | .14 | .26 |
| od Calories consumed per gm mouse tissue... | | | | .58 | 1.07 |

The digestibility of the experimental diets was
udied by collecting mouse feces in the cages for a
day period during each experiment. The feces were
ven-dried and the caloric value determined in the
omb calorimeter. By this method it was possible to
timate the amount of gross energy in the feed which
as undigested.

## STUDIES OF THE LEAST WEASEL

The energetics of the least weasel were given a
ore superficial treatment than those of the vegeta-
on, or of the *Microtus* population. Population esti-
ates were inferred from the capture of weasels in
ve traps during the mouse trapping program and
om counts of weasel tracks in the snow during
ecember, January, and February. During any one
apping period, captured individuals were identified
y weight under the assumption that only one indi-
idual of a particular weight would be present on
ae trap area. On the basis of trap records and
acking observations it appeared that there were two
dult weasels on the area of 2.5 ha in the late fall
f 1956. It was assumed that these weasels had been
resent and had produced young during the summer.
he number of litters produced per year (two) and
ie number of young per litter (five) were accepted
s reported by Burt (1948) and by Hall (1951).
une and August were arbitrarily chosen as the birth
ates of the litters.

Since no data on the growth of the least weasel
ere available, growth rates of adult and young
easels were estimated from the weights of captured
nimals. The initial weight for the adults in the
arly summer of 1956 was assumed to be 46 gm
average of 4 captures of young adults). These
dults were assumed to have grown to an average
dult weight of 60 gm by August (based on one cap-

ture) and to have maintained this weight through
the spring of 1957. It was further assumed that the
birth weight of the young was 3 gm and that each
individual in the litter grew approximately 6 gm per
month for the first 5 months and then 3 gm per
month for the next 5 months. As with *Microtus*,
production measurements were based on the instantaneous rate of growth of adults and young. Production was calculated separately for three 4-month
periods (Table 8). Biomass measurements were converted to their caloric equivalent by using the factor
obtained for mice carcasses.

Mortality was arbitrarily estimated as a loss of
approximately 5 young, weighing 15 gm each, from
September to December, 1956, and of one young,
weighing 35 gm, from January to May, 1957.

Food consumption and digestibility of food were
studied in the laboratory with one captured weasel
(Table 9). In the course of two feeding experiments,
one live mouse was placed in the weasel cage daily.
The remains of the dead carcass of the mouse fed the
previous day were transferred to a hardware-cloth
envelope within the cage to indicate evaporation loss
from the carcass. White mice (*Mus musculus*) were
fed in the first study and laboratory-raised *Microtus*
in the second study. Each experiment was run for a total
of 30 days.

During the feeding experiment using *Microtus*,
feces were collected for a 6-day period to measure
food digestibility. The caloric value of these feces
was determined in the bomb calorimeter.

The metabolic rate used for the least weasel was
that obtained by Morrison (1957).

## RESULTS

### SOLAR ENERGY

The annual insolation per ha for 1956 and 1957 is
shown in Table 10. Baten & Eichmeier (1951) indicate that the average agricultural growing season at
East Lansing is from May 8 to October 4, with extremes ranging from April 8 to November 16. Field
observations suggested that the growing season for
natural vegetation of the old field was slightly longer
than that for cultivated crops and extended from approximately April 1 (when spring plant growth became obvious) to approximately November 1 (when
the accumulated production peak was reached in
1956). The total insolation during the 1956 growing
season was $94.2 \times 10^8$ Cal per ha. Since approximately 50% of the incident energy (that in the ultraviolet and infrared portions of the spectrum) is not
used by plants in photosynthesis (Terrien, Truffaut &
Carles 1957, Daubenmire 1947), the total growing-
season insolation was divided by two to give the usable
insolation available to the plants. The data presented
in Table 10 represent total solar insolation at the
ground surface, and at the bottom of the table is
shown the 50% correction of growing-season insolation. The corrected insolation value for 1956 is used
in Fig. 1 and in all calculations of the ratio of insolation and production of the vegetation. The 50%

TABLE 8. Dynamics of least weasel population on one hectare.

| Season | Average Population Number | | Total Biomass Grams | | Proportionate Weight Change | | Production Grams | | Mortality Grams | | Respiration Loss Calories |
|---|---|---|---|---|---|---|---|---|---|---|---|
| | Adults | Young | Adults | Young | Adults | Young | Adults | Young | Adults | Young | |
| May-Aug...... | .80 | 2.0 | 42.4 | 10.3 | 1.30 | 2.58 | 11.1 | 10.0 | 0.0 | 0.0 | 1091 |
| Aug.-Dec...... | .80 | 2.8 | 48.0 | 34.9 | 0.00 | 3.04 | 0.0 | 38.8 | 0.0 | 31.5 | 1884 |
| Jan.-May..... | .80 | 1.6 | 48.0 | 61.9 | 0.00 | 1.76 | 0.0 | 35.5 | 0.0 | 10.5 | 2459 |

TABLE 9. Food consumption of the least weasel fed on live mice.

| Species | Food Consumption | | Caloric Value of Feces | Per Cent of Food Digested |
|---|---|---|---|---|
| | Grams | Calories | | |
| Microtus.... | 14.7 | 19.99 | 2.02 | 89.9 |
| White mice.. | 15.1 | 29.59 | — | — |

reduction may be excessive during April, May and June when the total insolation at ground surface is reduced due to increased cloudiness. Clouds reduce the amount of ultraviolet and infrared radiation because of diffusion and absorption by water molecules (Terrien, Truffaut & Carles 1957) and it might be anticipated that under clouds more than 50% of the insolation at the ground would be usable by the plants.

TABLE 10. Solar insolation on the study area in calories per hectare per month for 1956 and 1957.

| Month | 1956 | 1957 |
|---|---|---|
| January....................... | $4.2 \times 10^8$ | $5.0 \times 10^8$ |
| February...................... | 7.3 | 6.1 |
| March........................ | 9.5 | 11.0 |
| April......................... | 10.8 | 9.9 |
| May.......................... | 14.7 | 13.9 |
| June.......................... | 17.8 | 16.8 |
| July.......................... | 15.3 | 18.2 |
| August........................ | 13.6 | 15.2 |
| September..................... | 12.2 | 11.7 |
| October....................... | 9.8 | 7.9 |
| November..................... | 4.5 | 3.9 |
| December..................... | 2.7 | 3.8 |
| Total......................... | 122.4 | 123.4 |
| Total growing season (April 1 to Oct. 31).................... | 94.2 | 93.6 |
| Growing season correction[1]..... | 47.1 | 46.8 |

Data from the Michigan Hydrologic Research Station of the USDA and the Michigan Agricultural Experiment Station.
[1] 50 per cent of the total insolation during the growing season to allow for ultraviolet and infrared radiation which are not utilized in photosynthesis.

## DYNAMICS OF THE VEGETATION

The production of the vegetation can be separated into two different components: (1) the production of the plant tops and the root biomass over the growing season, and (2) the photosynthate which is lost to consumption by animals and to respiration of the plant biomass. The production of tops and roots plus the material eaten by animals comprise the net production; the inclusion of the respiration yields the gross production of the vegetation. In measure-

ments of net production by the harvest method, consumption of green plant material by animals often is not included in the estimate of total net production. Here, food consumption by the mouse population is added to the production of the roots and tops, while food consumption by insects and other herbivores is not estimated or included.

The dry weight standing crop of vegetation (Fig 2) shows a typical cycle of growth, death, and decay of vegetation. The grass-herb ratio shows cyclic fluctuations; grasses predominate in fall and winter with a tendency toward equality in midsummer. A slight change in caloric content of the vegetation also occurred seasonally (Tables 11, 12). The peak above ground standing crop was 385 gm per m² ($3.85 \times 10$ gm per ha) in 1956 and 251 gm per m² ($2.51 \times 10$ gm per ha) in 1957, these values being accepted a minimum estimates of production. The average caloric value of green vegetation was 4.08 Cal per g dry weight (average of the values in Table 2).

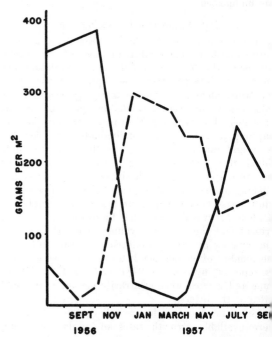

FIG. 2. The standing crops of living (solid line) and dead (broken line) vegetation by months in 1956 and 1957.

Standing crop of roots was measured three time during the 1957 growing season. The initial standing

TABLE 11. Above-ground standing crop of living and dead vegetation, and average caloric value of green grasses and herbs per square meter plot, and living grass-herb ratio.

| Date Collected | Number of Plots | STANDING CROP LIVE | | (GRAMS DRY WEIGHT) DEAD | | Caloric Values Cal/gram Dry Weight | Grass:Herbs (Weight) |
| | | Mean | SD | Mean | SD | | |
|---|---|---|---|---|---|---|---|
| 7/21/56............... | 2 | — | — | — | — | 4.12 | — |
| 8/ 8/56............... | 10 | 358.0 | ±49.2 | 55.6 | ±30.4 | 4.12 | 3.5:1 |
| 9/24/56............... | 16 | 372.4 | ±81.2 | 8.0 | — | 4.30 | 9.1:1 |
| 11/ 2/56............... | 20 | 385.2 | ±91.2 | 28.0 | — | 4.17 | 49.2:1 |
| 2/ 9/57............... | 10 | 31.2 | ±12.8 | 300.0 | ±60.0 | — | — |
| 3/22/57............... | 15 | 8.0 | ± 2.4 | 274.0 | ±75.2 | — | — |
| 4/24/57............... | 14 | 18.4 | ± 6.8 | 234.8 | ±97.2 | 3.99 | 16.0:1 |
| 5/22/57............... | 14 | 67.6 | ±12.8 | 236.0 | ±66.4 | 3.99 | 6.9:1 |
| 7/ 1/57............... | 15 | 147.2 | ±49.6 | 126.8 | ±47.6 | 3.90 | 2.6:1 |
| 8/ 5/57............... | 15 | 250.8 | ±71.2 | 140.4 | ±42.8 | — | 1.4:1 |
| 9/29/57............... | 14 | 184.0 | ±71.2 | 164.0 | ±42.4 | — | — |

TABLE 12. The caloric value per gram of oven-dried plant tissue for various plant species collected during the study.

| Date Collected | Species | Number of Samples | Cal/gm (Aver.) | S.D. |
|---|---|---|---|---|
| 7/22/56 | Poa compressa | 5 | 4.12 | ±.08 |
| 8/ 8/56 | Poa compressa | 9 | 4.18 | ±.20 |
| 9/24/56 | Poa compressa | 14 | 4.31 | ±.45 |
| 11/ 2/56 | Poa compressa | 15 | 4.18 | ±.08 |
| 5/22/57 | Poa compressa | 3 | 4.02 | ±.05 |
| 7/ 1/57 | Poa compressa | 3 | 3.99 | ±.11 |
| 8/ 8/56 | Linaria vulgaris | 5 | 4.28 | ±.07 |
| 9/24/56 | Linaria vulgaris | 5 | 4.34 | ±.10 |
| 8/ 8/56 | Daucus Carota | 5 | 3.92 | ±.45 |
| 8/ 8/56 | Cirsium arvense | 6 | 3.93 | ±.22 |
| 8/ 8/56 | Trifolium repens | 2 | 4.09 | ±.20 |
| 8/ 8/56 | Verbascum Thapsus | 3 | 3.98 | ±.14 |
| 8/ 8/56 | Plantago spp. | 2 | 3.79 | ±.09 |
| 8/ 8/56 | Dead grass | 6 | 3.91 | ±.05 |
| 2/ 9/57 | Dead grass | 15 | 4.25 | ±.06 |
| 4/24/57 | Grass and herbs | 3 | 3.99 | ±.10 |
| 5/22/57 | Herbs combined | 3 | 3.97 | ±.12 |
| 7/ 1/57 | Herbs combined | 3 | 3.81 | ±.12 |
| 8/ 8/56 | Roots | 6 | 3.30 | ±.20 |

TABLE 13. Food consumption of *Microtus* populations during the 1956 and 1957 growing seasons.

| Date | Interval Days | Density Mice Per Hectare | Individual Mean Weight Grams | Population Biomass Grams | Consumption Grams Per Hectare |
|---|---|---|---|---|---|
| 1956 | | | | | |
| April 1...... | 52 | 5.0 | 29 | 145 | 1,056 |
| May 22...... | 63 | 5.2 | 29 | 151 | 1,329 |
| July 24...... | 42 | 9.6 | 29 | 278 | 1,634 |
| Sept. 4...... | 35 | 16.5 | 29 | 479 | 2,349 |
| Oct. 9...... | 22 | 21.2 | 31 | 657 | 2,024 |
| Total...... | | | | | 8,392 |
| 1957 | | | | | |
| April 1...... | 53 | 64.2[1] | 32 | 2054 | 15,243 |
| May 23...... | 26 | 49.8 | 26 | 1295 | 4,714 |
| June 18...... | 36 | 65.4 | 28 | 1831 | 9,227 |
| July 24...... | 61 | 61.4 | 30 | 1842 | 15,732 |
| Sept. 23...... | 38 | 111.2 | 26 | 2891 | 15,379 |
| Total...... | | | | | 60,295 |

[1] Average of March and April population estimates.

gm of plant per night are shown in Table 14. The product of the rate of respiration in Cal, the mean standing crop of vegetation and the number of days between measurements of respiration yielded the Cal used in night respiration by the vegetation over the growing season, 146.2 Cal per m² plot or 1.46 × 10⁶ Cal per ha (Table 15).

TABLE 14. Night respiration of old field vegetation.

| Date | CO2 Produced cc./night | O2 Consumed cc./night | RQ | Calories per cc. Oxygen | Grams Vegetation[1] | Calories per Gram per Night |
|---|---|---|---|---|---|---|
| 5/17/57 | 1.96 | 3.50 | .56 | .0045 | .398 | .041 |
| 5/25/57 | 1.36 | 1.91 | .72 | .0047 | .589 | .016 |
| 6/13/57 | 1.17 | 1.20 | .97 | .0050 | .866 | .007 |
| 7/20/57 | .90 | .68 | 1.31 | .0053 | 1.905 | .002 |

[1] Grams of vegetation on area covered by cans (86.6 cm²) derived from the graph of standing crop of vegetation (Fig. 1).

crop (1493 gm per m², 15 cm deep) was measured on April 13, 1957 when the vegetation was beginning spring growth. The second measurement was made on July 11, when the root standing crop was 1805 gm per m². The peak standing crop was 2516 gm per m² on September 29, 1957. The difference between the peak and initial standing crop approximated the organic matter synthesized and stored in the roots above 15 cm depth over the growing season (1023 gm per m²) in 1957. It was assumed that this rate was also applicable to the 1956 season. The caloric value of the roots, determined for a sample collected in August 1956 was 3.30 Cal per gm dry weight (Table 12).

The amount of live vegetation calculated to have been consumed by mice during the growing seasons in 1956 and 1957 is shown in Table 13.

Data on respiration of the vegetation were collected during four nights in the summer of 1957. The CO₂ released, O₂ consumed, RQ, and Cal used per

Thomas & Hill (1949) in their field studies on the respiration of alfalfa showed that night respiration of the tops was approximately one-half the day respiration and that the root respiration was about equal to the combined day and night top respiration.

TABLE 15. Night respiration of the vegetation biomass during growing season.

| Date | Interval Days | Mean Standing Crop Vegetation Grams | Respiration Rate Cal/ gm/night | Respiration Loss/m² Cal. |
|---|---|---|---|---|
| April 1 to May 21....... | 51 | 6.1 | .041 | 50.4 |
| May 22 to June 2........ | 12 | 16.7 | .016 | 12.4 |
| June 3 to July 2......... | 30 | 27.6 | .007 | 23.2 |
| July 3 to Nov. 1......... | 121 | 62.2 | .002 | 60.2 |
| Total............... | | | | 146.2 |

If we assume that these findings can be applied to the old-field vegetation, the day respiration of the tops would equal $2.92 \times 10^6$ Cal per ha, and respiration of the roots, $4.38 \times 10^6$ Cal per ha. Total respiration of the entire plant biomass would be approximately $8.76 \times 10^6$ Cal per ha or 15% of the total assimilation. This estimate is slightly less than those of Transeau (1926) and Thomas & Hill (1949). These workers suggest that respiration of the plant biomass amounts to 25-35% of the total production. It is not known if the discrepancy between estimates made in this study and those by Transeau and Thomas & Hill is due to a diffusion of gases between the soil and air under the cans, or if it represents a real difference between the respiration of natural vegetation and cultivated crop plants.

In 1956 and 1957 the production was made up of the following components:

|  | 1956 | 1957 |
|---|---|---|
| Production of tops | $3.85 \times 10^6$gm/ha | $2.51 \times 10^6$gm/ha |
| Root production | $10.23 \times$ " | $10.23 \times$ " |
| Consumed by *Microtus* | $.01 \times$ " | $.06 \times$ " |
| Weight net production | $14.09 \times$ " | $12.80 \times$ " |
| Caloric net production | $49.51 \times 10^6$Cal/ha | $44.25 \times 10^6$Cal/ha |
| Respiration | $8.76 \times$ " | $8.76 \times$ " |
| Caloric gross production | $58.27 \times$ " | $53.01 \times$ " |

### THE DYNAMICS OF THE *Microtus* POPULATION

The energy dynamics of the Microtus population were separated into several components: (1) the tissue production, (2) energy expense of respiration, and (3) the intake of energy through foods. The estimate of tissue production was, in turn, based on determinations of the standing crop of mice, production of young, and rate of growth of mice in all age categories. To relate *Microtus* to the vegetation base of the food chain, determinations of consumption and digestibility of foods were used to estimate the percentage of the available food consumed by the mice, and the percentage of the consumed food used in metabolic processes and stored as tissue production. Finally, each separate component was brought together in Fig. 1 to show the entire exchange through the *Microtus* population.

### Standing Crop of *Microtus*

The standing crop of *Microtus* showed some unexpected variations during the investigation (Table 1). The population at the beginning of the study was at a very low level (5.2 mice per hectare). In fact, following the first trapping program in May 1956, an attempt was made to relocate the study on another area with a higher population of *Microtus*. It was not known whether this "low" was the result of adverse weather, heavy predation, or "cyclical behavior."

The estimated peak population (139 mice per hectare) determined in this study could not be considered unusual for the species. Other workers have arrived at greater estimates of population density for *Microtus pennsylvanicus*, 291 per hectare (Bole, 1939), 395-567 per hectare (Hamilton, 1937), and 165 per hectare (Townsend, 1935). The months in which the peak density occurred was unusual. Hamilton (1937), Martin (1956) and others showed that *Microtus* generally reach a peak population in the fall (September to November) after which the population decreases until breeding begins again in the spring. Linduska (1950), on the contrary, found that the annual peak population at Rose Lake, Michigan, approximately seven miles north of this study, occurred in January and February, as in the present study. Linduska was unable to explain the difference between his results and those of Hamilton, but suggested that the winter peak may be a local adaptation to "xerophytic" conditions.

A more detailed knowledge of the population density and topography of the study area enabled the writer to suggest another explanation for the winter population high. A region of dense cover, composed primarily of bluegrass sod, occurred in the center of the trap area. This dense cover may have served as a place of refuge for the mice during alternately wet and freezing weather occurring in January, February, and March. The number of new captures per day of trapping was correlated with snowfall (Table 16) suggesting that snow storms stimulated increased movement of the mice. Since in November and January the increased captures of new animals occurred late in the trapping period, it was thought that these captures represented new animals moving into the trap area rather than movement of the resident population. The movements immediately before and during snowfall were considered to be due to a migration of mice from upland areas into the areas with heavier cover, resulting in an increased population on the study area during the storm periods and possibly throughout the winter.

The fraction of animals captured in common to both lines decreased in January, February, and March (Table 1). This seasonal variation may have been

TABLE 16. Snowfall and new captures of *Microtus* in three winter months compared with a typical summer month.

| Day of Trapping | NOVEMBER | | JANUARY | | FEBRUARY | | JULY | |
|---|---|---|---|---|---|---|---|---|
| | Snow[1] | Captures | Snow | Captures | Snow | Captures | Snow | Captures |
| 1 | .00 | 2 | .00 | 1 | .00 | 3 | .00 | 4 |
| 2 | .00 | 3 | .05 | 1 | .00 | 4 | .00 | 11 |
| 3 | .00 | 4 | .01 | 2 | .10 | 10 | .00 | 4 |
| 4 | .00 | 3 | .28 | 8 | .00 | 9 | .00 | 6 |
| 5 | .10 | 8 | .17 | 2 | .00 | 3 | .00 | 9 |
| 6 | .50 | 2 | .01 | 1 | .00 | 7 | .00 | 3 |
| 7 | T | 0 | T | 2 | T | 1 | .00 | 2 |
| 8 | | | .85 | 11 | | | | |
| 9 | | | .05 | 0 | | | | |

[1] Snowfall or sleet in inches, taken from U. S. Department of Commerce, Local Climatological Date for East Lansing, Michigan.

the result of decreased size of the home range of the mice and consequent shorter daily movements. These in turn, may have resulted from increased density of mice or from some characteristic of winter weather acting on mouse behavior. Further information is needed before the cause for the decrease in number of captures in common in the winter can be established.

The observed fraction of animals captured in common to both lines for January (4.5%) was lower than that fraction used in Table 1. The January trapping period was interrupted by heavy snowfall and it was possible to run the trap lines only 3 days in one period and 4 days in another. If the unusually low fraction .045 is used to determine population density a very high population estimate (256 per ha) results. It was thought that this high a density was unlikely, since it would require a six-fold increase in the population in two months. Therefore, the fractions of common captures for the other winter months (February and March) were averaged and this average was used to estimate the January population.

### Caloric Value of Microtus Tissue

Since the objective of this study was to determine the energy transfer and losses between the levels of the food chain, it was necessary to convert the production data, calculated initially in terms of weight, into Calories (Table 17). In the process of preparing mice for calorific analysis, the mice lost approximately 71% of their body weight. Since mouse production figures were computed in terms of live weight, the average caloric value per gm of mouse tissue had to be converted from dry weight (4.65 Cal per gm) to live weight (1.37 Cal per gm).

### Mortality or Emigration of the Mice

Mortality and emigration both result in the disappearance of mice and are considered collectively in this report. When an animal was not caught again, it was impossible to determine whether it had died or had moved out of the trapping area. In a few instances animals were trapped in one month and not retrapped until several months later. Where these

TABLE 17. The wet weight, dry weight, and the average caloric value per gram dry *Microtus* tissue determined for four male mice (standard deviation in parenthesis).

| Individual | Age | Live Weight | Dry Weight | Caloric Value of Tissue |
|---|---|---|---|---|
| 1 | adult | 39.1 | 11.9 | 4.49 (± .21) |
| 2 | adult | 24.5 | 7.0 | 4.67 (± .25) |
| 3 | adult | 28.0 | 8.1 | 4.63 (± .26) |
| 4 | juvenile | 10.0 | 2.9 | 4.82 (± .07) |
| average (pooled data) | | | | 4.65 (± .21) |

animals resided in the intervening period is unknown, but it is here assumed that they were on the trap area.

The mortality of juveniles and adults was greatest immediately after the peak population was reached in February (Table 1). This peak was possibly correlated with periodic inundation of the low portions of the study area in February and March. As was mentioned previously this population decrease was expected to occur in December but may have been postponed by an immigration of mice into the trap area in January and February. Because of the fire on the study area in March, a measure of the mortality rate was unavailable for February. Mortality was assumed to be 55% in this month (based on the difference between the population estimates for February and March on the two adjacent areas).

### Production of Young by Adults

The potential number of young produced by the population showed a consistent increase from 24.8 mice per ha in May to 137.9 mice per ha in November 1956, and from 15.2 mice per ha in March to 79.3 mice per ha in April 1957 (Table 3). During January and February no females were judged to be in breeding condition and it was assumed that no breeding occurred. This assumption is consistent with the findings of Hamilton (1937). During the first four months of the study data on the breeding condition of the females were not collected. The pregnancy rate for these periods was later assumed to be approximately 90%.

TABLE 18. Population dynamics of nestling young on one hectare.

| Date | Potential Production Numbers | Replacements[1] Numbers | Survival Rate Per Cent | Mean Biomass of Young Grams | Mortality | | Immigration Numbers |
| | | | | | Grams | Calories | |
| --- | --- | --- | --- | --- | --- | --- | --- |
| May................. | 24.8 | 14.5 | 58 | 144 | 78 | 107 | — |
| July................. | 28.5 | 12.7 | 45 | 135 | 108 | 148 | — |
| Sept................. | 34.8 | 18.3 | 53 | 180 | 114 | 156 | — |
| Oct................. | 64.5 | 38.0 | 59 | 333 | 176 | 241 | — |
| Nov................. | 137.9 | 63.8 | 46 | 893 | 693 | 949 | — |
| Jan................. | 0.0 | 0.0 | — | — | — | — | 96.0 |
| Feb................. | 0.0 | 0.0 | — | — | — | — | — |
| March.............. | 15.2 | 27.4 | 100 | 100 | 0 | 0 | 13.4 |
| April.............. | 79.3 | 44.1 | 56 | 361 | 209 | 286 | — |

[1] Number of young replacing adults disappearing through death or migration.

The potential natality suggests the maximum possible number of young which could be produced by the population, and may be the source of most of the population increase and of replacements for adults disappearing from the population. The number of young entering the trap-susceptible population was assumed to be equal to the number of adults and juveniles disappearing between trapping periods. These replacement young also showed a consistent increase from spring to fall (Table 18) and in all but March were fewer in number than the potential production of young.

## Production of Tissue

Production of tissue in the mouse population was calculated for each trapping period from a knowledge of the average population biomass and the observed rates of growth. This calculation was carried out separately for the various weight classes, the production of tissue being estimated by methods described earlier. For each class the average biomass between times of trapping was estimated as the mean value of the corresponding population biomass determinations made at each trapping. The rates of growth were determined from weights of individual mice recaptured in two consecutive trapping periods.

On occasion certain weight classes, while obviously contributing to the population biomass, were not represented by recaptured animals, and hence, no growth rates were available for these classes. In Table 2 these instances are distinguished. Since it was known that some of the classes not represented by recaptured mice contributed to the production of tissue, it was necessary to estimate appropriate rates of growth for weight classes known to be producing tissue.

To estimate missing growth rates, use was made of the fact that growth rates decreased progressively with increasing weight, in each time period. This fact is obvious in Table 2 where the proportional weight changes, unadjusted for length of interval, show that over the year the average weight change for mice in the 11-20 gm class exceeded the average change for the 21-30 gm class by a factor of 0.66. Similarly, the 21-30 gm mice exceeded the 31-40 gm animals by 0.30. For those classes for which information was lacking on growth rates, as detailed above, substitute values were approximated by adding the above average increment in proportionate growth to the observed proportionate change for the next heaviest weight class. For example, in October 1956, 0.66 was added to the value of 1.20 observed for the 21-30 gm mice to estimate the missing value for the 11-20 gm animals.

In every instance survivors in the 41-50 gm class lost weight (Table 2). Hamilton (1941) suggests that the heavier adult mice lose weight only in the winter, but these data indicate that weight loss is characteristic of the 41-50 gm weight class throughout the year. This weight loss does not appear to be correlated with senility because in no instance did a heavy animal showing a weight loss disappear in the trapping period immediately following the loss in weight. Over the winter months of January and February mice in most other weight classes also lost weight. These losses probably represent the exhaustion of body fat stored over the fall months.

The weight distribution graph (Fig. 3) reflected the internal dynamics of the mouse population. Since weight may be considered a rough criterion of age, it would be expected that the greatest number of mice would fall in the lightest weight classes. However, no mice were caught in the 1-10 gm weight class, except in May. Whitmoyer (1956) found in his study of the growth rate of laboratory-raised *Microtus pennsylvanicus* that the eyes of all young were open at 11 days of age, at an average weight of 9 gm. Hamilton (1941) also showed that young *M. pennsylvanicus* did not leave the nest until they were 10 gm in weight, at 9-13 days of age. Therefore, it was assumed that nestling young did not leave the nest before they attained a weight of 10 gm, and that the probability of capturing an animal weighing less than 10 gm was very small.

Blair (1948) states that small meadow mice old enough to leave the nest may be caught by live traps. If the probability of capture were the same for all weight classes, in those months in which reproduction occurred we would expect the highest number of captures to be in the 11-20 gm class. However the 11-20 gm class in each month except one (May) had fewer mice than did the 21-30 gm class (Fig. 3). The home range of very young mice may be smaller than

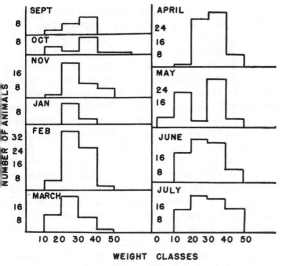

Fig. 3. The number of animals per weight class captured during each trapping period.

that of adults, resulting in a lower probability of capture of juvenile mice and a proportionately lower representation of this class of mice in the data. A second explanation for fewer animals in the 11-20 gm class than expected may be that the rapid growth of these mice shortens the period of exposure to trapping for individuals in this weight class. Hamilton (1941), observing the lower proportion of lightweight mice in his trapping data, suggested that exceptionally heavy mortality in this weight class may be further cause for the phenomenon. Whatever the cause, if the probability of capture for the 11-20 gm mice is less than for the 21 gm and heavier animals, the determination of the biomass of the population based on live-trapping data might underestimate the contribution of the 11-20 gm weight class.

The growth rates of nestling young (Table 4) were generally quite similar over the year since the growth rates were calculated from a constant birth weight of 3 gm and the relatively constant weight of the lightest juvenile captured in the traps. Since nestling young had the highest growth rates, they contributed a larger share of the tissue growth or production over the period of study (Table 4) than did the adults and juveniles (Table 2).

### Immigration into the Study Area

In January and March the potential production was insufficient to account for the increase in the population and/or the mortality of adults and juveniles. To account for the discrepancy between the potential production and the number of young entering the trap-susceptible population, it was assumed that mice migrated into the study area. In March this type of immigration was of a relatively minor nature, amounting to only 21% of the mean adult population. In January, however, the immigration was of greater importance since the population almost doubled between January and February (Table

1). There were no young produced in January; therefore, all of this increase must have been due to immigration. This assumption is supported by the previous information of the winter movements of mice immediately before or during snow storms (Table 16), which were interpreted to mean a migration of mice into the study area.

Theoretically, since the population increased in size over the period of study, the energy lost to mortality should not exceed that appearing in tissue production. However, Table 19 shows that mortality exceeded production in every period studied. Since the standing crop increased over the year by 1569 Cal (Table 1), production plus immigration must have exceeded mortality plus emigration by this amount. These last two processes exceeded production alone by approximately 12,000 Cal (Table 19).

Table 19. Tissue production, mortality, and respiration of mouse population in calories per hectare.

| Period | PRODUCTION | | MORTALITY | | RESPIRATION | |
|---|---|---|---|---|---|---|
| | Entire Period | Per Day | Entire Period | Per Day | Entire Period | Per Day |
| May to July | 331 | 5 | 500 | 8 | 4,871 | 76 |
| July to Sept. | 309 | 8 | 380 | 9 | 5,007 | 119 |
| Sept. to Oct. | 488 | 14 | 695 | 20 | 6,808 | 195 |
| Oct. to Nov. | 787 | 20 | 951 | 24 | 10,578 | 271 |
| Nov. to Jan. | 1742 | 29 | 2,111 | 35 | 33,245 | 575 |
| Jan. to Feb. | — | — | 1,245 | 36 | 27,055 | 773 |
| Feb. to March | — | — | 3,284 | 122 | 37,544 | 1391 |
| March to April | 727 | 20 | 987 | 26 | 27,710 | 770 |
| April to May | 786 | 28 | 2,217 | 79 | 17,059 | 609 |
| Total | 5170 | | 17,200 | | 169,877 | |

The conclusion follows that immigration (termed import in Fig. 1) must have contributed approximately 13,500 Cal. The estimates of immigration in Table 18 account only for the difference in calculated production of young and the young needed to replace trap-susceptible adults and juveniles. These estimates are included in the above calculations.

Energy leaving one population of mice by emigration joins another by immigration. Over all populations, these gains and losses must balance, just as production of all populations must equal the sum of mortality and population change. In this particular instance, immigration appears to have involved over twice as much energy transfer as production within the population itself. It is not known whether this population, sustaining a heavy population pressure as calculated from the weasels alone, represents a "sink" with energy flowing only inward, or whether it may approach an energy equilibrium, with the weasel and other predators being in equilibrium with the local production and there being a sizable exportation of energy from the population.

Immigration adds energy to a population, increasing the biomass, but not by any process defined here as production. Production of these animals took place elsewhere, and hence, cannot be credited to the local population. On the other hand, energy losses from the respiration of immigrants may have considerable influence on the energy balance in the community. Inspection of Table 1 and 19 will show that immigration increased the biomass greatly during January and February, accounting for a large part of the high population metabolism or respiration.

## Respiration of the Mouse Population

An estimate of the minimum number of Calories used by the mouse population in respiration was obtained from the fasting metabolic rate of *Microtus*. These rates showed very little variation seasonally (Table 5). Although an analysis of variance in the metabolic rates of individual groups in each calorimeter jar showed that no significant differences in the rates between seasons or within experiments, seasonal variations are to be expected. These were probably obscured by confining the mice in the laboratory at a constant temperature while measurements were being made. The average metabolic rate of 10 Cal per 24 hrs per mouse was used as the minimum metabolic constant to determine the minimum respiration of the mouse biomass (Table 20).

TABLE 20. Respiration of the mouse population.

| Date | Respiration of Young Calories per Hectare | Respiration of Adults |
|------|------|------|
| May | 1,575 | 3,296 |
| July | 975 | 4,032 |
| Sept. | 1,050 | 5,758 |
| Oct. | 2,329 | 8,249 |
| Nov. | 7,381 | 25,864 |
| Jan. | — | 27,055 |
| Feb. | — | 37,544 |
| March | 620 | 27,090 |
| April | 2,177 | 14,882 |
| Total | 16,107 | 153,770 |

The average metabolic rate determined in the present study, 2.75 cc $O_2$ per gm per hr, compares favorably with the determinations on *Microtus pennsylvanicus* made by Pearson (1947), 1.9—2.8 cc/gm/-hr, and Morrison (1948), 1.8—2.8 cc/gm/hr. Hatfield (1939) studied metabolism in *Microtus californicus* but arrived at a much higher figure of metabolism, 5.2 cc/gm/hr. Pearson suggested that the higher metabolic rates obtained by Hatfield were due to greater activity during the periods of measurements. The metabolic rate determined by this study was a minimal rate and when used in calculations of energy loss by respiration underestimated the actual loss. The average metabolic rate of *Microtus* in the wild is unknown. Morrison (1948) gives some indication of what this average rate would be; in his studies, the average metabolic rate of Microtus held in the calorimeter for 24 hrs, with food and water provided, was 18-42% above the minimum rate of metabolism.

## Summary of *Microtus* Energy Assimilation

The summary of the energy assimilation of the *Microtus* population (Table 19) shows the assimilation of a population changing from a low density to a higher density. With the exception of January and February, when growth of young and adult mice did not occur, tissue production rose continuously during the spring, summer, and fall of 1956, and the spring of 1957. Mortality, including the disappearance of mice from the population by death, predation, or emigration, also showed a smooth rise, with a disproportionate increase in February. Respiration was proportional to the population biomass and increased until the population drop in March. Following this, the energy loss due to respiration began a second increase. Laboratory metabolic measurements allowed no estimate to be made of expected seasonal changes in the respiration energy cost.

The respiration loss, though a minimal estimate, accounted for by far the greatest amount of energy used by the *Microtus* population. Respiration accounted for 68% of the energy passing through the mouse population yearly. In comparison, the mean biomass of mice (1900 Cal per ha) represented a storage at any one time of only 1.0% of the annual energy consumption; the maximum biomass (Table 1) was only 3% and the minimum biomass 0.1% of the annual energy consumption.

## Digestibility of Food

The amount of food ingested and its energy value may be understood in relation to the metabolism of the mouse population only through some knowledge of the digestive processes and their efficiency. The gross energy in the food minus the energy in the feces equals the digestible energy (Brody 1945). The feces include secretions and cells sloughing into the digestive tract. Thus the digestible energy indicates only the excess of food energy taken into the blood stream over excretion into the gut.

The digestibility of the food was investigated briefly in the laboratory, with results from three animals as indicated in Table 21. Although requiring confirmation, they indicate an exceptionally high digestibility for alfalfa in *Microtus* (90% of the gross energy as against the figure of 50% given by Morrison 1949 for cattle and sheep.) Further, with the diet of lettuce, carrots, and oatmeal, 82% of the gross energy was digested, equalling the presumed digestive efficiency of humans with the same diet, as calculated from the tables of Merrill & Watt (1955).

Further work in this direction is needed to understand the trophic ecology of *Microtus,* as well as other small mammals. Attempts should be made to determine the digestibility for various single dietary components and for complete diets. The qualitative composition of the diet also requires investigation, as suggested in the following section.

## Consumption of Food

The amount of food consumed, considered with digestibility, constitutes the trophic levy upon the

TABLE 21. Digestibility of laboratory diets.

| Day | Caloric Intake in Food | Caloric Loss in Feces | Undigested (per cent) |
|---|---|---|---|
| Alfalfa diet—2 female *Microtus* | | | |
| 1. | 128.7 | 20.2 | 15.7 |
| 2. | 183.1 | 15.2 | 8.3 |
| 3. | 83.3 | 12.9 | 15.5 |
| 4. | 143.5 | 12.0 | 9.0 |
| 5. | 176.1 | 12.4 | 7.0 |
| average (pooled data) | | | 10.2 (±4.2)[1] |
| Standard diet— 1 male *Microtus* | | | |
| 1. | 26.1 | 4.3 | 16.5 |
| 2. | 21.3 | 4.3 | 20.2 |
| 3. | 28.9 | 4.4 | 15.2 |
| 4. | 21.5 | 4.3 | 20.0 |
| 5. | 23.3 | 4.2 | 18.0 |
| average (pooled data) | | | 17.8 (±2.2) |

[1] Standard deviation in parenthesis.

environment by the population. Food consumption may be estimated in several ways; here it has been done by laboratory means (Table 7) and by examination of the stomach contents of wild mice (Table 22).

TABLE 22. Weight of stomach contents of snap-trapped mice.

| Season | Number Weighed | Mean Wgt Mice Grams | Mean Weight of Contents Grams | Standard Deviation Grams | Calculated[1] Daily Food Consumption Grams |
|---|---|---|---|---|---|
| Fall | 28 | 28 | 1.15 | ±.83 | 23.0 |
| Winter | 27 | 28 | 1.35 | ±.68 | 27.0 |
| Spring | 21 | 35 | 1.17 | ±.59 | 23.4 |
| Summer | 24 | 27 | 1.31 | ±.68 | 26.2 |
| average | | | | | 24.9 |

[1] Under the assumption that the mean weight of stomach contents represents one-half the stomach capacity and that the mice have 10 feeding periods per day.

Food consumption of *Microtus* has long been of interest to investigators, partly for economic reasons. Bailey (1924) fed *Microtus* a diet of clover, cantaloupe, grain, and seeds and found that they consumed 55% of their body weight daily. Regnier & Pussard (1926) obtained similar results with *Microtus arvalis* on a mixed diet of oat seeds, oat stems, and mangolds. In an experiment on which *Microtus* were fed a diet of dry feed (rolled oats, dry skim milk, dry meat, and seeds), Hatfield (1935) found an average consumption of 3.48 gm of food per mouse per day.

In the present study the mice on the standard diet consumed more fresh food than did the mice on the alfalfa diet. When dry weight of the food and caloric value was considered the reverse was true. It appears from these results and with comparison with Hatfield's findings that inclusion of dry foods in the diet re-

duced food consumption on a weight basis. The dry food materials (oatmeal, seed, etc.) have a much higher caloric value than fresh leafy foods such as lettuce and alfalfa, and animals on a fresh diet of succulent foods might have to consume a greater quantity of food to satisfy their energy requirements. In the present study, the mice on the alfalfa diet consumed 61% of their body weight daily and those on the "standard" diet consumed 86%. In both instances, the food consumption as a percentage of body weight was greater than that found by Bailey (1924) and Regnier & Pussard (1926).

Since blue grass appeared to be the dominant food plant of the environment in the study, attempts were made to maintain *Microtus* on a diet of fresh-cut, mature blue grass, with water available. In two attempts most of the animals lost considerable weight, or died, as indicated below:

| Trial | Number Mice | Number Dying | Number Losing Weight | Number Gaining Weight |
|---|---|---|---|---|
| 1 | 6 | 2 | 2 | 2 |
| 2 | 4 | 2 | 2 | 0 |

Dice (1922) was able to maintain *Microtus ochrogaster* on blue grass; possibly he fed immature grass or grass sod which might have a higher nutritive value. The energy content of the blue grass was 4.13 Cal per gm dry weight, which was closely similar to the caloric value of alfalfa (4.12 Cal per gm); however, the protein content of mature blue grass (6.6%, Morrison 1949) is much lower than that of alfalfa (14.8%, Morrison 1949). Lack of protein may be a cause of my failure to maintain *Microtus* on a blue grass diet. Regnier & Pussard (1926) found *Microtus arvalis* ate meat readily, consuming other voles and insects (Carabidae). They suggest that this consumption of protein might influence the numbers of mice during plague years. During one experiment in the present study, one *Microtus* ate 15 large grasshoppers within 24 hours. *Microtus* may thus supplement a low protein diet with insects or other high protein foods.

The stomach contents of animals taken by snap-traps reveal the proportional composition of the diet, assuming all components to be digested at the same rate (Table 6). To infer food consumption from the information on the volume of food in stomachs further, information on the rate of stomach clearance through digestion is required. Such information is not available, but one may infer from the observations of Hatfield (1940), Davis (1933), and Pearson (1947) that wild mice characteristically have 8-12 activity periods during a 24-hr day, and that these periods are concerned with feeding activity, to fill a nearly empty stomach.

The quantitative information on stomach contents (Table 22) may be examined, under the assumption of 10 activity periods a day, and a filling of the stomach to twice the mean observed contents at each activity period. The assumption that the mean stomach content equalled half a full stomach is supported not only by theoretical sampling considerations, but also by the observation that the observed stomachs ranged from full to almost empty, with most being "half-full."

The overall estimate of about 25 gm of food eaten per day (.86 gm wet food per gm mouse), for all sizes of capture-susceptible mice, agrees fairly well with the laboratory-determined values of 39 and 28 gm (.86 and .61 gm wet food per gm mouse) for two different diets. It is not known whether the indicated seasonal fluctuations are real or reflect bias from either shifting activity patterns, changing age structure, or sampling variation. However, this method of observation seems to offer a practical, if approximate, method of measuring food consumption.

The differential seasonal consumption of available food materials in Table 6 showed that grass (grass and sedges) was the dominant food at all seasons. Dead vegetation (with the exception of wood) was not found in the stomach slides, therefore, it was assumed that dead vegetation was not used by *Microtus*. Since the clip quadrat used to determine food availability and production of vegetation only sampled grasses and herbs and not mosses, fruit, and other foods, the separate percentages of grass and herbs in the stomachs were also calculated (Table 6).

The food consumption of the population was estimated by multiplying the biomass of the trap-susceptible population by the food consumption (.14 gm dry food per gm of mouse tissue per day or .58 Cal per gm of mouse tissue per day) of captive mice on the standard diet. Food consumption determined with the standard diet was used because it was thought that the standard diet more closely represented the diet of wild mice. Total consumption of vegetation per trap period by the mouse population was $250 \times 103$ Cal.

## THE LEAST WEASEL POPULATION

During the study least weasels were captured in 15 live-traps and were tracked on three different days during the winter. The largest number of individuals captured in one trap period was 4 (May 1957). Examination of the entire area on three days in winter (in each instance the morning following a snowfall of the previous day) yielded the tracks of one weasel in December, two in January, and three in February. According to Polderboer (1942) the maximum home range of the least weasel is 2 acres. Since the study area averaged 6.2 acres in size, it was assumed that at least three or four adult weasels could live on the area. Although the first evidence of weasels was not noted until July, 1956, it was assumed that two weasels were present at the beginning of the study in May, 1956.

Burt (1948) states that two litters of young are born per year. Litter size ranges from 4 to 10 (Burt 1948) and averages 5 (Hall 1951). If 2 litters of 5 young were produced by the weasels over the year, it is estimated that approximately 12 weasels were present on the area in September, 1956. This population of 12 animals decreased to 6 animals in May 1957.

The mean weight of the young dying in the period August to December was estimated at 15 gm, and in January to May at 35 gm. Although the population values may appear unusually high since the least weasel has been considered a rarity in Michigan (Hatt 1940), the evidence available supports these estimates.

Under the assumption that the population of least weasels followed the model developed in the section on methods and further elaborated in the above introductory paragraphs, the production of tissue by the weasels remained rather steady throughout the year (Table 8). In the summer, production of tissue was due to growth of both adults and young. In the fall and winter, the population of young, decreasing from 10 to approximately 5 animals, contributed all of the growth in this period. In the late winter and spring, the population of young, decreasing from 5 to 4 animals, again furnished all of the growth of tissue.

The respiration energy loss of the weasel population, based on an average minimum rate of $O_2$ consumption of 1.61 cc per gm per hr (Morrison 1957), increased over the year of study (Table 8). As observed with *Microtus*, the energy used in respiration of the weasel biomass was considerably greater than that involved in tissue production.

The laboratory feeding experiments were used to evaluate the role of the least weasel as a predator on *Microtus*. *Microtus* were assumed to be the sole food used by the weasel (Hatt 1940). In the laboratory experiments, the captive weasel consumed either 15.1 gm of white mice or 14.7 gm of *Microtus* per day (Table 9). Llewellyn (1942) found a similar rate of consumption in studies with a 32-gm weasel, i.e. 19.7 gm of mice per day. An average food consumption of 15 gm of mouse tissue per day was assumed to represent the true food consumption of adult weasels over the year. The young weasels, like other mammals (Morrison 1949), would probably use less food per day than the adults, and the daily food consumption of young was estimated to be 5 gm per day from May to August and 8 gm per day from August to December. Using these constants as a basis for calculating true food consumption, the effect of the weasel on the *Microtus* population was estimated. The weasel population consumed 5,824 Cal annually; this consumption was 3.07 times the mean biomass of *Microtus* (1900 Cal) over the year. Since net production of the *Microtus* population totaled only 5,170 Cal per ha annually, the weasel population appears to have required energy in excess of that produced by its principal prey. As previously noted, the production of the *Microtus* population did not allow for the energy imported by the mice which moved into the area. Further, it is possible that the weasel had other sources of food, such as *Blarina* which existed in moderately large numbers on the area, and insects which were abundant during the summer, or perhaps the calculations of weasel population density here are in error.

The percentage of the energy in the mouse car

casses which was digested by the least weasel was determined in the digestibility experiments. When the weasel was on the *Microtus* diet, he was able to digest 89.9% of the energy in the mouse bodies (Table 9). This rather high efficiency of digestion is comparable with the somewhat lower efficiency of digestion (70-80% of a dry-feed diet, McCay 1949) for the dog.

## DISCUSSION

In the transition of energy between two steps of the food chain there are two main pathways by which energy can be lost or diverted from the food chain itself. First, in tracing the energy from one population to the next not all the food organisms will be consumed by the consumer species; some of this energy could be dispersed to another food chain by migration of the food species out of the study area, by consumption of the food species by organisms outside of the food chain, or by death. These are considered to be energy losses of the first order. Second, not all the energy consumed is used in growth or in production of young; some of it is diverted to the maintenance of the organism and some passes through the body unused. These are energy losses of the second order. In energy losses of the first order the energy lost from the food chain is still in a form available for use by other animals. In energy losses of the second order, the loss is primarily heat derived from metabolic processes which is unavailable for further use by the food chain; that passing through the body is, of course, available to various other organisms in the food web.

### Energy Losses of the First Order

Of the solar energy available to the vegetation over the growing season (one-half of the total incident insolation during the growing season), 1.2% was utilized in the gross production, and 1.1% in the net production of the vegetation (Fig. 1). These figures can be compared with the giant ragweed ecosystem in Oklahoma, 1.2%, and alfalfa growing in experimental plots for 6 months, 3.1% (data converted from tabular material in Odum, 1959—net production was divided by incident energy data for Michigan). Data on the percentage of solar energy utilized by the vegetation of different communities are still too limited to allow any comparison of the efficiencies of a successional community with a stable one. At this time we may say only that terrestrial vegetation of the old field community on this soil, at this site, and for these years appeared to utilize approximately 1% of the available solar energy during the growing season.

The net production of the vegetation can be considered as the energy available to the herbivorous animals in the community. *Microtus* is primarily a herbivore, with animal food appearing only in trace amounts over the year (see Table 6). It was assumed in this study that only the production attributed to the above-ground vegetation could be utilized by *Microtus*. Some of the root biomass was undoubtedly

also used by the mice, but no estimate of the extent of root utilization was available. Lantz (1907) and Bailey (1924) state that consumption of roots is relatively unimportant, except during the winter, and roots were not recorded among the stomach contents in the present study. It is assumed here that use of roots was negligible.

Of the energy in the vegetation presumably available to the mice (15.8 $\times 10^6$ Cal), 1.6% was consumed, with 1.1% utilized by the mice in production and respiration. These percentages assume no loss of vegetation due to cutting of stems and leaves by *Microtus*. The utilization of the energy in the vegetation not consumed by mice was not traced further in this study. Some of this energy was probably diverted through invertebrate food chains. Wolcott (1937) indicated that insects ate .94 $\times 10^6$ gm (3.76 $\times 10^6$ Cal) of above-ground vegetation per ha in a pasture in New York over the summer. This level of consumption would amount to 23.9% of the available energy in the old field vegetation of the present study. If these data are correct, insects may be considered as more important herbivores in this old field community than are the meadow mice.

As mentioned previously, the energy in the *Microtus* population (production) available to predators was augmented by an import of energy through immigration of mice into the study area. This immigration was particularly noticeable in the winter and spring of 1957. Of the total energy available in the *Microtus* population (production plus immigration, Fig. 1) the least weasel consumed 31% as food and used 30% in production and respiration; considering only the production of the mice, the weasel consumed over 100%. When the energy consumed by the weasel and the energy retained in the mouse population through an increase in population size from May 1956 to May 1957 was subtracted from the production plus energy imported through immigration, 43% of the energy of the mouse population was unaccounted for. This loss may be attributed to emigration, to death from disease or accident, and degradation through microorganism food chains, or to capture in other predator chains. Some possible predators are *Blarina brevicauda* (Eadie 1952), *Felis domesticus* (Toner 1956, Korschgen 1957), or Owls, Red-tailed hawks, Red-shouldered hawks, and Cooper's hawks (Linduska 1950). All of these predators were seen on the study area during the investigation.

Most of the calculated production of the weasel population could be accounted for by the increase in the size of the population from May 1956 to May 1957. The expansion of the weasel population presumably was directly related to the expansion of the *Microtus* population. Only 10% of the production was not accounted for (Fig. 1). The least weasel may itself serve as food for certain predators, such as the great-horned owl, the barn owl, long-tailed weasel, and domestic cat (Hall 1951), but no information was gathered on mortality of weasels during this investigation.

## Energy Losses of the Second Order

The energy losses of the second order, due to respiration (fasting metabolism), nonassimilation of energy in the food, and the energy cost of maintaining the body under normal activity, can be further separated into energy losses available and unavailable to the biosphere. Energy losses available to the biosphere include the energy in fecal matter which is composed primarily of unassimilated food but also contains intestinal secretions and cellular debris. Energy in the feces would serve as the base for food chains of coprophagous organisms. The energy lost to the biosphere as heat derived from animal metabolism can be considered an increase in the positive entropy of the ecosystem.

Respiration loss (respiration energy/energy consumed) determined for each step of the food chain is as follows: Vegetation—15.0%, Mice—68.2%, Least Weasels—93.3%. The respiration coefficient for the vegetation may be underestimated as stated earlier; Transeau (1926) and Thomas & Hill (1949) suggest that it may run as high as 25-30%. The data confirm the statement of Lindeman (1942) that as energy passes through the trophic levels an increasing percentage is lost in respiration. It must be remembered that the percentages cited above for the mice and weasel were both determined as minimum metabolic rates and, therefore, indicate basic differences in the loss due to metabolism and not mere differences in activity. Taking activity into account would presumably act to increase the difference.

The energy consumed but not assimilated by *Microtus* and *Mustela* was measured in the digestion trials. Of the energy consumed, 10-18% was recovered in the feces of *Microtus* and 10% in the feces of *Mustela*.

When these losses were subtracted from the energy loss of the second order for each species, 14-22% of the energy consumed was unaccounted for in *Microtus* and all the energy loss was accounted for in the least weasel. It is highly unlikely that the energy loss in respiration and in the feces comprises the total energy losses in the organism. For instance, energy is also lost in the urine, in fermentation gases, and in specific dynamic action of feeding (energy used in the processes of food utilization). Estimates of the energy loss in the urine are 15% for cattle and 7% for rabbits after fecal losses are subtracted from the gross food energy (Brody 1945: 28), and the loss in specific dynamic action varies from 40% of the intake energy for lean meat, 15% for fat, and 6% for sucrose (Brody 1945: 61).

An additional energy loss not included above is the expense of normal body activity above rest. Very few investigators have been concerned with this maintenance cost according to Brody (1945), although he estimates that this loss is twice the basal metabolic rate. The minimum energy expended when the animal is confined and fasting (fasting metabolism) is known for *Microtus* and *Mustela* and was used to determine the loss of energy in respiration; but the energy used by these animals as they live in their natural environment is completely unknown. This latter energy expense reduces the efficiency of conversion by widening the gap between energy intake and production. The maintenance losses are reflected in the coefficient of production. Plants are the most sedentary and have the highest coefficient, 94.3% (net production/gross production). The weasel is the most active, since it must hunt for its food, and probably has the highest maintenance cost, with a low coefficient, 2.2% (production/energy intake). Possibly the energy expense of hunting by the predator will vary with different densities of the prey population. *Microtus* which is primarily dependent on vegetative material could be expected to have a low cost of maintenance and to display a higher coefficient than that shown in this study (2.1% production/energy intake). If the total energy losses in respiration and in the feces plus hypothetical maintenance cost are added to the production, the energy used totals more than the energy consumed by both the *Microtus* and *Mustela* populations. The reasons for this discrepancy were not determined, but food consumption rates estimated in the laboratory possibly underestimate the true food consumption of the more active animals in the field.

Since the maintenance cost is irreducible, the percentage of energy converted to production will be highest when the birth of new animals and the growth rate of living animals are the highest. This surge of production can most easily occur when sources of high energy food are available. *Microtus* conforms to this model, since the young are born and the rate of growth is highest during periods of greatest growth of the vegetation. It would further increase the year-round efficiency of the population to have the lowest population density during the period of little or no production by plants since at that time the dangers of over-exploitation of the food supply would be greatest. A low density at times of low plant production is the usual observation in field studies of the population dynamics of *Microtus* (Blair 1940, Martin 1956, Greenwald 1957, and others).

Finally, *Microtus* appears, on the basis of energy relationships, to be a relatively unimportant component of the community. Even when the energy consumption of insects (estimated as approximately 24% of the net production) is added to that of the mice only 25% of the net production of the plants is accounted for. Odum (1959) emphasizes the distinction between the herbivores which eat green plants directly and the delayed feeders which eat dead plant material. Apparently, in this stage of old field succession the major portion of the plant net production is directed through these decomposer food chains.

## SUMMARY

The energy dynamics of the perennial grass-herb vegetation—*Microtus pennsylvanicus*—*Mustela rixosa* food chain of the old field community was studied from May 1956 to September 1957.

Solar insolation for the growing season, measured

at East Lansing, Michigan, totaled $94.2 \times 10^8$ Cal per ha in 1956.

Primary net production by plants was broken down into the following components: (1) production of tops, (2) production of roots, and (3) consumption by *Microtus*. The net production of vegetation for 1956 was $49.5 \times 10^6$ Cal per ha and for 1957 was $44.3 \times 10^6$ Cal per ha. Respiration of the vegetation during the growing season amounted to approximately 15% of the net production, determined by crude field calorimetry. Gross primary production ranged from $58.27 \times 10^6$ Cal per ha in 1956 to $53.01 \times 10^6$ Cal per ha in 1957.

Population dynamics and weight changes of the *Microtus* population were studied by live-trapping. Tissue production of young and adult mice was 5,170 Cal per ha per yr. The fasting metabolic rate of mice determined in the laboratory was approximately 10 Cal per mouse per day. Energy lost to respiration equalled 169,877 Cal per ha per yr. The total energy used in growth of the weasel population were 130 Cal per ha per yr and in respiration, 5,434 Cal per ha per yr.

Stomach sample analysis indicated that *Microtus* ate primarily green grass and herbs. Weasels were assumed to feed predominantly on *Microtus*. Total yearly food consumption of the study area as determined from laboratory experiments, was 250,156 Cal per ha for Microtus and 5,284 Cal per ha for *Mustela*.

Of the solar energy available during the growing season, the vegetation used 1.2% in gross production and 1.1% in net production. These results compared favorably with the coefficients for primary production of terrestrial and aquatic communities determined by other workers. Of the energy available to the mice, 1.6% was consumed and 1.1% was utilized in growth and respiration. The weasel population consumed 31% of the energy available to it in the form of *Microtus*, and used 30% of the energy consumed in growth and respiration.

Twenty-one % of the production of the *Microtus* population and only 10% of the weasel production was lost from the food chain. These losses were diverted to other food chains through other predators or through micro-organisms.

Of the energy consumed only a portion was used in production; most of the energy went to respiration or passed through the digestive tract unused. Respiration cost increased from the vegetation level to the carnivore level of the food chain. The gross energy in the experimental diets which was recovered in the feces amounted to 10-18% for *Microtus* and 10% for *Mustela*.

## LITERATURE CITED

Bailey, V. 1924. Breeding, feeding and other life habits of meadow mice (Microtus). Jour. Agr. Res. 27: 523-536.

Baker, J. R. & R. M. Ranson. 1932. Factors affecting the breeding of the field mouse (*Microtus agrestis*) Part 1. Light. Proc. Royal Soc. London (B) 110: 313-322.

Baten, W. D. & A. H. Eichmeier. 1951. A summary of weather conditions at East Lansing, Michigan prior to 1950. Mich. State College Ag. Exp. Stat. 63 pp.

Beckwith, S. L. 1954. Ecological succession on abandoned farm lands and its relationship to wildlife management. Ecol. Monog. 24: 349-376.

Blair, W. F. 1940. Home range and population of the meadow vole in southern Michigan. Jour. Wildlife Mangt. 4: 149-161.

——. 1948. Population density, life span, and mortality rates of small mammals in the bluegrass meadow and bluegrass field associations of southern Michigan. Amer. Midland Nat. 40: 395-419.

Bole, B. P., Jr. 1939. The quadrat method of studying small mammal populations. Cleveland Mus. Nat. Hist. Sci. Publ. 5(4): 15-77.

Brody, S. 1945. Bioenergetics and growth. New York: Reinhold Publ. Corp. 1023 pp.

Burt, W. H. 1948. The mammals of Michigan. Ann Arbor: Univ. Mich. Press. 288 pp.

Clarke, G. L. 1946. Dynamics of production in a marine area. Ecol. Monog. 16: 321-335.

Clarke, G. L., W. T. Edmondson & W. E. Ricker. 1946. Mathematical formulation of biological productivity. Ecol. Monog. 16: 336-337.

Crabb, G. A., Jr. 1950a. Solar radiation investigations in Michigan. Mich. Agr. Expt. Sta. Tech. Bull. 222. 153 pp.

——. 1950b. The normal pattern of solar radiation at East Lansing, Michigan. Mich. Acad. Sci., Arts, and Letters 36: 173-176.

Daubenmire, R. F. 1947. Plants and Environment. New York: J. C. Wiley Co.

Davis, D. E. 1956. Manual for analysis of rodent populations. Ann Arbor, Mich.: Edwards Bros. 82 pp.

Davis, D. H. S. 1933. Rhythmic activity in the short-tailed vole, *Microtus*. Jour. Anim. Ecol. 2: 232-238.

Dice, L. R. 1922. Some factors affecting the distribution of the prairie vole, forest deer mouse, and prairie deer mouse. Ecology 3: 29-47.

Eadie, W. R. 1952. Shrew predation and vole populations on a localized area. Jour. Mammal. 33: 185-189.

Evans, F. C. & S. A. Cain. 1952. Preliminary studies on the vegetation of an old-field community in southeastern Michigan. Contrib. Lab. Vert. Biol. Univ. Mich. 51: 1-17.

Fernald, M. L. 1950. Gray's Manual of Botany. 8th Ed. New York: Amer. Book Co.

Greenwald, G. S. 1957. Reproduction in a coastal California population of the field mouse *Microtus californicus*. Calif. Univ. Pubs. Zool. 54: 421-446.

Hall, E. R. 1951. American weasels. Kans. Univ. Pubs. Mus. Nat. Hist. 4: 1-466.

Hamilton, W. J., Jr. 1937. The biology of microtine cycles. Jour. Agr. Res. 54: 779-790.

——. 1941. Reproduction of the field mouse, *Microtus pennsylvanicus* (Ord). Cornell Univ. Agr. Expt. Sta. Mem. 237.

Hatfield, D. M. 1935. A natural history study of *Microtus californicus*. Jour. Mammal. 16: 261-271.

————. 1939. Rate of metabolism in *Microtus* and *Peromyscus*. Murrelet 20: 54-56.

————. 1940. Activity and food consumption in *Microtus* and *Peromyscus*. Jour. Mammal. 21: 29-36.

Hatt, R. T. 1930. The biology of the voles of New York. Roosevelt Wildlife Bull. 5(4): 509-623.

————. 1940. The least weasel in Michigan. Jour. Mammal. 21: 412-416.

Korschgen, L. J. 1957. Food habits of coyotes, foxes, house cats, and bobcats in Missouri. Missouri Fish and Game Div. P-R Series No. 15. 63 pp.

Lantz, D. E. 1907. An economic study of field mice. USDA Biol. Surv. Bull. 31: 1-64.

Lindeman, R. L. 1942. The trophic-dynamic aspect of ecology. Ecology 23: 399-418.

Linduska, J. P. 1950. Ecological landuse relationships of small mammals on a Michigan farm. Mich. Dept. Cons. Game Div., Lansing. 144 pp.

Llewellen, L. M. 1942. Notes on the Alleghenian least weasel in Virginia. Jour. Mammal. 23: 439-441.

Martin, E. P. 1956. A population study of the prairie vole (*Microtus ochrogaster*) in northeastern Kansas. Kans. Univ. Pubs. Mus. Nat. Hist. 8(6): 361-416.

McCay, C. M. 1949. Nutrition of the dog. Ithaca, N.Y.: Comstock. 337 pp.

McLagen, N. F. & M. M. Sheahan. 1950. The measurement of oxygen consumption in small mammals by a closed circuit method. Jour. Endocrin. 6: 456-462.

Merrill, A. L. & B. K. Watt. 1955. Energy value of foods—basis and derivation. USDA Agr. Handbook No. 74. 105 pp.

Morrison, F. B. 1949. Feeds and Feeding. Ithaca, N.Y.: Morrison Publ. Co. 21st Ed. 1207 pp.

Morrison, P. R. 1948. Oxygen consumption in several small wild mammals. Jour. Cell. and Compar. Physiol. 31: 69-96.

Noddack, W. 1937. Der Kohlenstoff im Haushalt der Natur. Ztschr. f. Angew. Chem. 50: 505-510.

Odum, E. P. 1959. Fundamentals of Ecology. 2nd. Ed. Philadelphia: Saunders. 546 pp.

Odum, H. T. 1956. Efficiencies, size of organisms, and community structure. Ecology 37: 592-597.

Park, T. 1946. Some observations on the history and scope of population ecology. Ecol. Monog. 16: 313-320.

Pearsall, W. H. & E. Gorham. 1956. Production ecology. 1. Standing crops of natural vegetation. Oikos 7(2): 193-201.

Pearson, O. P. 1947. The rate of metabolism of some small mammals. Ecology 28: 127-145.

Polderboer, E. B. 1942. Habits of the least weasel (*Mustela rixosa*) in northeastern Iowa. Jour. Mammal. 23: 145-147.

Regnier, R. & R. Pussard. 1926. Le campagnol des champs (*Microtus arvalis* Pallas) et sa destruction. Ann. des Épiphyt. 12(6): 385-535.

Ricker, W. E. 1946. Production and utilization of fish populations. Ecol. Monog. 16: 373-391.

Shively, S. B. & J. E. Weaver. 1939. Amount of underground plant materials in different grassland climates. Nebr. Univ. Conserv. Bull. No. 21. 67 pp.

Tansley, A. G. 1935. The use and abuse of vegetational concepts and terms. Ecology 16: 284-307.

Terrien, J., G. Truffaut, & J. Carles. 1957. Light, vegetation and chlorophyll. New York: Philosoph. Libr. 228 pp.

Thomas, M. D. & G. R. Hill. 1949. Photosynthesis under field conditions. In, Photosynthesis in Plants, edited by J. Franck and W. E. Loomis. Ames: Iowa State Col. Press. 500 pp.

Toner, G. C. 1956. House cat predation on small animals. Jour. Mammal. 37: 119.

Townsend, M. T. 1935. Studies on some of the small mammals of central New York. Roosevelt Wildlife Ann. 4: 6-120.

Transeau, E. N. 1926. The accumulation of energy by plants. Ohio Jour. Sci. 26: 1-10.

Veatch, J. O., et al. 1941. Soil Survey of Ingham County, Michigan. USDA Soil Survey Series 1933, No. 36. 43 pp.

Whitmoyer, T. F. 1956. A laboratory study of growth rate in young *Microtus pennsylvanicus*. Unpubl. Master's thesis, Mich. State Univ. 62 pp.

Wolcott, G. N. 1937. An animal census of two pastures and a meadow in northern New York. Ecol. Monog. 7: 1-90

Wooster, H. A., Jr. & F. C. Blanck. 1950. Nutritional Data. Pittsburgh: H. J. Heinz Co. 114 pp.

# PART V

## COMMUNITY STRUCTURE AND POPULATION REGULATION

# HOMAGE TO SANTA ROSALIA

### or

# WHY ARE THERE SO MANY KINDS OF ANIMALS?*

## G. E. HUTCHINSON

Department of Zoology, Yale University, New Haven, Connecticut

When you did me the honor of asking me to fill your presidential chair, I accepted perhaps without duly considering the duties of the president of a society, founded largely to further the study of evolution, at the close of the year that marks the centenary of Darwin and Wallace's initial presentation of the theory of natural selection. It seemed to me that most of the significant aspects of modern evolutionary theory have come either from geneticists, or from those heroic museum workers who suffering through years of neglect, were able to establish about 20 years ago what has come to be called the "new systematics." You had, however, chosen an ecologist as your president and one of that school at times supposed to study the environment without any relation to the organism.

A few months later I happened to be in Sicily. An early interest in zoogeography and in aquatic insects led me to attempt to collect near Palermo, certain species of water-bugs, of the genus Corixa, described a century ago by Fieber and supposed to occur in the region, but never fully reinvestigated. It is hard to find suitable localities in so highly cultivated a landscape as the Concha d'Oro. Fortunately, I was driven up Monte Pellegrino, the hill that rises to the west of the city, to admire the view. A little below the summit, a church with a simple baroque facade stands in front of a cave in the limestone of the hill. Here in the 16th century a stalactite encrusted skeleton associated with a cross and twelve beads was discovered. Of this skeleton nothing is certainly known save that it is that of Santa Rosalia, a saint of whom little is reliably reported save that she seems to have lived in the 12th century, that her skeleton was found in this cave, and that she has been the chief patroness of Palermo ever since. Other limestone caverns on Monte Pellegrino had yielded bones of extinct pleistocene Equus, and on the walls of one of the rock shelters at the bottom of the hill there are beautiful Gravettian engravings. Moreover, a small relic of the saint that I saw in the treasury of the Cathedral of Monreale has a venerable and

---

*Address of the President, American Society of Naturalists, delivered at the annual meeting, Washington, D. C., December 30, 1958.

Reproduced with permission from The American Naturalist, XCIII: 145-159, 1959. Published by The American Society of Naturalists, Tempe, Arizona.

petrified appearance, as might be expected. Nothing in her history being known to the contrary, perhaps for the moment we may take Santa Rosalia as the patroness of evolutionary studies, for just below the sanctuary, fed no doubt by the water that percolates through the limestone cracks of the mountain, and which formed the sacred cave, lies a small artificial pond, and when I could get to the pond a few weeks later, I got from it a hint of what I was looking for.

Vast numbers of Corixidae were living in the water. At first I was rather disappointed because every specimen of the larger of the two species present was a female, and so lacking in most critical diagnostic features, while both sexes of the second slightly smaller species were present in about equal number. Examination of the material at leisure, and of the relevant literature, has convinced me that the two species are the common European *C. punctata* and *C. affinis*, and that the peculiar Mediterranean species are illusionary. The larger *C. punctata* was clearly at the end of its breeding season, the smaller *C. affinis* was probably just beginning to breed. This is the sort of observation that any naturalist can and does make all the time. It was not until I asked myself why the larger species should breed first, and then the more general question as to why there should be two and not 20 or 200 species of the genus in the pond, that ideas suitable to present to you began to emerge. These ideas finally prompted the very general question as to why there are such an enormous number of animal species.

There are at the present time supposed to be (Muller and Campbell, 1954; Hyman, 1955) about one million described species of animals. Of these about three-quarters are insects, of which a quite disproportionately large number are members of a single order, the Coleoptera.[1] The marine fauna although it has at its disposal a much greater area than has the terrestrial, lacks this astonishing diversity (Thorson, 1958). If the insects are excluded, it would seem to be more diverse. The proper answer to my initial question would be to develop a theory at least predicting an order of magnitude for the number of species of $10^6$ rather than $10^8$ or $10^4$. This I certainly cannot do. At most it is merely possible to point out some of the factors which would have to be considered if such a theory was ever to be constructed.

Before developing my ideas I should like to say that I subscribe to the view that the process of natural selection, coupled with isolation and later mutual invasion of ranges leads to the evolution of sympatric species, which at equilibrium occupy distinct niches, according to the Volterra-Gause principle. The empirical reasons for adopting this view and the correlative view that the boundaries of realized niches are set by competition are mainly indirect. So far as niches may be defined in terms of food, the subject has been carefully considered by Lack (1954). In general all the indirect evi-

[1] There is a story, possibly apocryphal, of the distinguished British biologist, J. B. S. Haldane, who found himself in the company of a group of theologians. On being asked what one could conclude as to the nature of the Creator from a study of his creation, Haldane is said to have answered, "An inordinate fondness for beetles."

dence is in accord with the view, which has the advantage of confirming theoretical expectation. Most of the opinions that have been held to the contrary appear to be due to misunderstandings and to loose formulation of the problem (Hutchinson, 1958).

In any study of evolutionary ecology, food relations appear as one of the most important aspects of the system of animate nature. There is quite obviously much more to living communities than the raw dictum "eat or be eaten," but in order to understand the higher intricacies of any ecological system, it is most easy to start from this crudely simple point of view.

## FOOD CHAINS

Animal ecologists frequently think in terms of food chains, of the form *individuals of species $S_1$ are eaten by those of $S_2$, of $S_2$ by $S_3$, of $S_3$ by $S_4$*, etc. In such a food chain $S_1$ will ordinarily be some holophylic organism or material derived from such organisms. The simplest case is that in which we have a true *predator chain* in Odum's (1953) convenient terminology, in which the lowest link is a green plant, the next a herbivorous animal, the next a primary carnivore, the next a secondary carnivore, etc. A specially important type of predator chain may be designated Eltonian, because in recent years C. S. Elton (1927) has emphasized its widespread significance, in which the predator at each level is larger and rarer than its prey. This phenomenon was recognized much earlier, notably by A. R. Wallace in his contribution to the 1858 communication to the Linnean Society of London.

In such a system we can make a theoretical guess of the order of magnitude of the diversity that a single food chain can introduce into a community. If we assume that in general 20 per cent of the energy passing through one link can enter the next link in the chain, which is overgenerous (cf. Lindeman, 1942; Slobodkin in an unpublished study finds 13 per cent as a reasonable upper limit) and if we suppose that each predator has twice the mass, (or 1.26 the linear dimensions) of its prey, which is a very low estimate of the size difference between links, the fifth animal link will have a population of one ten thousandth ($10^{-4}$) of the first, and the fiftieth animal link, if there was one, a population of $10^{-49}$ the size of the first. Five animal links are certainly possible, a few fairly clear cut cases having been in fact recorded. If, however, we wanted 50 links, starting with a protozoan or rotifer feeding on algae with a density of $10^6$ cells per ml, we should need a volume of $10^{26}$ cubic kilometers to accommodate on an average one specimen of the ultimate predator, and this is vastly greater than the volume of the world ocean. Clearly the Eltonian food-chain of itself cannot give any great diversity, and the same is almost certainly true of the other types of food chain, based on detritus feeding or on parasitism.

## Natural selection

Before proceeding to a further consideration of diversity, it is, however, desirable to consider the kinds of selective force that may operate on a food chain, for this may limit the possible diversity.

It is reasonably certain that natural selection will tend to maintain the efficiency of transfer from one level to another at a maximum. Any increase in the predatory efficiency of the $n^{th}$ link of a simple food chain will however always increase the possibility of the extermination of the $(n - 1)^{th}$ link. If this occurs either the species constituting the $n^{th}$ link must adapt itself to eating the $(n - 2)^{th}$ link or itself become extinct. This process will in fact tend to shortening of food chains. A lengthening can presumably occur most simply by the development of a new terminal carnivore link, as its niche is by definition previously empty. In most cases this is not likely to be easy. The evolution of the whale-bone whales, which at least in the case of *Balaenoptera borealis*, can feed largely on copepods and so rank on occasions as primary carnivores (Bigelow, 1926), presumably constitutes the most dramatic example of the shortening of a food chain. Mechanical considerations would have prevented the evolution of a larger rarer predator, until man developed essentially non-Eltonian methods of hunting whales.

### Effect of size

A second important limitation of the length of a food chain is due to the fact that ordinarily animals change their size during free life. If the terminal member of a chain were a fish that grew from say one cm to 150 cms in the course of an ordinary life, this size change would set a limit by competition to the possible number of otherwise conceivable links in the 1-150 cm range. At least in fishes this type of process (metaphoetesis) may involve the smaller specimens belonging to links below the larger and the chain length is thus lengthened, though under strong limitations, by cannibalism.

We may next enquire into what determines the number of food chains in a community. In part the answer is clear, though if we cease to be zoologists and become biologists, the answer begs the question. Within certain limits, the number of kinds of primary producers is certainly involved, because many herbivorous animals are somewhat eclectic in their tastes and many more limited by their size or by such structural adaptations for feeding that they have been able to develop.

### Effects of terrestrial plants

The extraordinary diversity of the terrestrial fauna, which is much greater than that of the marine fauna, is clearly due largely to the diversity provided by terrestrial plants. This diversity is actually two-fold. Firstly, since terrestrial plants compete for light, they have tended to evolve into structures growing into a gaseous medium of negligible buoyancy. This has led to the formation of specialized supporting, photosynthetic, and reproductive structures which inevitably differ in chemical and physical properties. The ancient Danes and Irish are supposed to have eaten elm-bark, and sometimes sawdust, in periods of stress, has been hydrolyzed to produce edible carbohydrate; but usually man, the most omnivorous of all animals, has avoided almost all parts of trees except fruits as sources of food, though various individual species of animals can deal with practically every tissue of many arboreal species. A major source of terrestrial diversity was thus introduced by the evolution of almost 200,000 species of flowering plants, and the three quarters of a million insects supposedly known today are in part a product of that diversity. But of itself merely providing five or ten kinds of food of different consistencies and compositions does not get us much further than the five or ten links of an Eltonian pyramid. On the whole the problem still remains, but in the new form: why are there so many kinds of plants? As a zoologist I do not want to attack that question directly, I want to stick with animals, but also to get the answer. Since, however, the plants are part of the general system of communities, any sufficiently abstract properties of such communities are likely to be relevant to plants as well as to herbivores and carnivores. It is, therefore, by being somewhat abstract, though with concrete zoological details as examples, that I intend to proceed.

## INTERRELATIONS OF FOOD CHAINS

Biological communities do not consist of independent food chains, but of food webs, of such a kind that an individual at any level (corresponding to a link in a single chain) can use some but not all of the food provided by species in the levels below it.

It has long been realized that the presence of two species at any level, either of which can be eaten by a predator at a level above, but which may differ in palatability, ease of capture or seasonal and local abundance, may provide alternative foods for the predator. The predator, therefore, will neither become extinct itself nor exterminate its usual prey, when for any reason, not dependent on prey-predator relationships, the usual prey happens to be abnormally scarce. This aspect of complicated food webs has been stressed by many ecologists, of whom the Chicago school as represented by Allee, Emerson, Park, Park and Schmidt (1949), Odum (1953) and Elton (1958), may in particular be mentioned. Recently MacArthur (1955) using an ingenious but simple application of information theory has generalized the points of view of earlier workers by providing a formal proof of the increase in stability of a community as the number of links in its food web increases.

MacArthur concludes that in the evolution of a natural community two partly antagonistic processes are occurring. More efficient species will replace less efficient species, but more stable communities will outlast less stable communities. In the process of community formation, the entry of a new species may involve one of three possibilities. It may completely displace an old species. This of itself does not necessarily change the stability, though it may do so if the new species inherently has a more stable population (cf. Slobodkin, 1956) than the old. Secondly, it may occupy an unfilled niche, which may, by providing new partially independent links, increase stability. Thirdly, it may partition a niche with a pre-existing species. Elton (1958) in a fascinating work largely devoted to the fate of species accidentally or purposefully introduced by man, concludes that in very diverse communities such introductions are difficult. Early in the history of a community we may suppose many niches will be empty and invasion will proceed easily; as the community becomes more diversified, the process will be progressively more difficult. Sometimes an extremely successful invader may oust a species but add little or nothing to stability, at other times the invader by some specialization will be able to compete successfully for the marginal parts of a niche. In all cases it is probable that invasion is most likely when one or more species happen to be fluctuating and are under-represented at a given moment. As the communities build up, these oppor-tunities will get progressively rarer. In this way a complex community con-taining some highly specialized species is constructed asymptotically.

Modern ecological theory therefore appears to answer our initial question at least partially by saying that there is a great diversity of organisms be-cause communities of many diversified organisms are better able to persist than are communities of fewer less diversified organisms. Even though the entry of an invader which takes over part of a niche will lead to the reduc-tion in the *average* population of the species originally present, it will also lead to an increase in stability reducing the risk of the original population being at times underrepresented to a dangerous degree. In this way loss of some niche space may be compensated by reduction in the amplitude of fluc-tuations in a way that can be advantageous to both species. The process however appears likely to be asymptotic and we have now to consider what sets the asymptote, or in simpler words why are there not more different kinds of animals?

## LIMITATION OF DIVERSITY

It is first obvious that the processes of evolution of communities must be under various sorts of external control, and that in some cases such control limits the possible diversity. Several investigators, notably Odum (1953) and MacArthur (1955), have pointed out that the more or less cyclical oscil-lations observed in arctic and boreal fauna may be due in part to the com-munities not being sufficiently complex to damp out oscillations. It is cer-tain that the fauna of any such region is qualitatively poorer than that of warm temperate and tropical areas of comparable effective precipitation. It is probably considered to be intuitively obvious that this should be so, but on analysis the obviousness tends to disappear. If we can have one or two species of a large family adapted to the rigors of Arctic existence, why can we not have more? It is reasonable to suppose that the total biomass may be involved. If the fundamental productivity of an area is limited by a short growing season to such a degree that the total biomass is less than under more favorable conditions, then the rarer species in a community may be so rare that they do not exist. It is also probable that certain absolute limita-tions on growth-forms of plants, such as those that make the development of forest impossible above a certain latitude, may in so acting, severely limit the number of niches. Dr. Robert MacArthur points out that the development of high tropical rain forest increases the bird fauna more than that of mammals, and Thorson (1957) likewise has shown that the so-called infauna show no increase of species toward the tropics while the marine epifauna becomes more diversified. The importance of this aspect of the plant or animal substratum, which depends largely on the length of the growing season and other aspects of productivity is related to that of the environmental mosaic discussed later.

We may also inquire, but at present cannot obtain any likely answer, whether the arctic fauna is not itself too young to have achieved its maximum diversity. Finally, the continual occurrence of catastrophes, as Wynne-Edwards (1952) has emphasized, may keep the arctic terrestrial community in a state of perennial though stunted youth.

Closely related to the problems of environmental rigor and stability, is the question of the absolute size of the habitat that can be colonized. Over much of western Europe there are three common species of small voles, namely *Microtus arvalis*, *M. agrestis* and *Clethrionomys glareolus*. These are sympatric but with somewhat different ecological preferences.

In the smaller islands off Britain and in the English channel, there is only one case of two species co-occurring on an island, namely *M. agrestis* and Clethrionomys on the island of Mull in the Inner Hebrides (Barrett-Hamilton and Hinton, 1911–1921). On the Orkneys the single species is *M. orcadensis*, which in morphology and cytology is a well-differentiated ally of *M. arvalis*; a comparable animal (*M. sarnius*) occurs on Guernsey. On most of the Scottish Islands only subspecies of *M. agrestis* occur, but on Mull and Raasay, on the Welsh island of Skomer, as well as on Jersey, races of Clethrionomys of somewhat uncertain status are found. No voles have reached Ireland, presumably for paleogeographic reasons, but they are also absent from a number of small islands, notably Alderney and Sark. The last named island must have been as well placed as Guernsey to receive *Microtus arvalis*. Still stranger is the fact that although it could not have got to the Orkneys without entering the mainland of Britain, no vole of the *arvalis* type now occurs in the latter country. Cases of this sort may be perhaps explained by the lack of favorable refuges in randomly distributed very unfavorable seasons or under special kinds of competition. This explanation is very reasonable as an explanation of the lack of Microtus on Sark, where it may have had difficulty in competing with *Rattus rattus* in a small area. It would be stretching one's credulity to suppose that the area of Great Britain is too small to permit the existence of two sympatric species of Microtus, but no other explanation seems to have been proposed.

It is a matter of considerable interest that Lack (1942) studying the populations of birds on some of these small British islands concluded that such populations are often unstable, and that the few species present often occupied larger niches than on the mainland in the presence of competitors. Such faunas provide examples of communities held at an early stage in development because there is not enough space for the evolution of a fuller and more stable community.

NICHE REQUIREMENTS

The various evolutionary tendencies, notably metaphoetesis, which operate on single food chains must operate equally on the food-web, but we also
have a new, if comparable, problem as to how much difference between two
species at the same level is needed to prevent them from occupying the same
niche. Where metric characters are involved we can gain some insight into
this extremely important problem by the study of what Brown and Wilson
(1956) have called *character displacement* or the divergence shown when
two partly allopatric species of comparable niche requirements become sympatric in part of their range.

I have collected together a number of cases of mammals and birds which
appear to exhibit the phenomenon (table 1). These cases involve metric
characters related to the trophic apparatus, the length of the culmen in birds
and of the skull in mammals appearing to provide appropriate measures.
Where the species co-occur, the ratio of the larger to the small form varies
from 1.1 to 1.4, the mean ratio being 1.28 or roughly 1.3. This latter figure
may tentatively be used as an indication of the kind of difference necessary
to permit two species to co-occur in different niches but at the same level
of a food-web. In the case of the aquatic insects with which I began my
address, we have over most of Europe three very closely allied species of
Corixa, the largest *punctata*, being about 116 per cent longer than the middle
sized species *macrocephala*, and 146 per cent longer than the small species
*affinis*. In northwestern Europe there is a fourth species, *C. dentipes*, as
large as *C. punctata* and very similar in appearance. A single observation
(Brown, 1948) suggests that this is what I have elsewhere (Hutchinson, 1951)
termed a fugitive species, maintaining itself in the face of competition mainly
on account of greater mobility. According to Macan (1954) while both *affinis*
and *macrocephala* may occur with *punctata* they never are found with each
other, so that all three species never occur together. In the eastern part of
the range, *macrocephala* drops out, and *punctata* appears to have a discontinuous distribution, being recorded as far east as Simla, but not in southern
Persia or Kashmir, where *affinis* occurs. In these eastern localities, where
it occurs by itself, *affinis* is larger and darker than in the west, and superficially looks like *macrocephala* (Hutchinson, 1940).

This case is very interesting because it looks as though character displacement is occurring, but that the size differences between the three species are just not great enough to allow them all to co-occur. Other characters than size are in fact clearly involved in the separation, *macrocephala*
preferring deeper water than *affinis* and the latter being more tolerant of
brackish conditions. It is also interesting because it calls attention to a
marked difference that must occur between hemimetabolous insects with annual life cycles involving relatively long growth periods, and birds or mammals in which the period of growth in length is short and of a very special
nature compared with the total life span. In the latter, niche separation may
be possible merely through genetic size differences, while in a pair of ani-

## TABLE 1

Mean character displacement in measurable trophic structures in mammals (skull) and birds (culmen); data for Mustela from Miller (1912); Apodemus from Cranbrook (1957); Sitta from Brown and Wilson (1956) after Vaurie; Galapagos finches from Lack (1947)

| | Locality and measurement when sympatric | Locality and measurement when allopatric | Ratio when sympatric |
|---|---|---|---|
| *Mustela nivalis* | Britain; skull ♂ 39.3 ♀ 33.6 mm. | (*boccamela*) S. France, Italy ♂ 42.9 ♀ 34.7 mm.<br>(*iberica*) Spain, Portugal ♂ 40.4 ♀ 36.0<br>(*bibernica*) Ireland ♂ 46.0 ♀ 41.9 | ♂ 100:128<br>♀ 100:134 |
| *M. erminea* | Britain; " ♂ 50.4 ♀ 45.0 | | |
| *Apodemus sylvaticus* | Britain; " 24.8 | unnamed races on Channel Islands 25.6–26.7 | 100:109 |
| *A. flavicollis* | Britain; " 27.0 | | |
| *Sitta tephronota* | Iran; culmen 29.0 | races east of overlap 25.5 | 100:124 |
| *S. neumayer* | Iran; " 23.5 | races west of overlap 26.0 | |
| *Geospiza fortis* | Indefatigable Isl.; culmen 12.0 | Daphne Isl. 10.5 | 100:143 |
| *G. fuliginosa* | Indefatigable Isl.; " 8.4 | Crossman Isl. 9.3 | |
| *Camarhynchus parvulus* | James Isl.; " 7.0<br>Indefatigable Isl.; " 7.5<br>S. Albemarle Isl.; " 7.3 | N. Albemarle Isl. 7.0<br>Chatham Isl. 8.0 | James 100:140:180<br>100:129 |
| *C. psittacula* | James Isl.; " 9.8<br>Indefatigable Isl.; " 9.6<br>S. Albemarle Isl.; " 8.5 | Abington Isl. 10.1<br>Bindloe Isl. 10.5 | Indefatigable 100:128:162<br>100:127 |
| *C. pallidus* | James Isl.; " 12.6<br>Indefatigable Isl.; " 12.1<br>S. Albemarle Isl.; " 11.2 | N. Albemarle Isl. 11.7<br>Chatham Isl. 10.8 | S. Albemarle 100:116:153<br>100:132 |
| | | | Mean ratio 100:128 |

mals like *C. punctata* and *C. affinis* we need not only a size difference but a seasonal one in reproduction; this is likely to be a rather complicated matter. For the larger of two species always to be larger, it must never breed later than the smaller one. I do not doubt that this is what was happening in the pond on Monte Pellegrino, but have no idea how the difference is achieved.

I want to emphasize the complexity of the adaptation necessary on the part of two species inhabiting adjacent niches in a given biotope, as it probably underlies a phenomenon which to some has appeared rather puzzling. MacArthur (1957) has shown that in a sufficiently large bird fauna, in a uniform undisturbed habitat, areas occupied by the different species appear to correspond to the random non-overlapping fractionation of a plane or volume. Kohn (1959) has found the same thing for the cone-shells (Conus) on the Hawaiian reefs. This type of arrangement almost certainly implies such individual and unpredictable complexities in the determination of the niche boundaries, and so of the actual areas colonized, that in any overall view, the process would appear random. It is fairly obvious that in different types of community the divisibility of niches will differ and so the degree of diversity that can be achieved. The fine details of the process have not been adequately investigated, though many data must already exist that could be organized to throw light on the problem.

### MOSAIC NATURE OF THE ENVIRONMENT

A final aspect of the limitation of possible diversity, and one that perhaps is of greatest importance, concerns what may be called the mosaic nature of the environment. Except perhaps in open water when only uniform quasi-horizontal surfaces are considered, every area colonized by organisms has some local diversity. The significance of such local diversity depends very largely on the size of the organisms under consideration. In another paper MacArthur and I (Hutchinson and MacArthur, 1959) have attempted a theoretical formulation of this property of living communities and have pointed out that even if we consider only the herbivorous level or only one of the carnivorous levels, there are likely, above a certain lower limit of size, to be more species of small or medium sized organisms than of large organisms. It is difficult to go much beyond crude qualitative impressions in testing this hypothesis, but we find that for mammal faunas, which contain such diverse organisms that they may well be regarded as models of whole faunas, there is a definite hint of the kind of theoretical distribution that we deduce. In qualitative terms the phenomenon can be exemplified by any of the larger species of ungulates which may require a number of different kinds of terrain within their home ranges, any one of which types of terrain might be the habitat of some small species. Most of the genera or even subfamilies of very large terrestrial animals contain only one or two sympatric species. In this connection I cannot refrain from pointing out the immense scientific importance of obtaining a really full insight into the ecology of the large mammals of Africa while they can still be studied under natural conditions. It is indeed quite possible that the results of studies on these wonderful animals would in long-range though purely practical terms pay for the establishment of greater reservations and National Parks than at present exist.

In the passerine birds the occurrence of five or six closely related sympatric species is a commonplace. In the mammal fauna of western Europe no genus appears to contain more than four strictly sympatric species. In Britain this number is not reached even by Mustela with three species, on the adjacent parts of the continent there may be three sympatric shrews of the genus Crocidura and in parts of Holland three of Microtus. In the same general region there are genera of insects containing hundreds of species, as in Athela in the Coleoptera and Dasyhelea in the Diptera Nematocera. The same phenomenon will be encountered whenever any well-studied fauna is considered. Irrespective of their position in a food chain, small size, by permitting animals to become specialized to the conditions offered by small diversified elements of the environmental mosaic, clearly makes possible a degree of diversity quite unknown among groups of larger organisms.

We may, therefore, conclude that the reason why there are so many species of animals is at least partly because a complex trophic organization of a community is more stable than a simple one, but that limits are set by the tendency of food chains to shorten or become blurred, by unfavorable physical factors, by space, by the fineness of possible subdivision of niches, and by those characters of the environmental mosaic which permit a greater diversity of small than of large allied species.

## CONCLUDING DISCUSSION

In conclusion I should like to point out three very general aspects of the sort of process I have described. One speculative approach to evolutionary theory arises from some of these conclusions. Just as adaptive evolution by natural selection is less easy in a small population of a species than in a larger one, because the total pool of genetic variability is inevitably less, so it is probable that a group containing many diversified species will be able to seize new evolutionary opportunities more easily than an undiversified group. There will be some limits to this process. Where large size permits the development of a brain capable of much new learnt behavior, the greater plasticity acquired by the individual species will offset the disadvantage of the small number of allied species characteristic of groups of large animals. Early during evolution the main process from the standpoint of community structure was the filling of all the niche space potentially available for producer and decomposer organisms and for herbivorous animals. As the latter, and still more as carnivorous animals began to appear, the persistence of more stable communities would imply splitting of niches previously occupied by single species as the communities became more diverse. As this process continued one would expect the overall rate of evolution to have increased, as the increasing diversity increased the probability of the existence of species preadapted to new and unusual niches. It is reasonable to suppose that strong predation among macroscopic metazoa did not begin until the late Precambrian, and that the appearance of powerful predators led to the appearance of fossilizable skeletons. This seems the only reasonable hypothesis, of those so far advanced, to account for the relatively sudden appearance of several fossilizable groups in the Lower Cambrian. The process of diversification would, according to this argument, be somewhat autocatakinetic even without the increased stability that it would produce; with the increase in stability it would be still more a self inducing process, but one, as we have seen, with an upper limit. Part of this upper limit is set by the impossibility of having many sympatric allied species of large animals. These however are the animals that can pass from primarily innate to highly modifiable behavior. From an evolutionary point of view, once they have appeared, there is perhaps less need for diversity, though from other points of view, as Elton (1958) has stressed in dealing with human activities, the stability provided by diversity can be valuable even to the most adaptable of all large animals. We may perhaps therefore see in the process of evolution an increase in diversity at an increasing rate till the early Paleozoic, by which time the familiar types of community structure were established. There followed then a long period in which various large and finally large-brained species became dominant, and then a period in which man has been reducing diversity by a rapidly increasing tendency to cause extinction of supposedly unwanted species, often in an indiscriminate manner. Finally we may hope for a limited reversal of this process when man becomes aware of the value of diversity no less in an economic than in an esthetic and scientific sense.

A second and much more metaphysical general point is perhaps worth a moment's discussion. The evolution of biological communities, though each species appears to fend for itself alone, produces integrated aggregates which increase in stability. There is nothing mysterious about this; it follows from mathematical theory and appears to be confirmed to some extent empirically. It is however a phenomenon which also finds analogies in other fields in which a more complex type of behavior, that we intuitively regard as higher, emerges as the result of the interaction of less complex types of behavior, that we call lower. The emergence of love as an antidote to aggression, as Lorenz pictures the process, or the development of cooperation from various forms of more or less inevitable group behavior that Allee (1931) has stressed are examples of this from the more complex types of biological systems.

In the ordinary sense of explanation in science, such phenomena are explicable. The types of holistic philosophy which import *ad hoc* mysteries into science whenever such a situation is met are obviously unnecessary. Yet perhaps we may wonder whether the empirical fact that it is the nature of things for this type of explicable emergence to occur is not something that itself requires an explanation. Many objections can be raised to such a view; a friendly organization of biologists could not occur in a universe in which cooperative behavior was impossible and without your cooperation I could not raise the problem. The question may in fact appear to certain types of philosophers not to be a real one, though I suspect such philosophers in their desire to demonstrate how often people talk nonsense, may sometimes show less ingenuity than would be desirable in finding some sense in such questions. Even if the answer to such a question were positive, it might not get us very far; to an existentialist, life would have merely provided yet one more problem; students of Whitehead might be made happier, though on the whole the obscurities of that great writer do not seem to generate unhappiness; the religious philosophers would welcome a positive answer but note that it told them nothing that they did not know before; Marxists might merely say, "I told you so." In spite of this I suspect that the question is worth raising, and that it could be phrased so as to provide some sort of real dichotomy between alternatives; I therefore raise it knowing that I cannot, and suspecting that at present others cannot, provide an intellectually satisfying answer.

My third general point is less metaphysical, but not without interest. If I am right that it is easier to have a greater diversity of small than of large organisms, then the evolutionary process in small organisms will differ somewhat from that of large ones. Wherever we have a great array of allied sympatric species there must be an emphasis on very accurate interspecific mating barriers which is unnecessary where virtually no sympatric allies occur. We ourselves are large animals in this sense; it would seem very unlikely that the peculiar lability that seems to exist in man, in which even the direction of normal sexual behavior must be learnt, could have developed to quite the existing extent if species recognition, involving closely related sympatric congeners, had been necessary. Elsewhere (Hutchinson, 1959) I have attempted to show that the difficulties that *Homo sapiens* has to face in this regard may imply various unsuspected processes in human evolutionary selection. But perhaps Santa Rosalia would find at this point that we are speculating too freely, so for the moment, while under her patronage, I will say no more.

### ACKNOWLEDGMENTS

Dr. A. Minganti of the University of Palermo enabled me to collect on Monte Pellegrino. Professor B. M. Knox of the Department of Classics of Yale University gave me a rare and elegant word from the Greek to express the blurring of a food chain. Dr. L. B. Slobodkin of the University of Michigan and Dr. R. H. MacArthur of the University of Pennsylvania provided me with their customary kinds of intellectual stimulation. To all these friends I am most grateful.

### LITERATURE CITED

Allee, W. C., 1931, Animal aggregations: a study in general sociology. vii, 431 pp. University of Chicago Press, Chicago, Illinois.

Allee, W. C., A. E. Emerson, O. Park, T. Park and K. P. Schmidt, 1949, Principles of animal ecology. xii, 837 pp. W. B. Saunders Co., Philadelphia, Pennsylvania.

Barrett-Hamilton, G. E. H., and M. A. C. Hinton, 1911–1921, A history of British mammals. Vol. 2. 748 pp. Gurney and Jackson, London, England.

Bigelow, H. B., 1926, Plankton of the offshore waters of the Gulf of Maine. Bull. U. S. Bur. Fisheries 40: 1–509.

Brown, E. S., 1958, A contribution towards an ecological survey of the aquatic and semi-aquatic Hemiptera-Heteroptera (water-bugs) of the British Isles etc. Trans. Soc. British Entom. 9: 151–195.

Brown, W. L., and E. O. Wilson, 1956, Character displacement. Systematic Zoology 5: 49–64.

Cranbrook, Lord, 1957, Long-tailed field mice (Apodemus) from the Channel Islands. Proc. Zool. Soc. London 128: 597–600.

Elton, C. S., 1958, The ecology of invasions by animals and plants. 159 pp. Methuen Ltd., London, England.

Hutchinson, G. E., 1951, Copepodology for the ornithologist. Ecology 32: 571–577.

    1958, Concluding remarks. Cold Spring Harbor Symp. Quant. Biol. 22: 415–427.

    1959, A speculative consideration of certain possible forms of sexual selection in man. Amer. Nat. 93: 81–92.

Hutchinson, G. E., and R. MacArthur, 1959, A theoretical ecological model of size distributions among species of animals. Amer. Nat. 93: 117–126.

Hyman, L. H., 1955, How many species? Systematic Zoology 4: 142–143.

Kohn, A. J., 1959, The ecology of Conus in Hawaii. Ecol. Monogr. (in press).

Lack, D., 1942, Ecological features of the bird faunas of British small islands. J. Animal Ecol. London 11: 9–36.

    1947, Darwin's Finches. x, 208 pp. Cambridge University Press, Cambridge, England.

    1954, The natural regulation of animal numbers. viii, 347 pp. Clarendon Press, Oxford, England.

Lindeman, R. L., 1942, The trophic-dynamic aspect of ecology. Ecology 23: 399–408.

Macan, T. T., 1954, A contribution to the study of the ecology of Corixidae (Hemipt). J. Animal Ecol. 23: 115–141.

MacArthur, R. H., 1955, Fluctuations of animal populations and a measure of community stability. Ecology 35: 533–536.

    1957, On the relative abundance of bird species. Proc. Nat. Acad. Sci. Wash. 43: 293–295.

Miller, G. S., Catalogue of the mammals of Western Europe. xv, 1019 pp. British Museum, London, England.

Muller, S. W., and A. Campbell, 1954, The relative number of living and fossil species of animals. Systematic Zoology 3: 168–170.

Odum, E. P., 1953, Fundamentals of ecology. xii, 387 pp. W. B. Saunders Co., Philadelphia, Pennsylvania, and London, England.

Slobodkin, L. B., 1955, Condition for population equilibrium. Ecology 35: 530–533.

Thorson, G., 1957, Bottom communities. Chap. 17 in Treatise on marine ecology and paleoecology. Vol. 1. Geol. Soc. Amer. Memoir 67: 461–534.

Wallace, A. R., 1858, On the tendency of varieties to depart indefinitely from the original type. In C. Darwin and A. R. Wallace, On the tendency of species to form varieties; and on the perpetuation of varieties and species by natural means of selection. J. Linn. Soc. (Zool.) 3: 45–62.

Wynne-Edwards, V. C., 1952, Zoology of the Baird Expedition (1950). I. The birds observed in central and southeast Baffin Island. Auk 69: 353–391.

# ON THE RELATIVE ABUNDANCE OF SPECIES

## ROBERT MacARTHUR

Department of Zoology, University of Pennsylvania,
Philadelphia, Pennsylvania

This paper will contain a discussion of the ecological consequences which can be deduced from data on the comparative abundances of species found together.

Let $N_i(t)$ be the abundance of the i-th species at time t. Then if $r_i(t)$ is defined by

$$r_i(t) = \frac{1}{N_i(t)} \frac{dN_i(t)}{dt},$$

integrating, we obtain

(1) $$\log N_i(t) = \log N_i(O) + \int_0^t r_i(t)dt.$$

Notice that r is permitted to vary. There are two opposed schools in ecology, one maintaining that the integral in equation (1) is important compared with $\log N_i(O)$ and the other maintaining that it is unimportant. These two views may lead to different ideas of the relative sizes of the $N_i(t)$ and so they will be discussed separately.

### OPPORTUNISTIC SPECIES

*Opinion 1:* $\int_0^t r_i(t)dt$ *is important compared with* $\log N_i(O)$. Such species are essentially opportunistic, being common when conditions have been good for some time; no equilibrium populations are maintained except perhaps as long-term averages. Basically, in this case, relative abundance is of little biological interest, because it is controlled by the vagaries of the climate and other aspects of the environment affecting r. However, it is often, but not always, possible to predict the relative abundance directly from equation (1). For, when the $r_i$ vary completely independently, their accumulated integrals undergo "random walks" and will become normally distributed (Feller, 1950; Margalef, 1957, has already pointed this out.) And, by our assumption, the $\log N_i(t)$ will be normally distributed and the $N_i(t)$ will therefore be log-normally distributed. A difficult and perhaps more important case leading to a log-normal distribution is discussed later. Notice that this distribution reflects nothing about the structure of the community; common species are those which lately have had large r's; at different times, or different places (within the same habitat) different species will be the most abundant. These conclusions form the easiest way to recognize opportunistic species. Thus, diatom species in polluted rivers show a log-normal distribution of abundances, and have common species with large r and with irregular distribution (Patrick, 1954, and personal communication). The insects studied by Ross (1957) had common species unpredictable in space and time; they too must be opportunistic. In fact, it is reasonable to suppose that many terrestrial invertebrates (Andrewartha and Birch, 1954) and plants (at least those characteristic of early stages in succession; Salisbury, 1942) fall in this category 1. And at least some vertebrates (for example, Cape May and bay-breasted warblers; MacArthur, 1958) are also opportunistic.

### EQUILIBRIUM SPECIES

*Opinion 2:* $\int_o^t r_i(t)dt$ *is unimportant compared with log* $N_i(O)$. This is the case of species in some sort of population equilibrium. Here, the study of relative abundance is important and may reveal structural features of the whole community. In this case, there will be as many models of relative abundance as there are models of species population interactions, and the results require a more elaborate discussion. The total abundance of a species over its whole range is different from its density in a local habitat, and the relative abundances of species over a large area will thus be quite different from those in a small section of the area. Which will be easier to understand? Two features will often make the relative abundances over a small area easier to understand. First, the environmental changes are relatively great in a large area; no theory of relative abundance can be expected to predict these. Second, there is some evidence on the evolution of population size (Fisher, 1958, p. 112). The population unit which undergoes natural selection is the hypothetical deme, even though this can not be delimited sharply. Thus, if relative abundances are measured on areas of size comparable to that usually occupied by a deme, then we may expect an evolutionary law of relative abundance of the type qualitatively outlined by Fisher. Such a theory would be very interesting. Fisher suggests that common species will increase faster than rare ones. If, as a first approximation, we assume that the rate of fixation of beneficial genes is proportional to the population size, so that the improvement each year is about proportional to population size, then as shown by Cramer (1946, pp. 218–221), population sizes will become log-normally distributed. This conclusion is of interest since one of the prominent theories of relative abundance, due to Preston (1948), shows that this curve fits observed data fairly well. However for ecological purposes it is useful to try to avoid the genetic assumptions involved in an evolutionary theory, and thereby to make alternative hypotheses which have a more purely ecological meaning. There are two principal alternatives.

(a) *The total number of individuals of all species together is essentially constant,* so that increases in the populations of some must result in decreases in others. There is a fairly natural model for this alternative. It will be illustrated with an example. Suppose there are ten individuals and four species; represent the individuals by ten i's in a row. We can then draw five vertical bars between the letters in any positions such that at least one bar is at each end of the row: $||ii|iiiii|iii|$. There are now four spaces between bars; these represent the four species, and the number of i's in the spaces are the numbers of individuals in the species. In the example, the left-hand species has no individuals, that is, is not represented in the census, and the other species have two, five and three individuals. The essential characteristic of this model is that an increase in one species' abundance, that is, a change in the position of one of the vertical bars, automatically involves a corresponding decrease in the abundances of other species.

Here, and for the rest of this paper, it is assumed that the species whose abundances are being compared are of roughly equal size, so that an individual of one species is comparable to an individual of any of the others. It is thus reasonable to consider the relative abundances of the bird species feeding on defoliating insects, and, separately, to consider the relative abundances of the parasitic insects. It is, however, both unreasonable and uninteresting to consider the relative abundances of the combined populations.

(b) *The abundances of different species are truly independent.* Here, an increase in the abundance of one species has no necessary effect on that of any others. The appropriate model in this case is a sequence of i's with a pair of vertical bars determining the abundance of each species; the position of each pair of bars is independent of that of the pairs of bars which determined the abundances of the other species.

These alternatives do not yet unambiguously determine relative abundances. Relative abundances are precisely determined, however, if we can assume that the bars are placed randomly among the i's. Mathematically, this is equivalent to having all positions of the bars equally probable. Now it is well known that a given species is usually common in one or two of the many habitats present in a region. In others it will be rare or absent and in still others it will have intermediate abundance. It is also well known that the different species have different habitat choices. Thus a census taker by a change in choice of homogenous habitat is quite likely to have many species change radically in abundance. And thus, in any given habitat the abundances are likely to be quite random.

These models, combined with the random element due to the census-taker, should determine the relative abundance of species, of approximately the same sizes, in communities obeying one of the two alternatives, a or b.

In an earlier paper (MacArthur, 1957), the formula for the expected abundance of the r–th rarest species was shown to be, for alternative a,

$$(2) \qquad \frac{m}{n} \sum_{i=1}^{r} \frac{1}{n-i+1}$$

where there are n species and m individuals, and for alternative b,

(3)
$$\frac{\sqrt{n-r+1} - \sqrt{n-r}}{\sqrt{n}}$$

Alternative a (total number of individuals constant) was shown to be closer to the truth, for birds at least, than alternative b (species abundances determined independently). This suggests that the subdivided segments of the sequence of i's in alternative a should correspond to a useful biological property of the organisms. Hutchinson (1957) defined "niche" in very elegant terms and was able to show that his "niche" and the non-overlapping segments of alternative a are closely related. It is thus appropriate to refer to a as "niches non-overlapping" and b as "niches overlapping."

Before passing on to a more detailed discussion of the evidence bearing on these alternatives, a different way of describing the same alternatives will be mentioned. If instead of ranking the species according to abundance and calculating the expected abundance of the r'th rarest species as was done in equations 2 and 3, one calculates the expected number of species with a given abundance (that is, the number of species with one individual, the number of species with two individuals, .., the number of species with i individuals, etc.) the following formulae result (see appendix for proofs):

For alternative a, non-overlapping niches, the most probable number $g_i$ of species with i individuals is given by the solution of

(2a)
$$\log_e g_i + 1/2 g_i = \lambda i + \mu$$

where $\lambda$ and $\mu$ are undetermined constants. This implies that if alternative a is holding, a graph of $\log_e g_i + 1/(2g_i)$ against i should yield a straight line. For alternative b, overlapping niches, the expected number $g_i$ of species with i individuals is given by

(3a)
$$g_i = a - bi$$

where a and b are constants. Thus a graph of $g_i$ against i should yield a straight line. The formulations of the results of alternatives a and b given in equations 2a and 3a are the same as those usually given to studies of relative abundance, but to the present author it is easier to think in terms of the formulation of equations 2 and 3, which dealt with ranked species.

In figure 1, alternatives a and b are compared with a bird census (Saunders, 1936) covering all of Quaker Run Valley in New York; in figure 2, the censuses of the component habitats (pasture, orchards, mature oak-hickory, etc.) are plotted. The expected curves for the two alternatives, based on equations 2 and 3, are plotted for comparison in figure 1. It is immediately clear that while as expected the total population of the valley fits neither alternative, the small, more homogenous habitats plotted in figure 2 are in very close agreement with alternative a as expressed by equation 2. (Any curve parallel to that for alternative a in figure 1 shows agreement with alternative a). The general close agreement is also very evident from figure 3 which is compiled from large tracts of virgin areas (three in Mexico

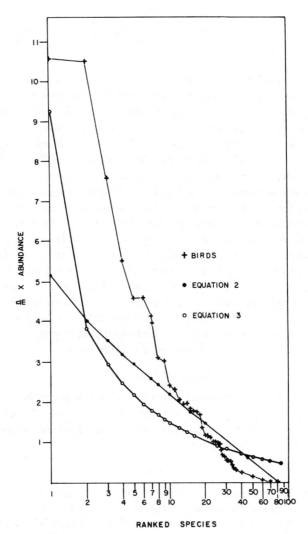

FIGURE 1. The abundances of the various bird species throughout Quaker Run Valley are ranked from commonest, on the left, to rarest, on the right, and plotted for comparison with the abundances expected from alternatives (a) and (b), which are given in equations 2 and 3.

[Davis, 1953, 1954, 1955], four in U.S.A. [Fables, 1957; Pugh, 1957; Longley, 1944; Hensley, 1954] and two in Canada [Stewart, 1955]).

These are all the censuses from virgin stands in extensive areas of that type which were analyzed. When bird censuses from mixed habitats are studied they reveal a divergence from the prediction of equation 2, however. This discrepancy is nearly always of the same type—common species are commoner than predicted and rare species are rarer—as was observed when the whole of Quaker Run Valley was compared with the formula of alternative a. Although two causes of this discrepancy will be discussed, the im-

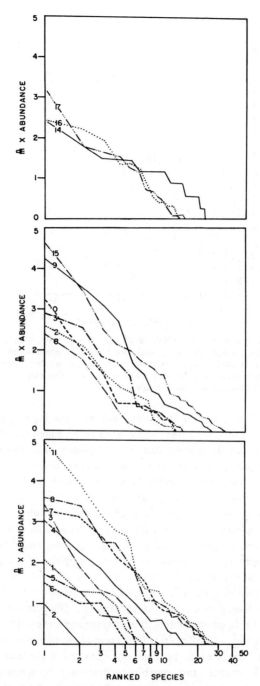

FIGURE 2. The bird species abundances of the component habitats of Quaker Run Valley are plotted separately, in the manner used in figure 1. A good fit to alternative (a) (equation 2) is indicated by the observed relative abundance curve being parallel to that curve in figure 1 which was calculated from equation 2.

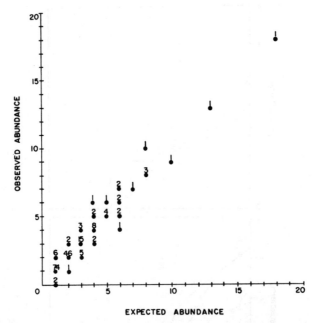

FIGURE 3. The observed abundances of species in nine tracts of virgin forest from Canada to Mexico are compared with the expected abundances calculated from equation 2. The expected abundances are taken as the nearest integer to the value predicted by the equation, and the parentheses enclose the number of species represented by the neighboring point on the graph.

portant thing to note is that it is always easier, that is, requires less information, to make a random system show excessive clumping than to make it excessively uniform. By moving any pair of points very close together one can always increase the clumping; to increase the uniformity one must have some knowledge of the configuration of nearby points, and move the pair accordingly. Thus any disturbance causing a departure from randomness is more likely to cause it in the direction of excessive clumping. Clumping in our model means clumping of the bars placed among the i's, which implies common species too common and rare too rare, as frequently observed. From a biological viewpoint, there seem to be two principal causes: (1) If the mean abundance of the species is different in two habitats, then the relative abundance in the combined area will depart from the expected. Thus, inclusion of an "edge" is likely to cause discrepancies. Hutchinson (1957) has appropriately called this phenomenon "heterogeneous diversity" and has discussed it thoroughly. (2) Empirically, common species in one habitat are more likely than rare ones to be common or at least present in neighboring habitats. For this reason, too, combining censuses from nearby habitats results in common species being unexpectedly common and rare species unexpectedly rare. Both of these causes operate in Quaker Run Valley where the individual habitats fitting equation 2 (and thus also 2a) combine to give a total census deviating greatly. Thus for birds at least it appears that the postulates of alternative a—that the total number of individuals is roughly constant and the individuals are partitioned among the species present—are correct and that when the census-taker, by his choice of small homogeneous census area, makes the partitioning random, then the relative abundances conform to equation 2.

So far, in comparing bird censuses with the alternatives of equilibrium species, it has been assumed that birds are indeed in equilibrium. Perhaps the most direct evidence that this is so comes from the long-term censuses carried out by Williams (1947, 1948, 1949, 1950) over 18 years. These show that birds are more likely to decrease when common and to increase when rare. Figure 4 shows this strikingly for the ovenbird.

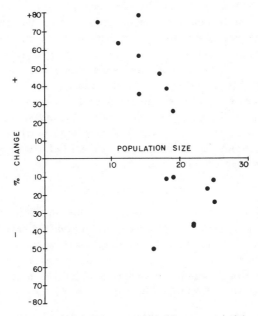

FIGURE 4. Increases and decreases over an 18-year period in the ovenbird population of a wood near Cleveland, Ohio, are plotted against the population size preceding the increase or decrease.

Data for other taxonomic groups are less convincing. Kohn (1959) has shown that Conus snails on Hawaiian reefs may agree closely with alternative a and equation 2, but otherwise, censuses of trees, fish, soil arthropods and other organisms deviate greatly from the expectation of alternative a and equation 2. Hairston and Byers (1954) feel that some species of soil arthropods show a local clumping and claim that this is not due to environmental heterogeneity. In this case, the environment is not being fully utilized and the postulates of alternative a, of course, fail to hold. Any closer agreement obtained by combining censuses from different areas is thus probably spurious. In the case of the trees, fish and perhaps some soil arthropods too, the census-taker almost certainly fails to effect the random subdivision of the individuals among the species, so that even if alternative a still holds for these groups, the relative abundances from censuses would not be expected to fit equation 2. Many of the censused areas are probably heterogeneously diverse also, so that an attempt to deduce ecological properties of these groups from their relative abundances cannot be made along these lines.

## SUMMARY

1. A distinction is made between opportunistic and equilibrium species.
2. There is little ecological interest in the relative abundances of opportunistic species, but such species abundances should frequently have a log-normal distribution.
3. The relative abundances of equilibrium species are of considerable ecological interest and frequently can be deduced from the assumption that increase in one species population results in a roughly equal decrease in the populations of other species. To make the formulae well-defined it is necessary to assume that the census-taker has sampled a small area and thus achieved a certain sort of randomness.
4. For bird populations, at least, discrepancies between observations and predictions are negligible except when the censused area is compounded from different habitats. The discrepancy is then partly due to the fact that common species in one habitat are more likely to be present in adjacent habitats than are rare ones.

## ACKNOWLEDGMENTS

G. E. Hutchinson has provided a continuous stream of good ideas on the subject for seven years since he first drew the author's attention to it. Drs. Peter Klopfer, Monte Lloyd, and David Lack made valuable comments and criticisms. The work was supported in part by a regular postdoctoral fellowship of the National Science Foundation which the author spent at the Edward Grey Institute of Field Ornithology at Oxford, England.

## LITERATURE CITED

Andrewartha, H. G., and L. C. Birch, 1954, The distribution and abundance of animals. University of Chicago Press, Chicago, Ill.

Cramer, H., 1946, Mathematical methods of statistics. Princeton University Press, Princeton, N. J.

Davis, L. I., 1953, Census 31. Audubon Field Notes 7: 352-353.
    1954, Census 40. Audubon Field Notes 8: 384.
    1955, Census 27. Audubon Field Notes 9: 425-426.

Fables, S., and D. Fables, 1957, Census 9. Audubon Field Notes 11: 440.

Feller, W., 1951, Probability theory and its applications. John Wiley & Sons, Inc., New York, N. Y.

Fisher, R. A., 1958, The genetical theory of natural selection. Dover Publications, Inc., New York, N. Y.

Hairston, N. G., and G. W. Byers, 1954, Soil arthropods of a field in southern Michigan: a study in community ecology. Cont. Lab. Vert. Biol. 64. 37 pp.

Hensley, M. M., 1954, Ecological relations of the breeding bird populations of the desert biome of southern Arizona. Ecol. Mon. 24: 185–207.

Hutchinson, G. E., 1957, Concluding remarks. Cold Spring Harbor Symp. Quant. Biol. XXII: 415–427.

Kohn, A., 1959, The ecology of Conus in Hawaii. Ecol. Mon. 29: 47–90.

Longley, W. H., 1944, Census 27. The Season (Suppl. to Audubon Mag.) CLI: 24.

MacArthur, R. H., 1957, On the relative abundance of bird species. Proc. Nat. Acad. Sci. 45: 293–295.

1958, Population ecology of some warblers of northeastern coniferous forests. Ecol. 39: 599–619.

Margalef, R., 1957, La teoria de la informacion en ecologia. Memorias de la Real Academia de Ciencias y Artes de Barcelona. XXXII, No. 13. 79 pp.

Patrick, R., 1954, A new method for determining the pattern of the diatom flora. Notulae Naturae of Acad. Nat. Sci. Philadelphia. No. 259: 1–12.

Preston, F. W., 1948, The commonness, and rarity, of species. Ecol. 29: 254–283.

Pugh, E., and R. Pugh, 1957, Census 10. Audubon Field Notes 11: 440–441.

Ross, H. H., 1957, Principles of natural coexistence indicated by leafhopper populations. Evolution 11: 113–129.

Salisbury, E. J., 1942, The reproductive capacity of plants. Bell, London.

Saunders, A. A., 1936, Ecology of the birds of Quaker Run Valley, Alleghany State Park, New York. The State University of New York, Albany, New York.

Stewart, R. W., 1955, Censuses 9, 10. Audubon Field Notes 9: 415–416.

Williams, A. B., 1947, Climax beech-maple forest with some hemlock (15 year summary). Audubon Field Notes 1: 205–210.

1948, Census 8. Audubon Field Notes 2: 231.

1949, Census 14. Audubon Field Notes 3: 262–263.

1950, Census 7. Audubon Field Notes 4: 297–298.

## APPENDIX

Suppose there are n species and m individuals. Let $g_i$ be the number of species with i individuals. The *most probable* values of $g_i$ will be computed for each type of randomness and for alternative a and b. To simplify manipulations it is useful to remember that, by Stirling's formula (cf. Feller, 1950, p. 43) $\log_e n!$ is very closely approximated by $\log_e (2)^{1/2} + (n + 1/2)\log_e n - n$, and thus the derivative of $\log_e n!$ is very nearly

$$(4) \qquad \frac{d}{dn} \log_e n! = \log_e n + \frac{1}{2n}.$$

Consider now the various cases. First, suppose total abundance is constant (niches non-overlapping) and the bars dividing the i's are moved randomly (niches continuous). As pointed out earlier, this means the i's are indistinguishable, and distinguishable combinations of i's and bars are equally probable. The number of distinguishable arrangements producing $g_1$ species of abundance 1, $g_2$ with two individuals, ... $g_i$ with i individuals, ..., is

$$\frac{n!}{g_1! \, g_2! \cdots g_i \cdots},$$

and since there are, in all, n species and m individuals,

$$(4') \qquad \sum_i i g_i = m, \qquad \text{and} \qquad \sum_i g_i = n.$$

By Lagrange's method of undetermined multipliers the state of greatest probability will be given by the solution for $g_i$ (8 = 1, 2, . . . .)

$$(5) \qquad \frac{\partial}{\partial g_i} \left( \log_e \frac{n!}{g_1! \, g_2! \cdots g_i! \cdots} + \lambda \sum_i i g_i + \mu \sum_i g_i \right) = 0;$$

In view of 2, this is equivalent to

$$(6) \qquad \log_e g_i + \frac{1}{2g_i} = \lambda i + \mu.$$

It would be possible to solve for $\lambda$ (approximately $-m/n$) and for $\mu$ (approximately $\log (n^2/m)$ because of conditions 4', but this seems unnecessary since equation 6 implies that a graph of $\log_e g_i + \frac{1}{2g_i}$ against i will be a straight line, provided the hypothesis (continuous, non-overlapping niches) is valid.

Consider, next, alternative b. Here the species abundances are determined independently, or equivalently, two bars are placed randomly among the i's and the number lying between them represents the abundance of a species; the process is repeated for each species. The total number of i's in the sequence is clearly not equal to the total number of individuals in the census, this time; it is an independent parameter, but fortunately one which has little effect on the relative abundances predicted. The problem is most easily solved as follows. Suppose, for instance, that there are ten i's. Construct a square array of 100 i's.

```
i i i i i i⁺i i i i
i i i i i⁺i i i i i
i i i i⁺i i i i i i
i i i⁺i i i i i i i
i i⁺i i i i i i i i⁺
i⁺i i i i i i i i⁺i
⁺i i i i i i i i⁺i i
i i i i i i i⁺i i i
i i i i i i⁺i i i i
i i i i i⁺i i i i i
    ⁺
```

Now two bars determined the abundance of the species in question; draw a vertical bar in the array in the position of the first bar determining the abundance, and a horizontal bar through the array in the position of the second bar determining abundance. Since each bar falls with uniform probability in each of the 11 positions available to it, all $11^2 = 121$ positions of the point of intersection of the two bars are equally probable. The probability that the two bars in the original sequence or the two coordinates in the square array differ by precisely four i's is then the fraction of the 121 coordinate points which satisfy this condition. The coordinates marked with a + sign are the ones, and their number is clearly $2(11 - 4) = 14$. In general, if there are p i's, the probability that two randomly placed bars enclose q i's is clearly given by

$$\frac{2(p + 1 - q)}{(p + 1)^2}.$$

When this probability is plotted against q, a straight line results. Therefore, since the expected number of species with q individuals under this alternative is proportional to the probability of q individuals, the number of species with q individuals would, if alternative b holds, be linearly related to q. Notice that the state of maximum probability was computed for alternative a while the mean or expected state was computed for alternative b. Presumably both distributions are sufficiently symmetrical so that the mean is approximately the state of maximum probability and conversely.

# THE ROLE OF SOIL ARTHROPODS IN THE
# ENERGETICS OF AN OLD FIELD COMMUNITY

MANFRED D. ENGELMANN

*Department of Zoology, University of Michigan, Ann Arbor, Mich.**

## INTRODUCTION

In a very stimulating paper (1942), the late R.L. Lindeman brought the problem of community energetics to the attention of the biologist, especially the ecologist. The study of this important problem did not spread, as one might have expected it to do, to all kinds of natural communities but remained focused upon the marine and fresh-water habitats. There are two reasons for the continued emphasis upon the aquatic habitats, the first and most important being the fact that the animal groups from these environments are comparatively well known taxonomically. Secondly, most of the support for studies in community energetics has come from various government and private agencies, who have recognized the implications of such work for fish production purposes. However, a critical evaluation of the general validity of Lindeman's concepts cannot be undertaken until data are obtained from a much wider spectrum of community types. This study is an attempt to apply the principles of community energetics to a terrestrial community with the intention of eventually broadening the scope of our knowledge in the area of community metabolism.

There are two aspects to any study of energetics: the field survey and the laboratory experiment. This division has led to two separate approaches to the problem which are ultimately dependent upon each other for the final answer. A field survey employs numerous methods to ascertain the density of each population present in the area. Such a study relies heavily upon the literature for information about the physiology and life history of various animals and plants in the community. An energy flow scheme is then constructed from the field data and the information in the literature. A few examples of this type of investigation are those of Lindeman (1942), and more recently Odum (1957) and Teal (1957). A laboratory study, on the other hand,

* Present address: Department of Natural Science, Michigan State University, East Lansing, Mich.

focuses attention upon the life history, physiology, and population dynamics of selected species under controlled conditions. The results of these investigations give information about the various efficiencies of which the species is capable. Examples of this type of study are those by Slobodkin (1959), Richman (1958), Trama (1957), and Armstrong (1960).

Several investigations have been concentrated upon the organisms living in various types of soil. Birch & Clark (1953) considered the status of the forest soil organisms as a study unit. Faunas of forest soils, especially in Europe, have been examined to a greater extent than those of prairie soils. Bornebusch (1930) pioneered with a study of several forest soils, ranging from pine woods to beech stands. He sampled the numbers and kinds of individuals in the soil, compared both species composition and numbers from the different stands, and attempted some studies of respiration and biomass on the soil animals. The sampling methods used by Bornebusch were inadequate, and his density estimates are low (Birch & Clark, 1953). Van der Drift (1950) has made one of the more recent studies on the forest arthropods, and this work contains an extensive bibliography. The work is mainly concerned with numbers of individuals and taxa, with the addition of some biomass estimates. Wallwork (1959) deals with several aspects of the population dynamics of some forest soil mites found in the United States. Extensions of the forest floor (such as tree holes) and specialized habitats have been considered by Park and his students (Park *et al.* 1950, Park & Auerbach 1954, Winston 1956).

Soil communities of fields and pastures have been studied by Salt *et al.* (1948), MacFadyen (1952), and Hairston & Byers (1954). Their papers are mainly concerned with numbers of individuals and distribution of animals in the community, although MacFadyen gives biomass data where possible. The Europeans have done more work on the soil arthrods because the taxonomy of their soil groups is atively well known. The taxonomic work on these ne groups in America has been neglected, with ny groups unworked for 40 years or more.

The soil arthropods of an abandoned field were osen for the study discussed in this paper. Both oratory and field studies were undertaken. The ld chosen for study is located on the University of chigan's Edwin S. George Reserve, 4.5 mi west Pinckney, Livingston Co., Mich. Evans & Cain 952) and Evans & Dahl (1955) have described e vegetation of this field; Talbot (1953, 1954) has vestigated the ant populations; Hairston & Byers 954) have sampled the soil arthropods; and Evans Lanham (1960) have examined the insect fauna the herbaceous stratum. According to Evans & hl, the climate is a humid, mesothermal one, with an monthly temperatures ranging from —4°C in nuary to 23°C in July, with a mean annual pre- oitation of 78 cm well distributed throughout the ar. The soil is a sandy loam with very good ainage. The humus layer of the soil ranges from 5 to 3.6 cm in depth. Vegetation of the field nsists of grasses (*Poa, Aristida, Setaria,* and *Lep- loma*), forbs (*Antennaria, Lespedeza, Rumex,* and *lidago*), mosses (*Ceratodon* and *Polytrichum*), and hens (*Cladonia*). The field has 2 distinct vege- tion types or associations. Several depressions or ales are found in various areas of the field. These pressions have a dense cover of Kentucky blue ass, *Poa pratensis,* interspersed with the common lkweed, *Asclepias syriaca.* The rest of the field higher and generally dominated by Canadian blue ass, *Poa compressa,* although there are patches other grasses which displace the Canadian blue ass. Hairston (1959) found a difference in the il fauna between the upland and the swales; erefore, these 2 areas are considered to be separate mmunities. In the present study only the upland mmunity was considered.

The major goals of this study were (1) to de- rmine the position of the oribatid mites in the od web, and (2) to indicate their role in the soil dustry. Secondary goals included (3) determination the ecological efficiency value for the soil her- vores, (4) comparison of this value with those tained from aquatic studies, and (5) evaluation the hypothesis that all communities operate on e same energetic principles.

I wish to acknowledge the following persons for eir assistance during the course of my work: J. Cantrall, for permission to work on the Edwin George Reserve; F. E. Smith and P. Ovenberg, r their help with the regression calculations; L. B. obodkin, for advice on ecological efficiencies; and . H. Lauff, for his sponsorship of the radioactive- beling work. Special thanks are due my wife, atricia, who typed the manuscript and helped with e editing; the members of my doctoral committee, . R. Dawson, F. C. Evans, and A. H. Smith, who ve assistance during the course of the investigation d in the writing of the manuscript; and my chair-

man, N. G. Hairston, who gave encouragement and valuable help through the entire period of this en- deavor.

## MATERIALS AND METHODS

In evaluating the role of the arthropods in the soil of the old field, the following information was considered necessary to make up an energy balance sheet: the number of individuals present during the year; their reproductive rates and generation times; their body weights, and the amount of energy repre- sented by these weights; and their metabolic energy. Despite the number of soil sampling studies, in- formation about the soil arthropods is scanty. Data necessary to draw up the energy balance sheet were obtained by the following sampling and experimental techniques.

### SAMPLING

A sampling program was employed to obtain estimates of the numbers of individuals present in the soil during the year. Hairston & Byers (1954) carried out an extensive program on the old field during the years 1949 and 1950; therefore, only a limited sampling program was undertaken in 1958. Sampling tubes 6.3 cm in diameter and 12.5 cm long were employed once each month to remove 3 plugs of soil from the central part of the old field. The sampling sites were chosen at random before the time of collection. The soil plugs were kept in the sample tubes and transported to the laboratory in plastic bags. This technique minimized moisture loss and kept the soil plug intact.

### EXTRACTION AND IDENTIFICATION

Tullgren extraction (Park & Auerbach 1954) was used to remove the arthropods from the soil plugs. The soil plug in its sample tube was placed upside down in the Tullgren funnel. A 40-watt bulb fur- nished the heat and light source. The arthropods were caught in a jar containing 70% alcohol. The animals were then counted under a dissecting micro- scope.

The oribatid mites were the most intensively studied group of the soil arthropods found in the old-field samples. These small mites are found in forest and prairie soils all over the world; those found on the old field ranged from .1 to .9 mm. in length. Some of these mites are soft-bodied in all stages; however, most of the individuals from the samples studied were of species in which the adult has a thick chitinous exoskeleton and differs in appear- ance from the immature stages.

Taxonomically this group has received little at- tention. Although in Europe the taxonomic rela- tionships of these mites are relatively well-known because of the work of men like Grandjean, work to date on forms from the Western Hemisphere has been of a pioneer nature. In recent years Dr. Tyler Woolley has begun a detailed study of the system- atics of the Oribatidae, but the task is a very compli- cated one, and it will be a long time before the picture is in any way complete. Hence, for the purpose of the research reported in this paper, a numbering device was substituted for species designations. The system was modeled after the one used by Hairston & Byers in their work on the field populations and proved a convenient tool for preliminary identification of different groups. Each recognized kind of mite was given a number and specimens were sent to specialists for future study. The immature forms which differ from the adults in appearance were probably placed in a different category. The immature forms, however, are rather infrequent in the samples. Therefore this source of error is probably not a major concern.

Live arthropods were caught in jars containing water (Engelmann 1956). The animals were cultured in jars which had a flooring of plaster of paris and charcoal (Rohde 1956). The jars were supplied with various types of food, and the plaster was kept moist. The most successful diet for the arthropods in culture consisted of washed, pulverized organic material found on the surface of the soil, supplemented with dried yeast (*Saccharomyces*) which had been suspended in water. The yeast was dropped onto the bottom of the "nest" in very small quantities. Funga (*Mycena, Aspergillus, Agaricus,* and others) were also used as a source of food at various times.

## WEIGHT AND RESPIRATION

A quartz-helix balance sensitive to 2.5 μg w used to weigh the arthropods. Many of the anim weighed less than a microgram, so that a number individuals had to be weighed at one time in ord to register on the scale; the weights are therefc averages in most cases. The animals were killed immersion in alcohol for a few minutes. They we then transferred to weighing pans and placed in desiccator for 24 hours or more. When remov from the desiccator, the dried animals began to ta up water from the air at a rapid rate, until equilibrium was reached in about 5 minutes. Co sequently some moisture was probably taken up the animals during this weighing procedure, whi required approximately 1.5 minutes per measureme

Respiration data for the soil arthropods we obtained with the Warburg respirometer (Umbr 1949) and a modification of the insect respiromet of Smith & Douglas (1949). This latter apparat proved to be most convenient and was used mc frequently. The Smith-Douglas respirometer w modified by substituting small glass vials with grou glass necks for the large brass chamber of the ori inal model. The bottom half of the vial was lin with moist filter paper and closed with a piece sterile cotton after the arthropods had been plac

TABLE 1. Numbers of individuals of the oribatid mite species found in 22 soil samples from an old field, Edw S. George Reserve, Livingston Co., Mich.
? indicates sample destroyed before species was counted.

| Oribatid mite species no. | Dec. 1, '57 | Dec. 1, '57 | Jan. 3, '58 | Feb. 8, '58 | Mar. 3, '58 | Apr. 13, '58 | Apr. 13, '58 | May 4, '58 | June 6, '58 | July 7, '58 | Aug. 8, '58 | Aug. 8, '58 | Sept. 2, '58 | Sept. 2, '58 | Oct. 4, '58 | Oct. 4, '58 | Oct. 31, '58 | Oct. 31, '58 | Dec. 12, '58 | Dec. 12, '58 | Jan. 9, '59 | Jan. 9, '59 | Totals |
|---|---|---|---|---|---|---|---|---|---|---|---|---|---|---|---|---|---|---|---|---|---|---|---|
| 101 | 31 | 12 | 12 | 19 | 25 | 37 | 14 | 4 | 27 | 19 | 28 | 79 | 0 | 13 | 5 | 0 | 5 | 7 | 5 | 20 | 26 | 12 | 4 |
| 102 | 0 | 0 | 2 | 10 | 1 | 50 | 1 | 2 | 1 | 0 | 0 | 0 | 0 | 0 | 4 | 0 | 12 | 3 | 16 | 2 | 1 | 4 | 1 |
| 103 | 7 | 2 | 4 | 0 | 0 | 0 | 0 | 0 | 0 | 0 | 0 | 0 | 0 | 1 | 0 | 0 | 0 | 1 | 0 | 0 | | | |
| 105 | 171 | 16 | 15 | 17 | 99 | 14 | 35 | 40 | 10 | 5 | 47 | 181 | 6 | 6 | 6 | 13 | 247 | 0 | 35 | 66 | 138 | 15 | 11 |
| 108a | 4 | 4 | 2 | 2 | 2 | 7 | 3 | 1 | 9 | 0 | 0 | 17 | 1 | 0 | 2 | 8 | 6 | 1 | 6 | 4 | 13 | 5 | |
| 108c | 3 | 6 | 0 | 11 | 0 | 25 | 5 | 0 | 0 | 0 | 0 | 1 | 0 | 1 | 1 | 1 | 19 | 6 | 12 | 2 | 1 | 0 | |
| 108d | 2 | 0 | 1 | 3 | 3 | 7 | 9 | 8 | 0 | 0 | 3 | 2 | 1 | 7 | 6 | 2 | 5 | 0 | 13 | 0 | 5 | 0 | |
| 108e | 0 | 0 | 0 | 0 | 0 | 4 | ? | 1 | 0 | 0 | 1 | 0 | 0 | 0 | 0 | 0 | 6 | 0 | 1 | 0 | 0 | 0 | |
| 109 | 0 | 0 | 1 | 2 | 0 | 2 | 0 | 0 | 0 | 0 | 0 | 0 | 0 | 0 | 0 | 0 | 0 | 1 | 23 | 0 | 1 | 0 | |
| 110 | 0 | 13 | 2 | 0 | 0 | 0 | 2 | 0 | 2 | 0 | 0 | 0 | 0 | 4 | 1 | 1 | 0 | 2 | 0 | 0 | 5 | 1 | |
| 111 | 0 | 0 | 0 | 0 | 0 | 0 | 0 | 0 | 0 | 0 | 0 | 10 | 0 | 0 | 1 | 0 | 1 | 0 | 0 | 0 | 0 | 0 | |
| 112a | 0 | 0 | 0 | 9 | 6 | 17 | 0 | 0 | 7 | 0 | 0 | 0 | 0 | 1 | 6 | 0 | 7 | 0 | 17 | 0 | 1 | 6 | |
| 112b | 0 | 0 | 0 | 0 | 0 | 0 | 0 | 2 | 7 | 2 | 0 | 3 | 0 | 3 | 3 | 0 | 0 | 0 | 0 | 0 | 0 | 0 | |
| 113 | 0 | 0 | 0 | 0 | 11 | 0 | 0 | 1 | 0 | 0 | 0 | 1 | 0 | 0 | 0 | 2 | 0 | 1 | 0 | 0 | 0 | 0 | |
| 114 | 4 | 4 | 17 | 7 | 1 | 1 | 2 | 0 | 0 | 0 | 1 | 8 | 0 | 1 | 0 | 15 | 0 | 0 | 1 | 0 | 0 | 6 | |
| 115 | 0 | 0 | 0 | 0 | 0 | 1 | 0 | 0 | 0 | 0 | 0 | 0 | 0 | 0 | 0 | 0 | 0 | 0 | 0 | 0 | 0 | 0 | |
| 116 | 0 | 0 | 0 | 0 | 0 | 0 | 0 | 0 | 2 | 0 | 0 | 4 | 0 | 1 | 2 | 0 | 3 | 0 | 1 | 0 | 0 | 0 | |
| 117 | 3 | 0 | 4 | 8 | 0 | 0 | 0 | 1 | 2 | 0 | 0 | 0 | 0 | 0 | 4 | 2 | 1 | 1 | 25 | 14 | 6 | 3 | |
| 118 | 0 | 0 | 1 | 0 | 0 | 0 | 0 | 0 | 0 | 0 | 0 | 0 | 0 | 0 | 0 | 0 | 0 | 0 | 0 | 0 | 0 | 0 | |
| 119 | 0 | 0 | 0 | 1 | 0 | 2 | 0 | 3 | 0 | 0 | 0 | 0 | 0 | 0 | 0 | 0 | 1 | 0 | 2 | 2 | 0 | 0 | |
| 120 | 0 | 0 | 0 | 25 | 8 | 66 | ? | 11 | 7 | 31 | 37 | 54 | 27 | 31 | 35 | 5 | 47 | 3 | 26 | 37 | 4 | 2 | 4 |
| 121 | 10 | 5 | 0 | 0 | 0 | 0 | 0 | 4 | 2 | 0 | 0 | 0 | 0 | 0 | 2 | 1 | 4 | 2 | 1 | 0 | 0 | 0 | |
| 126 | ? | ? | 7 | 89 | 6 | 42 | ? | 1 | 4 | 3 | 2 | 5 | 10 | 30 | 8 | 3 | 48 | 9 | 60 | 0 | 61 | 20 | 4 |
| 128 | ? | ? | 0 | 0 | 4 | 0 | ? | 32 | 7 | 4 | 15 | 8 | 0 | 8 | 155 | 11 | 46 | 0 | 139 | 153 | 0 | 2 | 5 |
| Total... | 235 | 62 | 68 | 203 | 166 | 275 | 71 | 111 | 87 | 64 | 134 | 373 | 45 | 107 | 241 | 64 | 458 | 36 | 383 | 301 | 262 | 76 | 38 |

on the filter paper. A roll of filter paper soaked in .1 molar NaOH was placed in the upper end of the vial. The manometer consisted of a length of thick-walled capillary tubing with a bore of .5 mm. Colored water containing a detergent was used as manometer fluid. The respirometers were immersed in a water bath which maintained a temperature of 24°-25° C during the course of the experiment.

### FEEDING AND ASSIMILATION

A radioactive labeling technique was used to make estimates of food ingestion and assimilation (Trama 1957). Yeast was labeled with radioactive glycine $C^{14}$. A known quantity of the yeast was plated on a counting planchet and radioactivity determined in a gas flow geiger counter. This procedure yielded an estimate of the number of disintegrations per unit of time per unit of weight of yeast. The yeast was then presented to the animals for a period of time, the animals were killed and dissolved in hot formamide and plated on a planchet. The disintegrations per unit of time obtained from the dissolved animals were then translated into grams of yeast contained in the body of the animal at the time of death. When the animals were allowed to post-absorb before being killed, an assimilation rate was estimated.

A bomb calorimeter was used to obtain estimates of the caloric contents of various substances including vascular plant material, fungi, and insect larvae (Richman 1958).

## PRESENTATION AND ANALYSIS OF DATA

The numbers of oribatid mites in the various species categories found in 22 samples taken over a 13-month period are given in Table 1. Species categories 101, 105, and 120 are found in most of the samples and are probably the more characteristic species of the field's upland. Species 115 and 118 were found only once and are most likely to be "accidentals". Yearly population patterns fell into 3 main types: populations with a relatively constant level through the year, populations largely restricted to the summer months, and populations showing increased numbers in both spring and fall. Species 101, 105, and 120 show no marked population peak, species 112b and 116 were taken only in summer, and the rest of the species show a spring population peak and a fall population peak. The fall population peak is usually greater than the one in the spring. This double peak has been observed in other oribatid populations (Sengbusch 1954) and has implications for the turnover rate of the populations concerned. Sengbusch believes that this double peak can be explained by the presence of two reproductive periods each year, one in the spring and one in the fall. Hairston & Byers (1954) give good evidence for the vertical migration of soil arthropods; therefore, the spring peak could also be explained by the return of the adults to the surface layers of the soil.

The total numbers of each species of mite in the 22 samples were divided by the number of sam-

TABLE 2. Numbers, weights, and biomasses of the oribatid mites found in an average soil sample (area 31.2 cm$^2$) from an abandoned field in southeastern Michigan, 1958.

| Species Category | Mean No. of Individuals Per Sample | Mean Wt. of Individual (µg) | Species Biomass (mg/m$^2$) |
|---|---|---|---|
| 101 | 18.20 | 1.50 | 8.750 |
| 102 | 5.00 | 2.00 | 3.205 |
| 103 | 0.68 | 15.60 | 3.397 |
| 105 | 53.70 | 0.70 | 12.019 |
| 108a | 4.40 | 1.00 | 1.410 |
| 108c | 4.30 | 0.51 | 0.705 |
| 108d | 3.50 | 0.43 | 0.481 |
| 108e | 0.60 | 0.33* | 0.064 |
| 109 | 1.40 | 2.43 | 1.090 |
| 110 | 1.50 | 5.00 | 2.404 |
| 111 | 0.50 | 12.00* | 1.923 |
| 112a | 3.50 | 0.74* | 0.833 |
| 112b | 0.90 | 0.89* | 0.250 |
| 113 | 0.70 | 0.71* | 0.151 |
| 114 | 3.10 | 5.49 | 5.449 |
| 115 | 0.05 | 4.00* | 0.074 |
| 116 | 0.60 | 0.33* | 0.077 |
| 117 | 3.40 | 1.00 | 1.090 |
| 118 | 0.05 | 2.00* | 0.029 |
| 119 | 0.50 | 0.20* | 0.035 |
| 120 | 21.70 | 3.50* | 2.436 |
| 121 | 1.40 | 7.15 | 3.205 |
| 126 | 21.50 | 0.31* | 2.147 |
| 128 | 30.70 | 0.27 | 2.660 |
| Totals | 181.88 | — | 53.884 |

* Weight derived from regression equation.

ples to secure "average sample" figures for the thirteen months (Table 2). Weights were also obtained for each mite species. These figures were used to calculate the biomass of the oribatids found in an average sample (Table 2).

### BIOMASS

Fig. 1 shows, on a double log plot, the relationship of the length-width index, i.e., the length times the width of the animal measured in microns, to the weight of the animal, in micrograms. The line was fitted to the points by means of the standard regression technique (the least squares method). The correlation coefficient of the points to the line is .85, and a $t$ value of 12.0 is significant at a probability of less than .01. The animals were measured after they had been mounted on slides in balsam. This point is important, for there is some compression of the animal on the slide which increases the lateral dimensions, thus increasing the frontal area about 20%. The weight of slide-mounted animals was estimated from the following formula: Log weight of animal in micrograms = 1.32 [log length + log width (in microns)] — 5.87. Neither length nor volume measurements showed a linear relationship when plotted against weight. The explanation for this is that the exoskeleton and muscles attached to it comprise most of the weight of these arthropods. Dry weight, therefore, becomes some function of the surface area rather than of volume. The length-

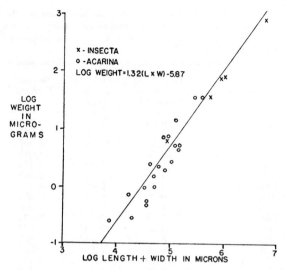

Fig. 1. The relationship of weight to length-width index in twenty five terrestrial arthropods. Data from Acarina (o) and Insecta (x) were used to make the plot.

width index is apparently some constant proportion of the total surface area (about 40%) and can therefore be used as a satisfactory measure.

The biomass for each species category was calculated from the weights obtained by direct weighing or from the regression equation (Table 2). A total of about 54 milligrams of oribatid mites was estimated for each square meter of upland of the old field. This estimate of standing crop was then converted into energy units by the assumption that a gram of arthropod protoplasm is equivalent to 5000 gram calories of energy. Culture methods did not allow the accumulation of enough material to make an actual assay of oribatid protoplasm; however, some calorimetry was done on fourth instar larvae of *Tenebrio molitor*. Larvae taken directly from culture and homogenized had a caloric content of 6578.9 cals/gm; fat-extracted individuals had a caloric content of 4858.1 cal/gm, and the exoskeletons (formamide-treated larvae) contained 4978.0 cals/gm. In a table compiled by Golley (1959), caloric values for the animal material tested ranged from 1900 cals/gm to 6200 cals/gm, with most of the values falling between 4000 and 5500 cals/gm. The assumption of 5000 cals/gm is, therefore, not an unreasonable approximation at the present time. The product of the total estimated standing crop (54 mg) times the mean caloric content (5000 cals/gm) gives an estimate of 270 cals of oribatid mites found to a depth of 12.5 cm on each square meter of upland.

When a population is in a "steady state" condition the total production biomass will remain the same from year to year, although during the year the standing crop biomass may fluctuate around some mean value. However, the standing crop gives little indication *per se* of the energy flow through the population. Energy flows into the population

in the form of food and flows out of the population in the form of respiration and dead individuals. As far as the population is concerned, egested or defecated food has never entered the protoplasm of the population. In this sense, then, the digestive tract of the animal can be considered an extension of the external environment. Therefore, only the functions of respiration rate, feeding rate, and death rate need be estimated to describe the basic energy characteristics of the population.

## Oxygen Consumption

Data on oxygen consumption by various arthropods were obtained with the aid of respirometers (Table 3). Technical difficulties prevented acquisition of respiration information from all of the soil arthropods; therefore, some other approach was needed to obtain estimates of the respiration of these animals. Data of Bornebusch (1931) were used with the data from Table 3 to plot the log of the total respiration of the individual against the log of the total body weight (Fig. 2). The slopes for the 2 sets of points are .74 and .85. The common regression line for all the points has a slope of .84. There is no significant difference between the 3

TABLE 3. Respiration of soil arthropods at 25°C in the laboratory.

| Species | Weight µg | µl/ ind./hr. (Mean) | Range | s | Coeff. of varia- tion | Avg. µl/ mg. per hour |
|---|---|---|---|---|---|---|
| Oribatidae *Oppia nova* . . . . . | 1.0 | .0065 | .0227- .0013 | .0066 | 1.01 | 6.5 |
| Oribatidae species 101 . . . . . . | 1.5 | .0024 | — | — | — | 1.6 |
| Oribatidae Species 102 . . . . . | 2.0 | .0044 | .0041- .0050 | .00052 | .118 | 2.2 |
| Acaridae *Tyroglyphus linteri* | 2.3 | .017 | .0035- .0110 | .01085 | .61 | 7.4 |
| Oribatidae Species 15 . . . . . . | 11.05 | .0215 | — | — | — | 1.95 |
| Scydmaenidae Species 7 Larva . . . . . . . . . . . . . . . | 13.6 | .08 | — | — | — | 5.9 |
| Oribatidae *Casmia* (mixed instars) . . . . . . . . . . . . . . | 15.56 | .0138 | — | — | — | 0.89 |
| Oribatidae Species 12 . . . . . . | 26.52 | .0107 | — | — | — | 0.4 |
| Mesostigmata Species 14 . . . | 40.1 | .0305 | — | — | — | 0.76 |
| Scydmaenidae Species 1 larva . . . . . . . . . . . . . . . . | 45.25 | .140 | — | — | — | 3.1 |
| Pselaphidae *Reichenbachia* . . | 76.6 | .145 | — | — | — | 1.9 |
| Staphylinidae Species 4 . . . . | 86.25 | .215 | — | — | — | 2.5 |
| Staphylinidae Species 3 . . . . | 88.75 | .061 | — | — | — | 0.7 |
| Staphylinidae Species 6 . . . . | 96.5 | .18 | — | — | — | 1.9 |
| Formicidae *Ponaria* (worker) | 187.3 | .24 | — | — | — | 1.3 |
| Isopoda *Armadillidium vulgare* (Juvenal) . . . . . . . | 636.2 | 1.118 | — | — | — | 1.8 |
| Carabidae Species 2 . . . . . . . . | 891.0 | .238 | — | — | — | 0.27 |
| Scarabaeidae *Geotrupes* . . . . . | 160300.0 | 120.5 | — | — | — | 0.75 |

lines. A slope of .85-.90 is common for a grea number of invertebrates (Zeuthen 1953). The test values for each of the regressions are highly sig nificant (P less than .01). The following formul was used to estimate the respiration of an anima when the weight was known:

Log respiration ($\mu$l $10^{-3}$) = .85 (log weight i micrograms) + .44.

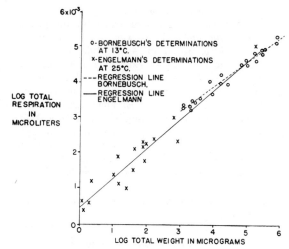

LOG TOTAL RESPIRATION IN MICROLITERS

o - BORNEBUSCH'S DETERMINATIONS AT 13°C.
x - ENGELMANN'S DETERMINATIONS AT 25°C.
--- REGRESSION LINE BORNEBUSCH.
— REGRESSION LINE ENGELMANN

LOG TOTAL WEIGHT IN MICROGRAMS

Fig. 2. Respiration-weight relationship in forty terrestrial arthropods. Data from the study of Bornebusch (1930) and from the present study were used to make the plot.

If the rates of oxygen consumption obtained from the respiration studies or from the regression equation are multiplied by the number of individuals in each species category, we obtain estimates of the

Table 4. Oxygen consumed and calories burned by the oribatid mites found in an average sample of 12.5 cm depth extrapolated to an area of 1 m², from an abandoned field in southeastern Michigan, 1958.

| Species category | Oxygen consumption** for total population µl O₂/day | Energy Expenditure of Total Population | |
| --- | --- | --- | --- |
| | | gm cal per 24 hours† | gm cal per year |
| 101 | 336.205* | 1.62173 | 192.98 |
| 102 | 169.224* | 0.81728 | 97.25 |
| 103 | 302.873 | 1.46148 | 173.91 |
| 105 | 838.428 | 4.04471 | 481.30 |
| 108a | 145.507* | 0.70190 | 83.52 |
| 108c | 50.639 | 0.24358 | 28.98 |
| 108d | 26.602 | 0.12820 | 15.26 |
| 108e | 4.808 | 0.02244 | 2.67 |
| 109 | 127.559 | 0.61536 | 73.22 |
| 110 | 124.675 | 0.60254 | 71.70 |
| 111 | 84.933 | 0.41024 | 48.82 |
| 112a | 58.331 | 0.28204 | 33.56 |
| 112b | 16.987 | 0.08333 | 9.92 |
| 113 | 8.654 | 0.04167 | 4.96 |
| 114 | 279.156 | 1.34610 | 160.18 |
| 115 | 3.846 | 0.01923 | 2.29 |
| 116 | 5.769 | 0.02885 | 3.43 |
| 117 | 72.113 | 0.34935 | 41.57 |
| 118 | 1.603 | 0.00641 | 0.76 |
| 119 | 2.885 | 0.01282 | 1.53 |
| 120 | 216.658 | 1.04483 | 124.32 |
| 121 | 126.277 | 0.60895 | 72.46 |
| 126 | 205.120 | 0.98714 | 117.46 |
| 128 | 214.735 | 1.03522 | 123.19 |
| Totals: | 3423.587 | 16.51538 | 1965.24 |

* From actual respiration measurement.
** Recorded at 25°C.
† Assuming an average value of .0048 calories per microliter.

amount of oxygen used by the population each hour, and these can be extrapolated to the daily oxygen consumption (Table 4). The total oribatid oxygen consumption per day was estimated at 3424 microliters. The caloric values of the oxygen consumed can be obtained if the RQ is known (Brody 1945: 310). Although no RQ is known for oribatid mites, the RQ of a resting insect is .82 (Roeder 1953), and the caloric equivalent of a microliter of oxygen at this RQ is .0048 cals. If this factor is applied to the data, an estimated 16.5 cals per day are burned by the total oribatid fauna (Table 4). Since these animals are poikilotherms, they will not function at the same rate throughout the year. The respiration-temperature curve of Krogh (1941: 6) and the monthly mean air temperatures of Ann Arbor (Clim. data, 1958) were used to determine the rates of respiration of the mites for each month. This was equivalent to 4 months of metabolic rate of 25° C. These calculations yield an estimate of 1965 calories respired by the oribatids over the period of a year (Table 4). An estimate of respiration based upon Krogh's curve may be too low, because many invertebrates are capable of some metabolic adjustment (Uvarov 1931, Agrell 1947, Bullock 1955, Fry 1958). Such adjustment could be advantageous to a soil dwelling organism, since the moist part of the year is usually the cold part of the year (spring, fall and winter). The soil arthropods require moist surroundings both because they are subject to desiccation, and because their food source requires moisture.

### Annual Caloric Flow Through the Mite Population

Information on the feeding rates of the oribatid mites came from two sources: direct weight experiments and radioactive tracer studies. The 2 methods yielded different results. The radio-tracer work gave an estimate of 40% body weight ingested at the end of a 24-hour feeding period, while the direct weighing technique gave estimates of from 90-110% body weight ingested after the same time interval. This discrepancy was explained when it became evident that the mites were contaminating their food source by fungi carried into the culture in their digestive tracts or on their bodies. The growing fungi as well as the mites consumed the food, and, therefore, the loss of weight in the food planchet was more than doubled. The use of food by both mites and fungi produced the apparent high ingestion rate of the weight experiments. Radio-tracer work gave an estimate of 8% body weight assimilated at the end of 24 hrs. The direct weighing technique gave an estimate of 13% body weight egested per day. Since the contamination factor would also affect the latter estimate, this should be multiplied by a factor of 2.3 (the rate of consumption of mite feces by fungi in the cultures). Thus the more probable value is approximately 30% of the body weight egested by the mites each day.

Using a respiration factor of 4 months of full activity as a year's activity and a value of 4000 calories per gram of food material, it was estimated that 10,248 calories are ingested by 54 mg of mites (the mite biomass in an average square meter) during a year. Caloric values of 3713 and 3999 calories per gram for the puff ball (*Astreus hygrometricus*) cortex were obtained by bomb calorimetry during the course of this study. Dried *Leptoloma* leaves gave values of 3825-4248 calories per gram. These figures agree with those compiled by Golley for the caloric values of plant material. Values for seeds in Golley's compilation, however, ran higher, ranging up to 6000 calories per gram.

An estimated 7686 calories are egested annually by the oribatid population. This figure was obtained by using the 30% egestion estimate and the same monthly factor and caloric values used in calculating ingestion rates above. If the animals assimilate 8% of their body weight per day, they will assimilate about 2058 calories each year, or 20% of the food ingested. Of these 2058 calories, 1965 are used in respiration.

Life cycle data become essential if we are to make estimates of the energies lost to the population through mortality. The complete life history of one oribatid mite, *Oppia nova,* was observed. In culture both adults and young fed upon yeasts and fungal mycelia. At 24° C the egg stage lasted 6-8 days, the larval instar lasted 8-9 days, first nymphal instar lasted 4-5 days, and the second nymphal instar 7-8 days. From the time of oviposition to the time of the emergence of the adult took 25-30 days. There was a 15-day maturation period before the adult laid its first egg; therefore, the minimum generation time would be 45 days. The adults lay about 1 egg every 7-10 days. This rate was obtained from a culture of several individuals which were allowed to oviposit for several days. The culture included both male and female individuals and the total number of eggs was averaged for the total number of individuals; therefore, 1 egg per 10 days per individual is an average population rate.

The long generation time and field data on the fluctuation of populations support the hypothesis that the oribatids completely replace their population once, or at the most twice each year if, as seems likely, reproduction is limited to the warmer months. If a yearly turnover rate is assumed, then 54 mg of mites, equal to 270 gram calories, will go to the next trophic level as dead adults. Adults, however, are not the only individuals which die in the course of the year, and in fact, the young are extremely vulnerable to predators. In culture, for example, the hard-bodied adults are almost ignored by predaceous mites and beetles, while the soft-bodied immature stages are attacked vigorously. Some estimate of the mortality of immature individuals must be attempted before the energy picture of the oribatids is complete. It has already been observed that the adults of *Oppia nova* lay, on the average, 1 egg every 10 days. The egg is about 3% of the body weight of the adult (Table 5). In an attempt to

define the length of the breeding period, the cleared, mounted specimens were scrutinized for the presence of eggs in the uteri. Eggs were found in the uteri of specimens captured in April, 1958 through late November of that same year. One individual captured in early December had a gravid uterus. On the basis of these observations a 6-month reproductive period is proposed. Eighteen eggs, then, will be produced each year by a single adult. In a state of population equilibrium, 1 egg must survive to replace the adult which produced it. Therefore, 17 eggs will die in some stage of the life cycle. Mortality from predation is probably heaviest in the larval instar.

TABLE 5. Relationship of egg weight to adult weight in selected mites.

| Species category | AVERAGE WEIGHT DETERMINED BY REGRESSION | | | | Egg wt as % adult wt |
| | Egg wt μg | s | Adult wt μg | s | |
| --- | --- | --- | --- | --- | --- |
| *Tyroglyphus linteri* | .085 | .0068 | 1.750 | .093 | 4.9 |
| Oribatid-102 | .174 | .0180 | 4.423 | .521 | 3.9 |
| Oribatid-109 | .187 | .0570 | 9.34 | — | 2.0 |
| Oribatid-110 | .185 | .0000 | 7.28 | — | 2.5 |
| Oribatid-111 | .337 | .1880 | 12.52 | — | 2.7 |
| Oribatid-114 | .204 | — | 9.16 | — | 2.2 |
| *Oppia nova* | .080 | — | 1.77 | — | 4.5 |
| Avg. Oribatid | | | | | 3.0% |
| Acarid | | | | | 5.0% |

The actual caloric value of the eggs is unknown; however, these structures are undoubtedly supplied with a quantity of "yolk" material which is in the form of fats and oils. The fat-laden fourth instar larva of *Tenebrio* yielded a caloric value of 6000 gram calories per gram, and this value was arbitrarily used for the caloric value of the mite eggs. The resulting quantity of energy passing out of the population in the form of dead "young" is therefore about 160 calories per year.

The caloric balance sheet for the oribatid biomass in an average square meter for 1 year may be summarized as follows: ingested—10,248 calories; egested—7,686 calories, or 75% of the ingested material; assimilated—2,058 calories, or 20% of the ingested material; respired—1,965 calories, or 96% of the assimilated calories; adult mortality—270 calories, or 13% of the assimilated calories; egg (young) mortality—160 calories, or 7.8% of the assimilated calories. Ninety-five % of the ingested calories has been accounted for in the number of calories egested and assimilated. Five %, or 504 calories, is unaccounted for; this is within the range of experimental error. One hundred and seventeen % of the assimilated calories is accounted for in respiration and total mortality, resulting in a surplus of 17% or 337 calories. Each figure was attained independently from various experimental and field data; none was derived from working only with "known" figures

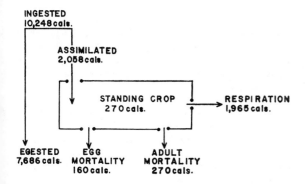

7,686+2,058=9,744 (504 cals. UNACCOUNTED FOR)
1,965+270+160=2395 (337 cals. OVERESTIMATED)

Fig. 3. Annual energy balance sheet for the oribatid mites found on a square meter of an abandoned field in Michigan, 1958. The arrows indicate the direction of energy flow. The rectangle represents the protoplasm of the oribatid population.

and solving for "unknowns". Hence, though there are arithmetical discrepancies, each estimate is a fairly close one, and all are supported by combined field and laboratory data. The caloric balance data are also summarized in Fig. 3.

### Changes in Species Composition

When this study was originally undertaken, it was hoped that the extensive collecting data of Hairston & Byers could be employed in a complete analysis of the energetics of the soil fauna. After careful comparison of the 1949-50 fauna and the 1958 fauna, it became clear that the oribatid mite populations had undergone a radical change in the years between 1950 and 1958. This change affected not only the species composition of the upland field, but also the biomass and respiration energies of the oribatid mites involved.

An analysis of the oribatid species composition of the field for the years 1949-50 and 1958 showed that only 5 species were common to the field during both samplings. Twenty-three species categories disappeared from the field after 1950 and were replaced by 19 new species. Numbers of individuals showed a similar decrease, since 33% fewer individuals were found per square meter in 1958. An analysis of the 5 species categories is made in Table 6. It is evident that 2 species have increased their numbers and biomass, 2 have decreased in numbers and biomass, and 1 has remained at about the same level. In spite of the decrease in the total numbers of individuals, there has been doubling of the biomass over the 1950 figure, and a near doubling of the respiration rate (Table 7). The increase in the biomass could be accounted for by the fact that the average individual in 1958 was heavier than the average individual of 1949-50; this is illustrated in Table 8, where an analysis is made of the portion of

TABLE 6. Comparison of the five species categories common to the old field in the years 1949-1950 and 1958.

| Species Code Number | | No. of Ind./m² | | Biomass in mg./m² | | Population trend |
|---|---|---|---|---|---|---|
| '49-'50 | '58 | '49-'50 | '58 | '49-'50 | '58 | |
| 5 | 120 | 6410.3 | 6954.8 | 1.733 | 2.436 | + |
| 6 | 105 | 3449.9 | 17210.9 | 2.471 | 12.019 | + |
| 7 | 115 | 46.6 | 16.0 | 0.311 | 0.074 | − |
| 9 | 126 | 21173.3 | 6890.8 | 3.815 | 2.147 | − |
| 10 | 109 | 170.9 | 448.7 | 0.956 | 1.090 | + |

+ represents an increase from 1950 to 1958.
− represents a decrease from 1950 to 1958.

TABLE 7. Comparison of various population characteristics of the oribatid mites in the top 12.5 cm of one square meter of the old field for the years 1949-1950 and 1958.

| Characteristic | Years '49-'50 | Year 1958 | % increase (+) or decrease (−) '58 over '50 |
|---|---|---|---|
| Total number of individuals...... | 87449.20 | 58293.10 | − 33.2 |
| Total biomass in mgs. | 26.96 | 53.88 | +100.0 |
| Total standing crop in calories....... | 134.75 | 269.48 | +100.0 |
| Respiration in μl's per total population per day..... | 1843.25 | 3423.59 | + 92.0 |
| Gm. cals. burned per day per total pop. | 8.85 | 16.52 | + 92.0 |
| Gm. cals. per year per population... | 1052.82 | 1965.24 | + 92.0 |

TABLE 8. Comparison of the biomass and weight of individual oribatid mites from the old field for the years 1949-1950 and 1958.

| Weight of individuals μg | Biomass '49-'50 | | Biomass 1958 | |
|---|---|---|---|---|
| | mg/m² | % | mg/m² | % |
| .1 and below.......... | 2.857 | 10.6 | 0.000 | 0.0 |
| .1-.49................ | 9.564 | 35.5 | 7.900 | 14.7 |
| .5-.99................ | 2.615 | 9.7 | 13.958 | 25.9 |
| 1.0-4.99.............. | 1.661 | 6.2 | 14.558 | 27.0 |
| 5.0-9.99.............. | 7.856 | 29.1 | 12.148 | 22.5 |
| 10.0-14.99............ | 2.409 | 8.9 | 1.923 | 3.6 |
| 15.0 and greater....... | 0.000 | 0.0 | 3.397 | 6.3 |
| Total.............. | 26.962 | 100.0 | 53.884 | 100.0 |

the total biomass contributed by individuals of various weight categories. Individuals in the .1-.49 and 5.0-9.9 microgram categories make up the greater part of the 1950 biomass, while the .5 through 9.9 microgram classes make up the greater proportion of the 1958 biomass. The milligram per square meter figures indicated that a greater number of heavier individuals produced the greater biomass in the 1958 samples. Apparently, the lighter species of 1949-50 have been replaced by heavier species in 1958.

It is evident then, that over this 8-year period, the oribatid populations have not been in a state of equilibrium, but have been undergoing marked change. The species present on the field during 1949-50 have disappeared, presenting certain difficulties in reconstructing the energy flow picture at that time. Nevertheless, a reasonable approximation of this energy flow system can be reached by studying the slides of the animals and using the area-weight equation and the weight-respiration equation.

The increase in oribatid biomass does not necessarily mean that the rest of the soil fauna has also increased. Evidence from 3 samples from the 1958 field in which all the animals were counted indicates that other groups have declined in numbers of species and numbers of individuals. There were no new species of eupodids and Collembola, but many of the species collected in 1949 and 1950 had disappeared. The implication is that the oribatids have replaced some of the other herbivores found in the old field soil.

It is possible that these drastic changes in the oribatid populations were correlated with corresponding changes in the above-ground system. The component of the latter most likely to exhibit significant modification is the vegetation. The plant cover of the old field was surveyed by Evans & Cain (1952) during the 1949-50 season; they recorded a total of 92 vascular plant species and an average of 148.2 g of air-dried vegetation per m². No formal plant investigation was undertaken in 1958, but clip-plot studies made in July of that year by U. N. Lanham (personal communication) yielded an average of 119.2 g of air-dried vegetation, and casual observations indicated that the same species reported by Evans & Cain and by Evans & Dahl (1954) were still present. That old-field production may remain fairly constant over a considerable period of time is also suggested by Odum's (1960) 6-yr study of abandoned fields on the Savannah River, Georgia, in which the net production underwent no significant change despite considerable alteration in species composition. Such evidence as is available, then, indicates that there has been no radical change in the old-field vegetation to correlate with changes in the oribatid populations.

## TROPHIC EFFICIENCIES

In theory the radiant energy taken up by a community is eventually given off as heat or respiration. If one could measure the total energy utilized by a particular community, one could use this as a basis for the comparison of communities. All too often, however, a total energy measurement is impractical, and therefore Lindeman (1942) proposed a series of efficiencies by which the various trophic levels within the community may be evaluated. These efficiencies have been summarized by Patten (1959: 227). The efficiency which is probably the most significant for use in the comparison of trophic levels of different communities is called the "efficiency

of transfer of ingested energy" by Patten and the "ecological efficiency" by Slobodkin (1960). For the purposes of the present study this efficiency is defined as the ratio of the calories ingested by the carnivore level to the number of calories ingested by the herbivore level:

$$EF = \frac{cals. \ ingested \ by \ carnivore}{cals. \ ingested \ by \ herbivore} \times 100$$

The population figures of Hairston & Byers were used to obtain the data needed for the efficiency equation. The numbers of individuals listed in Table 1 of Hairston & Byers were averaged, and then extrapolated to numbers of individuals per square meter. (In this case the depth of the square meter is 20.8 cm, rather than the 12.5 cm used by the present author in his study of the oribatid mite populations.) The mounted individuals were measured, and weight and oxygen consumptions were estimated by means of the regression equations.

It is evident that some of the animals found in the Hairston & Byers samples are not members of the soil community: e.g. thrips, true bugs, etc. Indeed, the classification of animals as members of the soil community presented several problems. Many animals appear to belong to the soil fauna but in actuality may not. The ants, carabid and staphylinid beetles, and dipteran larvae will be used as examples to illustrate this point. The most common ant on the field (*Lasius niger neoniger*) was observed to forage for dead animals, feed upon insects, root secretions and stem aphids (Talbot 1953). Plant material collected consisted of seeds, nectar and flower parts. The ants were parasitized by mites, and preyed upon by spiders, tiger beetles, and the flicker. Even though the ants burrow in the soil, their livelihood comes from the above-ground community, and from an energetics point of view they therefore are best considered part of the above-ground edaphon. The staphylinid and carabid beetles present greater problems, when an attempt is made to assign them to a particular community. In culture they have been observed to feed upon Collembola and mites, as well as upon meal worms, flies, leafhopper nymphs, etc. Occasionally in culture, they have even been observed to feed upon apple and banana (Needham *et al.* 1937)! A similar type of difficulty is presented by the small spiders and fly larvae found on the old field. A great amount of field and laboratory study is needed before these relationships can be resolved. These animals were eliminated from the efficiency analysis because of the lack of quantative data. It was decided to limit inclusion in the category of soil arthropods to the mites, Collembola, Protura, Symphyla, Pauropoda, and Japygida.

Knowing the food habits of an animal is of prime importance to an analysis of ecological efficiency. The literature on the food habits of the soil arthropods is indeed scant and extremely diffuse. Many times on the basis of one observation of one species a whole family has been assigned a particular food habit. This practice is deplorable but often leaves no alternative. The group called eupodoid by Hairston & Byers has proved to be a composite including members of the Acaridae, Trombididae and Eupodidae. In many cases the feeding habits of these animals were assigned on the basis of the mouth parts, and they were placed in questionable categories by the present author (Table 9). The japygids,

TABLE 9. Average numbers of individuals, biomass, and respiration of the soil arthropods found on 1 m² x 20.3 cm of the old field in the years 1949-1950.

| Category | Average number | Biomass in Mg. | Standing Crop Energy Gm. cals. | Resp. in cals. | Food habits |
|---|---|---|---|---|---|
| ACARINA | | | | | |
| Parasitoid....... | 12414.8 | 9.330 | 46.650 | 354.37 | Carn. |
| Oribatid........ | 87582.6 | 28.596 | 142.980 | 1115.96 | Herb. |
| Sarcoptoid..... | 4721.8 | 3.466 | 17.330 | 138.66 | Herb. |
| Trombidoid..... | 1797.8 | 1.722 | 8.610 | 53.33 | Carn. |
| Eupodoid....... | 9191.0 | 3.262 | 16.310 | 136.42 | Herb.? |
| | 20396.4 | 5.204 | 26.025 | 233.32 | Herb.? |
| | 2543.0 | 1.974 | 9.870 | 67.06 | Carn. |
| | 236.4 | 0.042 | 0.210 | 2.57 | Carn.? |
| Pauropoda...... | 679.9 | 0.244 | 1.220 | 10.73 | Herb. |
| Symphyla....... | 51.3 | 0.418 | 2.090 | 11.52 | Herb. |
| Protura......... | 662.1 | 2.387 | 11.935 | 66.53 | Herb. |
| INSECTA | | | | | |
| Japygida........ | 388.5 | 13.472 | 67.365 | 298.78 | ??? |
| Podurid........ | 7764.2 | 7.534 | 37.670 | 274.81 | Herb. |
| Entomobryid.... | 243.2 | 2.095 | 10.475 | 53.60 | Herb. |
| Sminthurid...... | 175.7 | 0.121 | 0.605 | 3.64 | Herb. |

which make up a considerable portion of the energy and biomass of the field soil arthropods, gave the most trouble. There is one citation in the literature given by Kühnelt in *Soil Zoology* (Kevan ed. 1955) in which he states that japygids are predators; however, intestinal analysis revealed both plant and animal substances. When observed in the laboratory during this investigation these animals huddled in cracks and crevices of the culture jars and slowly died off. They were never observed to feed. For this reason 3 separate analyses were made of the total data: 1), considering the japygids as herbivores; 2), considering them as carnivores; and 3), omitting the group entirely (Table 10).

As indicated above, ecological efficiency can be calculated if the numbers of calories ingested by both the herbivores and carnivores are known. Since feeding experiments were not carried out on the carnivores, the ingestion rates of these animals are not known. Nevertheless, an estimate of the calories involved can be obtained in the following way: if a steady-state condition is assumed, the respiration of the population plus the egestion-excretion of the population will equal the calories ingested. If the population is being preyed upon, then the calories respired and egested-excreted by the predators represent a portion of the ingested calories of the prey population. Therefore, these calories must be included with the egestion and respiration calories of the prey population. Assimilation rates vary with

TABLE 10. Ecological efficiency of the soil herbivores of the old field.

| ASSIMILATION % | | EFFICIENCY % | | |
|---|---|---|---|---|
| Carn. | Herb. | Without *Japex* | *Japex* Carn. | *Japex* Herb. |
| 32 | 32 | 18.9 | 27.5 | 16.9 |
| | 25 | 15.4 | 22.9 | 13.7 |
| | 14 | 9.6 | 14.7 | 8.5 |
| 25 | 32 | 23.0 | 32.7 | 20.7 |
| | 25 | 18.9 | 27.5 | 16.9 |
| | 14 | 12.0 | 18.1 | 10.6 |
| 14 | 32 | 32.9 | 45.4 | 30.1 |
| | 25 | 28.1 | 39.4 | 25.5 |
| | 14 | 18.9 | 27.5 | 16.9 |

the amount of food available, and since the food level of the soil herbivores is unknown for the field during 1949-1950, efficiencies for several assimilation rates have been calculated (Table 10). Richman found that *Daphnia* assimilated from 14 to 32% of the food ingested, depending upon the food level. The figure of 25% was selected as being a convenient number near the middle of that range. The ecological efficiencies were calculated by the following formula:

$$EF = \frac{Rc + Rc\left(\dfrac{100-A'}{A'}\right)}{Rh + Rh\left(\dfrac{100-A''}{A''}\right)}$$

where Rc is the respiration of the carnivore, Rh is the respiration of the herbivore, A' is the % assimilation of the carnivore, A'' is the % assimilation of the herbivore, and EF stands for ecological efficiency. In applying the data of this study to the formula given above, two variables were considered: (1) the assimilation rate of the herbivores and carnivores, and (2) the uncertain feeding status of the japygids. Hence, instead of obtaining a single efficiency, a range of efficiencies resulted from the several possible combinations of the variables.

The number of calories respired by the herbivores was 2045.19 when the japygids were omitted and also when they were included as carnivores, and 2343.97 when the japygids were considered to be herbivores. The numbers of calories respired by the carnivores was 477.33 when the japygids were omitted and also when they were included as herbivores, and 776.10 when the japygids were considered to be carnivores. Thus the total amount of respiration for combined herbivore and carnivore populations was 2522.52 calories when the japygids were omitted from both groups and 2821.30 calories when they were included in either herbivore or carnivore group. The above values are based upon the number of animals found in 1 square meter of soil, 20.8 cm deep, and over a year's period of time. The efficiencies range from 45.5% to 8.5% depending upon the various assimilation efficiencies proposed for the components of the system and the position of the japygids in the trophic scheme. It will be noted that wherever the assimilation rate for the carnivore and the herbivore is the same, i.e., 32%, 25%, 14%, for each, the EF for that column is the same: i.e., 18.9, 27.5, or 16.9. When A' and A" in the above equation are equal, EF becomes a ratio of the 2 respiration rates, thereby giving the same efficiency for all assumed assimilations.

Table 11 gives the range of the total calories consumed by the herbivores used in calculating the efficiencies found in Table 10. It will be noted that not only are there different caloric values for the same efficiency, but there are also the same caloric values for different efficiencies. Which value or values are the most reasonable? One approach is to determine how many calories the herbivores can produce over a year's time. Life history information showed that the acarid mites (*Caloglyphus* and *Tyroglyphus*) were capable of 2-3 generations per month (Table 12), and that they could deposit 56-235 eggs per lifetime per female. The oribatids have a lower reproductive rate and longer development time. It was found that the egg weight of

TABLE 11. Caloric consumption and ecological efficiency calculated for the soil herbivores found on the old field during 1949-1950.

| Consumption by herbivores cals. | Ecological efficiency % | Consumption by herbivores cals. | Ecological efficiency % |
|---|---|---|---|
| 7882.89 | 18.9 | 11713.09 | 45.4 |
| 8300.54 | 23.0 | 12174.25 | 28.1 |
| 8816.57 | 27.5 | 13369.81 | 25.5 |
| 8816.57 | 16.9 | 13502.65 | 39.4 |
| 9234.23 | 20.7 | 15515.87 | 9.6 |
| 9495.66 | 32.7 | 15933.53 | 12.0 |
| 9699.74 | 15.4 | 16449.56 | 14.7 |
| 10090.11 | 18.9 | 17128.65 | 18.1 |
| 10385.03 | 32.9 | 17564.65 | 8.5 |
| 10606.13 | 22.9 | 17982.31 | 10.6 |
| 10867.56 | 13.7 | 18103.38 | 18.9 |
| 11285.21 | 16.9 | 19346.08 | 27.5 |
| 11285.21 | 27.5 | 20152.27 | 16.9 |
| 11318.83 | 30.1 | | |

*Tyroglyphus linteri* was about 5% of the adult weight (Table 5). Using this information it was calculated that the herbivore population could produce 1928-3390 calories in eggs and adults for the maintenance of the predator populations. Most of the caloric requirements calculated for the carnivores in constructing Table 10 fell between 1260 and 3360 calories. However, the set of "*Japex* carn." efficiencies calculated at an assimilation level of 14% depended on a value of 5325 calories consumed each year by the carnivores. This value is more than the herbivores can possibly produce during a year, and the dependent set of efficiencies is therefore not a reasonable one.

Another way to try to narrow the choice of the

TABLE 12. Life cycle information of several herbivorous mites.

| Genus and species | Length of life | Eggs produced during life | Development time | Reference |
|---|---|---|---|---|
| Tetranychus telarus.... | 20-40 days | 70 | — | Metcalf & Flint 1939 |
| Tarsonemus pallidus... | 14 days | — | — | Metcalf & Flint 1939 |
| Rhizoglyphus hyacinthi. | 30-60 days | 50-100 | — | Metcalf & Flint 1939 |
| Rhizoglyphus echinopus. | 17-27 days | — | — | Baker & Wharton 1952 |
| Phyllocoptis oleivorus.. | 7-14 days | — | — | Metcalf & Flint 1939 |
| Paratetranychus pilosus | 21 days | 30-35 | — | Metcalf & Flint 1939 |
| Paratetranychus citrii.. | — | — | 21- 35 days | Metcalf & Flint 1939 |
| Halotydeus destructor.. | 25-50 days | — | — | Baker & Wharton 1952 |
| Caloglyphus mycophagus | 18-23 days | 235 | 4-9 days | Rohde 1959 |
| Tyroglyphus linteri.... | 32-84 days | 56-214 | 14- 25 days | Engelmann |
| Oppia nova.......... | — | .12 egg per day | 25- 30 days | Engelmann |
| Pseudotritia sp........ | — | — | 56 days (average) | Rohde 1955 |
| Euphthiracarus flavum. | — | — | 60 days | Rohde 1955 |
| Galumna elimatus..... | — | — | 72-107 days | Sengbusch 1954 |
| Galumna nervosus..... | — | — | 45- 50 days | Sengbusch 1954 |
| Galumna longiplume... | — | — | 58- 66 days | Sengbusch 1954 |

various efficiencies would be to calculate the amount of food material coming into the herbivore population. At the beginning of this study, it was believed that the population of herbivores fed upon the dead plant and animal material of the old field. It soon became evident that this was not so, and that the herbivores were feeding upon the organisms which were attacking the dead material; i.e., the mites were feeding upon the fungi and bacteria, and incidentally upon some of the dead material. If the various ecological efficiencies that were found for the herbivores are assumed to be the same for the bacteria and fungi, the result will be a series of estimated amounts of food available to the mites. The 148 grams of vascular plants which were found on 1 square meter of old field make up the greatest part of the dead material which falls to the decomposers each year. This amount of plant material is equivalent to 620,000 calories. If the lowest EF of 8.5 is used, the result will be an estimated 22,134 calories of fungi and bacteria ingested by the herbivores. This efficiency will adequately fill the needs for all the efficiencies calculated for the soil herbivores (Table 11). However, the 20,152.27 caloric value at 16.9% EF comes the closest to the 22,134 caloric estimate. One must keep in mind that other animals such as nematodes, rotifers, and protozoa also feed upon bacteria and fungi. Nematodes and rotifers were found in the soil of the old field, and it was estimated that the nematodes accounted for only about 360 calories per year. However, this is a very crude estimate, made on the basis of only 1 sampling, and they may consume more. The 16.9% efficiency was obtained by assuming a 14% assimilation rate for both herbivore and carnivore.

In a final attempt to narrow the range of ecological efficiencies the figure of 40% body weight ingested by the oribatid mites was applied to the total biomass of the herbivores. This weight, when converted into calories, gave estimates of 10,150.88 calories consumed when the japygids were omitted and 12,712.74 calories consumed when the japygids were included as herbivores. Using the 2 extremes in assimilation rate for the carnivores (i.e. 14% and 32% assimilation) the following efficiencies were obtained: when the japygids were considered to be herbivores, the ecological efficiency was 8-32%; when the japygids were considered to be carnivores, the ecological efficiency was 12-47%. It can be seen that even with 1 variable—the assimiliation efficiency of the predator—the range of possible ecological efficiencies is considerable. The 47% value is once again too high because it required 4,620 calories of ingested herbivore to support the carnivore population, 1230 calories greater than can be produced by the herbivores during the year. Even the 32% efficiency may be too high, for it required 4074 calories to support the carnivores.

At the present stage of knowledge, therefore, any ecological efficiency between 8% and 30% may be considered reasonable for soil herbivores.

## DISCUSSION

To create the proper setting for the discussion to follow, the use of the word "community" must be clarified. In most texts the community concept is supported and discussed with such assurance that the reader is led to believe that the concept is a rule in ecology. MacFadyen (1957: 238) points out that "the term community is a shibboleth and a label for a working hypothesis." Therefore, the discussion and re-definition of the term is not out of order. The definition of community used in this paper is as follows: an assemblage of populations coexisting in time and space, mutually regulative and interdependent, and depending ultimately upon some common energy source. This definition contains elements from several sources, principally Allee *et al.* (1949) and MacFadyen (1957). The stipulation about the energy source is lacking in most definitions; yet, it would seem that this requirement is basic to understanding of the community. The food web, if known, can be used to delimit one community from another. A common energy source, however, does not necessarily have to be solar radiation, but can be another form of energy, such as organic materials of various kinds, or even various simple chemical compounds which are capable of being broken down by microorganisms (e.g., sulphur and iron bacteria).

If there is a basic trophic scheme for all communities, then the energy relationships should be reflected in the community structure. Community structure has been approached from several points of view. Physical description came first, but this approach cannot be tested by the application of mathematical processes, and thus relies solely upon the acuity of the observer. Hairston (1955) has summarized another line of approach, that of comparing species abundance with mathematical models. Of all the models used, the ones by MacArthur (1957) re most appealing because they are based upon

biological principles rather than upon some theoretical mathematical curve. Data of relative species abundance best fit the MacArthur model which assumes that the niches are continuous but not overlapping. When the number of individuals per species (relative abundance) is plotted against the predicted curve, however, biological data do not fall along the predicted curve. Hairston attributed this difference between observed and expected plots to the fact that niche size is not determined randomly as suggested by MacArthur's model, but rather, niche size is a function of an organized system—the community. Hairston further pointed out that food is the one constituent of the community that will fit this model. Since, in all analyses mentioned by Hairston, numbers of individuals were used, it is possible to plot an energy function of these animals as related to their food (i.e., calories respired) against the theoretical curve. Figs. 4, 5, and 6 show the form of the observed data with respect to the predicted curves when numbers of individuals, biomass, and calories respired for a year are plotted for the oribatid mites found on the old-field in 1958. The observed curve for numbers of individuals is similar to those presented by Hairston (1959). Biomass gives a smoother curve, with a shape similar to that of the predicted curve, but still exhibiting the same

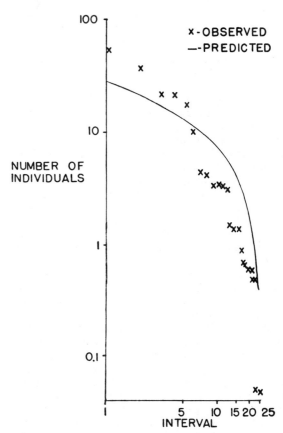

Fig. 4. Number of individuals of each species of oribatid mite found on the old field in 1958, compared with the model of MacArthur.

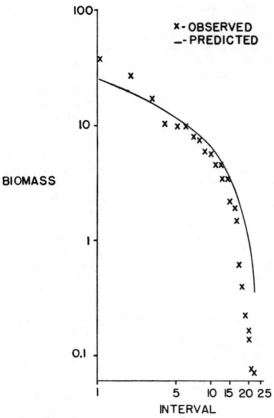

FIG. 5. Total biomass of each species of oribatid mite found on the old field in 1958, compared with the model of MacArthur.

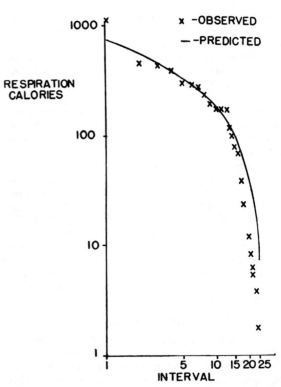

FIG. 6. Total respiration of each species of oribatid mite found on the old field in 1958, compared with the model of MacArthur.

distortions as did the previous curve. When respiration calories are plotted, the top half of the curve conforms to prediction, but the bottom half of the curve still falls away. This curve could be interpreted as meaning that the common organisms fit the model and have their niche size determined in a random manner, while the rare individuals do not fit the model and do not have their niche size determined at random. However, when the respirations for all of the soil arthropods found on the old field during 1949 and 1950 were plotted, the curve still showed the deviations of the plot for numbers of individuals. This may reflect the fact that several trophic levels are included in the total analysis of arthropods, while only part of one trophic level was considered in the analysis of the oribatids. It seems that for a single trophic level, at least, energy units more nearly fit the predicted curves. There is indication, then, that Hairston's assumption has validity and that the niche or status of an animal in the community might therefore be defined in terms of the amount and kind of food it eats, hence ultimately in terms of energy consumed.

The food web of the community is one of the more important concepts of community organization, and its complete qualitative and quantitative description should be the ultimate goal of the community ecol-

ogist. The food web of the soil community is poorly understood. The role of the soil arthropods in this food web will be considered next, because these organisms hold a key position in the soil community.

It is generally accepted that the soil arthropods play an important role in the soil-building process. Allee et al. (1949) review the classification of the soil organisms according to their food habits. This classification, based mostly upon the ideas of Fenton and Jacot, divided the soil organisms into 5 major groups: 1), chemical agents (bacteria and fungi); 2), ectophagous agents (species which eat whole green leaves and perform some chemical breakdown); 3), endophagous agents (agents which "mine" leaves and roots); 4), predators; and 5), shelterers (animals which use the soil as a retreat only). A common description of the process of soil building is as follows: first, the dead material falls to the ground; then the arthropods grind the material into small bits; and finally the bacteria and fungi attack the "grindings" and break the material down to an elemental state, which can once more be exploited by the plants. Many of the observations on food habits of soil arthropods seem to support this view. When van der Drift (1950) fed millipeds very moist leaf litter, they assimilated about 6% of the material. Gere (1956) fed millipeds as well as isopods on litter. He noted however, that the animals did much better on the litter from the Fx layer, or decomposed material just above the mineral soil, than they did on the newly fallen dead leaves. Wallwork (1958) and Rohde (1955) raised and maintained oribatid mites on leaf litter or decayed wood. Birch & Clark (1953) report Riha as stating that the oribatids feed upon wet dead leaves, wet dead wood, and that two species feed upon fungal mycelia.

In this study, however, the soil arthropods would not culture upon fresh dead, or dried plant material, even after it was wetted. Green plant material did not seem acceptable. *Oppia nova* was finally cultured on yeast. It was observed then that several other species of oribatid mites (family Eremaeidae) fed upon yeast, (*Saccharomyces cerevisiae*), mushrooms (*Mycena fibula, Agaricus campestris* and others) and the hyphae of *Aspergillus inornata*. A belbid mite specialized upon a mold (an imperfect) which grew upon decaying arthropod muscles. The particular fungus was very sticky and smaller mites would become trapped if they tried to cross it, but the long-legged belbid had no such difficulty and fed exclusively upon this mold in culture. Further search of the literature disclosed observations similar to those cited above. Van der Drift (1950) cites Dr. Rooseboom's observation that *Oppia neerlandica, Oribatula tibialis, Chamobotes schultze,* and *Galumna* cf. *dorsalis* all fed upon molds. Wallwork (1958) found fungal mycelia in the guts of most of the mites that he inspected. The guts were also filled with other material. Sengbusch found that the young of *Galumna* (several species) would feed on the alga *Protococcus,* while the adult fed upon moss. Rohde (1959) raised the mite *Caloglyphus* on fresh hamburger, and the same mite was cultured by D. Pimentel (personal communications) on *Neurospora.* Metcalf & Flint (1939) review the life histories of several mites which are pests on agricultural plants. Representatives of the same families including the agricultural pests are found in the soil of the old field. Finally, the volume edited and compiled by Needham *et al.* (1937) gives numerous culture methods of invertebrates. The food recommended for the milliped *Euryurus erythropygus* is moist decayed sapwood; for oribatids, and tyroglyphids, lichen, mosses, cheese mold, and moist dead wood. The mushroom mite, *Tyroglyphus linteri,* various Collembola (*Achorutes armatus, Proisotoma minuta, Lipidocyrtus cyaneus, L. albus,* and *Sminthurus caecus*), Diptera larva (*Sciara coprophila, Neosciara pauciseta, Calliceras* sp., and members of the Cecidomyidae) have all been raised on commercial mushroom spawn. Yeast has been used to culture *Proisotoma minuta* (Auerbach *et al.* 1957), and *Tyroglyphus linteri* (present author). Similar references on the food habits of soil-dwelling arthropods may be found in the work of Cloudsley-Thompson (1953), and Kevan (1955).

The question raised here is, do soil arthropods actually feed upon dead material, as has been so often reported, or are these animals actually deriving their nourishment from mycelia of fungi within the decaying litter? The definition of the word "feed" in the above question creates the problem, because an animal may ingest material and yet not be able to assimilate it. The majority of the dead matter falling to the floor stratum of a community is in the form of plant material, most of which is cellulose and hemicellulose. The starches and sugars contained in the living leaves of the plant have undoubtedly been used up by the cells of the plant as the leaves died, have been transported to other parts of the plant for storage, or have been leached from the leaf or oxidized before the leaf fell to the ground. Therefore, an organism must have cellulase in order to break down the cellulose for use as a food source. The lower plants (bacteria and fungi) are well-supplied with cellulase, as are many of the parasitic protozoa. However, when the metazoa are surveyed for the presence of cellulase (Prosser *et al.* 1950) it is found only in various Mollusca and the earthworm (*Lumbricus*). Symbiotic bacteria and/or protozoa are the usual source of cellulase in most wood-eating insects. Brues (1946) has shown dramatically the dependence of insects upon microorganisms. Using the fruit fly as an example, he points out that although the larvae appear to be feeding upon the banana medium, they are actually feeding upon yeasts growing in the medium. If the culture is kept completely sterile, the fly larvae die. In the same line, a soil arthropod may be *ingesting* dead plant material; however, it is *digesting* the living bodies of the fungal hyphae which are attacking the dead material. In each case where the food habits of a soil arthropod have been explored fully, it has been shown that fungus is a suitable food material. It is possible that the soil arthropods possess cellulase, but in view of the lack of the enzyme in the rest of the Metazoa, this possibility seems to be slight. Some soil arthropods may, of course, have intestinal symbionts. Rohde (1955) reports that the young of the box mite (*Pseudotritia* sp.) consume the feces of the adult, and that the adult's digestive tract is filled with rod-shaped bacteria. This feces-eating habit is common of other wood-feeding arthropods such as the passalid beetles and termites. New enzymes for the soil arthropods do not have to be postulated however, to allow for the break down of the dead plant material in the soil community. The bacteria and fungi already possess the necessary cellulases. These plants digest their food extracellularly and then absorb the dissolved sugars. An arthropod feeding upon the dead material, then, has access to the sugars digested by the fungus as well as to the fungal protoplasm. In culture glucose crystals were fed upon by galumnid and eremaeid mites, indicating that these animals were attracted to sugars.

Not all of the soil arthropods are herbivores; some are known to be carnivorous. All of the Parasitidae and Trombididae feed upon mites and Collembola or are parasitic upon vertebrates and large insects. These animals presumably act as population controls on the herbivores or upon the animals which they parasitize.

This review of the feeding habits of the soil arthropods, and especially of the food preferences of the mites, suggests that the traditional role of these animals in the soil community needs some revision. It follows from the above observations that the role of the soil arthropods is not merely that of a grinding mill. Rather, they form a control mechanism upon the fungus populations. The soil arthropods affect the fungi in at least three different ways. First, the arthropods feed directly upon fungi, thereby cutting the biomass of the plants in the immediate area. In this sense the arthropods act as a depressing factor upon the fungal population. Secondly the arthropods clear away material penetrated by hyphae, exposing new material to the action of the fungi. The oribatid mites also have a third important effect upon the fungi, since they defecate while they are feeding. The feces of these animals are usually filled with spores from some previous meal. The mite feces then inoculate newly-exposed material with new fungal spores. This action tends to accelerate the breakdown of the material in the immediate area, for it is known that the respiration of a rapidly growing fungus colony is greater that that of a mature colony (James 1953). Finally, of course, there is a certain amount of grinding or reduction of particle size in the feeding process, as well as the seeding of the feces with microorganisms. The reduction of particle size would seem more important for the bacteria, which can work only on the surfaces of materials, than for the fungi, which are capable of penetrating materials.

This analysis of community energetics further suggests that soil arthropods do not fit precisely into Lindeman's original scheme, or at least that they have not been properly elaborated upon in that scheme. A schematic representation of the energy flow of the old field is given in Fig. 7. Lindeman's symbols are retained in the interest of standardization and clarity. For each trophic level (capital lambda) there is a flow of energy into the level (small lambda) in the form of food or radiation depending upon the level, and the energy leaves that level in the form of respiration (R), decomposition (D), and energy consumed by the next level (small lambda). Each level is given a number: 1 for the green plants, 2 for the herbivores, 3, primary carnivores, and so forth. In the Lindeman scheme the "D" of decomposition of the trophic level either embraces the whole soil fauna, or it includes only the bacteria and fungi, thereby omitting the herbivores and carnivores which are directly dependent upon these plants for food. In the present modification of the scheme, the soil complex is represented by the double numbers: 11 for the fungi and bacteria, 22 for the herbivorous mites, Collembola, round worms, etc., and 33 for the carnivorous mites.

This trophic diagram of the old field indicates 2 major flows of energy, one above-ground and the other one in the soil. The above-ground system is powered directly by the sun's energy, captured by the green plants, while the soil system is powered

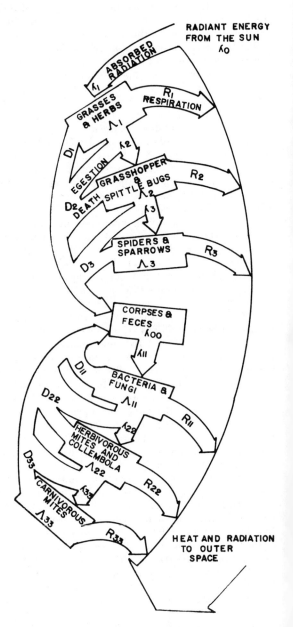

Fig. 7. A schematic energy flow diagram for the upland of an old field in Michigan. The symbols used are those of Lindeman. Note that "D" represents decomposition; this includes egestion, which has never become part of the protoplasm of the population, and death, which has been part of the protoplasm of the population.

directly by the dead bodies and feces of the above-ground members. The dead material, of course, was originally produced by the green plants. The soil plants can be placed in trophic levels equivalent to those of the above-ground system, and given a supply of energy, the soil system will continue to operate. The fact that the oribatid population underwent such a complete change, while the above-ground community changed little, tends to support the idea that the soil system is a separate community from the above-ground community. The surface of the soil then becomes an ecotone and animals such as spiders, staphylinids, and carabids can be considered ecotonal animals. These facts support the views of Birch & Clark (1953) that the soil is an ecological community in its own right.

The diagram depicts the energy flow of the old field only in its broadest outlines and is admittedly an over-simplification of the true picture. A single animal may not fall into a single trophic level, or may change food habits according to season: e.g., the chipping sparrow, which feeds mostly upon arthropods during the breeding season and mostly upon plant seeds during the rest of the summer. Imports and exports have also been ignored. In the old field, for example, windborne seeds and flying arthropods, are continually emigrating or immigrating. Rains leach materials from the soils. Carnivores often feed from several different trophic levels, thus complicating the picture further. Without information on these unknowns, the scheme is probably best left in simplified form.

A value of the Lindeman scheme is that it will allow the comparison of communities at all levels. At present this comparison is fairly rough because of imperfect methods of collecting needed data. On the population level the results for the oribatids compare favorably with those of Richman (1958) and Slobodkin (1959) for *Daphnia,* the water flea. The only outstanding difference between the two kinds of organisms involves the amount of energy put into reproduction by the populations. The *Daphnia* have a high reproductive rate, while the oribatids have a low rate. Assimilation rates and respiration vs. growth calories for non-reproductive adults of *Daphnia* and *Oppia-* are all in the same range. Richman has shown that the growth rates and assimilation rates of *Daphnia* are similar to those found for other animals including vertebrates. He reiterates that the basic biochemistry of all animals is very similar. When the ecological efficiency of the soil arthropods is compared with that of organisms in aquatic communities, the efficiencies also fall in the same range. The ecological efficiencies for the herbivores of several fresh water communities are summarized by Patten (1959). These efficiencies range from 5.5% to 21.0%. From the numerous efficiencies found for the soil arthropods it appears that anything from 8.5% to 30% would be a reasonable estimate. It may disturb some persons to have the ecological efficiency rating so variable. If one considers the efficiency of a population at monthly intervals, it will be seen that there are fluctuations which reflect food levels and predator levels. The overall yearly estimate, then, is an average of the population's efficiencies over the 12-month period. When food supply is abundant, per cent assimilation is low and more calories are "wasted" (defecated) by the population. At the other extreme, when food is scarce, greater amounts of food are assimilated and less is wasted. The ecological efficiency is variable just as a respiration rate is variably, but it should vary within a limited range. Slobodkin (1960) believes 5-15% to be the reasonable limits of this range. However, the data for the soil arthropods suggest that the upper limit may be 20% or higher.

Another efficiency that is a valuable tool in the comparison of several communities is the "efficiency of transfer to each level in terms of original input" (Patten 1959). If the above-ground system and the soil system are considered to be a single community, the primary energy source for the community, is, of course, the sun. The calculated efficiency of transfer of solar energy to the herbivore level of the soil arthropods is .02-.03%. The reason for such a low efficiency is that the soil arthropods are at least 3 trophic levels away from the original energy source. If, however, we consider the soil system to be a separate community, then the energy source and original input for the community is the amount of dead material available. This places the soil herbivores on a par with the above-ground herbivores with respect of trophic level within their communities. The efficiency of transfer thus calculated for the trophic level of the soil arthropods is in this instance 1.5-2.0%. Patten's summarized values for the efficiency of transfer to the herbivore level in aquatic communities ranged from .05 to 6.8%. The efficiency values for the soil arthropods fall well within this range.

In short, these data on the efficiencies of the soil arthropods, both at the population level and at the trophic level, lend support to the hypothesis that all communities function according to the same energetic principles.

## SUMMARY

1. In 1958 a field sampling program and laboratory studies were undertaken with the soil arthropods of an old field in south-eastern Michigan to elucidate the energy dynamics of the soil system. Laboratory methods involved Tullgren extraction, biomass determination, respiration studies and calorimetry.

2. An energy balance sheet was drawn up for the oribatid mites. It was calculated that these mites in 1 square meter 12.5 cm deep consumed 10,248 calories of food each year and assimilated 2,058 calories or 20% of the food ingested. Respiration accounted for 96%, and mortality for 20% of the assimilated material. The error for the calculation was 13%.

3. When comparison was made with the data obtained by Hairston & Byers (1954) on the same field, it was found that the oribatid mite populations had changed markedly. The species composition had changed completely save for 5 species. Numbers of individuals had decreased 33% between 1950 and 1958, but the biomass and calories of respiration had doubled or almost so. It is suggested that the oribatid fauna has probably

displaced other components of the soil, and that the total arthropod biomass has remained at a constant level.

4. The ecological efficiency was calculated for the soil arthropods. Due to the lack of certain feeding information, reasonable efficiencies ranged from 8% to 30% for the soil herbivores.

5. When energy units (respiration calories) were used in place of numbers of individuals in one of MacArthur's models, the observed curves more nearly fit the predicted curves, lending support to the idea that the niche is the amount and kind of food a population consumes.

6. The main role of the soil herbivores was found to be that of controlling the fungal and bacterial populations which are breaking down the dead materials. These arthropods can both accelerate and retard the growth of the decay organisms. The soil carnivores serve as population controls on the herbivores.

7. The soil system is considered for two reasons to be a community separate from the above-ground system. First, it has a trophic level system similar to that of the above-ground system, and secondly, changes in species composition in the soil arthropods are apparently independent of changes in the above-ground system.

8. Data on *Daphnia pulex*, the water flea, and *Oppia nova*, an oribatid mite, compared favorably with respect to their respiration and assimilation efficiencies. The range of ecological efficiencies (8.5-30%) for the soil herbivores compared favorably with ecological efficiencies for the same trophic level in the aquatic communities, and the 1.5-2.0% efficiency of transfer to each level in the soil community also fell within the range of efficiencies found for the aquatic communities. These data lend support to the hypothesis that all communities operate on the same energetic principles.

## LITERATURE CITED

Agrell, I. 1947. Some experiments concerning thermal adjustment and respiratory metabolism in insects. Arkiv. Zool. 39: 1-48.

Allee, W. C., A. E. Emerson, O. Park, T. Park, & K. P. Schmidt. 1949. Principles of Animal Ecology. Philadelphia: Saunders.

Armstrong, J. T. 1960. The dynamics of *Daphnia pulex* and of *Dugesia tigrina* populations as modified by immigration. Ph.D. Dissertation, Univ. of Mich.

Auerbach, S. I., D. A. Crossley, Jr., & M. D. Engelmann. 1957. Effects of gamma radiation on Collembola population growth. Science 126: 614.

Baker, E. W., & G. W. Wharton. 1952. An Introduction to Acarology. New York:Macmillan Company.

Birch, L. C., & P. D. Clark. 1953. Forest soil as an ecological community with special reference to the fauna. Quart. Rev. Biol. 28: 13-36.

Bornebusch, C. H. 1930. The Fauna of the Forest Soil. Copenhagen.

Brody, S. 1945. Bioenergetics and Growth, with Special Reference to the Efficiency Complex in Domestic Animals. New York: Reinhold.

Brues, C. T. 1946. Insect Dietary. Cambridge: Harvard U. Press

Bullock, T. H. 1955. Compensation for temperature in metabolism and activity of poikilotherms. Biol. Rev. 30: 311-342.

Cloudsley-Thompson, J. L. 1958. Spiders, Scorpions, Centipedes, and Mites. New York: Pergamon Press.

Engelmann, M. D. 1956. Observations on the feeding behavior of several pselaphid beetles. Ent. News 67: 19-24.

Evans, F. C., & S. A. Cain. 1952. Preliminary studies on the vegetation of an old-field community in southeastern Michigan. Cont. Lab. Vert. Biol. Univ. Mich. 51: 1-20.

Evans, F. C., & E. Dahl. 1955. The vegetational structure of an abandoned field in southeastern Michigan and its relation to environmental factors. Ecology 36: 685-706.

Evans, F. C. & U. N. Lanham. 1960. Distortion of the pyramid of numbers in a grassland insect community. Science 131: 1531-1532.

Fry, F. E. J. 1958. Temperature compensation. Ann. Rev. Phys. 20: 207-224.

Gere, G. 1956. The examination of the feeding biology and the humificative function of Diplopoda and Isopoda. Acta Biol. Hung. 6: 258-271.

Golley, F. B. 1959. Table of caloric equivalents. Mimeographed sheet. Available from the author, Dept. of Zool., Univ. of Georgia, Athens, Georgia.

Hairston, N. G. 1959. Species abundance and community organization. Ecology 40: 404-416.

Hairston, N. G., & G. W. Byers. 1954. A study in community ecology: the soil arthropods in a field in southern Michigan. Cont. Lab. Vert. Biol. Univ. Mich. 64: 1-37.

James, W. O. 1953. Plant Respiration. London: Oxford Press.

Kevan, D. K. McE. (ed.), 1955. Soil Zoology. London: Butterworths.

Krogh, A. 1941. The Comparative Physiology of Respiratory Mechanisms. Philadelphia: University of Pennsylvania Press.

Lindeman, R. L. 1942. The trophic-dynamic aspect of ecology. Ecology 23: 399-418.

MacFadyen, A. 1952. The small arthropods of a Molinia fen at Cothill. J. Anim. Ecol. 21: 87-117.

———. 1957. Animal Ecology; Aims and Methods. London: Pitman.

MacArthur, R. H. 1957. On the relative abundance of bird species. Proc. Nat. Acad. Sci. U. S. 43: 293-295.

Metcalf, C. L. & W. P. Flint. 1939. Destructive and Useful Insects. New York: McGraw-Hill.

Needham, J. G., F. E. Lutz, P. L. Welch, & P. S. Galtsoff. 1937. Culture Methods for Invertebrate Animals. New York: Dover.

Odum, E. P. 1960. Organic production and turnover in old field succession. Ecology 41: 34-49.

Odum, H. T. 1957. Trophic structure and productivity of Silver Springs, Florida. Ecol. Mono. 27: 55-112.

Park, O., S. Auerbach, & G. Corley. 1950. The tree-hole habitat with emphasis on the pselaphid beetle fauna. Bull. Chicago Acad. Sci. **9**: 19-57.

**Park, O., & S. I. Auerbach.** 1954. Further study of the tree-hole complex with emphasis on quantitative aspects of the fauna. Ecology **35**: 208-222.

**Patten, B. C.** 1959. An introduction to the cybernetics of the ecosystem: the trophic-dynamic aspect. Ecology **40**: 221-231.

**Prosser, C. L.** (ed.), 1950. Comparative Animal Physiology. Philadelphia: Saunders.

**Richman, S.** 1958. The transformation of energy by *Daphnia pulex*. Ecol. Mono. **28**: 273-291.

**Roeder, K. D.** (ed.), 1953. Insect Physiology. New York: Wiley.

**Rohde, C. J., Jr.** 1955. Studies on arthropods from a moss habitat with special emphasis on the life history of three oribatid mites. Ph.D. Dissertation, Northwestern Univ. Evanston, Illinois.

———. 1956. A modification of the plaster-charcoal technique for rearing of mites and other small arthropods. Ecology **37**: 843-844.

———. 1959. Studies on the biologies of two mite species, predator and prey, including some effects of gamma radiation on selected developmental stages. Ecology **40**: 572-579.

**Salt, G., F. S. J. Hollick, F. Raw, & M. V. Brian.** 1948. The arthropod population of pasture soil. J. Anim. Ecol. **17**: 139-150.

**Sengbusch, H.** 1954. Studies on the life histories of three oribatid mites with observations on other species. Ann. Ent. Soc. Amer. **47**: 646-668.

**Slobodkin, L. B.** 1959. Energetics in *Daphnia pulex* populations. Ecology **40**: 232-243.

———. 1960. Ecological energy relationships at the population level. Amer. Naturalist. **94**: 213-236.

**Smith, A. H., & J. R. Douglas.** 1949. An insect respirometer. Ann. Ent. Soc. Amer. **42**: 14-18.

**Talbot, M.** 1953. Ants of an old-field community on the Edwin S. George Reserve, Livingston county, Michigan. Cont. Vert. Lab. Biol. Univ. Mich. **63**: 1-13.

———. 1954. Populations of the ant *Aphaenogaster* (*Attomyrma*) *treatae* Forel on abandoned fields on the Edwin S. George Reserve. Cont. Vert. Lab. Biol. Univ. Mich. **69**: 1-9.

**Teal, M. J.** 1957. 'Community metabolism in a temperate cold spring. Ecol. Mono. **27**: 283-302.

**Trama, F.** 1957. The transformation of energy by an aquatic herbivore *Stenonema pulchelium* (Ephemeroptera). Ph.D. Dissertation, Univ. of Mich.

**Umbreit, W. W., R. H. Burris, & J. F. Stauffer.** 1949. Manometric techniques and tissue metabolism. Minneapolis: Burgess Pub. Co.

**United States Dept. Commerce.** 1958. Climatological Data: Annual Summary. **73**.

**Uvarov, B. P.** 1931. Insects and climate. Trans. Royal Ent. Soc. London **79**: 1-247.

**van der Drift, J.** 1950. Analysis of the Animal Community in a Beech Forest Floor. Wageningen.

**Wallwork, J.** 1958. Notes on the feeding behavior of some forest soil acarina. Oikos **9**: 260-271.

———. 1959. The distribution and dynamics of some forest soil mites. Ecology **40**: 557-563.

**Winston, P. W.** 1956. The acorn microsere, with special reference to arthropods. Ecology **37**: 120-132.

**Zeuthen, E.** 1953. Oxygen uptake as related to body size in organisms. Quart. Rev. Biol. **28**: 1-12.

# COMMUNITY STRUCTURE, POPULATION CONTROL, AND COMPETITION

NELSON G. HAIRSTON, FREDERICK E. SMITH,
AND LAWRENCE B. SLOBODKIN

Department of Zoology, The University of Michigan, Ann Arbor, Michigan

The methods whereby natural populations are limited in size have been debated with vigor during three decades, particularly during the last few years (see papers by Nicholson, Birch, Andrewartha, Milne, Reynoldson, and Hutchinson, and ensuing discussions in the Cold Spring Harbor Symposium, 1957). Few ecologists will deny the importance of the subject, since the method of regulation of populations must be known before we can understand nature and predict its behavior. Although discussion of the subject has usually been confined to single species populations, it is equally important in situations where two or more species are involved.

The purpose of this note is to demonstrate a pattern of population control in many communities which derives easily from a series of general, widely accepted observations. The logic used is not easily refuted. Furthermore, the pattern reconciles conflicting interpretations by showing that populations in different trophic levels are expected to differ in their methods of control.

Our first observation is that the accumulation of fossil fuels occurs at a rate that is negligible when compared with the rate of energy fixation through photosynthesis in the biosphere. Apparent exceptions to this observation, such as bogs and ponds, are successional stages, in which the failure of decomposition hastens the termination of the stage. The rate of accumulation when compared with that of photosynthesis has also been shown to be negligible over geologic time (Hutchinson, 1948).

If virtually all of the energy fixed in photosynthesis does indeed flow through the biosphere, it must follow that all organisms taken together are limited by the amount of energy fixed. In particular, the decomposers as a group must be food-limited, since by definition they comprise the trophic level which degrades organic debris. There is no a priori reason why predators, behavior, physiological changes induced by high densities, etc., could not limit decomposer populations. In fact, some decomposer populations may be limited in such ways. If so, however, others must consume the "left-over" food, so that the group as a whole remains food limited; otherwise fossil fuel would accumulate rapidly.

Any population which is not resource-limited must, of course, be limited to a level *below* that set by its resources.

Our next three observations are interrelated. They apply primarily to terrestrial communities. The first of these is that cases of obvious depletion of green plants by herbivores are exceptions to the general picture, in which

Reproduced with permission from The American Naturalist, XCIV: 421-425, 1960.
Published by The American Society of Naturalists, Tempe, Arizona.

the plants are abundant and largely intact. Moreover, cases of obvious mass destruction by meteorological catastrophes are exceptional in most areas. Taken together, these two observations mean that producers are neither herbivore-limited nor catastrophe-limited, and must therefore be limited by their own exhaustion of a resource. In many areas, the limiting resource is obviously light, but in arid regions water may be the critical factor, and there are spectacular cases of limitation through the exhaustion of a critical mineral. The final observation in this group is that there are temporary exceptions to the general lack of depletion of green plants by herbivores. This occurs when herbivores are protected either by man or natural events, and it indicates that the herbivores are able to deplete the vegetation whenever they become numerous enough, as in the cases of the Kaibab deer herd, rodent plagues, and many insect outbreaks. It therefore follows that the usual condition is for populations of herbivores *not* to be limited by their food supply.

The vagaries of weather have been suggested as an adequate method of control for herbivore populations. The best factual clues related to this argument are to be found in the analysis of the exceptional cases where terrestrial herbivores have become numerous enough to deplete the vegetation. This often occurs with introduced rather than native species. It is most difficult to suppose that a species had been unable to adapt so as to escape control by the weather to which it was exposed, and at the same time by sheer chance to be able to escape this control from weather to which it had not been previously exposed. This assumption is especially difficult when mutual invasions by different herbivores between two countries may in both cases result in pests. Even more difficult to accept, however, is the implication regarding the native herbivores. The assumption that the hundreds or thousands of species native to a forest have failed to escape from control by the weather despite long exposure and much selection, when an invader is able to defoliate without this past history, implies that "pre-adaptation" is more likely than ordinary adaptation. This we cannot accept.

The remaining general method of herbivore control is predation (in its broadest sense, including parasitism, etc.). It is important to note that this hypothesis is not denied by the presence of introduced pests, since it is necessary only to suppose that either their natural predators have been left behind, or that while the herbivore is able to exist in the new climate, its enemies are not. There are, furthermore, numerous examples of the direct effect of predator removal. The history of the Kaibab deer is the best known example, although deer across the northern portions of the country are in repeated danger of winter starvation as a result of protection and predator removal. Several rodent plagues have been attributed to the local destruction of predators. More recently, the extensive spraying of forests to kill caterpillars has resulted in outbreaks of scale insects. The latter are protected from the spray, while their beetle predators and other insect enemies are not.

Thus, although rigorous proof that herbivores are generally controlled by predation is lacking, supporting evidence is available, and the alternate hypothesis of control by weather leads to false or untenable implications.

The foregoing conclusion has an important implication in the mechanism of control of the predator populations. The predators and parasites, in controlling the populations of herbivores, must thereby limit their own resources, and as a group they must be food-limited. Although the populations of some carnivores are obviously limited by territoriality, this kind of internal check cannot operate for all carnivores taken together. If it did, the herbivores would normally expand to the point of depletion of the vegetation, as they do in the absence of their normal predators and parasites.

There thus exists either direct proof or a great preponderance of factual evidence that in terrestrial communities decomposers, producers, and predators, as whole trophic levels, are resource-limited in the classical density-dependent fashion. Each of these three can and does expand toward the limit of the appropriate resource. We may now examine the reasons why this is a frequent situation in nature.

Whatever the resource for which a set of terrestrial plant species compete, the competition ultimately expresses itself as competition for space. A community in which this space is frequently emptied through depletion by herbivores would run the continual risk of replacement by another assemblage of species in which the herbivores are held down in numbers by predation below the level at which they damage the vegetation. That space once held by a group of terrestrial plant species is not readily given up is shown by the cases where relict stands exist under climates no longer suitable for their return following deliberate or accidental destruction. Hence, the community in which herbivores are held down in numbers, and in which the producers are resource-limited will be the most persistent. The development of this pattern is less likely where high producer mortalities are inevitable. In lakes, for example, algal populations are prone to crash whether grazed or not. In the same environment, grazing depletion is much more common than in communities where the major producers are rooted plants.

A second general conclusion follows from the resource limitation of the species of three trophic levels. This conclusion is that if more than one species exists in one of these levels, they may avoid competition only if each species is limited by factors completely unutilized by any of the other species. It is a fact, of course, that many species occupy each level in most communities. It is also a fact that they are not sufficiently segregated in their needs to escape competition. Although isolated cases of non-overlap have been described, this has never been observed for an entire assemblage. Therefore, interspecific competition for resources exists among producers, among carnivores, and among decomposers.

It is satisfying to note the number of observations that fall into line with the foregoing deductions. Interspecific competition is a powerful selective force, and we should expect to find evidence of its operation. Moreover, the evidence should be most conclusive in trophic levels where it is necessarily present. Among decomposers we find the most obvious specific mechanisms for reducing populations of competitors. The abundance of antibiotic substances attests to the frequency with which these mechanisms have been developed in the trophic level in which interspecific competition is inevitable. The producer species are the next most likely to reveal evidence of competition, and here we find such phenomena as crowding, shading, and vegetational zonation.

Among the carnivores, however, obvious adaptations for interspecific competition are less common. Active competition in the form of mutual habitat-exclusion has been noted in the cases of flatworms (Beauchamp and Ullyott, 1932) and salamanders (Hairston, 1951). The commonest situation takes the form of niche diversification as the result of interspecific competition. This has been noted in birds (Lack, 1945; MacArthur, 1958), salamanders (Hairston, 1949), and other groups of carnivores. Quite likely, host specificity in parasites and parasitoid insects is at least partly due to the influence of interspecific competition.

Of equal significance is the frequent occurrence among herbivores of apparent exceptions to the influence of density-dependent factors. The grasshoppers described by Birch (1957) and the thrips described by Davidson and Andrewartha (1948) are well known examples. Moreover, it is among herbivores that we find cited examples of coexistence without evidence of competition for resources, such as the leafhoppers reported by Ross (1957), and the psocids described by Broadhead (1958). It should be pointed out that in these latter cases coexistence applies primarily to an identity of food and place, and other aspects of the niches of these organisms are not known to be identical.

## SUMMARY

In summary, then, our general conclusions are: (1) Populations of producers, carnivores, and decomposers are limited by their respective resources in the classical density-dependent fashion. (2) Interspecific competition must necessarily exist among the members of each of these three trophic levels. (3) Herbivores are seldom food-limited, appear most often to be predator-limited, and therefore are not likely to compete for common resources.

## LITERATURE CITED

Andrewartha, H. G., 1957, The use of conceptual models in population ecology. Cold Spring Harbor Symp. Quant. Biol. 22: 219–232.

Beauchamp, R. S. A., and P. Ullyott, 1932, Competitive relationships between certain species of fresh-water triclads. J. Ecology 20: 200–208.

Birch, L. C., 1957, The role of weather in determining the distribution and abundance of animals. Cold Spring Harbor Symp. Quant. Biol. 22: 217–263.

Broadhead, E., 1958, The psocid fauna of larch trees in northern England. J. Anim. Ecol. 27: 217–263.

Davidson, J., and H. G. Andrewartha, 1948, The influence of rainfall, evaporation and atmospheric temperature on fluctuations in the size of a natural population of *Thrips imaginis* (Thysanoptera). J. Anim. Ecol. 17: 200–222.

Hairston, N. G., 1949, The local distribution and ecology of the Plethodontid salamanders of the southern Appalachians. Ecol. Monog. 19: 47–73.

1951, Interspecies competition and its probable influence upon the vertical distribution of Appalachian salamanders of the genus Plethodon. Ecology 32: 266–274.

Hutchinson, G. E., 1948, Circular causal systems in ecology. Ann. N. Y. Acad. Sci. 50: 221–246.

1957, Concluding remarks. Cold Spring Harbor Symp. Quant. Biol. 22: 415–427.

Lack, D., 1945, The ecology of closely related species with special reference to cormorant (*Phalacrocorax carbo*) and shag (*P. aristotelis*). J. Anim. Ecol. 14: 12–16.

MacArthur, R. H., 1958, Population ecology of some warblers of northeastern coniferous forests. Ecology 39: 599–619.

Milne, A., 1957, Theories of natural control of insect populations. Cold Spring Harbor Symp. Quant. Biol. 22: 253–271.

Nicholson, A. J., 1957, The self-adjustment of populations to change. Cold Spring Harbor Symp. Quant. Biol. 22: 153–172.

Reynoldson, T. B., 1957, Population fluctuations in *Urceolaria mitra* (Peritricha) and *Enchytraeus albidus* (Oligochaeta) and their bearing on regulation. Cold Spring Harbor Symp. Quant. Biol. 22: 313–327.

Ross, H. H., 1957, Principles of natural coexistence indicated by leafhopper populations. Evolution 11: 113–129.

# "COMMUNITY STRUCTURE, POPULATION CONTROL, AND COMPETITION"—A CRITIQUE

WILLIAM W. MURDOCH*

Department of Zoology, University of Michigan, Ann Arbor

In attempting to formulate general theories of population control, ecologists are faced with the problem that every population is, in some sense, unique. Nevertheless, one persists in the attempt to arrive at general statements about a given class of phenomena by distinguishing these features which are common to different populations. The bulk of the present paper is an analysis of a publication by Hairston, Smith, and Slobodkin (1960) which is an interesting attempt to produce such a set of generalizations about broad groups of organisms, and as such is a rare event in ecology. The authors' conclusions, if valid, would be of great significance, and there is evidence in the literature (Hairston, 1964; Hazen [Introduction], 1964; Kormondy, 1965; Mayr, 1963) and in the absence of published contrary opinion, of their being accepted uncritically. At this point, therefore, it seems worthwhile recording some reasons for suspecting that this attempt at generality, though ingenious, is mistaken. In addition, if my interpretation is correct, problems of methodology are raised which are not obvious at first sight, and for this reason it is important to present criticism of this aspect of the paper under discussion.

It will be assumed that the reader is familiar with the contents of Hairston et al. The structure of that paper is as follows: (1) several observations are stated and (2) by a series of logical steps (3) certain conclusions are reached about how the abundance of organisms in nature is determined, in particular that "populations in different trophic levels are expected to differ in their methods of control." The conclusions concern producer, decomposer, herbivore and carnivore (predators and parasites) trophic levels, and, though some of the following criticisms apply to all groups, for brevity mainly herbivores and carnivores will be discussed here. The authors' arguments concerning these two groups may be summarized as follows: (1) Depletion of green plants by herbivores is rare. (2) Rare instances of depletion do occur when herbivores are naturally or artificially protected from their predators (Kaibab deer, spraying of forest insects). From these two observations it is concluded that "the usual condition is for populations of herbivores not to be limited by their food supply." (3) Herbivores are not limited by the weather. This point is supported by observations and arguments which are not the concern of the present paper. (4) It follows that since herbivores are neither food limited nor weather limited, "the remaining general method of herbivore control is predation."

*Present address: Department of Biological Sciences, University of California, Santa Barbara, California.

(5) Finally, "predators and parasites, in controlling the populations of herbivores, must thereby limit their own resources and as a group they must be food limited."

It is important to discuss the frame of reference of the criticisms before proceeding. Hairston et al. note certain observations about natural communities and argue that, given the truth of these observations, certain conclusions follow. The basic observations are that organic matter accumulates at a negligible rate and that vegetation is not seriously depleted by herbivores or climatic catastrophies. Appropriately they point out exceptions to these conditions, such as successional stages, and it must be noted that, since the basic conditions are not fulfilled there, the arguments based on them are unlikely to hold; therefore, it cannot with reason be expected that the conclusions will hold. It is possible that some climax terrestrial systems (which is what the authors are concerned with) exist where one or other of the original observations do not hold, for example organic matter may accumulate. However, I agree with the authors that such situations probably are rare and that their observations seem to be true for most climax terrestrial systems. These then are the "usual conditions" described by the authors and these are accepted for the rest of this paper. We are interested in the authors' conclusions that under "usual conditions" organisms in different trophic levels are limited in different ways. It should be noted, therefore, that the finding of a climax terrestrial community in which one of the observations does not hold would cast no doubt on the hypotheses concerning the usual condition of limitation, though it disproves a different generalization, (which the authors did not make explicitly) namely that the original observations hold universally in climax terrestrial systems. To state the position more succinctly, one of the observations from which the authors derive their ideas is that, in general, the world is green (to use Dr. Slobodkin's apt phrase); this is *not* the hypothesis. The hypothesis seeks to explain how the world remains green, and the existence of "non-green" situations does not test this hypothesis.

Finally, this critique does not seek to disprove the conclusions of the original paper. Thus it seems likely that many populations of herbivores are limited by predation, that many populations of producers, carnivores, and decomposers may be resource limited, and there is evidence from specific studies that competition may occur commonly in nature. The critique does seek to show that the conclusions do not follow irrevocably from the observations, that such conclusions cannot be arrived at deductively in any case, and that these conclusions, viewed as hypotheses, cannot be tested in their present form. Finally, the paper tries to suggest some ways in which the ideas might be modified to a testable form.

The original paper is essentially deductive, and one can attempt to criticize in three ways any hypothesis arrived at deductively by examining: (1) the material truth of the premises, (2) the formal structure and internal consistency of the argument, and (3) by challenging the conclusions on the basis of methodology. The following critique will include these kinds of criticisms, in order, though no attempt is made to make the critique exhaustive.

Two major premises or assumptions of the paper are disputed. The first is that we can conclude that herbivores are not food limited because green plants are not eaten out, and there are two reasons for rejecting it. (a) The first reason is that all of the green plant material may not be edible to the species present in a given area. In rejection of this idea it has been suggested that no part of the vegetation will be inedible to all the herbivores present; however the work of Painter (1951) and that summarized by Beck (1965) indicates that there is continual evolution of plants to avoid being eaten, just as there is evolution of the herbivores. In addition the above suggestion involves use of an assumption (that in any area over an appropriate span of time there are herbivores capable of getting at and eating all the vegetation) to support the theoretical proposition that herbivores are not food limited. (b) It is suggested that the first-mentioned premise can be rejected also because it ignores the possibility that organisms may be food limited without depleting their food supply. This point will be elaborated below.

The second premise to be disputed is not explicitly stated in the paper. It is that there are only three ways in which the numbers of animals (particularly herbivores) can be limited: i.e., by food depletion, by weather, and by predation, the argument being that if two of these are not responsible for limitation the third must be. However, this classification of modes of limitation is not exhaustive, and other possibilities do remain. They include limitation by (1) resources other than food supply, e.g., nesting or oviposition sites, or "space"; (2) self-regulatory systems of the type postulated by Chitty (1960), Wellington (1960) and others; and (3) kinds of food limitation not considered in the paper, e.g., relative shortage of food (Andrewartha and Birch, 1954), insufficient supply of the right kind of food (Dixon, 1963; Eisenberg, 1965). Well illustrated examples of these types of limitation are difficult to find, and the works quoted here generally are interpretations of situations rather than experimental demonstrations (as Drs. Hairston and Smith have pointed out). However, adequate experimental demonstrations of *any* kind of limitation, especially in climax terrestrial systems, are exceedingly rare. In any case it should be noted that since the argument in the 1960 paper is mostly a logical structure, there is no onus on the critic to show that many or most, or even some, herbivores are in fact limited in these ways; it is sufficient to point out the existence of such possibilities.

The question of food limitation mentioned here raises the general point that we cannot determine if some kind of limitation is occurring merely by making simple observations of the kind "green plants are abundant." Any causal relation between the density of a population and its food supply may be rather complex and not discernible from superficial observation (Murdoch, 1966; Huffaker, 1965), and it seems likely that food limitation cannot be demonstrated adequately without some kind of experimentation.

A final point needs to be made regarding these two premises. The conclusion that herbivores are not food limited because they do not deplete the vegetation clearly could apply only to those herbivore species in a given area which are capable of depleting the green matter; it says nothing of the many other herbivores which do not have this capacity. These include the pollen, nectar, seed and fruit eaters, and some of the plant sucking species, gall-formers, etc., and probably some populations which feed directly on the green parts. That is, this conclusion does not apply to the herbivores as a whole trophic level (if there is such a thing) but applies only to a segment of the herbivores. A consequence of this is that, unless predators "as a group" feed exclusively on this segment of herbivores (which is untrue), then step (5) of the argument on page 220 does not necessarily follow. That is, predators "as a group" need not be food limited.

The formal structure and internal consistency of the argument in Hairston et al. are also open to criticism. First, food limitation appears to have been used in different ways with reference to herbivores and to carnivores. Thus it was concluded that herbivores are not food limited because the green plants are not depleted, but by analogous logic it can be concluded that carnivores are not food limited since herbivores apparently are seldom eaten out by their predators. This conclusion is exactly contrary to one of the major conclusions in Hairston et al. Secondly, it is not clear from the paper if the conclusions apply to populations or to trophic levels. This is a crucial aspect of the paper, and will be discussed in the next section.

Finally, we can challenge the conclusions on methodological grounds. The paper, by its deductive nature, can state only a hypothesis, not a conclusion; it cannot state laws, but only suggest possible explanations. It is suggested here that, in its present form, the hypothesis formulated should be rejected for the following reason. A widely accepted criterion of a scientific hypothesis is its *falsifiability* (Popper, 1957; 1961); unless it is possible in principle to test an idea, i.e., make some observation or experiment which could conceivably *disprove* it, it must be rejected or restated. Thus the truth or falsity of a hypothesis cannot be inferred in any way from its material origin. That is, *conclusions* of the paper cannot be accepted on the basis of the premises, logic, and internal consistency alone, even if these are all sound, since the premises cannot be exhaustive in the absence of a complete knowledge of the natural world.

We must ask of the paper, then, what predictions it makes or leads to, and can we subject these predictions to test by observation or experiment? Three kinds of studies have to be considered as possible tests: studies on (1) single populations, (2) groups of populations, or (3) trophic levels, and I will deal with these in sequence. First, it has been pointed out by Hairston (1964) that the idea cannot be tested with reference to single instances of population control, that is, single contrary instances do not refute the idea. Thus it is agreed that the first type of test is unacceptable. Secondly, there is the suggestion that the conclusions are true of herbivores, carnivores, etc. in general. For example, the authors make the following statements: "The remaining general method of herbivore control is...," "although rigorous proof that herbivores are generally controlled by preda-is lacking...," "the usual condition is for populations of herbivores not to be limited by their food supply," and "demonstrate a pattern of popula-tion control in many communities...." How do we establish such a gen-eral pattern or trend? Does this require that, say, 75% or 80% of all herbivores, or of all herbivore species, are predator limited; or conversely, how many contrary instances are necessary to refute the hypothesis? Clearly the idea as stated in the paper provides no criteria for judging it in this way, and the second kind of test also is not appropriate. This second type of test also includes studies of groups of populations smaller than trophic levels, for example the dominant producers or those herbivores capable of depleting the vegetation. But such tests concern hypotheses about the group defined, and are not tests of ideas about a trophic level.

Finally we are left with the possibility of testing if the conclusions hold for trophic levels "as a whole" and this requires an examination of the nature of trophic levels. Unlike populations, trophic levels are ill-defined and have no distinguishable lateral limits; in addition tens of thousands of insect species, for example, live in more than one trophic level either si-multaneously or at different stages of their life histories. Thus trophic levels exist only as abstractions, and unlike populations they have no empirically measurable properties or parameters. In fact, organisms exist in populations and it is doubtful that nature is organized around the trophic level with regard to the processes involved in the limitation numbers. To test a hypothesis about a trophic level "as a whole," and not about a sub-set of it such as the dominant species, one must be able to identify the unit or some of its measurable attributes. Thus the last type of test is also inappropriate since the trophic level does not exist as an observable or experimental unit over the time span necessary for studying the limita-tion of numbers. It is suggested then that the idea, while it may serve as a basis for interesting polemic or as a stimulus to more rigorous formula-tions along these lines, is not amenable to testing and should be rejected as a useful hypothesis, at least in its present form.

This last section of the argument is treated in detail as it is a funda-mental area of disagreement. I suggest that unless "as a whole" means all populations in a given group or populations "in general" in that group, then the statements are untestable, and tests of types (1) and (2), outlined above, are irrelevant to such statements. Just as contrary evidence from a subset of a trophic level is insufficient to reject a hypothesis about the trophic level, so confirmatory evidence from a subset cannot constitute a check or test of the hypothesis. Perhaps an example will best illustrate this point. The original paper points out that, in climax terrestrial com-munities, organic debris does not accumulate as fossil fuel. It states fur-ther that although some decomposer populations may be limited below their food supply by, for example, predation or behavioral or physiological mechanisms, other populations must eat up the "left-over" food. It is concluded that the "group as a whole remains food limited." I suggest on the contrary, that, given appropriate experimental evidence, we could conclude only that those "other" populations were food limited, that the remainder were limited in some other way, and that no meaningful hypothesis could be reached about the method of limitation of the organisms in the group "as a whole."

## Some general methodological implications

The remainder of this paper is not a critique of Hairston et al., but is a presentation of some ideas which arose from the critique and its implications.

The particular instance of the non-testable idea which has been criticized here (if it is such an instance) is not unique in ecology, and such ideas seem to arise from attempts to reach statements about a broad range of undefined phenomena before statements about recognizable classes of events are achieved. Some ways in which a modification of the idea in Hairston et al. could be made testable have implications for much of theoretical ecology. Several steps are necessary. First, *operational* definitions of food limitation, predator limitation, and weather limitation are necessary. That is, those observations or experimental outcomes which will be accepted as necessary and sufficient evidence of each mode of limitation must be outlined before the observations and experiments are done. For example, food limitation might be demonstrated by a decrease in reproductive rate, an increase in mortality due to malnutrition, and a sustained increase in density following directly from artificial increase of the food supply. Secondly, the unit of study must be defined. It might be, for example, a single population or a group of populations of a recognizable type, etc. Finally, some criterion for rejection of the hypothesis must be presented. For example, to test the statements about a general method of control in Hairston et al., if 25 % of the species in the group were not limited in the postulated manner then the hypothesis could be rejected.

Finally, a problem which has become apparent in the present paper must be discussed, for it is present in several areas of theoretical ecology. It is the problem of definition, and it is more than a mere semantic one. Together with the idea of testability, the *kind* of definition used is central to a rigorous approach in ecology; and the failings of ecologists in these two areas have led directly to the present non-rigorous state of some areas of the discipline. That the experimental approach is important in empirical ecology has come to be accepted; but also theories in ecology must have implicit in them their experimental test, and this is not generally true at present. The rather notorious semantic arguments in ecology about definitions have arisen from this deficiency, as has the situation where a large part of the "checking" of ideas, and much theoretical controversy evolve around *a posteriori* analysis of data. Such data usually are open to varying interpretations which cannot be resolved partly because, of course, the

authors cannot agree on definitions, and partly because the data are analyzed *a posteriori* and were not collected in such a way as to test rigorously any particular *a priori* hypothesis. The worst kind of definition in
this respect is one which refers only to some concept or abstraction from
reality, since this kind is particularly susceptible to diverse interpretation
in the face of real data.

The resolution of theoretical problems can come only by recourse to
crucial experiments or observations designed to test rigorously stated hypotheses. Ecological hypotheses will be testable (i.e., disprovable) in
this way only when the definitions incorporated in them are operational
definitions.

## SUMMARY

The paper by Hairston et al. (1960) is examined critically with regard to
its premises, logic and internal consistency, and its methodology. It is
suggested that, either as conclusions or hypotheses, the major points made
in the paper are not acceptable. In the present paper the importance of
testability and of operational definitions in ecological hypotheses are
stressed.

## ACKNOWLEDGMENTS

I am grateful to the staff and graduate students in the University of
Michigan Ecology group for helpful discussions, and most particularly to
Professors Hairston, Smith, and Slobodkin, who, although not in agreement
with them, showed great patience and tolerance in listening to my argu-
ments. Dr. Charles Krebs kindly read and criticized the manuscript, and
Dr. Joseph Connell provided valuable discussion.

## LITERATURE CITED

Andrewartha, H. G., and L. C. Birch. 1954. The distribution and abundance
of animals. Univ. Chicago Press, Chicago. 782 p.
Beck, S. D. 1965. Resistance of plants to insects. Ann. Rev. Entomol.
10:207-232.
Chitty, D. H. 1960. Population processes in the vole and their relevance
to general theory. Can. J. Zool. 38:99-113.
Dixon, A. F. G. 1963. Reproductive activity of the sycamore aphid,
*Drepanosiphum platanoides* (Schr.) (Hemiptera, Aphididae). J.
Anim. Ecol. 32:33-48.
Eisenberg, R. M. 1965. The regulation of density in a natural population of
the pond snail, *Lymnaea elodes*. Ph.D. Thesis, Univ. Michigan.
Hairston, N. G. 1964. Studies on the organization of animal communities.
J. Anim. Ecol. 33 (Suppl.):227-239.
Hairston, N. G., F. E. Smith, and L. B. Slobodkin. 1960. Community struc-
ture, population control, and competition. Amer. Natur. 94:421-425.
Hazen, W. E. 1964. Readings in population and community ecology.
Saunders, Philadelphia. 388 p.

Huffaker, C. B. 1965. Population levels regulated by competition for food under different conditioning aspects of dispersion and density-unrelated stress. Bull. Ecol. Soc. Amer. 46:42.

Kormondy, E. J. 1965. Readings in ecology. Prentice Hall Inc., New Jersey. 219 p.

Mayr, E. 1963. Animal species and evolution. Belknap, Cambridge. 797 p.

Murdoch, W. W. 1966. Aspects of the population dynamics of some marsh Carabidae. J. Anim. Ecol. (In press).

Painter, R. H. 1951. Insect resistance in crop plants. Macmillan, New York.

Popper, K. R. 1957. Science, a personal report. *In* C. A. Mace [ed.], British Philosophy in the mid-century. Humanities Press, New York.

————. 1961. The logic of scientific discovery. Science Editions Inc., New York. (A translation of Logik der Forschung, 1935.)

Wellington, W. G. 1960. Qualitative changes in natural populations during changes in abundance. Can. J. Zool. 38:289–314.

# A REPLY TO DR. MURDOCH

We wish to thank the editors of *The American Naturalist* for inviting us to reply to Dr. Murdoch's paper. In spite of an extensive exchange of views with him, we remain in complete disagreement. We could, of course, present counter arguments, but we feel that little purpose would be served by our doing so. Readers who found the original paper convincing will find it easy to refute Dr. Murdoch's assertions for themselves; those who disagreed with us initially will doubtless continue to disagree, regardless of any arguments that we might present. It is clear that observation and experimentation, rather than argument, will eventually resolve the question.

Nelson G. Hairston, Department of Zoology
Frederick E. Smith, Department of Wildlife
and Fisheries
The University of Michigan

# THE "BALANCE OF NATURE" AND "POPULATION CONTROL"

P. R. EHRLICH* and L. C. BIRCH

Department of Biological Sciences, Stanford University, Stanford, California and
School of Biological Sciences, University of Sydney, Sydney, Australia

The idea that there is a "balance of nature" is commonly held by biologists. They feel that the organisms in a community are harmoniously adjusted to one another so that a state of dynamic equilibrium exists. In this equilibrium the numbers of the individuals of each species in the community remain relatively constant, and significant changes in numbers occur only when something upsets the natural "balance." This view of the "balance of nature" is perpetuated by popular magazines and nature films, and thus is part of the lore of the man-in-the-street. In our opinion, it is more difficult to explain why it persists in the writings of ecologists. In this paper we will first examine this idea as it appears in the ecological literature, and then present a realistic basis for models of "population control."

## THE "BALANCE OF NATURE"

The existence of a supposed balance of nature is usually argued somewhat as follows. Species X has been in existence for thousands or perhaps millions of generations, and yet its numbers have never increased to infinity or decreased to zero. The same is true of the millions of other species still extant. During the next 100 years, the numbers of all these species will fluctuate; yet none will increase indefinitely, and only a few will become extinct. Furthermore, most species have at least some populations living in areas where they are well able to cope with the climate, yet even these populations never increase indefinitely. Such "observations" are made the basis for the statement that population size is "controlled" or "regulated," and that drastic changes in size are the results of upsetting the "balance of nature." Sometimes this is put in other ways, such as "on the average, the species just replaces its numbers in successive generations" or "on the average, the numbers of individuals over a long period of time are constant." An extreme version can be found in Slobodkin (1962, p. 46). "Despite this enormous variation in reproductive patterns, each female adult animal alive now—in every species, in almost every location—will be replaced by pre-

*National Science Foundation Senior Postdoctoral Fellow, University of Sydney, 1965–66.

cisely one female alive a generation from now. If this were not the case, the size of animal populations would be changing permanently and strikingly at a much greater rate than any existing evidence indicates."

In this form, the "balance of nature" idea can be dealt with quite simply. Indeed, Slobodkin's statement may well be the most thoroughly falsified hypothesis still current in population biology. A survey of the literature fails to disclose a single case of a natural population behaving in the manner described. Even in those few situations in which the size of the population has been observed to remain relatively constant, "precise" one-for-one replacement does not occur.

A well-known statement about the balance of nature is "population densities are continually changing, but their values tend to oscillate about a mean which is relatively stable, though itself subject to change" (Smith, 1935, as quoted by Varley and Gradwell, 1958). Smith, unlike Slobodkin, at least recognized that numbers of organisms are continually changing; but the rest of his statement is almost meaningless for the following reasons. First, any set of values does not oscillate around a mean which is "relatively stable." The values oscillate around a mean that is fixed. The only ways the mean can be subjected to change are by weighting values, adding values, or subtracting values (or, of course, by substituting a different kind of mean). Any set of numbers which is not generally increasing or decreasing will oscillate around its mean. This, indeed, is the total information content of the second part of Smith's statement. Second, Smith's statement has been taken to imply that mean population size has an objective existence separate from the observed population sizes. This cannot be so. Some have also implied that a population will "strive" to return to this "mean." We are unable to attach any meaning to such an implication.

In saying that phrases such as "balance of nature" are rather meaningless, we are not denying that the numbers of some populations may be influenced by so-called "regulatory factors," i.e., whose depressive effect on rate of increase is positively correlated with density (Solomon, 1964). We would deny that there is any convincing evidence that the numbers of all populations are primarily determined by density regulating factors. We do not deny the role such "factors" play in some populations. Indeed, it would be quite an interesting exercise as Solomon (1964, p. 9) suggests to measure the effects of density-regulating and nondensity-regulating factors in any particular case. There are substantial problems in designing practical tests of regulation in natural populations, but these may not be insurmountable. We would expect the role of regulatory factors to vary among species, among populations of the same species, and through time.

## "BALANCE OF NATURE" AND DECOMPOSERS

A deceptively different version of the "balance of nature" idea is presented in a well-known paper by Hairston, Smith, and Slobodkin (1960). This version has been accepted fairly widely without criticism except for a recent brief critique by Murdoch (1966) which appeared after a final draft of this manuscript had been completed. We agree with all of Murdoch's criticisms but would go further. It seems desirable to do this as Hairston and Smith in their brief reply to Murdoch's critique at the end of his paper "remain in complete disagreement." Hairston, Smith, and Slobodkin did not commence their argument with the constancy of numbers of organisms but with the constancy of the amount of organic matter on the earth. Organic matter does not appear to accumulate on the earth; there is no evidence of large amounts of fossil fuel being laid down, nor is the earth becoming a vast dung heap. So they infer that "the decomposers as a group must be food-limited, since by definition they comprise the trophic level which degrades organic debris." This is their starting point of a demonstration of "a pattern of population control in many communities which derives easily from a series of general, widely accepted observations." We are told further that, "The logic used is not easily refuted."

As we will show below, many of the "general, widely accepted observations" about different trophic levels, although they may be widely accepted, are quite likely wrong. We will further show that, even if these "widely accepted observations" are 100% accurate, the conclusions about "population control" stated in the summary of Hairston, Smith, and Slobodkin's paper, do not necessarily follow. This latter point is also made by Murdoch (1966).

In the passage quoted above, Hairston, Smith, and Slobodkin state that "the decomposers as a group must be food-limited . . . ." Unfortunately, they do not define what they mean by "food-limited." You could say that the Cabbage-white butterfly is food-limited because the world could be planted with more cabbages than it is; and if it were, there would be more individuals of the butterfly around. But this can hardly be their meaning of food-limited. Alternatively, it could mean that at all times decomposers are present in greater numbers than their food can support. Such cannot be the case, for then the rate of increase of these organisms would be always negative and they would become extinct. We presume they mean that, at some times, in almost all places, decomposers are in greater numbers than their food can support. Now this is certainly a possibility, but it is not the *only* possibility. We can construct alternative models.

1. The simplest alternative would be that the decomposers are "self-regulated" in the manner of an experimental grain weevil colony (e.g., Birch, 1953). The experiment commences with $X$ grams of food in a vial together with a founding colony of beetles. Temperature and moisture are kept favorable. The food is replenished at regular intervals to the original quantity. The weevils increase rapidly until there are many of them in the vial. The experiment may be continued for years, yet the food is never completely used up between replenishings even though the beetles become very numerous. Factors other than the shortage of food limit the numbers of beetles. Mechanisms of "self-regulation," such as egg cannibalism, prevent the population from exhausting its food resource. The weevils do not die of starvation, yet the food resource does not accumulate. If food is added at a more rapid rate, the weevil colony grows larger; but food does not accumulate,

and weevils do not die of starvation. In short, the weevils are a model of a decomposer trophic level in which fossil fuel does not accumulate, and which is not "food-limited."

We have, of course, no basis for assuming that the weevil model can be used to generalize about the decomposer trophic level, any more than there is a basis for assuming that decomposers are "food-limited."

2. A second alternative model can be constructed on the following assumptions: (a) many different species of decomposers are involved in degrading organic matter in any one place, and (b) conditions favorable to one species may be unfavorable to another. Suppose that dead plants and animals are continually being deposited on a forest floor. Suppose, further, that some 100 different organisms are decomposers in the forest debris. It is realistic to assume that at some times organism A will be favored, at other times organism B will be favored, and so on. Suppose that in spring organism A increases in numbers and is then primarily responsible for the degradation of organic matter. But well before the organic matter is decomposed, the forest floor becomes too dry for A, which is killed off, except for some of its resistant spores. It is replaced by B, which is somewhat more resistant to dessication but less resistant to cold. Organism B, in turn, is replaced by C and D, which have somewhat different requirements, and so on throughout the year. Each population is prevented from continually increasing by the periodic arrival of unfavorable conditions. If conditions are unfavorable too long, the last spore may succumb and that population becomes extinct. It may then, of course, be replaced by another colony established by migrant spores. None of the populations of the 100 species are "food-limited," not one organism dies of starvation, food is continually added to the forest floor, and yet there is no significant accumulation of debris.

This sort of model is quite conceivable, but it is not at all favored by those ecologists who assume that all populations must be "controlled" by density-dependent factors.

This latter model can be made more realistic if the heterogeneity of the forest floor is taken into account. Different stages of the successional sequence would occur simultaneously at different places. Thus, A might persist in a moist depression, while C was building a large population at a nearby well-drained spot. The colony of species B might well become extinct when one area dried up completely; but, with the return of moisture, the colony of B in that area could quickly be reestablished by migration from the populations of B in places which remain moist throughout the year. This additional complexity in the model both increases the chance of survival of the species (though not of any particular local population), and also increases the probability that organic matter will not accumulate.

Finally, in our examination of this point let us ask the following question: What logical conclusions could be drawn if the present rate of accumulation of organic matter as fossil fuel was not "negligible"? The most likely conclusion would be that, in some manner, organic matter was being made rapidly unavailable to decomposers. This is the most likely explanation of past accumulations.

There would then be less food, not more food, available for the decomposers. This trend, if carried far enough, would increase the chances of decomposers running out of food. Hairston, Smith, and Slobodkin claim that nonaccumulation of fossil fuels means that decomposers as a group are "food-limited." This implies that if there were an accumulation of fossil fuel, then decomposers would not be "food-limited." As we have shown this does not follow.

There is, therefore, no compelling reason for making the assumption that decomposers are "food-limited" simply because organic matter does not seem to accumulate. Even if this assumption were in some sense correct, however, it tells us nothing about how populations of decomposers are "controlled" as Hairston, Smith, and Slobodkin claim. Suppose that there are 100 species of decomposers in a forest floor. According to Hairston, Smith, and Slobodkin at least one of them is "food-limited." Even if this were correct, the other 99 may be controlled by weather, predators, or they may be "self-regulated." This surely is not much of a contribution to the understanding of "population control."

### "BALANCE OF NATURE" AND HERBIVORES AND CARNIVORES

What about the other trophic levels? Hairston, Smith, and Slobodkin assume that all green plants (producers) are "limited by their own exhaustion of a resource." As examples of their meaning of a resource, they mention water and light. Again, we must in part guess as to their meaning of "limited." In this case we will assume that they mean limited in density where weather is favorable, since weather is clearly one of the most potent factors limiting plant populations. The overall generalization of Hairston, Smith, and Slobodkin rests on the following two statements: (1) "cases of obvious depletion of green plants by herbivores are exceptions..." and (2) "cases of obvious mass destruction by meteorological catastrophes are exceptional in most areas." Concerning (1), we can point to several cases where plants are known to be rare because of the presence of a successful herbivore in their environment. In each case, however, there is nothing "obvious" about the role the herbivore plays in keeping the plant rare. *Clidemia hirta* is relatively rare in the islands of Fiji. Its rarity is due to the herbivore *Liothrips urichi* which was introduced to Fiji from Hawaii. *Liothrips* is not common in Fiji today; it is not at all an obvious component in the environment of *Clidemia*. One would never guess from a casual visit that it keeps *Clidemia* rare. Nevertheless, *Clidemia* was abundant before *Liothrips* was introduced.

Similarly, a visitor to Eastern Queensland today would not guess that the rarity of Prickly-pear (*Opuntia*) was the direct result of the presence of an effective herbivore caterpillar, *Cactoblastis cactorum*, in its environment. One must search a great deal among the few *Opuntia* plants to find *Cactoblastis* today. Its role in keeping Prickly-pear rare is not at all obvious. Yet, we know the role of the herbivore because *Opuntia* covered thousands of square miles of Queensland before the caterpillar was introduced from South and Central America. Nor would a visit to South America today convince anyone that Prickly-pear is rare there because of a herbivore in its environment. We do not know enough about the effect of herbivores on the abundance of plants to say whether or not these examples are common. We must, however, avoid the simplistic assumption that because we do not see forest trees being defoliated before our eyes that herbivores are not a major factor in determining the density of plant populations. For instance, the most drastic effect of the grazing of game animals in East Africa and elsewhere is on young seedlings and may escape casual observation. This effect can be demonstrated by fencing off areas from game animals, or by otherwise reducing the herbivores. The great decline in numbers of rabbits in Australia following myxomatosis has had a dramatic effect in the regeneration of the native pine *Callitris* in Western New South Wales. Abundant evidence can be inferred on the important influence herbivores have had on plant evolution (e.g., Ehrlich and Raven, 1965). Any attempt to discount their influence on plant populations is, at best, premature.

Concerning the second statement of Hairston, Smith, and Slobodkin, we contend that weather may be primarily involved in determining the density of a plant population despite the absence of "obvious mass destruction by meteorological catastrophes." Two species of native palms are not uncommon in some places near Sydney, the Bangalow Palm, *Archontophoenix cunninghamiana,* and the Cabbage Tree Palm, *Livistona australis.* They are relatively common north of Sydney and are rare a little south of Sydney. Further south still they disappear. This is not due to a gradient in any resource. In the south, the weather is probably just too cold and the length of day too short for the plants to set seed. The chance of a seed germinating, of the seedling growing into a mature plant, and of the mature plant setting seed, becomes smaller and smaller as one proceeds south in Australia. This pattern of distribution is characteristic of many other species of rain forest trees in Australia. Similar changes in density doubtless occur in one place as the climate changes through relatively cool or warm periods. Again, the cause would not be obvious to the casual observer, especially in plants with a long length of life. Another of the many examples we could give is the distribution and abundance of the snow gum (*Eucalyptus pauciflora*) in the Australian Alps (Costin, 1954). On mountain slopes above the snow line, snow gums are common. However, in depressions on mountain slopes where cold air accumulates, the snow gums are sparse or absent altogether. They are not limited by resources, but simply by low temperature which kills the seedlings. A similar example is given by Watt (1950) for bracken, (*Pteridium aquilinum*) in England.

We do not deny that the density of plants may be limited by the amount of light or water available; numerous such cases have also been documented. We do deny that there is a basis for inferring that, in general, plants are "limited by their own exhaustion of a resource." We would suggest that there is only one way of knowing how plant populations in general are "limited." Having first defined "limited," it would then be necessary to sample a wide range of plant populations to see how they are "limited."

Turning to the trophic level of herbivores, Hairston, Smith, and Slobodkin further state "the usual condition is for populations of herbivores *not* to be limited by their food supply." They consider this to be a valid inference from the statement "causes of obvious depletion of green plants are exceptions...." As noted earlier, we must assume that Hairston, Smith, and Slobodkin do not refer to the meaning of "food-limited" that where there is no food for herbivores there are no herbivores. Presumably they mean that, in their view, it is rare for herbivores to reduce their food resources to the point where this reduction influences their chance to survive and multiply. With this we are inclined to agree, although one must be very careful in determining just what constitutes the "food supply." For instance, healthy Eucalypt trees may be a totally inadequate food for psyllids, which will starve to death in the presence of what appears to be a superabundant food supply (T. White, personal communication), or the spacing of plants may lead to starvation in the presence of food (Dethier, 1959). Furthermore, as Murdoch (1966) has noted, plants evolve characteristics, such as spines and secondary plant substances, that tend to prevent their being eaten (Ehrlich and Raven, 1965). However, if food does not ordinarily limit herbivore populations, what does? Hairston, Smith, and Slobodkin state that "although rigorous proof that herbivores are generally controlled by predation is lacking, supporting evidence is available, and the alternative hypothesis of control by weather leads to false or untenable implications." We would not deny that invasions, control of predators, and pesticides have given evidence that herbivore populations may be kept below a certain level by predators. When released from destruction by predators, introduced herbivores have increased and caused serious defoliation. But native species often do the same thing in the presence of their predators; this is well-documented, for instance, for forest Lepidoptera and grasshoppers. It is a basic error to assume that "control" by weather and "control" by predators are "alternative" hypotheses. There are others, some of which Murdoch (1966) lists and which we need not enumerate here. If we can draw any general conclusion from the work which has been done on natural populations, it is that single, neat "control" mechanisms are unlikely to explain fluctuations in the size of single populations, let alone numbers of all organisms of a trophic level.

Finally, Hairston, Smith, and Slobodkin assume that predators must generally be "food-limited." This conclusion falls down with the rest. There is no more reason to assume that predators are "food-limited" than to suppose that decomposers are "food-limited," or that herbivores are not "food-limited." The thesis of Hairston, Smith, and Slobodkin is an exercise based on premises which are very likely false. If they are indeed false, then the argument that rests on them is very likely false also. Even if the assumptions are completely true, however, it can be easily shown that conclusions on "population control" do not follow from them. This should be clear from the preceding discussion on decomposers.

"BALANCE OF NATURE" AND PERSISTENCE OF SPECIES

Following their argument about trophic levels, Hairston, Smith, and Slobodkin (1960, p. 424) draw the following conclusion: "Populations of producers, carnivores, and decomposers are limited by their respective resources in the classical density-dependent fashion." The literature on "population control" is so confused that it is not possible to assign a precise meaning to this statement. Considering the context of Hairston, Smith, and Slobodkin's paper, it seems safe to assume that their statement might be translated as follows: When populations at these three trophic levels grow too large, they begin to run out of energy or some essential resource. This leads to a decrease in numbers until resources are sufficiently abundant for the rate of increase once again to become positive. Thus, the population never becomes infinite, and rarely (perhaps in the case of catastrophe) becomes extinct.

Hairston, Smith, and Slobodkin make it clear that they consider it legitimate to argue logically from "trophic level" to "population." But this procedure is not valid. In the first place, a "trophic level" exists only as an abstraction. As Murdoch (1966) has pointed out, tens of thousands of species of insects, for example, live in more than one trophic level; and, unlike populations, a trophic level has no properties that can be measured. Secondly, the argument from trophic level to population involves the idea that persistence of species can be used as an argument for "population control." Since this proposition is one of the most common fallacies in population biology, we shall now examine it in some detail.

This is the supposition made by the so-called "density-dependent" school on "population control." The basic idea of this school is that, for a species that persists, "sooner or later" or "ultimately" the density of the population is the determining factor in whether or not the rate of increase will be positive or negative. For this to be so, the size of the population must in some way affect the individuals in the population. Now, consideration of numbers of individuals in a species cannot ordinarily throw light on the question of density-dependence. To investigate this one must investigate changes in local populations. For example, satyrine butterflies of the species *Erebia magdalena* live, among other places, on rock slides in Alaska and in the Colorado Rockies. A population explosion in an Alaskan colony will have no effect on the Colorado colonies, and a Colorado extinction will not affect the Alaskan *Erebia magdalena*. Changes in the size of the Colorado population in no way affect the individuals in the Alaskan population, and vice versa. If we had mapped and censused all colonies of *Erebia magdalena*, we would know the population size for the species. But if we were magically handed the population size 2,328,456 for the species, we would know nothing about the sizes of the colonies. If we had information on rates of movement among colonies, and about the probabilities of colony extinction, we could make an estimate of the chance of species extinction per generation. But if we were told that the chance of species extinction was $10^{-7}$ per generation, we would know virtually nothing about the probabilities of extinction of individual colonies. In short, statements about species without reference to their component populations are unlikely to tell us much about "population control."

An example is the three populations of the checkerspot butterfly *Euphydryas editha* on Stanford University's Jasper Ridge Biological Experimental Area.

Over the five years 1960–64, a casual observer wandering along the ridge would find *E. editha* butterflies on the wing there every spring. "How precise is the control of natural populations" he might say, "for are there not butterflies here every year?" He might even guess at the number of butterflies present each year. He could then add up his estimates, divide by the number of years, and come up with an average adult population size. Superimposing this average on a chart of his yearly estimates he would find the average presented as a straight line parallel to the time axis. It could not, of course, be otherwise. "Nature" he would say, "keeps the average size of this population constant."

Only if our observer had taken the trouble to determine that the Ridge was actually occupied by three discrete populations of *E. editha* would he have found out what was actually going on; that, in fact, he had witnessed one population increase steadily in size, another fluctuate in size, and the third decrease to extinction (Ehrlich, 1965).

When movement of individuals is such that populations do not have clear-cut boundaries, then proper framing of questions concerning population size becomes much more difficult. It is nevertheless clear that careful consideration must be given to definition of the population units involved. A series of isolated populations with an array of different densities (including extinctions and reestablishment by migrants) may give the same superficial impression as a continuous population under rather tight "control." That is, to the casual observer, the species will be present each year. However, from the point of view of the way numbers change in nature, the two situations are entirely different.

It hardly seems necessary to add that the same arguments, which apply to statements made about population "control" on the basis of observations of species, apply even more forcefully to arguments drawn for all organisms at a particular trophic level.

### A BASIS FOR MODELS OF "POPULATION CONTROL"

What, then, would be a reasonable set of propositions around which to build a theory concerned with the changes of numbers observed in populations?

The first might be a reversal of Slobodkin's statement quoted above. No female animal alive now, in any species or in any location, will be replaced by precisely one female alive a generation from now. A thorough search of the literature has failed to turn up a single case of exact replacement in a natural population, although admittedly the number of good studies is depressingly small. This surely is, however, a safer hypothesis than one which has been falsified in every single test known to us. The first proposition is, then, that all populations are constantly changing in size.

The second proposition is that the environments of organisms are constantly changing, with changes on different time scales (diurnal, seasonal, long-term, etc.) going on simultaneously.

The third proposition is that the local population, within which there is relatively free movement of individuals, must be recognized and investigated if changes in population size are to be understood. For example, if one is interested in the factors responsible for observed changes in numbers of individuals of a certain species, the first step in the investigation must be a study of the structure of the species population. Local populations must be identified by mapping, marking individuals, etc.; and some measure of the amount of migration among these populations must be obtained. The answer to the question at the "species level" will then be found in investigation of these local populations and the interactions among them.

The fourth proposition is that the influences of various components of the environment on population size will vary. That is, these components (weather, resources, etc.) will act differently on populations of different densities, on different populations of the same species, on populations of different species, and so on. Knowing what factors are primarily influencing the size of a Jasper Ridge *Euphydryas editha* population in 1966 will not necessarily tell us what the determinants of the size of that population will be in 1967. Nor will it necessarily tell us what factors are responsible for the size of the *E. editha* population at Woodside, California, in 1966. It is difficult enough to obtain the data necessary for generalizing about a single species, let alone for all the species at a particular trophic level. The most we can hope for in the way of broad generalizations are probabilistic statements such as "territorial animals are less likely to be limited by shortage of food than are non-territorial animals."

We are sympathetic with the goal of building simplified models to aid in our understanding of what determines the numbers of organisms. But such models are highly misleading if they are based on false assumptions and undefined terms such as "food-limited." It is our opinion that any realistic model must take into account the four propositions stated above. The necessary model will be stochastic, not deterministic. As digital computers become more sophisticated, it should be possible to advance from the pictorial model used by Andrewartha and Birch (1954, Chapter 14) to a more rigorous numerical treatment.

SUMMARY

1. The notion that nature is in some sort of "balance" with respect to population size, or that populations in general show relatively little fluctuation in size, is demonstrably false.

2. The thesis of Hairston, Smith, and Slobodkin that "populations of producers, carnivores, and decomposers are limited by their respective resources in the classical density-dependent fashion" is based on a series of assumptions about these trophic levels which are, in all probability, false. Even if the assumptions are true, this conclusion does not follow from them.

3. A realistic basis for building models dealing with the changes of numbers in populations would include the following propositions:

   a. All populations are constantly changing in size.

   b. The environments of all organisms are constantly changing.

   c. Local populations must be recognized and investigated if changes in population size are to be understood.

d. The influence on population size of various components of environment varies with population density, among species, among local populations, and through time.

ACKNOWLEDGMENTS

The following persons read and criticized the manuscript, and we are grateful for their advice: Professor H. G. Andrewartha, University of Adelaide; Dr. M. A. Bateman, Joint Unit of Animal Ecology, University of Sydney; Professor LaMont C. Cole, Cornell University; Professors R. W. Holm and P. H. Raven, Stanford University; and Dr. P. A. Labine, University of Michigan.

LITERATURE CITED

Andrewartha, H. G., and L. C. Birch. 1954. The distribution and abundance of animals. Univ. of Chicago Press, Chicago. 782 p.

Birch, L. C. 1953. Experimental background to the study of distribution and abundance of insects. II. The relation between innate capacity for increase in numbers and the abundance of three grain beetles in experimental populations. Ecology 34:712–726.

Costin, A. B. 1954. A study of the ecosystems of the Monaro region of New South Wales. Soil Conservation Service, New South Wales. 860 p.

Dethier, V. G. 1959. Food-plant distribution and density and larval dispersal as factors affecting insect populations. Canadian Entomol. 91:581–596.

Ehrlich, P. R. 1965. The population biology of the butterfly *Euphydryas editha*. II. The structure of the Jasper Ridge Colony. Evolution 19:327–336.

Ehrlich, P. R., and P. H. Raven. 1965. Butterflies and plants: A study in coevolution. Evolution 18:586–608.

Hairston, N. G., F. E. Smith, and L. B. Slobodkin. 1960. Community structure, population control, and competition. Amer. Natur. 94:421–425.

Murdoch, W. W. 1966. Community structure, population control, and competition—a critique. Amer. Natur. 100:219–226.

Smith, H. S. 1935. The role of biotic factors in the determination of population densities. J. Econ. Entom. 28:873–898.

Slobodkin, L. B. 1962. Growth and regulation of animal populations. Holt, Rinehart, and Winston, New York. 184 p.

Solomon, M. E. 1964. Analysis of processes involved in the natural control of insects. Adv. Ecol. Res. 2:1–58.

Varley, G. C., and G. R. Gradwell. 1958. Balance in insect populations. Proc. Xth Int. Congr. Entomol. 2:619–624.

Watt, A. S. 1950. Contributions to the ecology of Bracken *Pteridium aquilinum*. V. Bracken and frost. New Phytol. 49:308–327.

# REGULATION IN TERRESTRIAL ECOSYSTEMS, AND THE IMPLIED BALANCE OF NATURE*

## L. B. SLOBODKIN, F. E. SMITH, AND N. G. HAIRSTON

The University of Michigan, Ann Arbor, Michigan

## INTRODUCTION

We thank the editors of *The American Naturalist* for inviting us to reply to the criticisms by Ehrlich and Birch (1967) of Hairston, Smith, and Slobodkin (1960), which will be referred to henceforth as HSS. Other ecologists have expressed concern at our failure to reply in detail to the critique of Murdoch (1966), and we take this opportunity to reply to both papers since Ehrlich and Birch state that they agree with him. In the light of the published criticisms, and those of others since the original paper appeared, we regret the brevity of HSS. We must also apologize for some confusion of terminology which it contains.

Specifically in this rebuttal we will: demonstrate the internal inconsistency of the criticism of Ehrlich and Birch, clarify some of the considerations raised by Murdoch, and demonstrate in part the empirical validity of our earlier conclusions.

It must be made clear that the dispute is not simply verbiage, but rather the interpretation of commonly accepted observations and the use of these interpretations in prediction. Neither Murdoch nor Ehrlich and Birch deny the major empirical observations of HSS. They merely cite exceptions. But, as we point out below, the exceptions themselves are as predicted in the original paper.

A thoughtful reading of HSS shows that certain statements concern trophic levels as wholes, and may not necessarily apply to every subset of populations within trophic levels. The point is, we think, sufficiently clear in the body of the paper, but not in the summary. Murdoch is incorrect, therefore, when he substitutes "in general" for "as a whole." His thesis that our "hypotheses" cannot be tested derives from this misinterpretation of what we have said. We were not making statements about most herbivores, or most carnivores, but about these trophic levels as wholes. Our statements, then, apply to the quantitatively dominant species but not necessarily to the numerical majority of species in any ecosystem. We were, in fact, claiming a good deal less than many of our critics have thought.

We claimed, and still claim, that, with qualifications to be included below, certain biological methods of regulation are characteristic of certain trophic levels, while Ehrlich and Birch deny this. Ehrlich and Birch (but not Murdoch) affirm that biological regulation is not universal. Note that if

*We acknowledge the support of the National Science Foundation Environmental Biology Program grants GB-2364, 5306, 1595.

biological regulation exists, there is in some sense a balance of nature, which Ehrlich and Birch specifically deny.

We will take up the trophic levels in the same order as Ehrlich and Birch. The widespread occurrence of organisms that are not cleanly assignable to trophic level does not falsify the conclusions reached. In the interest of brevity, this statement will not be defended in detail, except for the remarks about "seed-eating carnivores" presented below.

## DECOMPOSERS

In their discussion of the decomposer trophic levels, Ehrlich and Birch deny that the complete consumption of organic debris is evidence that the decomposers as a group are food-limited. They provide two models, in one of which the size of a weevil population is proportional to the rate at which food is added (i.e., food-limited as defined in Slobodkin, 1954, p. 73). The normal usage of the concept of food-limitation has been precisely that the size of the population is limited by the food supply according to the general pattern of limiting factors developed by Blackman (1905, p. 289), namely, that if the supply of the limiting resource is increased, there will be an increase in the limited phenomenon. In the present case, an increase in food supply results in an increase of population size. This is the sense in which we used the term. It is not legitimate to criticize our logic by altering definitions. The meaning of food limitation as implying animals "dying of starvation" is a gratuitous addition by Ehrlich and Birch to the definition.

In short, their initial model is, in fact, based on food limitation in the accepted sense, and is in no sense an alternative to a model based on food-limitation. Therefore it cannot be a refutation of either our work, or that of Nicholson (1957), or that of any other worker.

The assertion that a population is food-limited does not deny the possibility of a simultaneous limitation by predation. For example, experimental Daphnia populations (Slobodkin, 1960) showed different linear relations with food supply at each of several rates of predation, so that population size could be increased by either more food or by relaxation of the rate of predation, or both. In these Daphnia experiments, at sufficiently high predation rates, further increase in the rate of food increment did not increase population size. Under these conditions, food was not eliminated from the containers and would have accumulated had it not been thrown away.

We can recognize operationally the nonlimiting nature of a necessary resource by the fact that an increment in its rate of supply does not produce an increase in its rate of utilization by the population under consideration. Such resources will accumulate indefinitely unless some separate process, independent of the population, compensates for its failure to utilize them.

The second model presented by Ehrlich and Birch supposes that numerous species of decomposers can consume all of the dead organic matter that is added regularly to the forest floor without being limited by the supply of this resource. That is, by our previous analysis either the resource is limiting or each and every one of their hypothetical 100 species must be alternately favored and damaged by the physical environment in such a way as to balance exactly the rate of addition of dead organic matter. Their second model is, in fact, an alternative to ours in that it postulates that the abundance of individual species in an assemblage is determined exclusively by the "arrival" (apparently the date of arrival) of unfavorable conditions. None of the individual species are permitted by the model to suffer from hunger. They actually say "...not one organism dies of starvation..." but dying of starvation is not an operational concept. Has a hunger-weakened animal that falls prey to disease died of starvation or not? The model further postulates that while "none of the species are food limited...yet there is no significant accumulation of debris." This last statement is a nonsequitur. Obviously, if they are assuming on the one hand 100 species each of which is limited by climate, they are free also to assume a forest floor on which debris does not accumulate; but it must be made emphatically clear that the lack of accumulation of debris in the hypothetical forest does not follow logically from the initial assertions of their model. In fact, a stronger statement is possible, namely, that the two assumptions are incompatible within the same model, unless one also assumes one or more food-limited species of decomposers in addition to the 100 non-food-limited species that they mention.

Consider any particular year, and let us assume with Ehrlich and Birch for at least this year, say $T_0$, the feeding activities of the 100 species are just appropriate to eliminate exactly the last bit of forest debris without any hunger and without any leftovers. We deny that this is more than a formal possibility, but agree to the assumption for the sake of the discussion. Ehrlich and Birch do not specify the relative feeding rates of their 100 species. But, for the sake of generality, we will consider the two extreme situations: first, that one species, say A, has a feeding rate per organism that is enormous compared with any and all other species, so that we can essentially consider species A alone as the eliminator of the forest debris; or, as an opposite alternative, we will consider that all of the 100 species have a precisely equivalent feeding rate per organism day.

What if A is the overwhelmingly significant feeder? If year $T_0$ is an average year, we can assume that the subsequent year, $T_1$, will differ in the date of the meteorological or climatological limit to feeding activity from the corresponding date in $T_0$ by the average deviation from the mean. Let us assume that $T_1$ is a better year than $T_0$. Species A will, therefore, persist longer; and the last few days of the active existence of species A will be days of hunger, on the reasonable assumption that the climatic benefit to species A is not exactly equal to the beneficial effect of the preceding year's weather on the organisms that produced the forest debris. On the equally tenable assumption that the weather in year $T_0$ permitted a greater production of debris than can be consumed by species A by the date of onset of unfavorable weather in year $T_1$, there will be forest litter left over. We see, therefore, that if we assume that only one species has a significant ability to consume debris, then it will almost always be the case that this species either gets hungry occasionally or that forest debris is left over. Either of these events would deny the contentions of Ehrlich and Birch, although they are, in fact, derived from precisely the model suggested by them.

Lest it appear that this depends on our assumption that feeding rates are impossibly different between species, let us make the opposite extreme assumption that all of the 100 species have identical feeding rates. Again let $T_0$ be an average year in which the food consumption by the 100 species precisely equals the debris production of the preceding year. Again, since each and every one of the possible climatic factors that influence any one of the 100 species of decomposers will have some variance over time, the year $T_1$ will almost certainly not be an average year. The last active individuals of the last active species in year $T_1$ will, therefore, be in precisely the same position as the last active members of species A in the first set of hypothetical feeding rates above. That is, they will either be hungry, or litter will accumulate in year $T_1$. Note that their model does not permit the consumption in year $T_2$ of any litter left over from year $T_1$, since this would require the response of one or more decomposer populations to the food supply, and would thus represent a food-limited situation.

Finally, we should note that the statement that food consumption precisely equals food supply in the absence of food-limitation requires two separate and independent empirical assumptions: one about the effect of nonbiological factors on the decomposers, and the other about the effect of nonbiological factors on the forest production in the preceding year.

In their second model, then, the statement "...yet debris does not accumulate" is not a consequence of the properties of the model. Since they state that no population is food-limited, this applies equally to the last population present. Food must, therefore, be left over; and this amount will accumulate.

If we wished to construct an internally consistent version of the second model of Ehrlich and Birch, we could do so in one of two ways: either

1. The amount of litter present must be regulated, not by the action of decomposers, but by some nonbiological means which eliminates litter during a hypothetical period when the decomposers are not active, or

2. We could make the assumption that the terminal individuals among the decomposers can predict the exact date of arrival of unfavorable meteorological conditions, and adjust their food consumption in advance so as to finish the last of the debris at the end of the last favorable day. A physiological mechanism for such a predictive ability is at present obscure, although its existence has been folkloristically postulated in the case of the woolybear caterpillars, *Isia isabella*.

It is possible to consider a system in which the environment improves as a result of debris accumulation. In this case, the temperature and humidity regimes may permit better decomposition as the layer of litter deepens. If this increased decomposition proceeds until the layer begins to thin, the environment may again deteriorate. Thus, a steady state can be achieved through the modification of the physical environment by accumulated debris.

Such a system falls within our definition of food-limitation, since an increased rate of leaf fall produces increased utilization, and vice versa. In fact, such a mechanism probably accounts for the difference between temperate forests and humid tropical forests in the depth of litter present.

## PRODUCERS, HERBIVORES, AND CARNIVORES

A major disagreement with our critics comes from their apparent position that herbivores and carnivores can be considered without reference to the other trophic levels. We do not accept this position, since our conclusions about these two trophic levels depend in part upon observations and deductions about both producers and decomposers. The point can be made best by reference to one of the examples cited by Erhlich and Birch. They point out that "You could say that the cabbage white butterfly is food-limited because the world could be planted with more cabbages than it is, and if it were there would be more individuals of the butterfly around." Despite the fact that cabbages are not natural plants, let us concede the point of Ehrlich and Birch that increasing the abundance of a species of plant will increase the abundance of herbivores that depend on this plant specifically for a major dietary component. In order to increase the abundance of this species of plant in a natural community, it will be necessary to decrease correspondingly the abundance of other species of plants (see below) and thereby reduce the abundance of the herbivores that depend on these other displaced species of plants. We, therefore, contend that the herbivore trophic level as a whole will not have been seriously influenced in quantity by these alterations.

## PRODUCERS

Although Murdoch does not dispute our conclusions about the resource-limitation of terrestrial vegetation, Ehrlich and Birch do disagree in part with this conclusion about the producer trophic level; and we, therefore, review the basis for the conclusion.

Wherever natural floras are well developed, a great proportion of one or another of the essential mineral nutrients is already taken up in the biota and is in an organic form. In many cases, most of the remaining inorganic nutrients are tightly bound in the soil, not available for utilization. Obviously, in such systems the total mass of protoplasm in the biota cannot increase much further. In particular, the capacity of the flora (the major component of the biota) to increase its standing crop of protoplasm is curtailed severely.

Equally significant is the rapid recovery of such floras following decimation. Recovery from a single severe defoliation is nearly complete in one year. After fire, both forests and prairies show rapid growth, often recovering the former density of plant protoplasm in a few seasons. There is no doubt that these floras as a whole have large capacities for increase that are expressed whenever the opportunity arises.

This combination of a large capacity for increase and limited nutrients produces a strongly limited system. Inasmuch as it is dynamic, it is a valid example of balance in nature.

Elegant details of regulation are seen in the compensatory changes among the components of the flora. The American Chestnut, *Castanea dentata* (Marsh) Borkh., was almost eradicated by an introduced disease organism within the space of a few years; yet it has not left holes in our forests today. Not one mature chestnut can be put back without displacing plants of other species. Similarly, as one walks from one soil type to another, the vegetation may change dramatically. For example, oak-hickory may give way to beech-maple. Along the zone of change, the two assemblages may be interspersed; but the total plant density in the zone of interspersion is not markedly greater than elsewhere. The boundaries between the two are not independent of each other, with some empty areas and some having double densities, but show extreme regulation of the whole. The same phenomenon is observed on a large scale for the geographic distributions of species. A species common in one region and absent from another does not thereby leave a reduced plant density in the latter. Other species replace it, producing a total density that is determined primarily by the local resources. The forests of Michigan are not thin because they lack live oaks, nor do those of Georgia suffer from a lack of spruce. We doubt the existence of vacant spaces south of Sydney, waiting for the palms to fill them. (See Ehrlich and Birch, p. 102) This concept has appeared already in the literature, for example: "When we travel from south to north, or from a damp region to a dry, we invariably see some species gradually getting rarer and rarer, and finally disappearing, and the change of climate being conspicuous, we are tempted to attribute the whole effect to its direct action. But this is a false view; we forget that each species, even where it most abounds, is constantly suffering enormous destruction at some period of its life, from enemies or competitors for the same place and food; and if these enemies or competitors be in the least degree favoured by any slight change of climate, they will increase in numbers; and as each area is already stocked full with inhabitants, the other species must decrease. When we travel southward and see a species decreasing in numbers, we may feel sure that the cause lies quite as much in other species being favoured, as in this one being hurt" (Darwin, 1859).

Thus, natural floras show every sign of being limited in density primarily by their resources. It is interesting to note in this respect that cases of invasion by exotics into undisturbed floras are extremely rare, while they are numerous where man has reduced plant competition. It is the overgrazed pasture or the cultivated field that accepts exotics (Elton, 1958).

Further confirmation of the resource-limitation of plants is found in the densities of those species that have suffered heavy grazing. They are sparse, and if formerly common, their place is now taken by other plants. In many cases, plants suffering heavy grazing cannot compete with plants suffering little grazing. As the grazed plants decrease in abundance through competition, their herbivores have more and more trouble finding them among the plants that have replaced them. If the grazed plant persists at all, it is because at some low density the grazing pressure is relieved enough to allow the plant to compete successfully. That is, grazing is now light, but would increase if the plant become more common.

We note that Ehrlich and Birch give three examples of the effect of herbivores in damaging the vegetation either at present or in the recent past (*Opuntia* and *Cactoblastis*, *Clidemia* and *Liothrips*, *Callitris* and *Oryctolagus*). All three are of introduced herbivores, and are thus exactly in accordance with our original contention that it is among the introduced species or among man-protected herbivores that deviations from the natural situation are to be found.

In summary, we contend that floras as wholes are resource-limited. In particular, this applies to the dominant component species. Also, we contend that heavily grazed plants are rare in natural systems.

## HERBIVORES

The question of what should be considered a herbivore was admittedly not discussed adequately in the original paper. "Herbivore" can be divided into two major groups: those that feed upon the producer itself and those that feed on its products. The original paper should have referred only to those herbivores that consume the vegetation itself. Seed-eaters, as well as nectar and pollen feeders, were ignored; and it is worthwhile to consider them now.

As was pointed out by Hairston (1964), many seed-eaters (ants, birds, mice, for example) are also carnivores, especially during the breeding season when demand on the general food supply is greatest. Moreover, these species often show evidence of food-limitation, or else show an evolutionary response (e.g., territoriality) to what must have been intraspecific competition for resources in the past. At any rate, this group of species, which can be referred to as omnivores, seem not to harm the producers. A second group of seed-eaters is obviously not carnivorous. These are frequently the smaller species, such as weevils. Like the larger seed-eaters, they have little direct effect on the vegetation.

Thus, a distinction between vegetation-consuming and plant-product-consuming herbivores is necessary.

Our assertions about the herbivore trophic level as a whole, like those on producers, should apply equally well to the quantitatively dominant herbivore species. However, we do distinguish two categories of herbivores as noted above, and intend that our comments apply primarily to those capable of destroying the living vegetation.

The validity of our statements requires that most such herbivores, but not necessarily most herbivore species, be able to feed upon the dominant plants, and that relatively few of these herbivores depend exclusively upon heavily grazed plants.

Murdoch says that our statement on the edibility of vegetation is an assumption. It is, in fact, one of the best supported statements in the literature. We challenge him to find, in any terrestrial community, a dominant plant species (i.e., involved in the bulk of net primary production) that does not harbor an insect capable of defoliation or capable of serious sap removal. Mass destruction of the vegetation has occurred in a sufficient variety of habitats to indicate that the burden of proof must be borne by anyone claiming the general inedibility of the major producers. Our paper does not discuss explicitly the minor components of the ecosystem.

We repeat our earlier observation that all green plants are edible. Within every native environment of every species, several herbivores (leaf eaters and sap suckers) can be found that are capable of extensive injury. The scarcity of most of these herbivores most of the time results in their food being largely unutilized. Thus, such herbivores as a whole cannot be food limited. This is most easily verified for the dominant plants, which are the most significant components in a trophic analysis.

Both Murdoch, and Ehrlich and Birch point out the fact that many plants are adapted to be unpalatable, resistant, or otherwise inaccessible to some herbivores. We are unaware of any such plant that is in fact free of herbivores. For example, poison ivy (*Rhus Toxicodendron* L.) is fed on by the diamond backed spittle bug, *Lepyronia quadrangularis* (Say). Many noxious insects derive their noxious property from eating plants that have evolved unpalatable qualities (Brower and Brower, 1964; Eisner, Kafatos, and Linsley, 1962; Lev Fishelson, personal communication to L. B. Slobodkin).

The evolutionary development of noxious characters in plants does not disprove the occurrence of interspecific competition among the green plants; nor does it suffice to demonstrate that the herbivore trophic level is food limited. When two species are in competition, as the terrestrial producers are, the outcome of competition can be influenced by losses due to one or both species being slightly consumed (Slobodkin, 1962; Fryer, 1965). Thus, it is not necessary to postulate food-limitation of the herbivore to invoke a selective pressure favoring unpalatability of the plant.

In our original paper we stated "...cases of obvious depletion of green plants by herbivores are exceptions to the general picture in which the plants are abundant and largely intact...It...follows that the usual condition is for populations of herbivores *not* to be limited by their food supply" (italics in the original).

Since the original preparation of our paper, several estimates of the proportion of food supply consumed by various herbivores have been published. These are presented in Table 1. As we have pointed out, seed eaters are expected to deviate from the low food utilization of other herbivores. The data strikingly confirm our published expectations, as do those of Wiegert and Evans (1964), who found that 90 % of the above-ground insects, excluding ants, consumed less than 1 % of the net primary production in an old-field ecosystem.

TABLE 1

Percentage utilization of net production of food by animals in three trophic categories (grazers and sapsuckers, seed-eaters, and a carnivore) (rearranged from Engelmann, 1966). No species has been omitted for which the percentage utilization has been estimated. That is, we have not selected the data.

|  | % Utilization | Investigator |
|---|---|---|
| *Grazers*: |  |  |
| *Orchelium fidicinum* (grasshopper) | 2 | Smalley, 1960 |
| Orthoptera (3 species)* | 2 to 7 | Odum, Connell, and Davenport, 1962 |
| Microtus (vole) | 1.6 | Golley, 1960 |
| *Loxodonta africana* (elephant) | 9.6 | Petrides and Swank, 1965 |
| *Sapsucker*: |  |  |
| *Prokelisia* sp (leafhopper) | 4.6 | Teal, 1962 |
| *Seed-eaters (omnivores)*: |  |  |
| *Pogonomyrmex badius* (ant) | 64 to 213 | Golley and Gentry, 1964 |
| *Passerculus* (sparrow)* | 10 to 50 | Odum, Connell, and Davenport, 1962 |
| *Peromyscus* (mouse)* | 10 to 50 | Odum, Connell, and Davenport, 1962 |
| *Carnivore*: |  |  |
| *Mustela* (weasel) | 31 | Golley, 1960 |

*All of these species were in the same ecosystem.

Odum, Connell, and Davenport (1962) fully recognized the relevance of their work to the predictions in HSS. They pointed out the fact that their data for *Passerculus* and *Peromyscus*, which they regarded as herbivores, did not conform fully to our expectations. We concur in this criticism; but, as we have discussed above, the distinction between grazers and seed-eaters strengthens the original conclusion rather than weakens it.

It is surprising that neither Murdoch nor Ehrlich and Birch offer any definite prediction as to the relative consumption rate of herbivores and carnivores. That is, the predictions made in 1960 have to a large degree been confirmed in subsequent studies by others. To discard the 1960 theory after these confirmations without at least demonstrating that there exists an alternative theory of equal or better predictive power does not seem legitimate. Murdoch suggests that our work has no testable prediction. The data of Table 1 are as we predicted.

## CARNIVORES

Ehrlich and Birch state that we assume that predators must generally be "...food limited. This conclusion falls down with the rest."

Since we have already demonstrated that the rest does not "fall down," it may seem superflous to discuss the problems of carnivores further. There were, however, certain problems relating to carnivores which were not adequately discussed in the original paper.

Murdoch argues, "The formal structure and internal consistency are ...open to criticism ...food limitation appears to have been used in different ways with reference to herbivores and carnivores. Thus it was concluded that herbivores are not food limited because the green plants are not depleted, but by analagous logic it can be concluded that carnivores are not food limited since herbivores apparently are seldom eaten out by their predators."

But note that terrestrial ecosystems are full of green plants, which give every evidence of being resource-limited and of competing for resources. Evidence for food-limitation of terrestrial herbivores is generally lacking among those species that feed upon the dominant producers themselves. The comparison has little relevance without these additional considerations.

Although the standing crop of plant protoplasm vastly exceeds that of herbivores in terrestrial systems, the standing crop of herbivore protoplasm exceeds the mass of predators by a very much smaller margin. Even allowing for the superior quality of animal protoplasm to plant protoplasm as a food, it is evident that food per predator is a much smaller number than food per herbivore (Odum, 1959, p. 63).

Obviously, HSS does not constitute a complete statement of a theory of ecological control. It does, however, summarize certain generalities which appear to us to be valid. Further data, collected and published since the original publication of HSS, have conformed very well to the predictions originally implied. In the face of these successful confirmations, and in the absence of either empirical counter-examples or of an alternative predictive theory, the strongest possible statement that can be made in support of Ehrlich and Birch or of Murdoch might be that they have demonstrated logical errors in HSS which would imply that the predictive success of our arguments was in some sense fortuitous. We have shown that this is not the case and, furthermore, that many of the criticisms themselves are either non-operational, internally inconsistent, based on erroneous definitions, or some combination of these.

### THE BALANCE OF NATURE

Until now, we have specifically not referred to the statement by Ehrlich and Birch on "balance of nature." Their statement that "a survey of the literature fails to disclose a single case of a natural population behaving in the manner described" is not accompanied by even one reference. We are, therefore, powerless to refute this absence of data; and we would be particularly interested in a bibliography of the literature searched.

The comments by Ehrlich and Birch on the work of Smith (1935) implying that numbers can only oscillate around a fixed mean seems naive.

We do not propose to defend every statement ever made by anyone on the subject of the balance of nature. Ehrlich and Birch do not state a definition of "the balance of nature," but it is clear by implication that they have chosen a point of view which rules out all stochastic events of any kind. Their quotation from Slobodkin (1962) is taken out of context. The statement was made in connection with a formal mathematical development of the intrinsic rate of natural increase, and was not intended to be a declaration about natural populations. The restricted nature of the statement is, for example, made clear on page 55 of the book. They have thus attacked a point of view which we would not defend. We doubt that many ecologists would care to defend the "balance of nature" as Ehrlich and Birch have by implication defined it. By "balance of nature" we refer to the persistence of ecological systems as a result of their tendency to compensate for perturbations.

The principal disagreement lies in the relative importance assigned to the inverse effect of density in determining the amount and direction of change in the numbers of organisms. They concede that such effects can be found in nature, but deny their universality. We have not made an exhaustive survey of the literature on this point; but we note that the frequently-cited examples of the absence of inverse effects are, in fact, either examples of the relationship between climate and distribution or the effect of seasonal changes in weather. Neither type of example is a legitimate exception to the existence of density-dependent factors.

While this manuscript was being prepared, Tanner (1966) published a review of density-dependent relations in a number of species. It is striking that he found a statistically significant inverse correlation between population growth rate and population size among 47 of the 64 species for which suitable data were available. Among the remaining 17 species, the relationship was also negative, but not significantly so in 15; and one of the two remaining was the human population of the world. Thus, Tanner's analysis gives strong, but not absolutely conclusive, evidence for the virtually universal operation of the effect of density on changes in population size. It is, therefore, worthwhile for us to state our reasons for contending that such effects are universal in nature.

In a continuously varying world, the process of replacement in populations is buffeted, rarely coming out even. Without density regulation, such disturbances accumulate in time, steadily increasing the size of the probable net change in density. The history of density in such a population is like a random walk in time: no matter what level the density has reached, it is as likely to increase or decrease. The more variable the environment, the more rapidly the density tends to wander away from some previous level.

Separating environmental effects in time does not alter the general properties of the system. Alternate periods of exponential growth (at variable rates in response to a varying environment) and of death (to varying degrees) produces a seasonal cycle that is reasonably repetitive in period and amplitude. Across the entire cycle, however, the process of replacement remains as before, rarely coming out even. If the amplitude of the cycle is large and variable, population density measured at any one point in the cycle (such as in a particular month) again follows a random walk that accomplishes wide excurions in time.

Separating environmental effects in space also does not alter the properties of the system. In some areas, the environment may be at times so unfavorable that local extinction occurs, while in other areas a more favorable environment allows local expansion. Random movement will, then, cause repopulation of all places, with a tendency to reduce densities where they have become high. Local populations may, therefore, be expected to remain within reasonable density limits. This argument is fallacious, however. By considering a larger area, sufficient to include both favorable and unfavorable subareas, the process of replacement remains one that rarely comes out even, and that accumulates a steadily increasing probable error in time. And as before, the more variable the centers of growth and decline become in time, the more rapidly the total density wanders.

If any reader believes that population density, over time, can drift at a rate slower than that predicted from the variance in the annual replacement rate, without resorting to regulatory devices, we urge him to test his hypotheses with mathematical analysis. To date no such model has ever been published.

The properties of a sum of unregulated populations depends upon the relations among them in their response to the varying environment. If these are generally uncorrelated responses, the variance in time of any sum of these responses, for example, over a trophic level, is the sum of the variance of the individual populations. If the populations tend to respond similarly to environmental disturbances, the variance of the sum is greater than this; while if the responses are inversely related, the variance of the sum is less. In all cases, however, the sum is like a random walk in time, as likely to increase or decrease in the future no matter what the present density happens to be.

Only if the relations among species are perfectly inverse, so that the sum of net losses by some species is always exactly balanced by a sum of net gains by others, will the total for the trophic level fail to wander. Such an event has a probability that is vanishingly small.

We know that some variations of the environment, such as moderate changes in temperature or moisture, may favor some species and harm others, thus producing inversely related effects. We also know that such effects as wind or freezing rain will affect most species adversely. In general, the variance of the sum of responses of many populations in a trophic level, if unregulated, will not be far from the sum of the separate variances.

The rate of drift of unregulated systems can be decreased if the environmental variables are negatively autocorrelated in time. It would become zero only if such variables were perfectly balanced in time, particularly in their effects upon the populations. It is not possible that all relevant variables are so constructed. Meteorological data, for example, shows poor autocorrelations over time. Thus, some rate of drift must remain, which would accumulate in populations, in whole trophic levels, and indeed in whole biotas.

The only regulatory mechanisms that can operate from within populations or groups of populations are those in which density itself is inversely related to the changes in density. This can occur if internal aggression increases with density, if resources per organism decrease measurably with increase in density, if predation pressure expands in response to density increase, etc. Such mechanisms must not only be present, but must be powerful enough to cope with the continual disturbance of the system. Only then will the population density be constrained in time to remain between limits, and tend toward some set of values defined by the system as a whole. The effect of regulation is to erase the impact of past disturbances, which otherwise persists indefinitely into the future.

The operation of a regulated system in a variable world is complex. Population density is directly affected by density-independent factors, and the level toward which regulatory mechanisms move density is also changing. The result is a frequency distribution of observed densities defined by these two sources of variance. Hence, densities may be relatable to various environmental parameters, including density-independent factors. But the existence of predictable densities at all is entirely a consequence of the presence of regulatory mechanisms which determine whether the population remains within a range of densities; all factors, including density-independent factors, determine where that range lies.

The highest densities populations can reach are those set by their resources. These densities are attained only if loss rates are small and if the limiting resource is not shared through competition. As stated in our earlier paper, any population not limited by its resources must exist at lower densities.

If predation, in the widest sense, is the major regulatory mechanism, the density will be well below that set by resources alone. In part, this is due to the need for relatively abundant resources, so that high loss rates can be matched by high reproduction rates. Predation will eliminate a species from a habitat altogether if this balance cannot be made.

These two regulatory mechanisms can coexist in the sense that some degree of food shortage plus some degree of predation may combine to be effective. A modest resource supply can balance a moderate loss rate. It is probably never correct to say that resources or predators act alone. Operationally, a system can be defined as resource limited if predation is relatively minor and if densities reached are close to the limits set by resources alone. Conversely, a system can be defined as predator limited if resources are only slightly utilized and if loss rates due to predation are nearly the maximum that the population can sustain in that environment.

Density-independent factors can cause additional losses, further depressing the densities achieved. They can have a considerable effect without disrupting the system. Although they form a part of the system, they do not define a regulatory level; this is defined necessarily by density-dependent mechanisms, which take the density-independent losses into account.

## ON THE QUESTION OF FALSIFIABILITY

Murdoch questions the scientific relevance of HSS on the grounds that the conclusions are not testable. As pointed out above, the data in Table

1 constitute a general refutation of Murdoch, but we feel it is necessary to refute his claim in detail.

The argument in the critique is based upon Murdoch's implication that studies cannot be imagined which would have an outcome that would falsify the conclusions in our paper. Although he concerns himself with only two of the conclusions, we shall consider all of them.

1. The first and most important conclusion is, "...it must follow that all organisms taken together are limited by the amount of energy fixed. In particular, the decomposers as a group must be food-limited...."

This conclusion can be falsified if an ecosystem is found in which an appreciable proportion of the annual primary production accumulates. As in the original paper, we except "...successional stages, in which the failure of decomposition hastens the termination of the state."

2. The second conclusion is, "...producers are neither herbivore-limited nor catastrophe-limited and must therefore be limited by their own exhaustion of a resource."

This conclusion can be falsified in three different ways: (a) if a terrestrial community is found in which the major part of the net primary production is consumed by herbivores (see Table 1); (b) if a terrestrial ecosystem is found in which mass destruction of the dominant producers by meteorological catastrophes is common enough to prevent their being resource-limited; and (c) if a terrestrial community is found in which the dominant producers are not resource-limited.

3. The third conclusion is, "It therefore follows that the usual condition is for populations of herbivores *not* to be limited by their food supply."

There are several possible ways in which this conclusion could be falsified. In fact, the three methods suggested for the foregoing conclusion could in principle yield damaging results. In addition to these, we suggest the following: (a) if a terrestrial ecosystem can be found in which no herbivore present is capable of damaging the dominant producers (see the challenge on p. 116) and (b) if all herbivores capable of damaging the dominant vegetation of a terrestrial ecosystem are limited in abundance by weather factors only. It should be noted that if a single one of these species is not weather-limited, this disproof is not available.

4. The fourth conclusion is, "...although rigorous proof that herbivores are generally controlled by predation is lacking, supporting evidence is available, and the alternate hypothesis of control by weather leads to false or untenable implications."

In addition to very damaging results theoretically available from previously stated suggestions, this conclusion can be falsified if none of the herbivores capable of damaging the dominant vegetation is predator limited. A study to make this observation need only be concerned with the herbivores present in the ecosystem and capable of destroying the dominant producers.

5. The fifth conclusion is, "The predators and parasites, in controlling the populations of herbivores, must thereby limit their own resources, and as a group they must be food-limited."

This conclusion is falsifiable if raising the density of the existing herbivores in a terrestrial ecosystem does not result in an increase in the density of predators and parasites as a whole. In a more restricted sense, the conclusion (and some of the preceding ones) is falsifiable if increasing the number of herbivores present that are capable of destroying any one of the dominant plant species fails to increase the total abundance of predators.

6. The final conclusion is, "...interspecific competition exists among producers, among carnivores, and among decomposers." Since this conclusion depends upon the first, second, and fifth conclusions listed above, if they are falsified, this one must also be falsified.

We do not maintain that the necessary observations in the foregoing suggestions are easily made, nor that they have any likelihood of falsifying the conclusions. We only point out that they have hypothetically possible outcomes that could falsify the respective conclusions. This is sufficient to refute Murdoch's claim.

## LITERATURE CITED

Blackman, F. F. 1905. Optima and limiting factors. Ann. Bot. 19:281–295.

Brower, L. P., and J. V. Z. Brower. 1964. Birds, butterflies, and plant poisons: a study in ecological chemistry. Zoologica 49:137–159.

Darwin, C. 1859. On the origin of species by means of natural selection, or the preservation of favoured races in the struggle for life. John Murray, London. 426 p.

Ehrlich, P. R., and L. C. Birch. 1967. The "balance of nature" and "population control." Amer. Natur. 101:97.

Eisner, T., F. C. Kafatos, and E. G. Linsley. 1962. Lycid predation by mimetic adult Cerambycidae (Coleoptera). Evolution 16:316–324.

Elton, C. S. 1958. The ecology of invasions by animals and plants. John Wiley & Sons, Inc., New York. 181 p.

Engelmann, M. D. 1966. Energetics, terrestrial field studies, and animal productivity, p. 73–115. In J. B. Cragg [Ed.], Advances in Ecological Research. Vol. 3. Academic Press, London.

Fryer, G. 1965. Predation and its effects on migration and speciation in African fishes: a comment. Proc. Zool. Soc. London 144:301–310.

Golley, F. B. 1960. Energy dynamics of a food chain of an old-field community. Ecol. Monogr. 30:187–206.

Golley, F. B., and J. D. Gentry. 1964. Bioenergetics of the southern harvest ant, Pogonomyrmex badius. Ecology 45:217–225.

Hairston, N. G. 1964. Studies on the organization of animal communities. J. Anim. Ecol., Jubilee Symp. Suppl. 33:227–239.

Hairston, N. G., F. E. Smith, and L. B. Slobodkin. 1960. Community structure, population control, and competition. Amer. Natur. 94:421–425.

Murdoch, W. W. 1966. Community structure, population control, and competition—a critique. Amer. Natur. 100:219–226.

Nicholson, A. J. 1957. The self-adjustment of populations to change. Cold Spring Harb. Symp. Quant. Biol. 22:153–172.

Odum, E. P. 1959. Fundamentals of ecology. W. B. Saunders Co., Philadelphia. 546 p.

Odum, E. P., C. E. Connell, and L. B. Davenport. 1962. Population energy flow of three primary consumer components of old-field ecosystems. Ecology 43:88–96.

Petrides, G. A., and W. G. Swank. 1965. Estimating the productivity and energy relations of an African elephant population. Proc. 9th Int. Grasslands Congr., São Paulo, Brazil.

Slobodkin, L. B. 1954. Population dynamics in *Daphnia obtusa* Kurz. Ecol. Monogr. 24:69–88.

_____. 1960. Ecological energy relationships at the population level. Amer. Natur. 94:213–236.

_____. 1962. Growth and regulation of animal populations. Holt, Rinehart and Winston, New York. 184 p.

Smalley, A. E. 1960. Energy flow of a salt marsh grasshopper population. Ecology 41:672–677.

Smith, H. S. 1935. The role of biotic factors in the determination of population densities. J. Econ. Entomol. 28:873–898.

Tanner, J. T. 1966. Effects of population density on growth rates of animal populations. Ecology 47:733–745.

Teal, J. M. 1962. Energy flow in the salt marsh ecosystem of Georgia. Ecology 43:614–624.

Wiegert, R. G., and F. C. Evans. 1964. Primary production and the disappearance of dead vegetation on an old-field in southeastern Michigan. Ecology 45:49–63.